Hindu and Arabian Period 200 B.C. to 1250 A.D.
Hindu-Arabic numeral system; Arab absorption of Hindu arithmetic and Greek geometry

Modern Period (Early) 1450 A.D. to 1800 A.D.
Logarithms; modern number theory; analytic geometry; calculus; the exploitation of the calculus

Period of Transmission 1250 A.D. to 1500 A.D.
Learning preserved by Arabs slowly transmitted to Western Europe

0 TO 500 A.D.

Chinese begin to use negative numbers.

Zero symbol is invented.

Hypatia studies number theory, geometry, and astronomy; her death in Alexandria is followed by decline of Alexandria as center of learning.

– – –

Jesus Christ's teachings establish new religion.

Under Emperor Claudius, Romans conquer Britain.

Roman Empire is divided into east and west.

Visigoths sack Rome.

Christianity becomes official religion of Roman Empire.

500 A.D. TO 1000 A.D.

al-Khowarizmi composes key book on algebra and Hindu numerals.

Early computing algorithms are developed.

Omar Khayyam creates geometric solutions of cubic equations and calendric problems.

– – –

Justinian's legal code is instituted.

Hegira of Muhammad takes place.

Chinese invent compass, gunpowder, and printing.

Charlemagne is crowned Holy Roman Emperor.

1000 A.D. TO 1500 A.D.

Fibonacci's Liber Abaci advocates Hindu-Arabic numeral system, which supplants Roman system.

– – –

Jerusalem is captured in First Crusade.

Genghis Khan rules.

Marco Polo travels through the East.

Universities are established at Bologna, Paris, Oxford, and Cambridge.

Bubonic plague kills one-fourth of Europe's population.

Printing with movable type is invented; rise of humanism occurs.

Columbus discovers New World.

1500 A.D. TO 1700 A.D.

Francois Viète simplifies algebraic notation.

Galileo Galilei applies math to experiments with falling bodies.

John Napier invents logarithms.

René Descartes and Blaise Pascal unify algebra and geometry.

Pierre de Fermat develops modern number theory.

Fermat and Pascal help lay foundations for theory of probability.

Isaac Newton and Gottfried Leibniz independently discover calculus.

Bernoulli family makes numerous contributions in analysis.

Newton's Principia Mathematica has enormous impact throughout Europe.

Johannes Kepler describes laws governing planetary movement (important to geometry and astronomy).

Works of da Vinci, Michelangelo, Raphael, Titian, and others mark the High Renaissance in Italy.

Protestant Reformation begins with Martin Luther's ninety-five theses.

Nicolas Copernicus attacks theory of geocentric universe.

Elizabeth accedes the throne. Sir Francis Drake defeats Spanish Armada.

William Shakespeare's plays are published.

Galileo invents telescope.

Mayflower lands at Plymouth Rock.

Newton formulates laws of gravity.

MATHEMATICAL IDEAS

CUSTOM EDITION FOR
HUDSON VALLEY COMMUNITY COLLEGE

CHARLES D. MILLER

VERN E. HEEREN

JOHN HORNSBY

MARGARET L. MORROW

JILL VAN NEWENHIZEN

Taken from:
Mathematical Ideas, Expanded Eleventh Edition
by Charles D. Miller, Vern E. Heeren, John Hornsby, Margaret L. Morrow, and Jill Van Newenhizen

Learning Solutions

New York   Boston   San Francisco
London   Toronto   Sydney   Tokyo   Singapore   Madrid
Mexico City   Munich   Paris   Cape Town   Hong Kong   Montreal

Cover Art: Chicago053; Chicago077

Taken from:

Mathematical Ideas, Expanded Eleventh Edition
by Charles D. Miller, Vern E. Heeren, John Hornsby, Margaret L. Morrow, and Jill Van Newenhizen
Copyright © 2008 by Pearson Education, Inc.
Published by Pearson Addison Wesley
Boston, Massachusetts 02116

Pearson Learning Solutions, 501 Boylston Street, Suite 900, Boston, MA 02116
A Pearson Education Company
www.pearsoned.com

Printed in the United States of America

3 4 5 6 7 8 9 10 V202 15 14 13 12

000200010270580277

KB

ISBN 10: 0-558-71318-1
ISBN 13: 978-0-558-71318-8

To my classmates in the 1967 graduating class of Catholic High School of Pointe Coupee, New Roads, Louisiana: Eleanor André, Mary Lynn Brumfield, Marilyn Cazayoux, Greg Chustz, Suzanne Chustz, Fellman Chutz, Alexis Cotten, Gay Dabadie, Cathie Ducote, Johnny Forbes, Bonnie Garrett, Gregory Langlois, Hilary Langlois, Paul Lorio, Garrett Olinde, Lynne Olinde, J. D. Patin, Loretta Ramagos, Kackie Smith, Buddy Vosburg, Allen Wells—In memory of Shootie Gosserand and Tippy Hurst—And to the coolest teacher and the most influential priest ever: Sister Margaret Maggio (Stephen) and Fr. Jerome Dugas. I love you all.

JOHNNY

To all my math students, over these many years.

V. E. H.

CONTENTS

PREFACE

After ten editions and nearly forty years, *Mathematical Ideas* continues to be one of the premier textbooks in liberal arts mathematics education. We are proud to present the eleventh edition of a text that offers non-physical science students a practical coverage that connects mathematics to the world around them. It is a flexible book that has evolved alongside changing trends but remains steadfast to its original objectives.

For the first time, this book features a theme that spans its entire contents. Movies and television have become entrenched in our society and appeal to a broad range of interests. With this in mind, we have rewritten every chapter opener with reference to a popular movie or television show, including discussion of a scene that deals with the mathematics covered in the chapter. The margin notes, long a popular hallmark of the book, have been updated to include similar references as well. These references are indicated with a movie camera icon 🎥. We hope that users of this edition will enjoy visiting Hollywood while learning mathematics.

Mathematical Ideas is written with a variety of students in mind. It is well suited for several courses, including those geared toward the aforementioned liberal arts audience and survey courses in mathematics, finite mathematics, and mathematics for prospective and in-service elementary and middle-school teachers. Numerous topics are included for a two-term course, yet the variety of topics and flexibility of sequence makes the text suitable for shorter courses as well. Our main objectives continue to be comprehensive coverage, appropriate organization, clear exposition, an abundance of examples, and well-planned exercise sets with numerous applications.

Overview of Chapters

- **Chapter 1 (The Art of Problem Solving)** introduces the student to inductive reasoning, pattern recognition, and problem-solving techniques. Many of the new problems are taken from the popular monthly calendars found in the NCTM publication *Mathematics Teacher.*

- **Chapter 2 (The Basic Concepts of Set Theory)** and **Chapter 3 (Introduction to Logic)** give brief overviews of set theory and elementary logic. Instructors wishing to do so may cover Chapter 3 before Chapter 2.

- **Chapter 4 (Numeration and Mathematical Systems)** covers various types of numeration systems and group theory, as well as clock arithmetic and modular number systems.

- **Chapter 5 (Number Theory)** presents an introduction to topics such as prime and composite numbers, the Fibonacci sequence, and magic squares. There is updated information on new developments in the field of prime numbers. New to this edition is an extension on modern crypotography.

- **Chapter 6 (The Real Numbers and Their Representations)** introduces some of the basic concepts of real numbers, their various forms of representation, and operations of arithmetic with them.

- **Chapter 7 (The Basic Concepts of Algebra) and Chapter 8 (Graphs, Functions, and Systems of Equations and Inequalities)** offer numerous new applications that help form the core of the text's algebra component.

- **Chapter 9 (Geometry)** covers the standard topics of elementary plane geometry, a section on transformational geometry, an extension on constructions, non-Euclidean geometry, and material on chaos and fractals.

- **Chapter 10 (Trigonometry)** includes angles in standard position, right angle trigonometry, and the laws of sines and cosines.

- **Chapter 11 (Counting Methods)** focuses on elementary counting techniques, in preparation for the chapter to follow.

- **Chapter 12 (Probability)** covers the basics of probability, odds, and expected value.

- **Chapter 13 (Statistics)** has been revised to include new data in examples and exercises.

- **Chapter 14 (Personal Financial Management)** provides the student with the basics of the mathematics of finance as applied to inflation, consumer debt, and house buying. The chapter includes a section on investing, with emphasis on stocks, bonds, and mutual funds. Examples and exercises have been updated to reflect current interest rates and investment returns.

The following chapters are available in the Expanded Edition of this text:

- **Chapter 15 (Graph Theory)** covers the basic concepts of graph theory and its applications. Material on graph coloring is new to this edition.

- **Chapter 16 (Voting and Apportionment)** deals with issues in voting methods and apportionment of votes, topics which have become increasingly popular in liberal arts mathematics courses.

Course Outline Considerations

For the most part, the chapters in the text are independent and may be covered in the order chosen by the instructor. The few exceptions are as follows: Chapter 6 contains some material dependent on the ideas found in Chapter 5; Chapter 6 should be covered before Chapter 7 if student background so dictates; Chapters 7 and 8 form an algebraic "package" and should be covered in sequential order; a thorough coverage of Chapter 12 depends on knowledge of Chapter 11 material, although probability can be covered without teaching extensive counting methods by avoiding the more difficult exercises; and the latter part of Chapter 13, on inferential statistics, depends on an understanding of probability (Chapter 12).

Features of the Eleventh Edition

New: **Chapter Openers**   In keeping with the Hollywood theme of this edition, all chapter openers have been rewritten to address a scene or situation from a popular movie or a television series. Some openers illustrate the correct use of mathematics, while others address how mathematics is misused. In the latter case, we subscribe to the premise that we can all learn from the mistakes of others. Some openers (e.g., Chapters 1 and 9) include a problem statement that the reader is asked to solve. We hope that you enjoy reading these chapter openers as much as we have enjoyed preparing them.

Enhanced: Varied Exercise Sets   We continue to present a variety of exercises that integrate drill, conceptual, and applied problems. The text contains a wealth of exercises to provide students with opportunities to practice, apply, connect, and extend the mathematical skills they are learning. We have updated the exercises that focus on real-life data and have retained their titles for easy identification. Several chapters are enriched with new applications, particularly Chapters 7, 8, 10, and 14. We continue to use graphs, tables, and charts when appropriate. Many of the graphs use a style similar to that seen by students in today's print and electronic media.

Enhanced: Margin Notes   This popular feature is a hallmark of this text and has been retained and updated where appropriate. These notes are interspersed throughout the text and deal with various subjects such as lives of mathematicians, historical vignettes, philatelic and numismatic reproductions, anecdotes on mathematics textbooks of the past, newspaper and magazine articles, and current research in mathematics. Completely new Hollywood-related margin notes have been included as well.

Collaborative Investigations   The importance of cooperative learning is addressed in this end-of-chapter feature.

Problem-Solving Hints   Special paragraphs labeled "Problem-Solving Hint" relate the discussion of problem-solving strategies to techniques that have been presented earlier.

Optional Graphing Technology   We continue to provide sample graphing calculator screens (generated by a TI-83/84 Plus calculator) to show how technology can be used to support results found analytically. It is not essential, however, that a student have a graphing calculator to study from this text; *the technology component is optional.*

Flexibility   Some topics in the first six chapters require a basic knowledge of equation solving. Depending on the background of the students, the instructor may omit topics that require this skill. On the other hand, the two algebra chapters (Chapters 7 and 8) provide an excellent overview of algebra, and because of the flexibility of the text, they may be covered at almost any time.

Art Program   The text continues to feature a full-color design. Color is used for instructional emphasis in text discussions, examples, graphs, and figures. New and striking photos have been incorporated to enhance applications and provide visual appeal.

For Further Thought   These entries encourage students to share amongst themselves their reasoning processes in order to gain a deeper understanding of key mathematical concepts.

New: Example Titles The numerous, carefully selected examples that illustrate concepts and skills are now titled so that students can see at a glance the topic under consideration. They prepare students for the exercises that follow.

Updated: Emphasis on Real Data in the Form of Graphs, Charts, and Tables We continue to use up-to-date information from magazines, newspapers, and the Internet to create real applications that are relevant and meaningful.

Chapter Tests Each chapter concludes with a chapter test so that students can check their mastery of the material.

MEDIA GUIDE

MathXL®

MathXL is a powerful online homework, tutorial, and assessment system that accompanies this Addison-Wesley textbook. With MathXL, instructors can create, edit, and assign online homework and tests using algorithmically generated exercises correlated at the objective level to the text. Instructors can also create and assign their own online exercises and import TestGen tests for added flexibility. All student work is tracked in MathXL's online gradebook. Students can take chapter tests in MathXL and receive personalized study plans based on their test results. The study plan diagnoses weaknesses and links students directly to tutorial exercises for the objectives they need to study and on which they need to be retested. Students can also access supplemental animations and video clips directly from selected exercises. MathXL is available to qualified adopters. For more information, visit our Web site at www.mathxl.com or contact your local sales representative.

MathXL® Tutorials on CD ISBN: 0-321-36972-6

This interactive tutorial CD-ROM provides algorithmically generated practice exercises that are correlated at the objective level to the exercises in the textbook. Every practice exercise is accompanied by an example and a guided solution designed to involve students in the solution process. Selected exercises may also include a video clip to help students visualize concepts. The software provides helpful feedback for incorrect answers and can generate printed summaries of students' progress.

MyMathLab

MyMathLab is a series of text-specific, easily customizable online courses for Addison-Wesley textbooks in mathematics and statistics. MyMathLab is powered by CourseCompass™—Pearson Education's online teaching and learning environment—and by MathXL—our online homework, tutorial, and assessment system. MyMathLab gives instructors the tools needed to deliver all or a portion of their course online, whether students are in a lab setting or working from home. MyMathLab provides a rich and flexible set of course materials, featuring free-response exercises that are algorithmically generated for unlimited practice and mastery. Students can also use online tools, such as video lectures, animations, and a multimedia textbook, to independently improve their understanding and performance. Instructors can use MyMathLab's homework and test managers to select and assign online exercises correlated directly to the textbook, and they can also create and assign their own online exercises and import TestGen tests for added flexibility. MyMathLab's online gradebook—designed specifically for mathematics and statistics—automatically tracks students' homework and test results and gives the instructor control over how to calculate final grades. Instructors can also add off-line (paper-and-pencil) grades to the gradebook. MyMathLab is available to qualified adopters. For more information, visit our Web site at www.mymathlab.com or contact your local sales representative.

InterAct Math Tutorial Web site www.interactmath.com

Get practice and tutorial help online! This interactive tutorial Web site provides algorithmically generated practice exercises that correlate directly to the exercises in the textbook. Students can retry an exercise as many times as they like, with new values each time, for unlimited practice and mastery. Every exercise is accompanied by an interactive guided solution that provides helpful feedback for incorrect answers, and students can also view a worked-out sample problem that steps them through an exercise similar to the one they are working on.

Video Lectures on CD with Optional Captioning

In this comprehensive video series, an engaging team of instructors provide chapter- and section-based instruction on every topic in the textbook. These lessons present key concepts and show students how to work exercises, providing extra instruction for students who have missed a class or who are in need of a little extra help. The lectures are available on CD-ROM, for purchase with the text at minimal cost. Affordable and portable for students, this series makes it easy and convenient for students to watch the videos from a computer at home or on campus.

SUPPLEMENTS to accompany MATHEMATICAL IDEAS
Eleventh Edition ● Expanded Eleventh Edition

STUDENT SUPPLEMENTS

Student's Study Guide and Solutions Manual

- By Emmett Larson, *Brevard Community College*
- This manual provides solutions to the odd-numbered exercises in the exercise sets, the Extensions, and the Appendix exercises, as well as solutions for all the Chapter Test exercises. Chapter summaries review key points in the text, providing extra examples, and enumerate major topic objectives.
  ISBN 0-321-36971-8

Video Lectures on CD with Optional Captions

- This is a complete set of digitized videos for student use at home or on campus, making it ideal for distance learning or supplemental instruction.
  ISBN 0-321-36954-8

Addison-Wesley Math Tutor Center

- The Tutor Center provides tutoring through a registration number that can be packaged with a new textbook or purchased separately. The Tutor Center is staffed by qualified college mathematics instructors who provide students with tutoring on examples and odd-numbered exercises from the textbook. It is accessible via toll-free telephone, toll-free fax, e-mail, and the Internet (www.aw-bc.com/tutorcenter).

INSTRUCTOR SUPPLEMENTS

NEW! Annotated Instructor's Edition

- This special edition of the text provides answers next to text exercises for quick reference, where possible. The remaining answers are found in the answer section.
  ISBN 0-321-36147-4

Instructor's Solutions Manual

- By Emmett Larson, *Brevard Community College*
- This manual contains solutions to all end-of-section exercises, Extension, Chapter Test, and Appendix exercises.
  ISBN 0-321-36970-X

Instructor's Testing Manual

- This manual contains four tests for each chapter of the text. Answer keys are included.
  ISBN 0-321-36969-6

TestGen®

- TestGen enables instructors to build, edit, print, and administer tests using a computerized bank of questions developed to cover all text objectives. The software is available on a dual-platform Windows/ Macintosh CD-ROM.
  ISBN 0-321-36966-1

NEW! Insider's Guide to Teaching with Mathematical Ideas, 11e

- The Insider's Guide includes resources to help faculty with course preparation and classroom management. It provides helpful teaching tips correlated to each section of the text, as well as general teaching advice.
  ISBN 0-321-49090-8

PowerPoint Lecture Presentation

- The PowerPoint classroom presentation slides are geared specifically to sequence this textbook. They are available within MyMathLab or at www.aw-bc. com/irc.

NEW! Adjunct Support Center

- The Center offers consultation on suggested syllabi, helpful tips on using the textbook support package, assistance with content, and advice on classroom strategies. It is available Sunday through Thursday evenings from 5 P.M. to midnight EST; telephone: 1-800-435-4084; e-mail: adjunctsupport @aw.com; fax: 1-877-262-9774.

ACKNOWLEDGMENTS

We wish to thank the following reviewers for their helpful comments and suggestions for this and previous editions of the text. (Reviewers of the eleventh edition are noted with an asterisk.)

H. Achepohl, *College of DuPage*

Shahrokh Ahmadi, *Northern Virginia Community College*

Richard Andrews, *Florida A&M University*

Cindy Anfinson, *Palomar College*

Elaine Barber, *Germanna Community College*

Anna Baumgartner, *Carthage College*

James E. Beamer, *Northeastern State University*

Elliot Benjamin, *Unity College*

Jaime Bestard, *Barry University*

Joyce Blair, *Belmont University*

Gus Brar, *Delaware County Community College*

Roger L. Brown, *Davenport College*

Douglas Burke, *Malcolm X College*

John Busovicki, *Indiana University of Pennsylvania*

Ann Cascarelle, *St. Petersburg Junior College*

Kenneth Chapman, *St. Petersburg Junior College*

Gordon M. Clarke, *University of the Incarnate Word*

M. Marsha Cupitt, *Durham Technical Community College*

James Curry, *American River College*

*Rosemary Danaher, *Sacred Heart University*

Ken Davis, *Mesa State College*

Nancy Davis, *Brunswick Community College*

George DeRise, *Thomas Nelson Community College*

Catherine Dermott, *Hudson Valley Community College*

*Greg Dietrich, *Florida Community College at Jacksonville*

Diana C. Dwan, *Yavapai College*

Laura Dyer, *Belleville Area College*

Jan Eardley, *Barat College*

Joe Eitel, *Folsom College*

Azin Enshai, *American River College*

Gayle Farmer, *Northeastern State University*

Michael Farndale, *Waldorf College*

Gordon Feathers, *Passaic County Community College*

Thomas Flohr, *New River Community College*

Bill Fulton, *Black Hawk College—East*

Anne Gardner, *Wenatchee Valley College*

Donald Goral, *Northern Virginia Community College*

Glen Granzow, *Idaho State University*

Larry Green, *Lake Tahoe Community College*

Arthur D. Grissinger, *Lock Haven University*

Don Hancock, *Pepperdine University*

Denis Hanson, *University of Regina*

Marilyn Hasty, *Southern Illinois University*

Shelby L. Hawthorne, *Thomas Nelson Community College*

Jeff Heiking, *St. Petersburg Junior College*

*Laura Hillerbrand, *Broward Community College*

*Jacqueline Jensen, *Sam Houston State University*

Emanuel Jinich, *Endicott College*

*Frank Juric, *Brevard Community College-Palm Bay*

Karla Karstens, *University of Vermont*

Hilary Kight, *Wesleyan College*

Barbara J. Kniepkamp, *Southern Illinois University at Edwardsville*

Suda Kunyosying, *Shepherd College*

*Yu-Ju Kuo, *Indiana University of Pennsylvania*

Pam Lamb, *J. Sargeant Reynolds Community College*

John W. Legge, *Pikeville College*

*John Lattanzio, *Indiana University of Pennsylvania*

Leo Lusk, *Gulf Coast Community College*

Sherrie Lutsch, *Northwest Indian College*

Rhonda Macleod, *Florida State University*

Andrew Markoe, *Rider University*

Darlene Marnich, *Point Park College*

Victoria Martinez, *Okaloosa Walton Community College*

Chris Mason, *Community College of Vermont*

Mark Maxwell, *Maryville University*

Carol McCarron, *Harrisburg Area Community College*

Delois McCormick, *Germanna Community College*

Daisy McCoy, *Lyndon State College*

Cynthia McGinnis, *Okaloosa Walton Community College*

Vena McGrath, *Davenport College*

Robert Moyer, *Fort Valley State University*

Shai Neumann, *Brevard Community College*

*Vladimir Nikiforov, *University of Memphis*

Barbara Nienstedt, *Gloucester County College*

Chaitanya Nigam, *Gateway Community-Technical College*

Jean Okumura, *Windward Community College*

Bob Phillips, *Mesabi Range Community College*

Kathy Pinchback, *University of Memphis*

Priscilla Putman, *New Jersey City University*

Scott C. Radtke, *Davenport College*

John Reily, *Montclair State University*

Beth Reynolds, *Mater Dei College*

Shirley I. Robertson, *High Point University*

Andrew M. Rockett, *CW Post Campus of Long Island University*

Kathleen Rodak, *St. Mary's College of Ave Maria University*

*Abby Roscum, *Marshalltown Community College*

D. Schraeder, *McLennan Community College*

Wilfred Schulte, *Cosumnes River College*

Melinda Schulteis, *Concordia University*

Gary D. Shaffer, *Allegany College of Maryland*

*Doug Shaw, *University of North Iowa*

Jane Sinibaldi, *York College of Pennsylvania*

Larry Smith, *Peninsula College*

Marguerite Smith, *Merced College*

Charlene D. Snow, *Lower Columbia College*

H. Jeannette Stephens, *Whatcom Community College*

Suzanne J. Stock, *Oakton Community College*

Dian Thom, *McKendree College*

Claude C. Thompson, *Hollins University*

Mark Tom, *College of the Sequoias*

Ida Umphers, *University of Arkansas at Little Rock*

Karen Villarreal, *University of New Orleans*

Wayne Wanamaker, *Central Florida Community College*

David Wasilewski, *Luzerne County Community College*

William Watkins, *California State University, Northridge*

Susan Williford, *Columbia State Community College*

Tom Witten, *Southwest Virginia Community College*

Fred Worth, *Henderson State University*

Rob Wylie, *Carl Albert State College*

Henry Wyzinski, *Indiana University Northwest*

A project of this magnitude cannot be accomplished without the help of many other dedicated individuals. Anne Kelly served as sponsoring editor for this edition. Jeff Houck of Progressive Publishing Alternatives provided excellent production supervision. Ashley O'Shaughnessy, Greg Tobin, Barbara Atkinson, Becky Anderson, Peggy McMahon, Beth Anderson, and Joanne Ha of Addison-Wesley gave us their unwavering support. Terry McGinnis provided her usual excellent behind-the-scenes guidance. Thanks go to Dr. Margaret L. Morrow of Plattsburgh State University and Dr. Jill Van Newenhizen of Lake Forest College, who wrote the material on graph theory and voting/apportionment, respectively, for the Expanded Edition. Perian Herring, Cheryl Davids, Patricia Nelson, and Alicia Gordon did an outstanding job of accuracy- and answer-checking, and Becky Troutman provided the *Index of Applications*. And finally, we thank our loyal users over the past four decades for making this book one of the most successful in its market.

Vern E. Heeren
John Hornsby

1

THE ART OF PROBLEM SOLVING

The 1995 movie *Die Hard: With a Vengeance* is the third in a series of action films starring Bruce Willis as New York Detective John McClane. In this film, McClane is tormented by villain Simon Gruber (Jeremy Irons) who plants bombs around the city and poses riddles and puzzles for disarming them. In one situation, as McClane and store owner Zeus Carver (Samuel L. Jackson) open a briefcase containing a timer connected to a bomb near a park fountain, Simon relates the following riddle by telephone and gives them 5 minutes to solve it:

On the fountain there should be two jugs. Do you see them? A 5-gallon and a 3-gallon. Fill one of the jugs with exactly 4 gallons of water, and place it on the scale, and the timer will stop. You must be precise. One ounce more or less will result in detonation.

McClane and Carver were able to solve the riddle and defuse the bomb. Can you solve it? Variations of this problem have been around for many years. The answer is on page 26.

1.1 Solving Problems by Inductive Reasoning

Characteristics of Inductive and Deductive Reasoning • Pitfalls of Inductive Reasoning

The **Moscow papyrus,** which dates back to about 1850 B.C., provides an example of **inductive reasoning** by the early Egyptian mathematicians. Problem 14 in the document reads:

You are given a truncated pyramid of 6 for the vertical height by 4 on the base by 2 on the top. You are to square this 4, result 16. You are to double 4, result 8. You are to square 2, result 4. You are to add the 16, the 8, and the 4, result 28. You are to take one-third of 6, result 2. You are to take 28 twice, result 56. See, it is 56. You will find it right.

What does all this mean? A *frustum* of a pyramid is that part of the pyramid remaining after its top has been cut off by a plane parallel to the base of the pyramid. The formula for finding the volume of the frustum of a pyramid with a square base is

$$V = \frac{1}{3}h(b^2 + bB + B^2),$$

where *b* is the area of the upper base, *B* is the area of the lower base, and *h* is the height (or altitude). The writer of the problem is giving a method of determining the volume of the frustum of a pyramid with square bases on the top and bottom, with bottom base side of length 4, top base side of length 2, and height equal to 6.

A truncated pyramid, or frustum of a pyramid

Characteristics of Inductive and Deductive Reasoning The development of mathematics can be traced to the Egyptian and Babylonian cultures (3000 B.C.–A.D. 260) as a necessity for problem solving. To solve a problem or perform an operation, a cookbook-like recipe was given, and it was performed repeatedly to solve similar problems. During the classical Greek period (600 B.C.–A.D. 450), general concepts were applied to specific problems, resulting in a structured, logical development of mathematics.

By observing that a specific method worked for a certain type of problem, the Babylonians and the Egyptians concluded that the same method would work for any similar type of problem. Such a conclusion is called a *conjecture*. A **conjecture** is an educated guess based on repeated observations of a particular process or pattern. The method of reasoning we have just described is called *inductive reasoning*.

Inductive Reasoning

Inductive reasoning is characterized by drawing a general conclusion (making a conjecture) from repeated observations of specific examples. The conjecture may or may not be true.

In testing a conjecture obtained by inductive reasoning, it takes only one example that does not work in order to prove the conjecture false. Such an example is called a **counterexample.**

Inductive reasoning provides a powerful method of drawing conclusions, but there is no assurance that the observed conjecture will always be true. For this reason, mathematicians are reluctant to accept a conjecture as an absolute truth until it is formally proved using methods of *deductive reasoning*. Deductive reasoning characterized the development and approach of Greek mathematics, as seen in the works of Euclid, Pythagoras, Archimedes, and others.

Deductive Reasoning

Deductive reasoning is characterized by applying general principles to specific examples.

We now look at examples of these two types of reasoning. In this chapter, we often refer to the **natural** or **counting numbers:**

$$1, 2, 3, \ldots \quad \text{Natural (counting) numbers}$$

↑
Ellipsis points

The three dots (*ellipsis points*) indicate that the numbers continue indefinitely in the pattern that has been established. The most probable rule for continuing this pattern is "add 1 to the previous number," and this is indeed the rule that we follow.

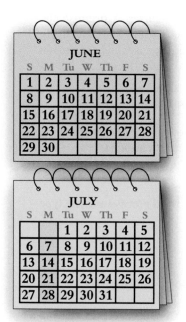

FIGURE 1

Now consider the following list of natural numbers: 2, 9, 16, 23, 30. What is the next number of this list? What is the pattern? After studying the numbers, we might see that $2 + 7 = 9$, and $9 + 7 = 16$. Do we add 16 and 7 to get 23? Do we add 23 and 7 to get 30? Yes; any number in the given list can be found by adding 7 to the preceding number, so the next number in the list should be $30 + 7 = 37$.

We set out to find the "next number" by reasoning from observation of the numbers in the list. We may have jumped from these observations to the general statement that any number in the list is 7 more than the preceding number. This is an example of *inductive reasoning*.

By using inductive reasoning, we concluded that 37 was the next number in the list. But this is wrong. We've been tricked into drawing an incorrect conclusion. The person making up the list has another answer in mind. The list of numbers

$$2, 9, 16, 23, 30$$

actually gives the dates of Mondays in June if June 1 falls on a Sunday. The next Monday after June 30 is July 7. With this pattern, the list continues as

$$2, 9, 16, 23, 30, 7, 14, 21, 28, \ldots .$$

See the calendar in Figure 1. The process used to obtain the rule "add 7" in the preceding list reveals one main flaw of inductive reasoning. We can never be sure that what is true in a specific case will be true in general. Inductive reasoning does not guarantee a true result, but it does provide a means of making a conjecture.

Throughout this book, we use *exponents* to represent repeated multiplication. For example, in the expression 4^3 the exponent is 3:

$$4^3 = 4 \cdot 4 \cdot 4 = 64. \qquad \text{4 is used as a factor 3 times.}$$

Exponential Expression

If a is a number and n is a counting number (1, 2, 3, . . .), then the exponential expression a^n is defined as

$$a^n = \underbrace{a \cdot a \cdot a \cdot \ldots \cdot a.}_{n \text{ factors of } a}$$

The number a is the *base* and n is the exponent.

With deductive reasoning, we use general statements and apply them to specific situations. For example, one of the best-known rules in mathematics is the Pythagorean theorem: In any right triangle, the sum of the squares of the legs (shorter sides) is equal to the square of the hypotenuse (longest side). Thus, if we know that the lengths of the shorter sides are 3 inches and 4 inches, we can find the length of the longest side. Let h represent the longest side.

$$3^2 + 4^2 = h^2 \qquad \text{Pythagorean theorem}$$
$$9 + 16 = h^2 \qquad 3^2 = 3 \cdot 3 = 9;\, 4^2 = 4 \cdot 4 = 16$$
$$25 = h^2 \qquad \text{Add.}$$
$$5 = h \qquad \text{The positive square root of 25 is 5.}$$

Thus, the longest side measures 5 inches. We used the general rule (the Pythagorean theorem) and applied it to the specific situation.

Reasoning through a problem usually requires certain *premises*. A **premise** can be an assumption, law, rule, widely held idea, or observation. Then reason inductively or deductively from the premises to obtain a **conclusion.** The premises and conclusion make up a **logical argument.**

EXAMPLE 1 Identifying Premises and Conclusions

Identify each premise and the conclusion in each of the following arguments. Then tell whether each argument is an example of inductive or deductive reasoning.

(a) Our house is made of brick. Both of my next-door neighbors have brick houses. Therefore, all houses in our neighborhood are made of brick.

(b) All word processors will type the symbol @. I have a word processor. I can type the symbol @.

(c) Today is Monday. Tomorrow will be Tuesday.

SOLUTION

(a) The premises are "Our house is made of brick" and "Both of my next-door neighbors have brick houses." The conclusion is "Therefore, all houses in our neighborhood are made of brick." Because the reasoning goes from specific examples to a general statement, the argument is an example of inductive reasoning (although it may very well have a false conclusion).

(b) Here, the premises are "All word processors will type the symbol @" and "I have a word processor." The conclusion is "I can type the symbol @." This reasoning goes from general to specific, so deductive reasoning was used.

(c) There is only one premise here, "Today is Monday." The conclusion is "Tomorrow will be Tuesday." The fact that Tuesday immediately follows Monday is being used, even though this fact is not explicitly stated. Because the conclusion comes from general facts that apply to this special case, deductive reasoning was used.

The earlier calendar example illustrated how inductive reasoning may, at times, lead to false conclusions. However, in many cases, inductive reasoning does provide correct results if we look for the most *probable* answer.

EXAMPLE 2 Predicting the Next Number in a Sequence

Use inductive reasoning to determine the *probable* next number in each list below.

(a) 5, 9, 13, 17, 21, 25 **(b)** 1, 1, 2, 3, 5, 8, 13, 21 **(c)** 2, 4, 8, 16, 32

SOLUTION

(a) Each number in the list is obtained by adding 4 to the previous number. The probable next number is $25 + 4 = 29$.

(b) Beginning with the third number in the list, 2, each number is obtained by adding the two previous numbers in the list. That is,

$$1 + 1 = 2, \qquad 1 + 2 = 3, \qquad 2 + 3 = 5,$$

and so on. The probable next number in the list is $13 + 21 = 34$. (These are the first few terms of the famous *Fibonacci sequence*.)

In the 2003 movie *A Wrinkle in Time*, young Calvin O'Keefe, played by Gregory Smith, is challenged to identify a particular sequence of numbers. He correctly identifies it as the **Fibonacci sequence.**

(c) It appears here that to obtain each number after the first, we must double the previous number. Therefore, the most probable next number is $32 \times 2 = 64$. ■

Inductive reasoning often can be used to predict an answer in a list of similarly constructed computation exercises, as shown in the next example.

EXAMPLE 3 Predicting the Product of Two Numbers

$37 \times 3 = 111$

$37 \times 6 = 222$

$37 \times 9 = 333$

$37 \times 12 = 444$

Consider the list of equations in the margin. Use the list to predict the next multiplication fact in the list.

SOLUTION

In each case, the left side of the equation has two factors, the first 37 and the second a multiple of 3, beginning with 3. The product (answer) in each case consists of three digits, all the same, beginning with 111 for 37×3. For this pattern to continue, the next multiplication fact would be $37 \times 15 = 555$, which is indeed true. (*Note:* You might want to investigate what occurs after 30 is reached for the right-hand factor, and make conjectures based on those products.) ■

TABLE 1

Number of Points	Number of Regions
1	1
2	2
3	4
4	8
5	16

Pitfalls of Inductive Reasoning There are pitfalls associated with inductive reasoning. A classic example involves the maximum number of regions formed when chords are constructed in a circle. When two points on a circle are joined with a line segment, a *chord* is formed. Locate a single point on a circle. Because no chords are formed, a single interior region is formed. See Figure 2(a). Locate two points and draw a chord. Two interior regions are formed, as shown in Figure 2(b). Continue this pattern. Locate three points, and draw all possible chords. Four interior regions are formed, as shown in Figure 2(c). Four points yield 8 regions and five points yield 16 regions. See Figures 2(d) and 2(e).

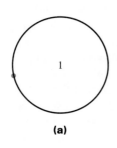 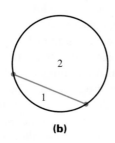 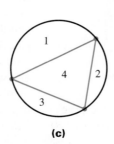 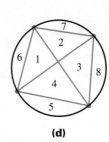 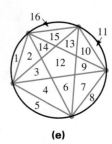

(a)   (b)   (c)   (d)   (e)

FIGURE 2

FIGURE 3

The results of the preceding observations are summarized in Table 1 in the margin. The pattern formed in the column headed "Number of Regions" is the same one we saw in Example 2(c), where we predicted that the next number would be 64. It seems here that for each additional point on the circle, the number of regions doubles. A reasonable inductive conjecture would be that for six points, 32 regions would be formed. But as Figure 3 indicates, there are only 31 regions! The pattern of doubling ends when the sixth point is considered. Adding a seventh point would yield 57 regions. The numbers obtained here are

$$1, 2, 4, 8, 16, 31, 57.$$

For n points on the circle, the number of regions is given by the formula

$$\frac{n^4 - 6n^3 + 23n^2 - 18n + 24}{24}.\text{*}$$

We can use a graphing calculator to construct a table of values that indicates the number of regions for various numbers of points. Using X rather than n, we can define Y_1 using the expression above (see Figure 4(a) on the next page). Then, creating a table of values, as in Figure 4(b), we see how many regions (indicated by Y_1) there are for any number of points (X).

As indicated earlier, not until a general relationship is proved can one be sure about a conjecture because one counterexample is always sufficient to make the conjecture false.

For Further Thought

Inductive Reasoning Anecdote

The following anecdote concerning inductive reasoning appears in the first volume of the *In Mathematical Circles* series by Howard Eves (PWS-KENT Publishing Company).

A scientist had two large jars before him on the laboratory table. The jar on his left contained 100 fleas; the jar on his right was empty. The scientist carefully lifted a flea from the jar on the left, placed the flea on the table between the two jars, stepped back, and in a loud voice said, "Jump." The flea jumped and was put in the jar on the right. A second flea was carefully lifted from the jar on the left and placed on the table between the two jars. Again the scientist stepped back and in a loud voice said, "Jump." The flea jumped and was put in the jar on the right. In the same manner, the scientist treated each of the 100 fleas in the jar on the left, and each flea jumped as ordered. The two jars were then interchanged and the experiment continued with a slight difference. This time the scientist carefully lifted a flea from the jar on the left, yanked off its hind legs, placed the flea on the table between the jars, stepped back, and in a loud voice said, "Jump." The flea did not jump, and was put in the jar on the right. A second flea was carefully lifted from the jar on the left, its hind legs yanked off, and then placed on the table between the two jars. Again the scientist stepped back and in a loud voice said, "Jump." The flea did not jump, and was put in the jar on the right. In this manner, the scientist treated each of the 100 fleas in the jar on the left, and in no case did a flea jump when ordered. So the scientist recorded in his notebook the following induction: "A flea, if its hind legs are yanked off, cannot hear."

For Group Discussion or Individual Investigation

Discuss or research examples from advertising on television, in newspapers, magazines, etc., that lead consumers to draw incorrect conclusions.

---

*For more information on this and other similar patterns, see "Counting Pizza Pieces and Other Combinatorial Problems," by Eugene Maier, in the January 1988 issue of *Mathematics Teacher*, pp. 22–26.

Note the careful use of parentheses. →

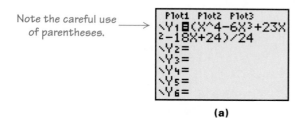

(a)

(b)

FIGURE 4

1.1 EXERCISES

In Exercises 1–12, determine whether the reasoning is an example of deductive or inductive reasoning.

1. If the mechanic says that it will take seven days to repair your car, then it will actually take ten days. The mechanic says, "I figure it'll take a week to fix it, ma'am." Then you can expect it to be ready ten days from now.

2. If you take your medicine, you'll feel a lot better. You take your medicine. Therefore, you'll feel a lot better.

3. It has rained every day for the past nine days, and it is raining today as well. So it will also rain tomorrow.

4. Marin's first three children were boys. If she has another baby, it will be a boy.

5. Finley had 95 baseball cards. His mom gave him 20 more for his birthday. Therefore, he now has 115 of them.

6. If the same number is subtracted from both sides of a true equation, the new equation is also true. I know that $9 + 18 = 27$. Therefore, $(9 + 18) - 12 = 27 - 12$.

7. If you build it, they will come. You build it. Therefore, they will come.

8. All men are mortal. Socrates is a man. Therefore, Socrates is mortal.

9. It is a fact that every student who ever attended Geekville University was accepted into graduate school. Because I am attending Geekville, I can expect to be accepted to graduate school, too.

10. For the past 53 years, a rare plant has bloomed in Columbia each summer, alternating between yellow and green flowers. Last summer, it bloomed with green flowers, so this summer it will bloom with yellow flowers.

11. In the sequence 5, 10, 15, 20, . . . , the most probable next number is 25.

12. Carrie Underwood's last four single releases have reached the Top Ten country list, so her current release will also reach the Top Ten.

13. Discuss the differences between inductive and deductive reasoning. Give an example of each.

14. Give an example of faulty inductive reasoning.

Determine the most probable next term in each list of numbers.

15. 6, 9, 12, 15, 18

16. 13, 18, 23, 28, 33

17. 3, 12, 48, 192, 768

18. 32, 16, 8, 4, 2

19. 3, 6, 9, 15, 24, 39

20. $\dfrac{1}{3}, \dfrac{3}{5}, \dfrac{5}{7}, \dfrac{7}{9}, \dfrac{9}{11}$

21. $\dfrac{1}{2}, \dfrac{3}{4}, \dfrac{5}{6}, \dfrac{7}{8}, \dfrac{9}{10}$

22. 1, 4, 9, 16, 25

23. 1, 8, 27, 64, 125

24. 2, 6, 12, 20, 30, 42

25. 4, 7, 12, 19, 28, 39

26. $-1, 2, -3, 4, -5, 6$

27. 5, 3, 5, 5, 3, 5, 5, 5, 3, 5, 5, 5, 5, 3, 5, 5, 5, 5

28. 8, 2, 8, 2, 2, 8, 2, 2, 2, 8, 2, 2, 2, 2, 8, 2, 2, 2, 2

29. Construct a list of numbers similar to those in Exercise 15 such that the most probable next number in the list is 60.

30. Construct a list of numbers similar to those in Exercise 26 such that the most probable next number in the list is 9.

In Exercises 31–42, a list of equations is given. Use the list and inductive reasoning to predict the next equation, and then verify your conjecture.

31. $(9 \times 9) + 7 = 88$
    $(98 \times 9) + 6 = 888$
    $(987 \times 9) + 5 = 8888$
    $(9876 \times 9) + 4 = 88{,}888$

32. $(1 \times 9) + 2 = 11$
    $(12 \times 9) + 3 = 111$
    $(123 \times 9) + 4 = 1111$
    $(1234 \times 9) + 5 = 11{,}111$

33. $3367 \times 3 = 10{,}101$
    $3367 \times 6 = 20{,}202$
    $3367 \times 9 = 30{,}303$
    $3367 \times 12 = 40{,}404$

34. $15873 \times 7 = 111{,}111$
    $15873 \times 14 = 222{,}222$
    $15873 \times 21 = 333{,}333$
    $15873 \times 28 = 444{,}444$

35. $34 \times 34 = 1156$
    $334 \times 334 = 111{,}556$
    $3334 \times 3334 = 11{,}115{,}556$

36. $11 \times 11 = 121$
    $111 \times 111 = 12{,}321$
    $1111 \times 1111 = 1{,}234{,}321$

37.
$$3 = \frac{3(2)}{2}$$
$$3 + 6 = \frac{6(3)}{2}$$
$$3 + 6 + 9 = \frac{9(4)}{2}$$
$$3 + 6 + 9 + 12 = \frac{12(5)}{2}$$

38.
$$2 = 4 - 2$$
$$2 + 4 = 8 - 2$$
$$2 + 4 + 8 = 16 - 2$$
$$2 + 4 + 8 + 16 = 32 - 2$$

39.
$$5(6) = 6(6 - 1)$$
$$5(6) + 5(36) = 6(36 - 1)$$
$$5(6) + 5(36) + 5(216) = 6(216 - 1)$$
$$5(6) + 5(36) + 5(216) + 5(1296) = 6(1296 - 1)$$

40.
$$3 = \frac{3(3 - 1)}{2}$$
$$3 + 9 = \frac{3(9 - 1)}{2}$$
$$3 + 9 + 27 = \frac{3(27 - 1)}{2}$$
$$3 + 9 + 27 + 81 = \frac{3(81 - 1)}{2}$$

41.
$$\frac{1}{2} = 1 - \frac{1}{2}$$
$$\frac{1}{2} + \frac{1}{4} = 1 - \frac{1}{4}$$
$$\frac{1}{2} + \frac{1}{4} + \frac{1}{8} = 1 - \frac{1}{8}$$
$$\frac{1}{2} + \frac{1}{4} + \frac{1}{8} + \frac{1}{16} = 1 - \frac{1}{16}$$

42.
$$\frac{1}{1 \cdot 2} = \frac{1}{2}$$
$$\frac{1}{1 \cdot 2} + \frac{1}{2 \cdot 3} = \frac{2}{3}$$
$$\frac{1}{1 \cdot 2} + \frac{1}{2 \cdot 3} + \frac{1}{3 \cdot 4} = \frac{3}{4}$$
$$\frac{1}{1 \cdot 2} + \frac{1}{2 \cdot 3} + \frac{1}{3 \cdot 4} + \frac{1}{4 \cdot 5} = \frac{4}{5}$$

A story is often told about how the great mathematician Carl Friedrich Gauss (1777–1855) at a very young age was told by his teacher to find the sum of the first 100 counting numbers. While his classmates toiled at the problem, Carl simply wrote down a single number and handed it in to his teacher. His answer was correct. When asked how he did it, the young Carl explained that he observed that there were 50 pairs of numbers that each added up to 101. (See below.) So the sum of all the numbers must be 50 × 101 = 5050.

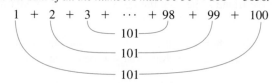

50 sums of 101 = 50 × 101 = 5050

Use the method of Gauss to find each sum.

43. $1 + 2 + 3 + \cdots + 200$

44. $1 + 2 + 3 + \cdots + 400$

45. $1 + 2 + 3 + \cdots + 800$

46. $1 + 2 + 3 + \cdots + 2000$

47. Modify the procedure of Gauss to find the sum $1 + 2 + 3 + \cdots + 175$.

48. Explain in your own words how the procedure of Gauss can be modified to find the sum $1 + 2 + 3 + \cdots + n$, where n is an odd natural number. (When an odd natural number is divided by 2, it leaves a remainder of 1.)

49. Modify the procedure of Gauss to find the sum $2 + 4 + 6 + \cdots + 100$.

50. Use the result of Exercise 49 to find the sum $4 + 8 + 12 + \cdots + 200$.

51. Find a pattern in the following figures and use inductive reasoning to predict the next figure.

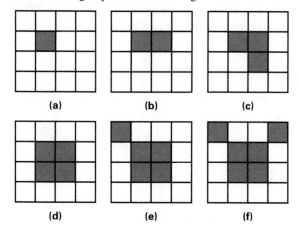

52. Consider the following table.

0	2	2	2	0	0	0	0	0
0	2	4	6	4	2	0	0	0
0	2	6	12	14	12	6	2	0
0	2	8	20	32	38	32	20	8

Find a pattern and predict the next row of the table.

53. What is the most probable next number in this list? 12, 1, 1, 1, 2, 1, 3 (*Hint:* Think about a clock.)

54. What is the next term in this list? O, T, T, F, F, S, S, E, N, T (*Hint:* Think about words and their relationship to numbers.)

55. (a) Choose any three-digit number with all different digits. Now reverse the digits, and subtract the smaller from the larger. Record your result. Choose another three-digit number and repeat this process. Do this as many times as it takes for you to see a pattern in the different results you obtain. (*Hint:* What is the middle digit? What is the sum of the first and third digits?)

(b) Write an explanation of this pattern. You may want to use this exercise as a "number trick" to amuse your friends.

56. Choose any number, and follow these steps.
   (a) Multiply by 2.
   (b) Add 6.
   (c) Divide by 2.
   (d) Subtract the number you started with.
   (e) Record your result.

   Repeat the process, except in Step (b), add 8. Record your final result. Repeat the process once more, except in Step (b), add 10. Record your final result.

   (f) Observe what you have done; use inductive reasoning to explain how to predict the final result. You may want to use this exercise as a "number trick" to amuse your friends.

57. Complete the following.

$$142,857 \times 1 = \underline{\hspace{2cm}}$$
$$142,857 \times 2 = \underline{\hspace{2cm}}$$
$$142,857 \times 3 = \underline{\hspace{2cm}}$$
$$142,857 \times 4 = \underline{\hspace{2cm}}$$
$$142,857 \times 5 = \underline{\hspace{2cm}}$$
$$142,857 \times 6 = \underline{\hspace{2cm}}$$

What pattern exists in the successive answers? Now multiply 142,857 by 7 to obtain an interesting result.

58. Complete the following.

$$12{,}345{,}679 \times \ 9 = \underline{\hspace{2cm}}$$
$$12{,}345{,}679 \times 18 = \underline{\hspace{2cm}}$$
$$12{,}345{,}679 \times 27 = \underline{\hspace{2cm}}$$

By what number would you have to multiply 12,345,679 to get an answer of 888,888,888?

59. Refer to Figures 2(b)–(e) and 3. Instead of counting interior regions of the circle, count the chords formed. Use inductive reasoning to predict the number of chords that would be formed if seven points were used.

60. The following number trick can be performed on one of your friends. It was provided by Dr. George DeRise of Thomas Nelson Community College.
  (a) Ask your friend to write down his or her age. (Only whole numbers are allowed.)
  (b) Multiply the number by 4.
  (c) Add 10.
  (d) Multiply by 25.
  (e) Subtract the number of days in a non-leap year.
  (f) Add the amount of change (less than a dollar, in cents) in his or her pocket.
  (g) Ask your friend for the final answer.

If you add 115 to the answer, the first two digits are the friend's age, and the last two give the amount of change.

61. Explain how a toddler might use inductive reasoning to decide on something that will be of benefit to him or her.

62. Discuss one example of inductive reasoning that you have used recently in your life. Test your premises and your conjecture. Did your conclusion ultimately prove to be true or false?

1.2 | An Application of Inductive Reasoning: Number Patterns

Number Sequences • Successive Differences • Number Patterns and Sum Formulas • Figurate Numbers

Number Sequences
An ordered list of numbers such as

$$3, 9, 15, 21, 27, \ldots,$$

is called a *sequence*. A **number sequence** is a list of numbers having a first number, a second number, a third number, and so on, called the **terms** of the sequence. The sequences in Examples 2(a) and 2(c) in the previous section are called *arithmetic* and *geometric sequences,* respectively. An **arithmetic sequence** has a common *difference* between successive terms, while a **geometric sequence** has a common *ratio* between successive terms.

Successive Differences
The sequences seen in the previous section were usually simple enough for us to make an obvious conjecture about the next term. However, some sequences may provide more difficulty in making such a conjecture, and often the **method of successive differences** may be applied to determine the next term if it is not obvious at first glance. Consider the sequence

$$2, 6, 22, 56, 114, \ldots.$$

Because the next term is not obvious, subtract the first term from the second term, the second from the third, the third from the fourth, and so on.

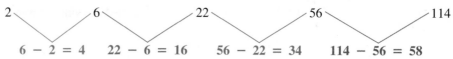

$$6 - 2 = 4 \qquad 22 - 6 = 16 \qquad 56 - 22 = 34 \qquad 114 - 56 = 58$$

Now repeat the process with the sequence 4, 16, 34, 58 and continue repeating until the difference is a constant value, as shown in line (4):

Once a line of constant values is obtained, simply work "backward" by adding until the desired term of the given sequence is obtained. Thus, for this pattern to continue, another 6 should appear in line (4), meaning that the next term in line (3) would have to be $24 + 6 = 30$. The next term in line (2) would be $58 + 30 = 88$. Finally, the next term in the given sequence would be $114 + 88 = \mathbf{202}$. The final scheme of numbers is shown below.

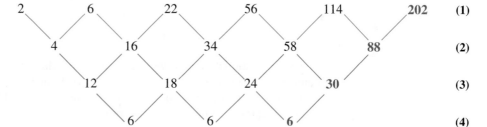

EXAMPLE 1 Using Successive Differences

Use the method of successive differences to determine the next number in each sequence.

(a) 14, 22, 32, 44, . . . **(b)** 5, 15, 37, 77, 141, . . .

SOLUTION

(a) Using the scheme described above, obtain the following:

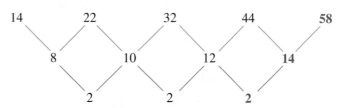

Once the row of 2s was obtained and extended, we were able to get $12 + 2 = 14$, and $44 + 14 = 58$, as shown above. The next number in the sequence is **58**.

(b) Proceeding as before, obtain the following diagram.

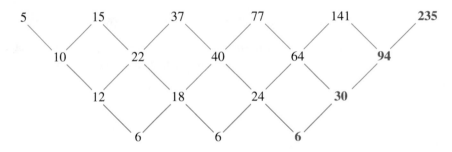

The next number in the sequence is **235**.

The method of successive differences will not always work. For example, try it on the Fibonacci sequence in Example 2(b) of Section 1.1 and see what happens!

Number Patterns and Sum Formulas   Mathematics features a seemingly endless variety of number patterns. Observe the following pattern:

$$1 = 1^2$$
$$1 + 3 = 2^2$$
$$1 + 3 + 5 = 3^2$$
$$1 + 3 + 5 + 7 = 4^2$$
$$1 + 3 + 5 + 7 + 9 = 5^2.$$

In each case, the left side of the equation is the indicated sum of the consecutive odd counting numbers beginning with 1, and the right side is the square of the number of terms on the left side. You should verify this in each case. Inductive reasoning would suggest that the next line in this pattern is

$$1 + 3 + 5 + 7 + 9 + 11 = 6^2.$$

Evaluating each side shows that each side simplifies to 36.

We cannot conclude that this pattern will continue indefinitely, because observation of a finite number of examples does not guarantee that the pattern will continue. However, mathematicians have proved that this pattern does indeed continue indefinitely, using a method of proof called *mathematical induction*. (See any standard college algebra text.)

Any even counting number may be written in the form $2k$, where k is a counting number. It follows that the kth odd counting number is written $2k - 1$. For example, the third odd counting number, 5, can be written $2(3) - 1$. Using these ideas, we can write the result obtained above as follows.

Sum of the First *n* Odd Counting Numbers

If *n* is any counting number, then

$$1 + 3 + 5 + \cdots + (2n - 1) = n^2.$$

EXAMPLE 2 Predicting the Next Equation in a List

In each of the following, several equations are given illustrating a suspected number pattern. Determine what the next equation would be, and verify that it is indeed a true statement.

(a)
$$1^2 = 1^3$$
$$(1 + 2)^2 = 1^3 + 2^3$$
$$(1 + 2 + 3)^2 = 1^3 + 2^3 + 3^3$$
$$(1 + 2 + 3 + 4)^2 = 1^3 + 2^3 + 3^3 + 4^3$$

(b)
$$1 = 1^3$$
$$3 + 5 = 2^3$$
$$7 + 9 + 11 = 3^3$$
$$13 + 15 + 17 + 19 = 4^3$$

(c)
$$1 = \frac{1 \cdot 2}{2}$$
$$1 + 2 = \frac{2 \cdot 3}{2}$$
$$1 + 2 + 3 = \frac{3 \cdot 4}{2}$$
$$1 + 2 + 3 + 4 = \frac{4 \cdot 5}{2}$$

SOLUTION

(a) The left side of each equation is the square of the sum of the first n counting numbers, while the right side is the sum of their cubes. The next equation in the pattern would be

$$(1 + 2 + 3 + 4 + 5)^2 = 1^3 + 2^3 + 3^3 + 4^3 + 5^3.$$

Each side simplifies to 225, so the pattern is true for this equation.

(b) The left sides of the equations contain the sum of odd counting numbers, starting with the first (1) in the first equation, the second and third (3 and 5) in the second equation, the fourth, fifth, and sixth (7, 9, and 11) in the third equation, and so on. The right side contains the cube (third power) of the number of terms on the left side in each case. Following this pattern, the next equation would be

$$21 + 23 + 25 + 27 + 29 = 5^3,$$

which can be verified by computation.

(c) The left side of each equation gives the indicated sum of the first n counting numbers, and the right side is always of the form

$$\frac{n(n + 1)}{2}.$$

For the pattern to continue, the next equation would be

$$1 + 2 + 3 + 4 + 5 = \frac{5 \cdot 6}{2}.$$

Because each side simplifies to 15, the pattern is true for this equation. ∎

The patterns established in Examples 2(a) and 2(c) can be written as follows.

Special Sum Formulas

For any counting number n,

$$(1 + 2 + 3 + \cdots + n)^2 = 1^3 + 2^3 + 3^3 + \cdots + n^3$$

and

$$1 + 2 + 3 + \cdots + n = \frac{n(n + 1)}{2}.$$

The second formula given is a generalization of the method first explained preceding Exercise 43 in the previous section, relating the story of young Carl Gauss. We can provide a general, deductive argument showing how this equation is obtained. Suppose that we let S represent the sum $1 + 2 + 3 + \cdots + n$. This sum can also be written as $S = n + (n - 1) + (n - 2) + \cdots + 1$. Now write these two equations as follows.

$$
\begin{array}{l}
S = 1 \quad\quad + 2 \quad\quad + 3 \quad\quad + \cdots + n \\
\underline{S = n \quad\quad + (n - 1) + (n - 2) + \cdots + 1} \\
2S = (n + 1) + (n + 1) + (n + 1) + \cdots + (n + 1) \quad\text{Add the corresponding sides.}\\
2S = n(n + 1) \quad\text{There are } n \text{ terms of } n + 1.\\
S = \dfrac{n(n + 1)}{2} \quad\text{Divide both sides by 2.}
\end{array}
$$

We can now apply deductive reasoning to find the sum of the first n counting numbers for any given value of n.

Figurate Numbers

Pythagoras and his Pythagorean brotherhood (see the margin note) studied numbers of geometric arrangements of points, such as *triangular numbers, square numbers*, and *pentagonal numbers*. Figure 5 illustrates the first few of each of these types of numbers.

The *figurate numbers* possess numerous interesting patterns. Every square number greater than 1 is the sum of two consecutive triangular numbers. (For example, $9 = 3 + 6$ and $25 = 10 + 15$.) Every pentagonal number can be represented as the sum of a square number and a triangular number. (For example, $5 = 4 + 1$ and $12 = 9 + 3$.)

In the expression T_n, n is called a **subscript.** T_n is read **"T sub n,"** and it represents the triangular number in the nth position in the sequence. For example,

$$T_1 = 1, \quad T_2 = 3, \quad T_3 = 6, \quad \text{and} \quad T_4 = 10.$$

S_n and P_n represent the nth square and pentagonal numbers, respectively.

In the 1959 Disney animation *Donald in Mathmagic Land*, Donald Duck travels back in time to meet the Greek mathematician **Pythagoras** (c. 540 B.C.), who with his fellow mathematicians formed the Pythagorean brotherhood. The brotherhood devoted its time to the study of mathematics and music.

Formulas for Triangular, Square, and Pentagonal Numbers

For any natural number n,

the nth triangular number is given by $\quad T_n = \dfrac{n(n + 1)}{2},$

the nth square number is given by $\quad\quad S_n = n^2,$ and

the nth pentagonal number is given by $\quad P_n = \dfrac{n(3n - 1)}{2}.$

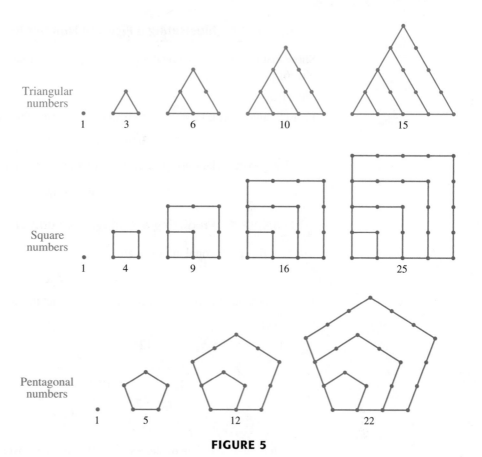

FIGURE 5

EXAMPLE 3 Using the Formulas for Figurate Numbers

Use the formulas to find each of the following.

(a) seventh triangular number
(b) twelfth square number
(c) sixth pentagonal number

SOLUTION

(a) $T_7 = \dfrac{n(n+1)}{2} = \dfrac{7(7+1)}{2} = \dfrac{7(8)}{2} = \dfrac{56}{2} = 28$ Formula for a triangular number, $n = 7$

(b) $S_{12} = n^2 = 12^2 = 144$ Formula for a square number, $n = 12$

$$12^2 = 12 \cdot 12$$

(c) $P_6 = \dfrac{n(3n-1)}{2} = \dfrac{6[3(6)-1]}{2} = \dfrac{6(18-1)}{2} = \dfrac{6(17)}{2} = 51$

Inside the brackets,
multiply first and
then subtract.

EXAMPLE 4 Illustrating a Figurate Number Relationship

Show that the sixth pentagonal number is equal to 3 times the fifth triangular number, plus 6.

SOLUTION

From Example 3(c), $P_6 = 51$. The fifth triangular number is 15. Thus,

$$51 = 3(15) + 6 = 45 + 6 = 51.$$

The general relationship examined in Example 4 can be written as follows.

$$P_n = 3 \cdot T_{n-1} + n \quad (n \geq 2)$$

EXAMPLE 5 Predicting a Pentagonal Number

The first five pentagonal numbers are

$$1, 5, 12, 22, 35.$$

Use the method of successive differences to predict the sixth pentagonal number.

SOLUTION

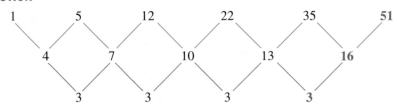

After the second line of successive differences, we work backward to find that the sixth pentagonal number is 51, which was also found in Example 3(c).

For Further Thought

Kaprekar Numbers

Take any three-digit number whose digits are not all the same. Arrange the digits in decreasing order, and then arrange them in increasing order. Now subtract. Repeat the process, using a 0 if necessary in the event that the difference consists of only two digits. For example, suppose that we choose a number whose digits are 1, 4, and 8, such as 841.

$$
\begin{array}{rrr}
841 & 963 & 954 \\
-148 & -369 & -459 \\
\hline
693 & 594 & 495 \\
\end{array}
$$

Notice that we have obtained the number 495, and the process will lead to 495 again. The number 495 is called a **Kaprekar number.** The number 495 will eventually always be generated if this process is applied to such a three-digit number.

For Group Discussion or Individual Investigation

1. Apply the process of Kaprekar to a two-digit number, in which the digits are not the same. (Interpret 9 as 09 if necessary.) Compare the results. What seems to be true?
2. Repeat the process for four digits, comparing results after several steps. What conjecture can be made for this situation?

1.2 EXERCISES

Use the method of successive differences to determine the next number in each sequence.

1. 1, 4, 11, 22, 37, 56, . . .

2. 3, 14, 31, 54, 83, 118, . . .

3. 6, 20, 50, 102, 182, 296, . . .

4. 1, 11, 35, 79, 149, 251, . . .

5. 0, 12, 72, 240, 600, 1260, 2352, . . .

6. 2, 57, 220, 575, 1230, 2317, . . .

7. 5, 34, 243, 1022, 3121, 7770, 16799, . . .

8. 3, 19, 165, 771, 2503, 6483, 14409, . . .

9. Refer to Figures 2 and 3 in Section 1.1. The method of successive differences can be applied to the sequence of interior regions,

$$1, 2, 4, 8, 16, 31,$$

to find the number of regions determined by seven points on the circle. What is the next term in this sequence? How many regions would be determined by eight points? Verify this using the formula given at the end of that section.

10. Suppose that the expression $n^2 + 3n + 1$ determines the nth term in a sequence. That is, to find the first term, let $n = 1$; to find the second term, let $n = 2$, and so on.
   (a) Find the first four terms of the sequence.
   (b) Use the method of successive differences to predict the fifth term of the sequence.
   (c) Find the fifth term by letting $n = 5$ in the expression $n^2 + 3n + 1$. Does your result agree with the one you found in part (b)?

In Exercises 11–20, several equations are given illustrating a suspected number pattern. Determine what the next equation would be, and verify that it is indeed a true statement.

11. $(1 \times 9) - 1 = 8$
   $(21 \times 9) - 1 = 188$
   $(321 \times 9) - 1 = 2888$

12. $(1 \times 8) + 1 = 9$
   $(12 \times 8) + 2 = 98$
   $(123 \times 8) + 3 = 987$

13. $999{,}999 \times 2 = 1{,}999{,}998$
   $999{,}999 \times 3 = 2{,}999{,}997$

14. $101 \times 101 = 10{,}201$
   $10{,}101 \times 10{,}101 = 102{,}030{,}201$

15. $\quad 3^2 - 1^2 = 2^3$
   $\quad 6^2 - 3^2 = 3^3$
   $\quad 10^2 - 6^2 = 4^3$
   $\quad 15^2 - 10^2 = 5^3$

16. $1 = 1^2$
   $1 + 2 + 1 = 2^2$
   $1 + 2 + 3 + 2 + 1 = 3^2$
   $1 + 2 + 3 + 4 + 3 + 2 + 1 = 4^2$

17. $2^2 - 1^2 = 2 + 1$
   $3^2 - 2^2 = 3 + 2$
   $4^2 - 3^2 = 4 + 3$

18. $1^2 + 1 = 2^2 - 2$
   $2^2 + 2 = 3^2 - 3$
   $3^2 + 3 = 4^2 - 4$

19. $1 = 1 \times 1$
   $1 + 5 = 2 \times 3$
   $1 + 5 + 9 = 3 \times 5$

20. $1 + 2 = 3$
   $4 + 5 + 6 = 7 + 8$
   $9 + 10 + 11 + 12 = 13 + 14 + 15$

Use the formula $S = \dfrac{n(n + 1)}{2}$ to find each sum.

21. $1 + 2 + 3 + \cdots + 300$

22. $1 + 2 + 3 + \cdots + 500$

23. $1 + 2 + 3 + \cdots + 675$

24. $1 + 2 + 3 + \cdots + 825$

Use the formula $S = n^2$ to find each sum. (Hint: To find n, add 1 to the last term and divide by 2.)

25. $1 + 3 + 5 + \cdots + 101$

26. $1 + 3 + 5 + \cdots + 49$

27. $1 + 3 + 5 + \cdots + 999$

28. $1 + 3 + 5 + \cdots + 301$

29. Use the formula for finding the sum

$$1 + 2 + 3 + \cdots + n$$

to discover a formula for finding the sum

$$2 + 4 + 6 + \cdots + 2n.$$

30. State in your own words the following formula discussed in this section:

$$(1 + 2 + 3 + \cdots + n)^2 = 1^3 + 2^3 + 3^3 + \cdots + n^3.$$

31. Explain how the following diagram geometrically illustrates the formula $1 + 3 + 5 + 7 + 9 = 5^2$.

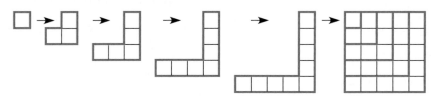

32. Explain how the following diagram geometrically illustrates the formula $1 + 2 + 3 + 4 = \dfrac{4 \times 5}{2}$.

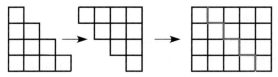

33. Use patterns to complete the table below.

Figurate Number	1st	2nd	3rd	4th	5th	6th	7th	8th
Triangular	1	3	6	10	15	21		
Square	1	4	9	16	25			
Pentagonal	1	5	12	22				
Hexagonal	1	6	15					
Heptagonal	1	7						
Octagonal	1							

34. The first five triangular, square, and pentagonal numbers may be obtained using sums of terms of sequences, as shown below.

Triangular	Square	Pentagonal
$1 = 1$	$1 = 1$	$1 = 1$
$3 = 1 + 2$	$4 = 1 + 3$	$5 = 1 + 4$
$6 = 1 + 2 + 3$	$9 = 1 + 3 + 5$	$12 = 1 + 4 + 7$
$10 = 1 + 2 + 3 + 4$	$16 = 1 + 3 + 5 + 7$	$22 = 1 + 4 + 7 + 10$
$15 = 1 + 2 + 3 + 4 + 5$	$25 = 1 + 3 + 5 + 7 + 9$	$35 = 1 + 4 + 7 + 10 + 13$

Notice the successive differences of the added terms on the right sides of the equations. The next type of figurate number is the **hexagonal** number. (A hexagon has six sides.) Use the patterns above to predict the first five hexagonal numbers.

35. Eight times any triangular number, plus 1, is a square number. Show that this is true for the first four triangular numbers.

36. Divide the first triangular number by 3 and record the remainder. Divide the second triangular number by 3 and record the remainder. Repeat this procedure several more times. Do you notice a pattern?

37. Repeat Exercise 36, but instead use square numbers and divide by 4. What pattern is determined?

38. Exercises 36 and 37 are specific cases of the following: In general, when the numbers in the sequence of n-agonal numbers are divided by n, the sequence of remainders obtained is a repeating sequence. Verify this for $n = 5$ and $n = 6$.

39. Every square number can be written as the sum of two triangular numbers. For example, 16 = 6 + 10. This can be represented geometrically by dividing a square array of dots with a line as shown.

The triangular arrangement above the line represents 6, the one below the line represents 10, and the whole arrangement represents 16. Show how the square numbers 25 and 36 may likewise be geometrically represented as the sum of two triangular numbers.

40. A fraction is in *lowest terms* if the greatest common factor of its numerator and its denominator is 1. For example, $\frac{3}{8}$ is in lowest terms, but $\frac{4}{12}$ is not.

(a) For $n = 2$ to $n = 8$, form the fractions

$$\frac{n\text{th square number}}{(n + 1)\text{th square number}}$$

(b) Repeat part (a), but use triangular numbers instead.

(c) Use inductive reasoning to make a conjecture based on your results from parts (a) and (b), observing whether the fractions are in lowest terms.

41. Complete the following table.

n	2	3	4	5	6	7	8
A Square of n							
B (Square of n) + n							
C One-half of Row B entry							
D (Row A entry) − n							
E One-half of Row D entry							

Use your results to answer the following, using inductive reasoning.

(a) What kind of figurate number is obtained when you find the average of n^2 and n? (See Row C.)

(b) If you square n and then subtract n from the result, and then divide by 2, what kind of figurate number is obtained? (See Row E.)

42. Find the least integer N greater than 1 such that two different figurate numbers equal N. What are they?

*In addition to the formulas for T_n, S_n, and P_n, the following formulas are true for **hexagonal** numbers (H), **heptagonal** numbers (Hp), and **octagonal** numbers (O):*

$$\mathbf{H}_n = \frac{n(4n - 2)}{2}, \quad \mathbf{Hp}_n = \frac{n(5n - 3)}{2}, \quad \mathbf{O}_n = \frac{n(6n - 4)}{2}.$$

Use these formulas to find each of the following.

43. the sixteenth square number

44. the eleventh triangular number

45. the ninth pentagonal number

46. the seventh hexagonal number

47. the tenth heptagonal number

48. the twelfth octagonal number

49. Observe the formulas given for H_n, Hp_n, and O_n, and use patterns and inductive reasoning to predict the formula for N_n, the nth **nonagonal** number. (A nonagon has nine sides.) Then use the fact that the sixth nonagonal number is 111 to further confirm your conjecture.

50. Use the result of Exercise 49 to find the tenth nonagonal number.

Use inductive reasoning to answer each question.

51. If you add two consecutive triangular numbers, what kind of figurate number do you get?

52. If you add the squares of two consecutive triangular numbers, what kind of figurate number do you get?

53. Square a triangular number. Square the next triangular number. Subtract the smaller result from the larger. What kind of number do you get?

54. Choose a value of n greater than or equal to 2. Find T_{n-1}, multiply it by 3, and add n. What kind of figurate number do you get?

1.3 Strategies for Problem Solving

A General Problem-Solving Method • Using a Table or Chart • Working Backward • Using Trial and Error • Guessing and Checking • Considering a Similar Simpler Problem • Drawing a Sketch • Using Common Sense

George Polya, author of the classic *How to Solve it*, died at the age of 97 on September 7, 1985. A native of Budapest, Hungary, he was once asked why there were so many good mathematicians to come out of Hungary at the turn of the century. He theorized that it was because mathematics is the cheapest science. It does not require any expensive equipment, only pencil and paper. He authored or coauthored more than 250 papers in many languages, wrote a number of books, and was a brilliant lecturer and teacher. Yet, interestingly enough, he never learned to drive a car.

A General Problem-Solving Method In the first two sections of this chapter we stressed the importance of pattern recognition and the use of inductive reasoning in solving problems. There are other useful approaches. These ideas are used throughout the text.

Probably the most famous study of problem-solving techniques was developed by George Polya (1888–1985), among whose many publications was the modern classic *How to Solve It*. In this book, Polya proposed a four-step method for problem solving.

Polya's Four-Step Method for Problem Solving

Step 1 **Understand the problem.** You cannot solve a problem if you do not understand what you are asked to find. The problem must be read and analyzed carefully. You may need to read it several times. After you have done so, ask yourself, "What must I find?"

Step 2 **Devise a plan.** There are many ways to attack a problem. Decide what plan is appropriate for the particular problem you are solving.

Step 3 **Carry out the plan.** Once you know how to approach the problem, carry out your plan. You may run into "dead ends" and unforeseen roadblocks, but be persistent.

Step 4 **Look back and check.** Check your answer to see that it is reasonable. Does it satisfy the conditions of the problem? Have you answered all the questions the problem asks? Can you solve the problem a different way and come up with the same answer?

In Step 2 of Polya's problem-solving method, we are told to devise a plan. Here are some strategies that may prove useful.

Problem-Solving Strategies

Make a table or a chart.	If a formula applies, use it.
Look for a pattern.	Work backward.
Solve a similar simpler problem.	Guess and check.
Draw a sketch.	Use trial and error.
Use inductive reasoning.	Use common sense.
Write an equation and solve it.	Look for a "catch" if an answer seems too obvious or impossible.

A particular problem solution may involve one or more of the strategies listed here, and you should try to be creative in your problem-solving techniques. The examples that follow illustrate some of these strategies.

Fibonacci (1170–1250) discovered the sequence named after him in a problem on rabbits. Fibonacci (son of Bonaccio) is one of several names for Leonardo of Pisa. His father managed a warehouse in present-day Bougie (or Bejaia), in Algeria. Thus it was that Leonardo Pisano studied with a Moorish teacher and learned the "Indian" numbers that the Moors and other Moslems brought with them in their westward drive.

Fibonacci wrote books on algebra, geometry, and trigonometry.

Using a Table or Chart

EXAMPLE 1   Solving Fibonacci's Rabbit Problem

A man put a pair of rabbits in a cage. During the first month the rabbits produced no offspring but each month thereafter produced one new pair of rabbits. If each new pair thus produced reproduces in the same manner, how many pairs of rabbits will there be at the end of 1 year? (This problem is a famous one in the history of mathematics and first appeared in *Liber Abaci,* a book written by the Italian mathematician Leonardo Pisano (also known as Fibonacci) in the year 1202.)

SOLUTION

We apply Polya's method.

Step 1   **Understand the problem.** After several readings, we can reword the problem as follows:

> *How many pairs of rabbits will the man have at the end of one year if he starts with one pair, and they reproduce this way: During the first month of life, each pair produces no new rabbits, but each month thereafter each pair produces one new pair?*

Step 2   **Devise a plan.** Because there is a definite pattern to how the rabbits will reproduce, we can construct Table 2. Once the table is completed, the final entry in the final column is our answer.

TABLE 2

Month	Number of Pairs at Start	Number of New Pairs Produced	Number of Pairs at End of Month
1st			
2nd			
3rd			
4th			
5th			
6th			
7th			
8th			
9th			
10th			
11th			
12th			

The answer will go here.

Step 3   **Carry out the plan.** At the start of the first month, there is only one pair of rabbits. No new pairs are produced during the first month, so there is $1 + 0 = 1$ pair present at the end of the first month. This pattern continues. In the table, we

TEXAS INSTRUMENTS

(X) NATIONAL COUNCIL OF
NCTM TEACHERS OF MATHEMATICS

🎥 On January 23, 2005, the CBS television network presented the first episode of *NUMB3RS*, a show focusing on how mathematics is used in solving crimes. David Krumholtz plays Charlie Eppes, a brilliant mathematician who assists his FBI agent brother (Rob Morrow). In the first-season episode "Sabotage" (2/25/2005), one of the agents admits that she "never saw how math relates to the real world," and Charlie uses the **Fibonacci sequence** and its relationship to nature to enlighten her.

add the number in the first column of numbers to the number in the second column to get the number in the third.

Month	Number of Pairs at Start	+	Number of New Pairs Produced	=	Number of Pairs at End of Month	
1st	1		0		1	$1 + 0 = 1$
2nd	1		1		2	$1 + 1 = 2$
3rd	2		1		3	$2 + 1 = 3$
4th	3		2		5	·
5th	5		3		8	·
6th	8		5		13	·
7th	13		8		21	·
8th	21		13		34	·
9th	34		21		55	·
10th	55		34		89	·
11th	89		55		144	·
12th	144		89		**233** ←	$144 + 89 = 233$

The answer is the final entry.

There will be 233 pairs of rabbits at the end of one year.

Step 4 **Look back and check.** This problem can be checked by going back and making sure that we have interpreted it correctly, which we have. Double-check the arithmetic. We have answered the question posed by the problem, so the problem is solved. ▪

The sequence shown in color in the table in Example 1 is the Fibonacci sequence, mentioned in Example 1 of the previous section. In the remaining examples of this section, we use Polya's process but do not list the steps specifically as we did in Example 1.

Working Backward

EXAMPLE 2 Determining a Wager at the Track

Rob Zwettler goes to the racetrack with his buddies on a weekly basis. One week he tripled his money, but then lost $12. He took his money back the next week, doubled it, but then lost $40. The following week he tried again, taking his money back with him. He quadrupled it, and then played well enough to take that much home with him, a total of $224. How much did he start with the first week?

SOLUTION

This problem asks us to find Rob's starting amount, given information about his winnings and losses. We also know his final amount. The method of working backward can be applied quite easily.

Because his final amount was $224 and this represents four times the amount he started with on the third week, we *divide* $224 by 4 to find that he started the third week with $56. Before he lost $40 the second week, he had this $56 plus the $40 he lost, giving him $96. This represented double what he started with, so he started with $96 *divided by* 2, or $48, the second week. Repeating this process once more for the first week, before his $12 loss he had

$$\$48 + \$12 = \$60,$$

which represents triple what he started with. Therefore, he started with

$$\$60 \div 3 = \$20. \quad \text{Answer}$$

To check, observe the following equations that depict winnings and losses:

First week: $(3 \times \$20) - \$12 = \$60 - \$12 = \$48$
Second week: $(2 \times \$48) - \$40 = \$96 - \$40 = \$56$
Third week: $(4 \times \$56) = \$224.$ His final amount

Augustus De Morgan was an English mathematician and philosopher, who served as professor at the University of London. He wrote numerous books, one of which was *A Budget of Paradoxes*. His work in set theory and logic led to laws that bear his name and are covered in other chapters. He died in the same year as Charles Babbage.

Using Trial and Error

Recall that $5^2 = 5 \cdot 5 = 25$, that is, 5 squared is 25. Thus, 25 is called a **perfect square.** Other perfect squares include

$$1, \quad 4, \quad 9, \quad 16, \quad 36, \quad \text{and so on.} \quad \text{Perfect squares}$$

The next example uses the idea of perfect square.

EXAMPLE 3 Finding Augustus De Morgan's Birth Year

The mathematician Augustus De Morgan lived in the nineteenth century. He made the following statement: "I was x years old in the year x^2." In what year was he born?

SOLUTION

We must find the year of De Morgan's birth. The problem tells us that he lived in the nineteenth century, which is another way of saying that he lived during the 1800s. One year of his life was a perfect square, so we must find a number between 1800 and 1900 that is a perfect square. Use trial and error.

$$42^2 = 1764$$
$$43^2 = \mathbf{1849} \quad \text{1849 is between 1800 and 1900.}$$
$$44^2 = 1936$$

The only natural number whose square is between 1800 and 1900 is 43, since $43^2 = 1849$. Therefore, De Morgan was 43 years old in 1849. The final step in solving the problem is to subtract 43 from 1849 to find the year of his birth:

$$1849 - 43 = \mathbf{1806}. \quad \text{He was born in 1806.}$$

Although the following suggestion for a check may seem unorthodox, it works: Look up De Morgan's birth date in a book dealing with mathematics history, such as *An Introduction to the History of Mathematics*, Sixth Edition, by Howard W. Eves.

Guessing and Checking

As mentioned above, $5^2 = 25$. The inverse (opposite) of squaring a number is called taking the **square root**. We indicate the positive square root using a **radical sign** $\sqrt{}$. Thus, $\sqrt{25} = 5$. Also,

$$\sqrt{4} = 2, \quad \sqrt{9} = 3, \quad \sqrt{16} = 4, \quad \text{and so on.} \quad \text{Square roots}$$

The next problem deals with a square root, and dates back to Hindu mathematics, circa 850.

EXAMPLE 4 Finding the Number of Camels

One-fourth of a herd of camels was seen in the forest; twice the square root of that herd had gone to the mountain slopes; and 3 times 5 camels remained on the river-bank. What is the numerical measure of that herd of camels?

SOLUTION

The numerical measure of a herd of camels must be a counting number. Because the problem mentions "one-fourth of a herd" and "the square root of that herd," the number of camels must be both a multiple of 4 and a perfect square, so that only whole numbers are used. The least counting number that satisfies both conditions is 4. We write an equation where x represents the numerical measure of the herd, and then substitute 4 for x to see if it is a solution.

$$\underbrace{\text{One-fourth of the herd}} + \underbrace{\text{Twice the square root of that herd}} + \underbrace{\text{3 times 5 camels}} = \underbrace{\text{The numerical measure of the herd.}}$$

$$\frac{1}{4}x \quad + \quad 2\sqrt{x} \quad + \quad 3 \cdot 5 \quad = \quad x$$

$$\frac{1}{4}(4) + 2\sqrt{4} + 3 \cdot 5 = 4 \qquad \text{Let } x = 4.$$

$$1 + 4 + 15 = 4 \quad ? \quad \sqrt{4} = 2$$

$$20 \neq 4$$

Because 4 is not the solution, try 16, the next perfect square that is a multiple of 4.

$$\frac{1}{4}(16) + 2\sqrt{16} + 3 \cdot 5 = 16 \qquad \text{Let } x = 16.$$

$$4 + 8 + 15 = 16 \quad ? \quad \sqrt{16} = 4$$

$$27 \neq 16$$

Because 16 is not a solution, try 36.

$$\frac{1}{4}(36) + 2\sqrt{36} + 3 \cdot 5 = 36 \qquad \text{Let } x = 36.$$

$$9 + 12 + 15 = 36 \quad ? \quad \sqrt{36} = 6$$

$$36 = 36$$

We see that 36 is the numerical measure of the herd. Check in the words of the problem: "One-fourth of 36, plus twice the square root of 36, plus 3 times 5" gives 9 plus 12 plus 15, which equals 36. (Algebra shows that 36 is the *only* correct answer.)

Considering a Similar Simpler Problem

EXAMPLE 5 Finding the Units Digit of a Power

The digit farthest to the right in a counting number is called the *ones* or *units* digit, because it tells how many ones are contained in the number when grouping by tens is considered. What is the ones (or units) digit in 2^{4000}?

The 1952 film *Hans Christian Andersen* features Danny Kaye as the Danish writer of fairy tales. In a scene outside a schoolhouse, he sings a song to an inchworm: "Inchworm, inchworm, measuring the marigolds, you and your arithmetic, you'll probably go far." Following the scene, students in the schoolhouse are heard singing arithmetic facts:

Two and two are four,
Four and four are eight,
Eight and eight are sixteen,
Sixteen and sixteen are
thirty-two.

Their answers are all **powers of 2.**

SOLUTION

Recall that 2^{4000} means that 2 is used as a factor 4000 times:

$$2^{4000} = \underbrace{2 \times 2 \times 2 \times \ldots \times 2.}_{4000 \text{ factors}}$$

Certainly, we are not expected to evaluate this number. To answer the question, we examine some smaller powers of 2 and then look for a pattern. We start with the exponent 1 and look at the first twelve powers of 2.

$$\begin{array}{lll} 2^1 = 2 & 2^5 = 32 & 2^9 = 512 \\ 2^2 = 4 & 2^6 = 64 & 2^{10} = 1024 \\ 2^3 = 8 & 2^7 = 128 & 2^{11} = 2048 \\ 2^4 = 16 & 2^8 = 256 & 2^{12} = 4096 \end{array}$$

Notice that in each of the four rows above, the ones digit is the same. The final row, which contains the exponents 4, 8, and 12, has the ones digit 6. Each of these exponents is divisible by 4, and because 4000 is divisible by 4, we can use inductive reasoning to predict that the units digit in 2^{4000} is 6.

(*Note*: The units digit for any other power can be found if we divide the exponent by 4 and consider the remainder. Then compare the result to the list of powers above. For example, to find the units digit of 2^{543}, divide 543 by 4 to get a quotient of 135 and a remainder of 3. The units digit is the same as that of 2^3, which is 8.) ■

Drawing a Sketch

EXAMPLE 6 Connecting the Dots

An array of nine dots is arranged in a 3×3 square, as shown in Figure 6. Is it possible to join the dots with exactly four straight line segments if you are not allowed to pick up your pencil from the paper and may not trace over a segment that has already been drawn? If so, show how.

FIGURE 6

SOLUTION

Figure 7 shows three attempts. In each case, something is wrong. In the first sketch, one dot is not joined. In the second, the figure cannot be drawn without picking up your pencil from the paper or tracing over a line that has already been drawn. In the third figure, all dots have been joined, but you have used five line segments as well as retraced over the figure.

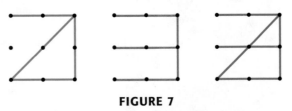

FIGURE 7

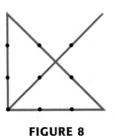

FIGURE 8

The conditions of the problem can be satisfied, as shown in Figure 8. We "went outside of the box," which was not prohibited by the conditions of the problem. This is an example of creative thinking—we used a strategy that is usually not considered at first. ■

In *Die Hard: With a Vengeance* (see the Chapter Opener), Simon taunts McClane with a riddle that has its origins in Egyptian mathematics.

*As I was going to St. Ives,
I met a man with seven wives.
Every wife had seven sacks,
Every sack had seven cats,
Every cat had seven kittens.
Kittens, cats, sacks and wives,
How many were going to St. Ives?*

"My phone number is 555 and the answer. Call me in 30 seconds or die."

By calling 555-0001, he was able to contact Simon. Do you see why 1 is the answer to this riddle? (Use **common sense**.)

Using Common Sense The final example falls into a category of problems that involve a "catch." Some of these problems seem too easy or perhaps impossible at first because we tend to overlook an obvious situation. Look carefully at the use of language in such problems. And, of course, never forget to use common sense.

EXAMPLE 7 Determining Coin Denominations

Two currently minted United States coins together have a total value of $1.05. One is not a dollar. What are the two coins?

SOLUTION

Our initial reaction might be, "The only way to have two such coins with a total of $1.05 is to have a nickel and a dollar, but the problem says that one of them is not a dollar." This statement is indeed true. What we must realize here is that the one that is not a dollar is the nickel, and the *other* coin is a dollar! So the two coins are a dollar and a nickel. ◾

Solution to the Chapter Opener Problem This is one way to do it: With both jugs empty, fill the 3-gallon jug and pour its contents into the 5-gallon jug. Then fill the 3-gallon jug again, and pour it into the 5-gallon jug until the latter is filled. There is now $(3 + 3) - 5 = 1$ gallon in the 3-gallon jug. Empty the 5-gallon jug, and pour the 1 gallon of water from the 3-gallon jug into the 5-gallon jug. Finally, fill the 3-gallon jug and pour all of it into the 5-gallon jug, resulting in $1 + 3 = 4$ gallons in the 5-gallon jug.

(*Note*: There is another way to solve this problem. See if you can discover the alternative solution.)

For Further Thought

A Brain Teaser

Various forms of the following problem have been around for many years.

In Farmer Jack's will, Jack bequeathed $\frac{1}{2}$ of his horses to his son Johnny, $\frac{1}{3}$ to his daughter Linda, and $\frac{1}{9}$ to his son Jeff. Jack had 17 horses, so how were they to comply with the terms of the will? Certainly, horses cannot be divided up into fractions. Their attorney, Garbarino, came to their rescue, and was able to execute the will to the satisfaction of all. How did she do it?

Here is the solution:

Garbarino added one of her horses to the 17, giving a total of 18. Johnny received $\frac{1}{2}$ of 18, or 9, Linda received $\frac{1}{3}$ of 18, or 6, and Jeff received $\frac{1}{9}$ of 18, or 2. That accounted for a total of $9 + 6 + 2 = 17$ horses. Then Garbarino took back her horse, and everyone was happy.

For Group Discussion or Individual Investigation

Make up a similar problem involving fractions. Check your work.

1.3 EXERCISES

One of the most popular features in the journal Mathematics Teacher, *published by the National Council of Teachers of Mathematics, is the monthly calendar, which provides an interesting, unusual, or challenging problem for each day of the month. Problems are contributed by the editors of the journal, teachers, and students, and the contributors are cited in each issue. Exercises 1–35 are problems chosen from these calendars over the past several years, with the day, month, and year for the problem indicated. The authors want to thank the many contributors for permission to use these problems.*

Use the various problem-solving strategies to solve each problem. In many cases there is more than one possible approach, so be creative.

1. ***Catwoman's Cats*** If you ask Batman's nemesis, Catwoman, how many cats she has, she answers with a riddle: "Five-sixths of my cats plus seven." How many cats does Catwoman have? (April 20, 2003)

2. ***Pencil Collection*** Bob gave four-fifths of his pencils to Barbara, then he gave two-thirds of the remaining pencils to Bonnie. If he ended up with ten pencils for himself, with how many did he start? (October 12, 2003)

3. ***Adding Gasoline*** The gasoline gauge on a van initially read $\frac{1}{8}$ full. When 15 gallons were added to the tank, the gauge read $\frac{3}{4}$ full. How many more gallons are needed to fill the tank? (November 25, 2004)

4. ***Gasoline Tank Capacity*** When 6 gallons of gasoline are put into a car's tank, the indicator goes from $\frac{1}{4}$ of a tank to $\frac{5}{8}$. What is the total capacity of the gasoline tank? (February 21, 2004)

5. ***Number Pattern*** What is the relationship between the rows of numbers?

18,	38,	24,	46,	42
8,	24,	8,	24,	8

(May 26, 2005)

6. ***Unknown Number*** The number in an unshaded square is obtained by adding the numbers connected with it from the row above. (The 11 is one such number.) What is the value of *x*? (August 9, 2004)

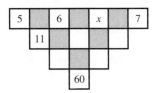

7. ***Locking Boxes*** You and I each have one lock and a corresponding key. I want to mail you a box with a ring in it, but any box that is not locked will be emptied before it reaches its recipient. How can I safely send you the ring? (Note that you and I each have keys to our own lock but not to the other lock.) (May 4, 2004)

8. ***Woodchuck Chucking Wood*** Nine woodchucks can chuck eight pieces of wood in 3 hours. How much wood can a woodchuck chuck in 1 hour? (May 24, 2004)

9. *Number in a Sequence* In the sequence 16, 80, 48, 64, A, B, C, D, each term beyond the second term is the arithmetic mean (average) of the two previous terms. What is the value of D? (April 26, 2004)

10. *Unknown Number* Cindy was asked by her teacher to subtract 3 from a certain number and then divide the result by 9. Instead, she subtracted 9 and then divided the result by 3, giving an answer of 43. What would her answer have been if she had worked the problem correctly? (September 3, 2004)

11. *Labeling Boxes* You are working in a store that has been very careless with the stock. Three boxes of socks are each incorrectly labeled. The labels say *red socks, green socks*, and *red and green socks*. How can you relabel the boxes correctly by taking only one sock out of one box, without looking inside the boxes? (October 22, 2001)

12. *Vertical Symmetry in States' Names* (If a vertical line is drawn through the center of a figure and the left and right sides are reflections of each other across this line, the figure is said to have vertical symmetry.) When spelled with all capital letters, each letter in HAWAII has vertical symmetry. Find the name of a state whose letters all have vertical and horizontal symmetry. (September 11, 2001)

13. *Sum of Hidden Dots on Dice* Three dice with faces numbered 1 through 6 are stacked as shown. Seven of the eighteen faces are visible, leaving eleven faces hidden on the back, on the bottom, and between dice. The total number of dots not visible in this view is

.

A. 21
B. 22
C. 31
D. 41
E. 53
(September 17, 2001)

14. *Mr. Green's Age* At his birthday party, Mr. Green would not directly tell how old he was. He said, "If you add the year of my birth to this year, subtract the year of my tenth birthday and the year of my fiftieth birthday, and then add my present age, the result is eighty." How old was Mr Green? (December 14, 1997)

15. *Unfolding and Folding a Box* An unfolded box is shown below.

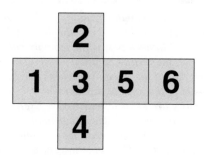

Which figure shows the box folded up? (November 7, 2001)

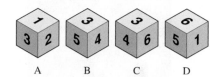

16. *Age of the Bus Driver* Today is your first day driving a city bus. When you leave downtown, you have twenty-three passengers. At the first stop, three people exit and five people get on the bus. At the second stop, eleven people exit and eight people get on the bus. At the third stop, five people exit and ten people get on. How old is the bus driver? (April 1, 2002)

17. *Matching Triangles and Squares* How can you connect each square with the triangle that has the same number? Lines cannot cross, enter a square or triangle, or go outside the diagram. (October 15, 1999)

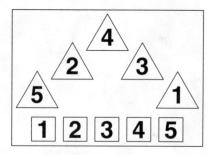

18. *Ticktacktoe Strategy* You and a friend are playing ticktacktoe, where three in a row loses. (See the next page.) You are O. If you want to win, what must your next move be? (October 21, 2001)

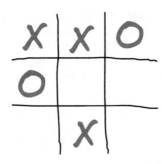

19. Forming Perfect Square Sums How must one place the integers from 1 to 15 in each of the spaces below in such a way that no number is repeated and the sum of the numbers in any two consecutive spaces is a perfect square? (November 11, 2001)

20. How Old? Pat and Chris have the same birthday. Pat is twice as old as Chris was when Pat was as old as Chris is now. If Pat is now 24 years old, how old is Chris? (December 3, 2001)

21. Difference Triangle Balls numbered 1 through 6 are arranged in a *difference triangle*. Note that in any row, the difference between the larger and the smaller of two successive balls is the number of the ball that appears below them. Arrange balls numbered 1 through 10 in a *difference triangle*. (May 6, 1998)

22. Clock Face By drawing two straight lines, divide the face of a clock into three regions such that the numbers in the regions have the same total. (October 28, 1998)

23. Alphametric If *a*, *b*, and *c* are digits for which

$$\begin{array}{r} 7\ a\ 2 \\ -4\ 8\ b \\ \hline c\ 7\ 3, \end{array}$$

then $a + b + c =$ _____.
A. 14 **B.** 15 **C.** 16 **D.** 17 **E.** 18
(September 22, 1999)

24. Perfect Square Only one of these numbers is a perfect square. Which one is it? (October 8, 1997)

329476   389372   964328
326047   724203

25. Sleeping on the Way to Grandma's House While traveling to his grandmother's for Christmas, George fell asleep halfway through the journey. When he awoke, he still had to travel half the distance that he had traveled while sleeping. For what part of the entire journey had he been asleep? (December 25, 1998)

26. Counting Puzzle (Rectangles) How many rectangles of any size are in the figure shown? (September 10, 2001)

27. Buckets of Water You have brought two unmarked buckets to a stream. The buckets hold 7 gallons and 3 gallons of water, respectively. How can you obtain exactly 5 gallons of water to take home? (October 19, 1997)

28. Collecting Acorns Chipper and Dalie collected thirty-two acorns on Monday and stored them with their acorn supply. After Chipper fell asleep, Dalie ate half the acorns. This pattern continued through Friday night, with thirty-two acorns being added and half the supply being eaten. On Saturday morning, Chipper counted the acorns and found that they had only thirty-five. How many acorns had they started with on Monday morning? (March 12, 1997)

29. Counting Puzzle (Rectangles) How many rectangles are in the figure? (March 27, 1997)

30. Digit Puzzle Place each of the digits 1, 2, 3, 4, 5, 6, 7, and 8 in separate boxes so that boxes that share common corners do not contain successive digits. (November 29, 1997)

31. Palindromic Number (*Note:* A *palindromic* number is a number whose digits read the same left to right as right to left. For example, 383, 12321, and 9876789 are palindromic.) The odometer of the family car read 15951 when the driver noticed that the number was palindromic. "Curious," said the driver to herself. "It will be a long time before that happens again." But 2 hours later, the odometer showed a new palindromic number. (*Author's note:* Assume it was the next possible one.) How fast was the car driving in those 2 hours? (December 26, 1998)

32. Exchange Rate An island has no currency; it instead has the following exchange rate:

$$50 \text{ bananas} = 20 \text{ coconuts}$$
$$30 \text{ coconuts} = 12 \text{ fish}$$
$$100 \text{ fish} = 1 \text{ hammock}$$

How many bananas equal 1 hammock? (April 16, 1998)

33. Final Digits of a Power of 7 What are the final two digits of 7^{1997}? (November 29, 1997)

34. Brightness of a Clock Display If a digital clock is the only light in an otherwise totally dark room, when will the room be darkest? Brightest? (May 1, 1996)

35. Value of Coins Which is worth more, a kilogram of $10 gold pieces or half a kilogram of $20 gold pieces? (March 20, 1995)

36. Units Digit of a Power of 3 If you raise 3 to the 324th power, what is the units digit of the result?

37. Units Digit of a Power of 7 What is the units digit in 7^{491}?

38. Money Spent at a Bazaar Ashley O'Shaughnessy bought a book for $10 and then spent half her remaining money on a train ticket. She then bought lunch for $4 and spent half her remaining money at a bazaar. She left the bazaar with $8. How much money did she start with?

39. Unknown Number I am thinking of a positive number. If I square it, double the result, take half of that result, and then add 12, I get 37. What is my number?

40. Frog Climbing up a Well A frog is at the bottom of a 20-foot well. Each day it crawls up 4 feet, but each night it slips back 3 feet. After how many days will the frog reach the top of the well?

41. Matching Socks A drawer contains 20 black socks and 20 white socks. If the light is off and you reach into the drawer to get your socks, what is the minimum number of socks you must pull out in order to be sure that you have a matching pair?

42. Counting Puzzle (Squares) How many squares are in the following figure?

43. Counting Puzzle (Triangles) How many triangles are in the following figure?

44. **Children in a Circle** Some children are standing in a circular arrangement. They are evenly spaced and marked in numerical order. The fourth child is standing directly opposite the twelfth child. How many children are there in the circle?

45. **Perfect Number** A *perfect number* is a counting number that is equal to the sum of all its counting number divisors except itself. For example, 28 is a perfect number because its divisors other than itself are 1, 2, 4, 7, and 14, and 1 + 2 + 4 + 7 + 14 = 28. What is the least perfect number?

46. **Naming Children** Becky's mother has three daughters. She named her first daughter Penny and her second daughter Nichole. What did she name her third daughter?

47. **Growth of a Lily Pad** A lily pad grows so that each day it doubles its size. On the twentieth day of its life, it completely covers a pond. On what day was the pond half covered?

48. **Interesting Property of a Sentence** Comment on an interesting property of this sentence: "A man, a plan, a canal, Panama." (*Hint:* See Exercise 31.)

49. **High School Graduation Year of Author** One of the authors of this book graduated from high school in the year that satisfies these conditions: (1) The sum of the digits is 23; (2) The hundreds digit is 3 more than the tens digit; (3) No digit is an 8. In what year did he graduate?

50. **Relative Heights** Donna is taller than David but shorter than Bill. Dan is shorter than Bob. What is the first letter in the name of the tallest person?

51. **Adam and Eve's Assets** Eve said to Adam, "If you give me one dollar, then we will have the same amount of money." Adam then replied, "Eve, if you give me one dollar, I will have double the amount of money you are left with." How much does each have?

52. **Missing Digits Puzzle** In the addition problem at the top of the next column, some digits are missing as indicated by the blanks. If the problem is done correctly, what is the sum of the missing digits?

$$
\begin{array}{ccc}
\_ & 3 & 5 \\
8 & \_ & 6 \\
+ \quad 1 & 4 & \_ \\
\hline
\_ \quad 4 & 0 & 8 \\
\end{array}
$$

53. **Missing Digits Puzzle** Fill in the blanks so that the multiplication problem below uses all digits 0, 1, 2, 3, . . . , 9 exactly once, and is correctly worked.

$$
\begin{array}{r}
\_ \quad 0 \quad 2 \\
\times \quad \_ \quad 3 \quad \_ \\
\hline
\_ \quad 5, \_ \_ \_ \\
\end{array}
$$

54. **Magic Square** A *magic square* is a square array of numbers that has the property that the sum of the numbers in any row, column, or diagonal is the same. Fill in the square below so that it becomes a magic square, and all digits 1, 2, 3, . . . , 9 are used exactly once.

6		8
	5	
		4

55. **Magic Square** Refer to Exercise 54. Complete the magic square below so that all counting numbers 1, 2, 3, . . . ,16 are used exactly once, and the sum in each row, column, or diagonal is 34.

6			9
	15		14
11		10	
16		13	

56. **Paying for a Mint** Brian Altobello has an unlimited number of cents (pennies), nickels, and dimes. In how many different ways can he pay 15¢ for a chocolate mint? (For example, one way is 1 dime and 5 pennies.)

57. **Pitches in a Baseball Game** What is the minimum number of pitches that a baseball player who pitches a complete game can make in a regulation 9-inning baseball game?

58. **Weighing Coins** You have eight coins. Seven are genuine and one is a fake, which weighs a little less than the other seven. You have a balance scale, which you may use only three times. Tell how to locate the bad coin in three weighings. (Then show how to detect the bad coin in only *two* weighings.)

59. **Geometry Puzzle** When the diagram shown is folded to form a cube, what letter is opposite the face marked Z?

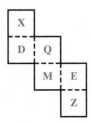

60. **Picture Puzzle** Draw a square in the following figure so that no two cats share the same region.

61. **Geometry Puzzle** Draw the following figure without picking up your pencil from the paper and without tracing over a line you have already drawn.

62. **Geometry Puzzle** Repeat Exercise 61 for this figure.

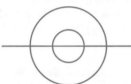

63. **Decimal Digit** What is the 100th digit in the decimal representation for $\frac{1}{7}$?

64. **Books on a Shelf** Volumes 1 and 2 of *The Complete Works of Wally Smart* are standing in numerical order from left to right on your bookshelf. Volume 1 has 450 pages and Volume 2 has 475 pages. Excluding the covers, how many pages are between page 1 of Volume 1 and page 475 of Volume 2?

65. **Oh Brother!** The brother of the chief executive officer (CEO) of a major industrial firm died. The man who died had no brother. How is this possible?

66. **Teenager's Age** A teenager's age increased by 2 gives a perfect square. Her age decreased by 10 gives the square root of that perfect square. She is 5 years older than her brother. How old is her brother?

67. **Ages** James, Dan, Jessica, and Cathy form a pair of married couples. Their ages are 36, 31, 30, and 29. Jessica is married to the oldest person in the group. James is older than Jessica but younger than Cathy. Who is married to whom, and what are their ages?

68. **Making Change** In how many different ways can you make change for a half dollar using currently minted U.S. coins, if cents (pennies) are not allowed?

69. **Days in a Month** Some months have 30 days and some have 31 days. How many months have 28 days?

70. **Dirt in a Hole** How much dirt is there in a cubical hole, 6 feet on each side?

71. **Fibonacci Property** Refer to Example 1, and observe the sequence of numbers in color. Choose any four successive terms. Multiply the first one chosen by the fourth; then multiply the two middle terms. Repeat this process. What do you notice when the two products are compared?

72. **Palindromic Greeting** The first man introduced himself to the first woman with a brief "palindromic" greeting. What was the greeting? (*Hint:* See Exercises 31, 48, and 51.)

73. **Geometry Puzzle** What is the maximum number of small squares in which we may place crosses (×) and not have any row, column, or diagonal completely filled with crosses? Illustrate your answer.

74. **_Determining Operations_** Place one of the arithmetic operations $+$, $-$, $\times$, or $\div$ between each pair of successive numbers on the left side of this equation to make it true. Any operation may be used more than once or not at all. Use parentheses as necessary.

$$1 \quad 2 \quad 3 \quad 4 \quad 5 \quad 6 \quad 7 \quad 8 \quad 9 = 100$$

1.4 Calculating, Estimating, and Reading Graphs

Calculation • Estimation • Interpretation of Graphs

Calculation The search for easier ways to calculate and compute has culminated in the development of hand-held calculators and computers. This text assumes that all students have access to calculators, allowing them to spend more time on the conceptual nature of mathematics and less time on computation with paper and pencil. For the general population, a calculator that performs the operations of arithmetic and a few other functions is sufficient. These are known as **four-function calculators.** Students who take higher mathematics courses (engineers, for example) usually need the added power of **scientific calculators. Graphing calculators,** which actually plot graphs on small screens, are also available. Remember the following.

The photograph shows the **Sharp Elsimate EL-330M,** a typical four-function calculator.

Since the introduction of hand-held calculators in the early 1970s, the methods of everyday arithmetic have been drastically altered. One of the first consumer models available was the Texas Instruments SR-10, which sold for nearly $150 in 1973. It could perform the four operations of arithmetic and take square roots, but could do very little more.

> Always refer to your owner's manual if you need assistance in performing an operation with your calculator. If you need further help, ask your instructor or another student who is using the same model.

Graphing calculators have become the standard in the world of advanced hand-held calculators. One of the main advantages of a graphing calculator is that both the information the user inputs into the calculator and the result generated by that calculator can be viewed on the same screen. In this way, the user can verify that the information entered into the calculator is correct. Although it is not necessary to have a graphing calculator to study the material presented in this text, we occasionally include graphing calculator screens to support results obtained or to provide supplemental information.*

The screens that follow illustrate some common entries and operations.

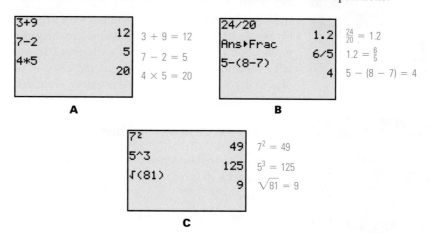

$3 + 9 = 12$

$7 - 2 = 5$

$4 \times 5 = 20$

A

$\frac{24}{20} = 1.2$

$1.2 = \frac{6}{5}$

$5 - (8 - 7) = 4$

B

$7^2 = 49$

$5^3 = 125$

$\sqrt{81} = 9$

C

---

*Because they are the most popular models of graphing calculators, we include screens generated by TI-83 Plus and TI-84 Plus models from Texas Instruments.

Screen A illustrates how two numbers can be added, subtracted, or multiplied. Screen B shows how two numbers can be divided, how the decimal quotient (stored in the memory cell Ans) can be converted into a fraction, and how parentheses can be used in a computation. Screen C shows how a number can be squared, how it can be cubed, and how its square root can be taken.

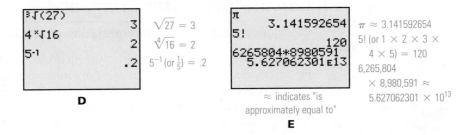

$\sqrt[3]{27} = 3$	$\pi \approx 3.141592654$
$\sqrt[4]{16} = 2$	$5!$ (or $1 \times 2 \times 3 \times 4 \times 5$) $= 120$
5^{-1} (or $\frac{1}{5}$) $= .2$	$6,265,804 \times 8,980,591 \approx 5.627062301 \times 10^{13}$

D

≈ indicates "is approximately equal to"

E

Any calculator (particularly a graphing calculator) consists of two components: the electronic "box" and the owner's manual that explains how to use it. The **TI-84 Plus** graphing calculator is shown.

Screen D shows how other roots (cube root and fourth root) can be found, and how the reciprocal of a number can be found using -1 as an exponent. Screen E shows how π can be accessed with its own special key, how a *factorial* (as indicated by !) can be found and how a result might be displayed in *scientific notation*. (The "E13" following 5.627062301 means that this number is multiplied by 10^{13}. This answer is still only an approximation, because the product $6{,}265{,}804 \times 8{,}980{,}591$ contains more digits than the calculator can display.)

Estimation   Although calculators can make life easier when it comes to computations, many times we need only estimate an answer to a problem, and in these cases a calculator may not be necessary or appropriate.

EXAMPLE 1 Estimating an Appropriate Number of Birdhouses

A birdhouse for swallows can accommodate up to 8 nests. How many birdhouses would be necessary to accommodate 58 nests?

SOLUTION

If we divide 58 by 8 either by hand or with a calculator, we get 7.25. Can this possibly be the desired number? Of course not, because we cannot consider fractions of birdhouses. Do we need 7 or 8 birdhouses? To provide nesting space for the nests left over after the 7 birdhouses (as indicated by the decimal fraction), we should plan to use 8 birdhouses. In this problem, we must round our answer *up* to the next counting number.

EXAMPLE 2 Approximating Average Number of Yards per Carry

In 2004, Tiki Barber of the New York Giants carried the football 322 times for 1518 yards (*Source:* nfl.com). Approximate his average number of yards per carry.

SOLUTION

Because we are are asked only to find Tiki's approximate average, we can say that he carried about 300 times for about 1500 yards, and his average was about $\frac{1500}{300} = 5$ yards per carry. (A calculator shows that his average to the nearest tenth was 4.7 yards per carry. Verify this.)

EXAMPLE 3 Comparing Proportions of Workers by Age Groups

In a recent year, there were approximately 127,000 males in the 25–29-year age bracket working on farms. This represented part of the total of 238,000 farm workers in that age bracket. Of the 331,000 farm workers in the 40–44-year age bracket, 160,000 were males. Without using a calculator, determine which age bracket had a larger proportion of males.

SOLUTION

Here, it is best to think in terms of thousands instead of dealing with all the zeros. First, let us analyze the age bracket 25–29 years. Because there were a total of 238 thousand workers, of which 127 thousand were males, there were $238 - 127 = 111$ thousand female workers. Here, more than half of the workers were males. In the 40–44-year age bracket, of the 331 thousand workers, there were 160 thousand males, giving $331 - 160 = 171$ thousand females, meaning fewer than half were males. A comparison, then, shows that the 25–29-year age bracket had the larger proportion of males. ▪

Interpretation of Graphs

Using graphs is an efficient means of transmitting information in a concise way. Any issue of the newspaper *USA Today* will verify this. *Circle graphs* or *pie charts, bar graphs,* and *line graphs* are the most common.

A **circle graph** or **pie chart** is used to give a pictorial representation of data. A circle is used to indicate the total of all the categories represented. The circle is divided into sectors, or wedges (like pieces of a pie), whose sizes show the relative magnitudes of the categories. The sum of all the fractional parts must be 1 (for 1 whole circle).

EXAMPLE 4 Interpreting Information in a Circle Graph

Use the circle graph in Figure 9 to determine how much of the amount spent for a $3.50 gallon of gasoline in California goes to refinery margin and to crude oil cost.

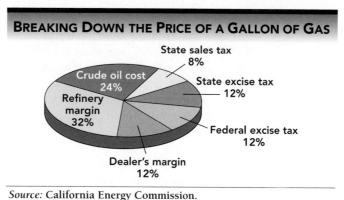

BREAKING DOWN THE PRICE OF A GALLON OF GAS

State sales tax 8%
Crude oil cost 24%
State excise tax 12%
Refinery margin 32%
Federal excise tax 12%
Dealer's margin 12%

Source: California Energy Commission.

FIGURE 9

SOLUTION

The sectors are sized to match how the price is divided. For example, most of the price (32%) goes to the refinery, while the least portion (8%) goes for state sales tax. As expected, the percents total 100%. If the price of gasoline is $3.50 per gallon,

Refinery margin: $3.50 × .32 = $1.12   Crude oil cost: $3.50 × .24 = $.84. ▪

32% converted to a decimal   24% converted to a decimal

A **bar graph** is used to show comparisons. We illustrate with a bar graph where we must estimate the heights of the bars.

EXAMPLE 5 Interpreting Information in a Bar Graph

The bar graph in Figure 10 shows sales in millions of dollars for CarMax Auto Super-stores, Inc. The graph compares sales for 5 years.

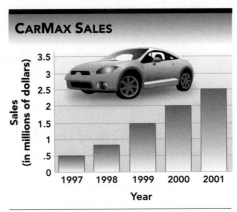

Source: Circuit City CarMax Group.

FIGURE 10

(a) Estimate sales in 1998.
(b) In what years were sales greater than $1 million?
(c) As the years progress, describe the change in sales.

SOLUTION

(a) Move horizontally from the top of the bar for 1998 to the scale on the left to see that sales in 1998 were about $.8 million.
(b) Locate 1 on the vertical scale and follow the line across to the right. Three years—1999, 2000, and 2001—have bars that extend above the line for 1, so sales were greater than $1 million in those years.
(c) Sales increase steadily as the years progress, from about $.5 million to $2.5 million.

A **line graph** is used to show changes or trends in data over time. To form a line graph, we connect a series of points representing data with line segments.

EXAMPLE 6 Interpreting Information in a Line Graph

The line graph in Figure 11 shows average prices for all types of gasoline in the U.S. for the years 1999 through 2004.

(a) In which years shown did the average price decrease from the previous year?
(b) What was the general trend in gasoline prices from 1999 to 2004?
(c) Estimate the average prices for 2002 and 2004. About how much did gasoline price rise from 2002 to 2004?

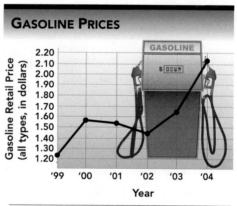

Source: Energy Information Administration.

FIGURE 11

SOLUTION

(a) The line segments joining the points for the years 2000, 2001, and 2002 fall from left to right. This indicates that average prices decreased from the previous years in 2001 and 2002.

(b) Although the prices fell in 2001 and 2002, the general trend is that prices rose from 1999 to 2004, as indicated by the overall rise of the line graph from left to right.

(c) It appears that in 2002 the average price was about \$1.44 and in 2004 about \$2.12. Thus, the price rose about \$2.12 − \$1.44 = \$.68 per gallon. ∎

For Further Thought

Are You "Numerate"?

Letter is to *number* as *literacy* is to *numeracy*. Much has been written about how important it is that the general population be "numerate." The essay "Quantity" by James T. Fey in *On the Shoulders of Giants: New Approaches to Numeracy* contains this description of an approach to numeracy.

Given the fundamental role of quantitative reasoning in applications of mathematics as well as the innate human attraction to numbers, it is not surprising that number concepts and skills form the core of school mathematics. In the earliest grades all children start on a mathematical path designed to develop computational procedures of arithmetic together with corresponding conceptual understanding that is required to solve quantitative problems and make informed decisions. Children learn many ways to describe quantitative data and relationships using numerical, graphic, and symbolic representations; to plan arithmetic and algebraic operations and to execute those plans using effective procedures; and to interpret quantitative information, to draw inferences, and to test the conclusions for reasonableness.

For Group Discussion or Individual Investigation

With calculator in hand, fill in the boxes with the digits 3, 4, 5, 6, 7, or 8, using each digit at most once. See how close you can come to the "goal number." You are allowed 1 minute per round. Good luck!

Round I   ☐ × ☐☐☐☐ = 30,000

Round II   ☐ × ☐☐☐☐ = 40,000

Round III   ☐ × ☐☐☐☐ = 50,000

Round IV ☐☐ × ☐☐☐☐ = 30,000

Round V   ☐☐ × ☐☐☐☐ = 60,000

1.4 EXERCISES

Exercises 1–20 are designed to give you practice in learning how to do some basic operations on your calculator. Perform the indicated operations and give as many digits in your answer as shown on your calculator display. (The number of displayed digits may vary depending on the model used.)

1. $39.7 + (8.2 - 4.1)$

2. $2.8 \times (3.2 - 1.1)$

3. $\sqrt{5.56440921}$

4. $\sqrt{37.38711025}$

5. $\sqrt[3]{418.508992}$

6. $\sqrt[3]{700.227072}$

7. 2.67^2

8. 3.49^3

9. 5.76^5

10. 1.48^6

11. $\dfrac{14.32 - 8.1}{2 \times 3.11}$

12. $\dfrac{12.3 + 18.276}{3 \times 1.04}$

13. $\sqrt[5]{1.35}$

14. $\sqrt[6]{3.21}$

15. $\dfrac{\pi}{\sqrt{2}}$

16. $\dfrac{2\pi}{\sqrt{3}}$

17. $\sqrt[4]{\dfrac{2143}{22}}$

18. $\dfrac{12{,}345{,}679 \times 72}{\sqrt[3]{27}}$

19. $\dfrac{\sqrt{2}}{\sqrt[3]{6}}$

20. $\dfrac{\sqrt[3]{12}}{\sqrt{3}}$

21. Choose any number consisting of five digits. Multiply it by 9 on your calculator. Now add the digits in the answer. If the sum is more than 9, add the digits of this sum, and repeat until the sum is less than 10. Your answer will always be 9. Repeat the exercise with a number consisting of six digits. Does the same result hold?

22. Use your calculator to *square* the following two-digit numbers ending in 5: 15, 25, 35, 45, 55, 65, 75, 85. Write down your results, and examine the pattern that develops. Then use inductive reasoning to predict the value of 95^2. Write an explanation of how you can mentally square a two-digit number ending in 5.

By examining several similar computation problems and their answers obtained on a calculator, we can use inductive reasoning to make conjectures about certain rules, laws, properties, and definitions in mathematics. Perform each calculation and observe the answers. Then fill in the blank with the appropriate response.

(Justification of these results will be discussed later in the book.)

23. $(-3) \times (-8)$; $(-5) \times (-4)$; $(-2.7) \times (-4.3)$
Multiplying a negative number by another negative number gives a _____ product.
(negative/positive)

24. $5 \times (-4)$; -3×8; $2.7 \times (-4.3)$
Multiplying a negative number by a positive number gives a _____ product.
(negative/positive)

25. 5.6^0; π^0; 2^0; 120^0; $.5^0$
Raising a nonzero number to the power 0 gives a result of _____.

26. 1^2; 1^3; 1^{-3}; 1^0; 1^{13}
Raising 1 to any power gives a result of _____.

27. $1/7$; $1/(-9)$; $1/3$; $1/(-8)$
The sign of the reciprocal of a number is _____ the sign of the number.
(the same as/different from)

28. $5/0$; $9/0$; $\pi/0$; $-3/0$; $0/0$
Dividing a number by 0 gives a(n) _____ on a calculator.

29. $0/8$; $0/2$; $0/(-3)$; $0/\pi$
Zero divided by a nonzero number gives a quotient of _____.

30. $(-3) \times (-4) \times (-5)$; $(-3) \times (-4) \times (-5) \times (-6) \times (-7)$; $(-3) \times (-4) \times (-5) \times (-6) \times (-7) \times (-8) \times (-9)$
Multiplying an *odd* number of negative numbers gives a _____ product.
(positive/negative)

31. $(-3) \times (-4)$; $(-3) \times (-4) \times (-5) \times (-6)$; $(-3) \times (-4) \times (-5) \times (-6) \times (-7) \times (-8)$
Multiplying an *even* number of negative numbers gives a _____ product.
(positive/negative)

32. $\sqrt{-3}$; $\sqrt{-5}$; $\sqrt{-6}$; $\sqrt{-10}$
Taking the square root of a negative number gives a(n) _____ on a calculator.

33. Find the decimal representation of $1/6$ on your calculator. Following the decimal point will be a 1 and a string of 6s. The final digit will be a 7 if your calculator *rounds off* or a 6 if it *truncates*. Which kind of calculator do you have?

34. Choose any three-digit number and enter the digits into a calculator. Then enter them again to get a six-digit number. Divide this six-digit number by 7. Divide the result by 13. Divide the result by 11. What is your answer? Explain why this happens.

35. Choose any digit except 0. Multiply it by 429. Now multiply the result by 259. What is your answer? Explain why this happens.

36. Choose two natural numbers. Add 1 to the second and divide by the first to get a third. Add 1 to the third and divide by the second to get a fourth. Add 1 to the fourth and divide by the third to get a fifth. Continue this process until you discover a pattern. What is the pattern?

When a four-function or scientific calculator (not a graphing calculator, however) is turned upside down, the digits in the display correspond to letters of the English alphabet as follows:

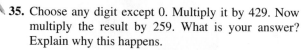

$$0 \leftrightarrow O \quad 3 \leftrightarrow E \quad 7 \leftrightarrow L$$
$$1 \leftrightarrow I \quad 4 \leftrightarrow h \quad 8 \leftrightarrow B$$
$$2 \leftrightarrow Z \quad 5 \leftrightarrow S \quad 9 \leftrightarrow G.$$

Perform the indicated calculation on a four-function or scientific calculator. Then turn your calculator upside down to read the word that belongs in the blank in the accompanying sentence.

37. $(100 \div 20) \times 14,215,469$
I filled my tank with gasoline from the _____ station.

38. $\dfrac{10 \times 10,609}{\sqrt{4}}$
"It's got to be the _____."

39. $60^2 - \dfrac{368}{4}$
The electronics manufacturer _____ produces the Wave Radio.

40. $187^2 + \sqrt{1600}$
Have you ever read *Mother* _____ nursery rhymes?

41. Make up your own exercise similar to Exercises 37–40.

42. Displayed digits on some calculators show some or all of the parts in the pattern as in the figure at the top of the next column. For the digits 0 through 9:
    (a) Which part is used most frequently?
    (b) Which part is used the least?

    (c) Which digit uses the most parts?
    (d) Which digit uses the fewest parts?

Give an appropriate counting number answer to each question in Exercises 43–46. (Find the least counting number that will work.)

43. **Pages to Store Trading Cards** A plastic page designed to hold trading cards will hold up to 9 cards. How many pages will be needed to store 563 cards?

44. **Drawers for Videocassettes** A sliding drawer designed to hold videocassettes has 20 compartments. If Chris wants to house his collection of 408 Disney videotapes, how many such drawers will he need?

45. **Containers for African Violets** A gardener wants to fertilize 800 African violets. Each container of fertilizer will supply up to 60 plants. How many containers will she need to do the job?

46. **Fifth-Grade Teachers Needed** False River Academy has 155 fifth-grade students. The principal, Butch LeBeau, has decided that each fifth-grade teacher should have a maximum of 24 students. How many fifth-grade teachers does he need?

In Exercises 47–52, use estimation to determine the choice closest to the correct answer.

47. **Price per Acre of Land** To build a "millennium clock" on Mount Washington in Nevada that would tick once each year, chime once each century, and last at least 10,000 years, the nonprofit Long Now Foundation

purchased 80 acres of land for $140,000. Which one of the following is the closest estimate to the price per acre?
A. $1000   **B.** $2000   **C.** $4000   **D.** $11,200

48. **Time of a Round Trip** The distance from Seattle, Washington, to Sprinfield, Missouri, is 2009 miles. About how many hours would a roundtrip from Seattle to Springfield and back take a bus that averages 50 miles per hour for the entire trip?
A. 60   **B.** 70   **C.** 80   **D.** 90

49. **People per Square Mile** Buffalo County in Nebraska has a population of 40,249 and covers 968 square miles. About how many people per square mile live in Buffalo County?
A. 40   **B.** 400   **C.** 4000   **D.** 40,000

50. **Revolutions of Mercury** The planet Mercury takes 88.0 Earth days to revolve around the sun once. Pluto takes 90,824.2 days to do the same. When Pluto has revolved around the sun once, about how many times will Mercury have revolved around the sun?
A. 100,000   **B.** 10,000   **C.** 1000   **D.** 100

51. **Rushing Average** In 2004, Muhsin Muhammad of the Carolina Panthers caught 93 passes for 1405 yards. His approximate number of yards gained per catch was _____.
A. $\dfrac{9}{14}$ **B.** 140   **C.** 1.4   **D.** 14

52. **Area of the Sistine Chapel** The Sistine Chapel in Vatican City measures 40.5 meters by 13.5 meters.

Which is the closest approximation to its area?
A. 110 meters   **B.** 55 meters
C. 110 square meters   **D.** 600 square meters

The circle graph at the top of the next column shows the approximate percent of immigrants admitted into the United States during the 1990s. Use the graph to answer the questions in Exercises 53–56.

53. What percent of the immigrants were from the "Other" group of countries?

U.S. IMMIGRANTS BY REGION OF BIRTH

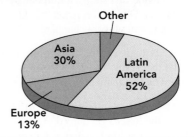

Source: U.S. Bureau of the Census.

54. What percent of the immigrants were not from Asia?

55. In a group of 2,000,000 immigrants, how many would you expect to be from Europe?

56. In a group of 4,000,000 immigrants, how many more would there be from Latin America than all the other regions combined?

The bar graph shows the amount of personal savings, in billions of dollars, accumulated during the years 1997 through 2001. Use the graph to answer the questions in Exercises 57–60.

PERSONAL SAVINGS IN THE UNITED STATES

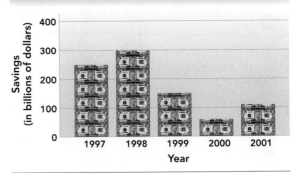

Source: U.S. Bureau of Economic Analysis.

57. Which year had the greatest amount of savings? Which had the least?

58. Which years had amounts greater than $200 billion?

59. Approximately how much was the amount for 1997? for 1998?

60. Approximately how much more was saved in 1998 than 1997?

The line graph indicates that current projections for Medicare funding will not cover its costs unless the program changes. Use the graph to answer the questions in Exercises 61–64.

61. Which is the only period in which Medicare funds are predicted to increase?

62. By approximately how much will the funds decrease between the years 2005 and 2006?

63. How do the amounts for 2004 and 2007 compare?

64. In which year will funds first show a deficit?

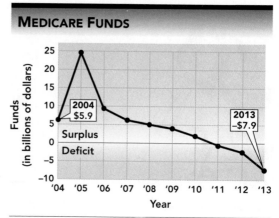

MEDICARE FUNDS

Source: Centers for Medicare and Medicaid Services.

EXTENSION
Using Writing to Learn About Mathematics

Research has indicated that the ability to express mathematical observations in writing can serve as a positive force in one's continued development as a mathematics student. The implementation of writing in the mathematics class can use several approaches.

Journals   One way of using writing in mathematics is to keep a journal in which you spend a few minutes explaining what happened in class that day. The journal entries may be general or specific, depending on the topic covered, the degree to which you understand the topic, your interest level at the time, and so on. Journal entries are usually written in informal language, and are often an effective means of communicating to yourself, your classmates, and your instructor what feelings, perceptions, and concerns you are having at the time.

Learning Logs   Although journal entries are for the most part unstructured writings in which the student's thoughts are allowed to roam freely, entries in learning logs are typically more structured. An instructor may pose a specific question for a student to answer in a learning log. In this text, we intersperse writing exercises in each exercise set that are appropriate for answering in a learning log. For example, consider Exercise 13 in the exercise set for the opening section in this chapter.

Discuss the differences between inductive and deductive reasoning. Give an example of each.

(continued)

Here is a possible response to this exercise.

> *Deductive reasoning occurs when you go from general ideas to specific ones. For example, I know that I can multiply both sides of $\frac{1}{2}x = 6$ by 2 to get $x = 12$, because I can multiply both sides of any equation by whatever I want (except 0). Inductive reasoning goes the other way. If I make a general conclusion from specific observations, that's inductive reasoning. Example — in the numbers 4, 8, 12, 16, and so on, I can conclude that the next number is 20, since I always add 4 to get the next number.*

Mathematical writing takes many forms. One of the most famous author/mathematicians was **Charles Dodgson** (1832–1898), who used the pen name **Lewis Carroll.**

Dodgson was a mathematics lecturer at Oxford University in England. Queen Victoria told Dodgson how much she enjoyed *Alice's Adventures in Wonderland* and how much she wanted to read his next book; he is said to have sent her *Symbolic Logic,* his most famous mathematical work.

The *Alice* books made Carroll famous. Late in life, however, Dodgson shunned attention and denied that he and Carroll were the same person, even though he gave away hundreds of signed copies to children and children's hospitals.

Reports on Articles from Mathematics Publications   The motto "Publish or perish" has long been around, implying that a scholar in pursuit of an academic position must publish in a journal in his or her field. There are numerous journals that publish papers in mathematics research and/or mathematics education. In Activity 3 at the end of this section, we provide some suggestions of articles that have appeared within the last few years. A report on such an article can help you understand what mathematicians do and what ideas mathematics teachers use to convey concepts to their students.

Term Papers   Professors in mathematics survey courses are, in increasing numbers, requiring short term papers of their students. In this way, you can become aware of the plethora of books and articles on mathematics and mathematicians, many written specifically for the layperson. In Activities 5 and 6 at the end of this section, we provide a list of possible term paper topics.

EXTENSION ACTIVITIES

Rather than include a typical exercise set, we list some suggested activities in which writing can be used to enhance awareness and learning of mathematics.

Activity 1   Keep a journal. After each class, write for a few minutes on your perceptions about the class, the topics covered, or whatever you feel is appropriate. You may want to use the following guidelines.

> **Journal Writing***
>
> 1. *WHO should write in your journal?* You should.
>
> 2. *WHAT should you write in your journal?* New words, ideas, formulas, or concepts; profound thoughts; wonderings, musings, problems to solve; reflections on the class; questions—both answerable and unanswerable; writing ideas
>
> 3. *WHEN should you write in your journal?* After class each day; as you are preparing, reading, or studying for class; anytime an insight or question hits you.
>
> 4. *WHERE should you write in your journal?* Anywhere—so keep it with you when possible.
>
> 5. *WHY should you write in your journal?* It will help you record ideas that you might otherwise forget. It will be worthwhile for you to read later on so that you can note your growth. It will facilitate your learning, problem solving, writing, reading, and discussion in class.
>
> 6. *HOW should you write in your journal?* In wonderful, long, flowing sentences with perfect punctuation and perfect spelling and in perfect handwriting; or in single words that express your ideas, in short phrases, in sketches, in numbers, in maps, in diagrams, in sentences. (You may even prefer to organize your journal entries on your desktop, notebook, or palmtop computer.)

Activity 2 Keep a learning log, answering at least one writing exercise from each exercise set covered in your class syllabus. Ask your teacher for suggestions of other types of specific writing assignments. For example, you might want to choose a numbered example from a section in the text and write your own solution to the problem, or comment on the method that the authors use to solve the problem. Don't be afraid to be critical of the method used in the text.

Activity 3 The National Council of Teachers of Mathematics publishes journals in mathematics education: *Teaching Children Mathematics* (formerly called *Arithmetic Teacher*) and *Mathematics Teacher* are two of them. These journals can be found in the periodicals section of most college and university libraries. We have chosen several recent articles in each of these journals. There are thousands of other articles from which to choose. Write a short report on one of these articles according to guidelines specified by your instructor.

From *Mathematics Teacher*
2001

Johnson, Craig M. "Functions of Number Theory in Music." Vol. 94, No. 8, November 2001, p. 700.

Lightner, James E. "Mathematics Didn't Just Happen." Vol. 94, No. 9, December 2001, p. 780.

---

*"Journal Writing" from "No Time for Writing in Your Class?" by Margaret E. McIntosh in *Mathematics Teacher,* September 1991, p. 431. Reprinted by permission.

(continued)

McNeill, Sheila A. "The Mayan Zeros." Vol. 94, No. 7, October 2001, p. 590.

Socha, Susan. "Less Is Sometimes More." Vol. 94, No. 6, September 2001, p. 450.

2002

Houser, Don. "Roots in Music." Vol. 95, No. 1, January 2002, p. 16.

Howe, Roger. "Hermione Granger's Solution." Vol. 95, No. 2, February 2002, p. 86.

Kolpas, Sidney J. "Let Your Fingers Do the Multiplying." Vol. 95, No. 4, April 2002, p. 246.

Van Dresar, Vickie J. "Opening Young Minds to Closure Properties." Vol. 95, No. 5, May 2002, p. 326.

2003

McDaniel, Michael. "Not Just Another Theorem: A Cultural and Historical Event." Vol. 96, No. 4, April 2003, p. 282.

Nelson, Joanne E., Margaret Coffey, and Edie Huffman. "Stop This Runaway Truck, Please." Vol. 96, No. 8, November 2003, p. 548.

Roberts, David L., and Angela L. E. Walmsley. "The Original New Math: Storytelling versus History." Vol. 96, No. 7, October 2003, p. 468.

Yoshinobu, Stan T. "Mathematics, Politics, and Greenhouse Gas Intensity: An Example of Using Polya's Problem-Solving Strategy." Vol. 96, No. 9, December 2003, p. 646.

2004

Devaney, Robert L. "Fractal Patterns and Chaos Games." Vol. 98, No. 4, November 2004, p. 228.

Francis, Richard L. "New Worlds to Conquer." Vol. 98, No. 3, October 2004, p. 166.

Hansen, Will. "War and Pieces." Vol. 98, No. 2, September 2004, p. 70.

Mahoney, John F. "How Many Votes Are Needed to Be Elected President?" Vol. 98, No. 3, October 2004, p. 154.

From *Teaching Children Mathematics*

2001

Karp, Karen S., and E. Todd Brown. "Geo-Dolls: Traveling in a Mathematical World." Vol. 8, No. 3, November 2001, p. 132.

Randolph, Tamela D., and Helene J. Sherman. "Alternative Algorithms: Increasing Options, Reducing Errors." Vol. 7, No. 8, April 2001, p. 480.

Sun, Wei, and Joanne Y. Zhang. "Teaching Addition and Subtraction Facts: A Chinese Perspective." Vol. 8, No. 1, September 2001, p. 28.

Whitenack, Joy W., et. al. "Second Graders Circumvent Addition and Subtraction Difficulties." Vol. 8, No. 4, December 2001, p. 228.

2002

Agosto, Melinda. "Cool Mathematics for Kids." Vol. 8, No. 7, March 2002, p. 397.

Huniker, DeAnn. "Calculators as Learning Tools for Young Children's Explorations of Number." Vol. 8, No. 6, February 2002, p. 316.

Strutchens, Marilyn E. "Multicultural Literature as a Context for Problem Solving: Children and Parents Learning Together." Vol. 8, No. 8, April 2002, p. 448.

Whitin, David J. "The Potentials and Pitfalls of Integrating Literature into the Mathematics Program." Vol. 8, No. 9, May 2002, p. 503.

2003

Arvold, Bridget, Gina Stone, and Lynn Carter. "What Do You Get When You Cross a Math Professor and a Body Builder?" Vol. 9, No. 7, March 2003, p. 408.

Edelson, R. Jill, and Gretchen L. Johnson. "Integrating Music and Mathematics in the Elementary Classroom." Vol. 9, No. 8, April 2003, p. 474.

Phillips, Linda J. "When Flash Cards Are Not Enough." Vol. 9, No. 6, February 2003, p. 358.

Uy, Frederick L. "The Chinese Numeration System and Place Value." Vol. 9, No. 5, January 2003, p. 243.

2004

Anthony, Glenda J., and Margaret A. Walshaw. "Zero: A 'None' Number?" Vol. 11, No. 1, August 2004, p. 38.

Buschman, Larry. "Teaching Problem Solving in Mathematics." Vol. 10, No. 6, February 2004, p. 302.

Joram, Elana, Christina Hartman, and Paul R. Trafton. "'As People Get Older, They Get Taller': An Integrated Unit on Measurement, Linear Relationships, and Data Analysis." Vol. 10, No. 7, March 2004, p. 344.

Mann, Rebecca L. "Balancing Act: The Truth Behind the Equals Sign." Vol. 11, No. 2, September 2004, p. 65.

Activity 4   One of the most popular mathematical films of all time is *Donald in Mathmagic Land*, produced by Disney in 1959. Spend an entertaining half-hour watching this film, and write a report on it according to the guidelines of your instructor.

Activity 5   Write a report according to the guidelines of your instructor on one of the following mathematicians, philosophers, and scientists.

Abel, N.	Cardano, G.	Gauss, C.	Noether, E.
Agnesi, M. G.	Copernicus, N.	Hilbert, D.	Pascal, B.
Agnesi, M. T.	De Morgan, A.	Kepler, J.	Plato
Al-Khowârizmi	Descartes, R.	Kronecker, L.	Polya, G.
Apollonius	Euler, L.	Lagrange, J.	Pythagoras
Archimedes	Fermat, P.	Leibniz, G.	Ramanujan, S.
Aristotle	Fibonacci	L'Hospital, G.	Riemann, G.
Babbage, C.	(Leonardo	Lobachevsky, N.	Russell, B.
Bernoulli, Jakob	of Pisa)	Mandelbrot, B.	Somerville, M.
Bernoulli,	Galileo (Galileo	Napier, J.	Tartaglia, N.
Johann	Galilei)	Nash, J.	Whitehead, A.
Cantor, G.	Galois, E.	Newton, I.	Wiles, A.

(continued)

Activity 6 Write a term paper on one of the following topics in mathematics according to the guidelines of your instructor.

Babylonian mathematics
Egyptian mathematics
The origin of zero
Plimpton 322
The Rhind papyrus
Origins of the Pythagorean
  theorem
The regular (Platonic) solids
The Pythagorean brotherhood
The Golden Ratio (Golden
  Section)
The three famous construction
  problems of the Greeks
The history of the approximations
  of π
Euclid and his "Elements"
Early Chinese mathematics
Early Hindu mathematics
Origin of the word *algebra*
Magic squares
Figurate numbers
The Fibonacci sequence
The Cardano/Tartaglia controversy
Historical methods of computation
  (logarithms, the abacus, Napier's
  rods, the slide rule, etc.)

Pascal's triangle
The origins of probability theory
Women in mathematics
Mathematical paradoxes
Unsolved problems in
  mathematics
The four color theorem
The proof of Fermat's Last
  Theorem
The search for large primes
Fractal geometry
The co-inventors of calculus
The role of the computer in the
  study of mathematics
Mathematics and music
Police mathematics
The origins of complex numbers
Goldbach's conjecture
The use of the Internet in
  mathematics education
The development of graphing
  calculators
Mathematics education reform
  movement
Multicultural mathematics
The Riemann Hypothesis

Activity 7 Investigate a computer program that focuses on teaching children elementary mathematics and write a critical review of it as if you were writing for a journal that contains software reviews of educational material. Be sure to address the higher-level thinking skills in addition to drill and practice.

Activity 8 The following Web sites provide a fascinating list of mathematics-related topics. Go to one of them, choose a topic that interests you, and report on it, according to the guidelines of your instructor.

www.mathworld.wolfram.com

www.world.std.com/~reinhold/mathmovies.html

www.mcs.surrey.ac.uk/Personal/R.Knott/

www.dir.yahoo.com/Science/Mathematics/

www.cut-the-knot.com/

www.ics.uci.edu/~eppstein/recmath.html

🎥 ***Activity 9***   A theme of mathematics-related scenes in movies and television is found throughout this book. Prepare a report on one or more such scenes, and determine whether the mathematics involved is correct or incorrect. If correct, show why; if incorrect, find the correct answer. The Website

www.world.std.com/~reinhold/mathmovies.html

provides a wealth of information on mathematics in the movies.

🎥 ***Activity 10***   The longest running animated television show is *The Simpsons*, having begun in 1989. The Website

www.simpsonsmath.com

explores the occurrence of mathematics in the episodes on a season-by-season basis. Watch several episodes and elaborate on the mathematics found in them.

COLLABORATIVE INVESTIGATION

Discovering Patterns in Pascal's Triangle

One fascinating array of numbers, *Pascal's triangle,* consists of rows of numbers, each of which contains one more entry than the one before. The first five rows are shown here.

```
        1
      1   1
    1   2   1
  1   3   3   1
1   4   6   4   1
```

To discover some of its patterns, divide the class into groups of four students each. Within each group designate one student as A, one as B, one as C, and one as D. Then perform the following activities in order.

1. Discuss among group members some of the properties of the triangle that are obvious from observing the first five rows shown.

2. It is fairly obvious that each row begins and ends with 1. Discover a method whereby the other entries in a row can be determined from the entries in the

row immediately above it. (*Hint:* In the fifth row, $6 = 3 + 3$.) Then, as a group, find the next four rows of the triangle, and have each member prepare his or her own copy of the entire first nine rows for later reference.

3. Now each student in the group will investigate a particular property of the triangle. In some cases, a calculator will be helpful. All students should begin working at the same time. (A discussion follows.)

Student A: Find the sum of the entries in each row. Notice the pattern that emerges. Now write the tenth row of the triangle.

Student B: Investigate the successive differences in the diagonals from upper left to lower right. For example, in the diagonal that begins 1, 2, 3, 4, . . . , the successive differences are all 1; in the diagonal that begins 1, 3, 6, . . . , the successive differences are 2, 3, 4, and so on. Do this up through the diagonal that begins 1, 6, 21, ...

Student C: Find the values of the first five powers of the number 11, starting with 11^0 (recall $11^0 = 1$).

Student D: Arrange the nine rows of the triangle with all rows "flush left," and then draw lightly dashed arrows as shown:

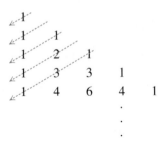

and so on. Then add along the diagonals. Write these sums in order from left to right.

4. After all students have concluded their individual investigations in Item 3, return to a group discussion.

   (a) Have student A report the result found in Item 3, and then make a prediction concerning the sum of the entries in the tenth row.

(b) Have student B report the successive differences discovered in the diagonals. Then have all students in the group investigate the successive differences in the diagonal that begins 1, 7, 28. . . . (It may be necessary to write a few more rows of the triangle.)

(c) Have student C report the relationship between the powers of 11 found, and then determine the value of 11^5. Why does the pattern not continue here?

(d) Have student D report the sequence of numbers found. Then, as a group, predict what the next sum will be by observing the pattern in the sequence. Confirm your prediction by actual computation.

5. Choose a representative from each group to report to the entire class the observations made throughout this investigation.

6. Find a reference to Pascal's triangle using a search engine of the Internet and prepare a report on the reference.

CHAPTER 1 TEST

In Exercises 1 and 2, decide whether the reasoning involved is an example of inductive or deductive reasoning.

1. Jane Fleming is a sales representative for a publishing company. For the past 14 years, she has exceeded her annual sales goal, primarily by selling mathematics textbooks. Therefore, she will also exceed her annual sales goal this year.

2. For all natural numbers n, n^2 is also a natural number. 101 is a natural number. Therefore, 101^2 is a natural number.

3. What are the fourth and fifth numbers in this sequence?

$$1, 4, 27, \underline{\hspace{1cm}}, \underline{\hspace{1cm}}, 46656, \ldots$$

(From *Mathematics Teacher* monthly calendar, April 25, 1994)

4. Use the list of equations and inductive reasoning to predict the next equation, and then verify your conjecture.

$$65,359,477,124,183 \times 17 = 1,111,111,111,111,111$$
$$65,359,477,124,183 \times 34 = 2,222,222,222,222,222$$
$$65,359,477,124,183 \times 51 = 3,333,333,333,333,333$$

5. Use the method of successive differences to find the next term in the sequence

$$3, 11, 31, 69, 131, 223, \ldots.$$

6. Find the sum $1 + 2 + 3 + \cdots + 250$.

7. Consider the following equations, where the left side of each is an octagonal number.

$$1 = 1$$
$$8 = 1 + 7$$
$$21 = 1 + 7 + 13$$
$$40 = 1 + 7 + 13 + 19$$

Use the pattern established on the right sides to predict the next octagonal number. What is the next equation in the list?

8. Use the result of Exercise 7 and the method of successive differences to find the first eight octagonal numbers. Then divide each by 4 and record the remainder. What is the pattern obtained?

9. Describe the pattern used to obtain the terms of the Fibonacci sequence 1, 1, 2, 3, 5, 8, 13, 21, ...

Use problem-solving strategies to solve each problem, taken from the date indicated in the monthly calendar of Mathematics Teacher.

10. *Building a Fraction* Each of the four digits 2, 4, 6, and 9 is placed in one of the boxes to form a fraction. The numerator and the denominator are both two-digit whole numbers. What is the smallest value of all the common fractions that can be formed? Express your answer as a common fraction. (November 17, 2004)

11. *Units Digit of a Power of 9* What is the units digit (ones digit) in the decimal representation of 9^{1997}? (January 27, 1997)

12. *Counting Puzzle (Triangles)* How many triangles are in this figure? (January 6, 2000)

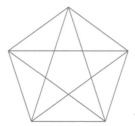

13. *Devising a Correct Addition Problem* Can you put the digits 1 through 9, each used once, in the boxes of the problem below to make an addition problem that has carrying and that is correct? If so, find a solution. If not, explain why no solution exists. (April 10, 2002)

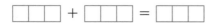

14. *Missing Pages in a Newspaper* A sixty-page newspaper, which consists of only one section, has the sheet with page 7 missing. What other pages are missing? (February 6, 1998)

15. *Units Digit of a Sum* Find the units digit (ones digit) of the decimal numeral representing the number $11^{11} + 14^{14} + 16^{16}$. (February 14, 1994)

16. Based on your knowledge of elementary arithmetic, describe the pattern that can be observed when the following operations are performed: 9×1, 9×2, $9 \times 3, \ldots, 9 \times 9$. (*Hint:* Add the digits in the answers. What do you notice?)

Use your calculator to evaluate each of the following. Give as many decimal places as the calculator displays.

17. $\sqrt{98.16}$

18. 3.25^3

19. *Basketball Scoring Results* During her NCAA women's basketball career, Seimone Augustus of LSU made 800 of her 1488 field goal attempts. This means that for every 15 attempts, she made approximately _____ of them.
A. 4 **B.** 8 **C.** 6 **D.** 2

20. *Women in Mathematics* The accompanying graph shows the number of women in mathematics or computer science professions during the past three decades.

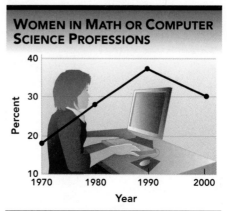

Source: U.S. Bureau of the Census and Bureau of Labor Statistics.

(a) In what decade (10-year period) did the percent of women in math or computer science professions decrease?
(b) When did the percent of women in math or computer science professions reach a maximum?
(c) In what year was the percent of women in math or computer science professions about 27%?

THE BASIC CONCEPTS OF SET THEORY

In the 1994 movie *I.Q.*, Meg Ryan plays Catherine Boyd, Alfred Einstein's brilliant niece, who is attracted to blue-collar worker Ed Walters (Tim Robbins). Ed pretends to be a physicist so that Catherine will not know his real background. In a charming scene, Catherine and Ed are standing a few feet apart while music is playing in the background.

ED: I think your uncle wants us to dance.

CATHERINE: Oh, now, don't be irrelevant, Ed. You can't get from there to here.

ED: Why not?

CATHERINE: Now don't tell me that a famous and brilliant scientist such as yourself doesn't know about Zeno's paradox.

ED: Remind me.

CATHERINE: You can't get from there to here because you always have to cover half the remaining distance, like from me to you. (Moving in increments of one-half) I have to cover half of it. Then, see, I still have half of that remaining, so I cover half that. I still have half of that left, so I cover half of that. Half of that . . . half of that . . . half of that . . . and since there are infinite halves left, I can't ever get there.

ED (reaching out and taking her in his arms and starting to dance): So how did that happen?

CATHERINE: I don't know.

Something in our human nature encourages us to collect things: baseball cards, Barbie dolls, coins, stamps, cars, and so on. A collection of objects is called a *set*, and this chapter deals with the mathematical aspects of sets. Prior to the twentieth century some ideas in set theory were considered *paradoxes* (wrong opinions). Zeno's paradox, as described by Catherine and seen in Exercises 51 and 52 of Section 2.5, has been around in several forms for thousands of years.

51

2.1 | Symbols and Terminology

Designating Sets • Sets of Numbers and Cardinality • Finite and Infinite Sets • Equality of Sets

The basic ideas of set theory were developed by the German mathematician **Georg Cantor** (1845–1918) in about 1875. Cantor created a new field of theory and at the same time continued the long debate over infinity that began in ancient times. He developed counting by one-to-one correspondence to determine how many objects are contained in a set. Infinite sets differ from finite sets by not obeying the familiar law that the whole is greater than any of its parts.

Designating Sets The human mind likes to create collections. Instead of seeing a group of five stars as five separate items, people tend to see them as one group of stars. The mind tries to find order and patterns. In mathematics this tendency to create collections is represented with the idea of a *set*. A **set** is a collection of objects. The objects belonging to the set are called the **elements**, or **members**, of the set.

Sets are designated using the following three methods: (1) *word description*, (2) the *listing method*, and (3) *set-builder notation*. A given set may be more conveniently denoted by one method rather than another, but most sets can be given in any of the three ways, as shown.

The set of even counting numbers less than 10   Word description

$\{2, 4, 6, 8\}$ Listing method

$\{x \mid x$ is an even counting number less than $10\}$ Set-builder notation

In the listing and set-builder notations, the braces at the beginning and ending indicate a set. Also, in the listing method, the commas between successive entries are essential. The set-builder notation above is read "the set of all x such that x is an even counting number less than 10."

Set-builder notation uses the algebraic idea of a *variable*. (Any symbol would do, but just as in other algebraic applications, the letter x is a common choice.) Before the vertical line we give the variable, which represents an element in general, and after the vertical line we state the criteria by which an element qualifies for membership in the set. By including *all* objects that meet the stated criteria, we generate (or build) the entire set.

Sets are commonly given names (usually capital letters). If E is selected as a name for the set of all letters of the English alphabet, then we can write

$$E = \{a, b, c, d, e, f, g, h, i, j, k, l, m, n, o, p, q, r, s, t, u, v, w, x, y, z\}.$$

The listing notation can often be shortened by establishing the pattern of elements included, and using ellipsis points to indicate a continuation of the pattern. Thus,

$$E = \{a, b, c, d, \ldots, x, y, z\} \quad \text{or} \quad E = \{a, b, c, d, e, \ldots, z\}.$$

The set containing no elements is called the **empty set**, or **null set**. The symbol $\emptyset$ is used to denote the empty set, so $\emptyset$ and { } have the same meaning. We do *not* denote the empty set with the symbol $\{\emptyset\}$ because this notation represents a set with one element (that element being the empty set).

EXAMPLE 1   Listing Elements of Sets

Give a complete listing of all the elements of each of the following sets.

(a) the set of counting numbers between six and thirteen
(b) $\{5, 6, 7, \ldots, 13\}$
(c) $\{x \mid x$ is a counting number between 6 and 7$\}$

SOLUTION

(a) This set can be denoted {7, 8, 9, 10, 11, 12}. (Notice that the word *between* excludes the endpoint values.)

(b) This set begins with the element 5, then 6, then 7, and so on, with each element obtained by adding 1 to the previous element in the list. This pattern stops at 13, so a complete listing is

$$\{5, 6, 7, 8, 9, 10, 11, 12, 13\}.$$

(c) There are no counting numbers between 6 and 7, and thus this is the empty set $\emptyset$. ▪

For a set to be useful, it must be well defined. This means that if a particular set and some particular element are given, it must be possible to tell whether the element belongs to the set. For example, the preceding set E of the letters of the English alphabet is well defined. Given the letter q, we know that q is an element of E. Given the Greek letter θ (theta), we know that it is not an element of set E.

However, given the set C of all fat chickens, and a particular chicken, Hortense, it is not possible to say whether

Hortense is an element of C or   Hortense is *not* an element of C.

The problem is the word "fat"; how fat is fat? Because we cannot necessarily decide whether a given chicken belongs to set C, set C is not well defined.

The letter q is an element of set E, where E is the set of all the letters of the English alphabet. To show this, $\in$ is used to replace the words "is an element of," or

$$q \in E,$$

which is read "q is an element of set E." The letter θ is not an element of E. To show this, $\in$ with a slash mark is used to replace the words "is not an element of," written

$$\theta \notin E.$$

This is read "θ is not an element of set E."

> **EXAMPLE 2   Applying the Symbol $\in$**

Decide whether each statement is true or false.

(a) $3 \in \{1, 2, 5, 9, 13\}$

(b) $0 \in \{0, 1, 2, 3\}$

(c) $\dfrac{1}{5} \notin \left\{\dfrac{1}{3}, \dfrac{1}{4}, \dfrac{1}{6}\right\}$

SOLUTION

(a) Because 3 is *not* an element of the set {1, 2, 5, 9, 13}, the statement is false.

(b) Because 0 is indeed an element of the set {0, 1, 2, 3}, the statement is true.

(c) This statement says that $\frac{1}{5}$ is not an element of the set $\left\{\frac{1}{3}, \frac{1}{4}, \frac{1}{6}\right\}$, which is true. ▪

Sets of Numbers and Cardinality

Example 1 referred to counting numbers (or natural numbers), which were introduced in Section 1.1. Other important categories of numbers, which are used throughout the text, are summarized on the next page.

Sets of Numbers

Natural or Counting numbers $\{1, 2, 3, 4, \ldots\}$

Whole numbers $\{0, 1, 2, 3, 4, \ldots\}$

Integers $\{\ldots, -3, -2, -1, 0, 1, 2, 3, \ldots\}$

Rational numbers $\left\{\frac{p}{q} \mid p \text{ and } q \text{ are integers, and } q \neq 0\right\}$
(Some examples of rational numbers are $\frac{3}{5}$, $-\frac{7}{9}$, 5, and 0. Any rational number may be written as a terminating decimal number, like .25, or a repeating decimal number, like .666 . . . .)

Real numbers $\{x \mid x \text{ is a number that can be expressed as a decimal}\}$

Irrational numbers $\{x \mid x \text{ is a real number and } x \text{ cannot be expressed as a quotient of integers}\}$
(Some examples of irrational numbers are $\sqrt{2}$, $\sqrt[3]{4}$, and π. Decimal representations of irrational numbers never terminate and never repeat.)

The number of elements in a set is called the **cardinal number,** or **cardinality,** of the set. The symbol $\textbf{\textit{n}}(\textbf{\textit{A}})$, which is read **"*n* of *A*,"** represents the cardinal number of set A.

If elements are repeated in a set listing, they should not be counted more than once when determining the cardinal number of the set. For example, the set

$$B = \{1, 1, 2, 2, 3\}$$

has only three distinct elements, and so

$$n(B) = 3.$$

EXAMPLE 3 Finding Cardinal Numbers

Find the cardinal number of each set.

(a) $K = \{2, 4, 8, 16\}$ (b) $M = \{0\}$
(c) $R = \{4, 5, \ldots, 12, 13\}$ (d) $\emptyset$

SOLUTION

(a) Set K contains four elements, so the cardinal number of set K is 4, and $n(K) = 4$.
(b) Set M contains only one element, zero, so $n(M) = 1$.
(c) There are only four elements listed, but the ellipsis points indicate that there are other elements in the set. Counting them, we find that there are ten elements, so $n(R) = 10$.
(d) The empty set, $\emptyset$, contains no elements, and $n(\emptyset) = 0$. ◼

A close-up of a camera lens shows the **infinity symbol, ∞**, defined as any distance greater than 1000 times the focal length of a lens.

The sign was invented by the mathematician John Wallis in 1655. Wallis used 1/∞ to represent an infinitely small quantity.

Finite and Infinite Sets If the cardinal number of a set is a particular whole number (0 or a counting number), as in all parts of Example 3, we call that set a **finite set.** Given enough time, we could finish counting all the elements of any finite set and arrive at its cardinal number. Some sets, however, are so large that we could never finish the counting process. The counting numbers themselves are such a set. Whenever a set is so large that its cardinal number is not found among the whole numbers, we call that set an **infinite set**. Infinite sets can be designated using the three methods already mentioned.

EXAMPLE 4 Designating an Infinite Set

Designate all odd counting numbers by the three common methods of set notation.

SOLUTION

The set of all odd counting numbers   Word description

$\{1, 3, 5, 7, 9, \ldots\}$ Listing method

$\{x | x \text{ is an odd counting number}\}$ Set-builder notation

Equality of Sets

Set Equality

Set A is **equal** to set B provided the following two conditions are met:

1. Every element of A is an element of B, and
2. Every element of B is an element of A.

Informally, two sets are equal if they contain exactly the same elements, regardless of order. For example,

$\{a, b, c, d\} = \{a, c, d, b\}.$ Both sets contain exactly the same elements.

Because repetition of elements in a set listing does not add new elements,

$\{1, 0, 1, 2, 3, 3\} = \{0, 1, 2, 3\}$ Both sets contain exactly the same elements.

EXAMPLE 5 Determining Whether Two Sets are Equal

Are $\{-4, 3, 2, 5\}$ and $\{-4, 0, 3, 2, 5\}$ equal sets?

SOLUTION

Every element of the first set is an element of the second; however, 0 is an element of the second and not the first. In other words, the sets do not contain exactly the same elements, so they are not equal: $\{-4, 3, 2, 5\} \neq \{-4, 0, 3, 2, 5\}.$

EXAMPLE 6 Determining Whether Two Sets are Equal

Decide whether each statement is *true* or *false*.

(a) $\{3\} = \{x | x \text{ is a counting number between 1 and 5}\}$
(b) $\{x | x \text{ is a negative natural number}\} = \{y | y \text{ is a number that is both rational and irrational}\}$

SOLUTION

(a) The set on the right contains *all* counting numbers between 1 and 5, namely 2, 3, and 4, while the set on the left contains *only* the number 3. Because the sets do not contain exactly the same elements, they are not equal. The statement is false.
(b) All natural numbers are positive, so the set on the left is $\emptyset$. By definition, if a number is rational, it cannot be irrational, so the set on the right is also $\emptyset$. Because each set is the empty set, the sets are equal. The statement is true.

2.1 EXERCISES

Match each set in Column I with the appropriate description in Column II.

I	II
1. {2, 4, 6, 8}	**A.** the set of all even integers
2. {$x \mid x$ is an even integer greater than 4 and less than 6}	**B.** the set of the five least positive integer powers of 2
3. {. . . , −4, −3, −2, −1}	**C.** the set of even positive integers less than 10
4. {. . . , −6, −4, −2, 0, 2, 4, 6, . . .}	**D.** the set of all odd integers
5. {2, 4, 8, 16, 32}	**E.** the set of all negative integers
6. {. . . , −5, −3, −1, 1, 3, 5, . . .}	**F.** the set of odd positive integers less than 10
7. {2, 4, 6, 8, 10}	**G.** ∅
8. {1, 3, 5, 7, 9}	**H.** the set of the five least positive integer multiples of 2

List all the elements of each set. Use set notation and the listing method to describe the set.

9. the set of all counting numbers less than or equal to 6

10. the set of all whole numbers greater than 8 and less than 18

11. the set of all whole numbers not greater than 4

12. the set of all counting numbers between 4 and 14

13. {6, 7, 8, . . . , 14}

14. {3, 6, 9, 12, . . . , 30}

15. {−15, −13, −11, . . . , −1}

16. {−4, −3, −2, . . . , 4}

17. {2, 4, 8, . . . , 256}

18. {90, 87, 84, . . . , 69}

19. {$x \mid x$ is an even whole number less than 11}

20. {$x \mid x$ is an odd integer between −8 and 7}

Denote each set by the listing method. There may be more than one correct answer.

21. the set of all counting numbers greater than 20

22. the set of all integers between −200 and 500

23. the set of Great Lakes

24. the set of U.S. presidents who served after Lyndon Johnson and before George W. Bush

25. {$x \mid x$ is a positive multiple of 5}

26. {$x \mid x$ is a negative multiple of 6}

27. {$x \mid x$ is the reciprocal of a natural number}

28. {$x \mid x$ is a positive integer power of 4}

Denote each set by set-builder notation, using x as the variable. There may be more than one correct answer.

29. the set of all rational numbers

30. the set of all even natural numbers

31. {1, 3, 5, . . . , 75}

32. {35, 40, 45, . . . , 95}

Identify each set as finite *or* infinite.

33. {2, 4, 6, . . . , 32}

34. {6, 12, 18}

35. $\left\{ \dfrac{1}{2}, \dfrac{2}{3}, \dfrac{3}{4}, \ldots \right\}$

36. {−10, −8, −6, . . .}

37. $\{x \mid x \text{ is a natural number greater than } 50\}$

38. $\{x \mid x \text{ is a natural number less than } 50\}$

39. $\{x \mid x \text{ is a rational number}\}$

40. $\{x \mid x \text{ is a rational number between } 0 \text{ and } 1\}$

Find n(A) for each set.

41. $A = \{0, 1, 2, 3, 4, 5, 6, 7\}$

42. $A = \{-3, -1, 1, 3, 5, 7, 9\}$

43. $A = \{2, 4, 6, \ldots, 1000\}$

44. $A = \{0, 1, 2, 3, \ldots, 3000\}$

45. $A = \{a, b, c, \ldots, z\}$

46. $A = \{x \mid x \text{ is a vowel in the English alphabet}\}$

47. $A = \text{the set of integers between } -20 \text{ and } 20$

48. $A = \text{the set of current U.S. senators}$

49. $A = \left\{ \dfrac{1}{3}, \dfrac{2}{4}, \dfrac{3}{5}, \dfrac{4}{6}, \ldots, \dfrac{27}{29}, \dfrac{28}{30} \right\}$

50. $A = \left\{ \dfrac{1}{2}, -\dfrac{1}{2}, \dfrac{1}{3}, -\dfrac{1}{3}, \ldots, \dfrac{1}{10}, -\dfrac{1}{10} \right\}$

51. Explain why it is acceptable to write the statement "*x* is a vowel in the English alphabet" in the set for Exercise 46, despite the fact that *x* is a consonant.

52. Explain how Exercise 49 can be answered without actually listing and then counting all the elements.

Identify each set as well defined *or* not well defined.

53. $\{x \mid x \text{ is a real number}\}$

54. $\{x \mid x \text{ is a negative number}\}$

55. $\{x \mid x \text{ is a good athlete}\}$

56. $\{x \mid x \text{ is a skillful typist}\}$

57. $\{x \mid x \text{ is a difficult course}\}$

58. $\{x \mid x \text{ is a counting number less than } 2\}$

Fill each blank with either $\in$ *or* $\notin$ *to make each statement true.*

59. 5 _____ $\{2, 4, 5, 7\}$

60. 8 _____ $\{3, -2, 5, 7, 8\}$

61. -4 _____ $\{4, 7, 8, 12\}$

62. -12 _____ $\{3, 8, 12, 18\}$

63. 0 _____ $\{-2, 0, 5, 9\}$

64. 0 _____ $\{3, 4, 6, 8, 10\}$

65. $\{3\}$ _____ $\{2, 3, 4, 6\}$

66. $\{6\}$ _____ $\{2 + 1, 3 + 1, 4 + 1, 5 + 1, 6 + 1\}$

67. 8 _____ $\{11 - 2, 10 - 2, 9 - 2, 8 - 2\}$

68. The statement $3 \in \{9 - 6, 8 - 6, 7 - 6\}$ is true even though the *symbol* 3 does not appear in the set. Explain.

Write true *or* false *for each statement.*

69. $3 \in \{2, 5, 6, 8\}$

70. $6 \in \{-2, 5, 8, 9\}$

71. $b \in \{h, c, d, a, b\}$

72. $m \in \{l, m, n, o, p\}$

73. $9 \notin \{6, 3, 4, 8\}$

74. $2 \notin \{7, 6, 5, 4\}$

75. $\{k, c, r, a\} = \{k, c, a, r\}$

76. $\{e, h, a, n\} = \{a, h, e, n\}$

77. $\{5, 8, 9\} = \{5, 8, 9, 0\}$

78. $\{3, 7, 12, 14\} = \{3, 7, 12, 14, 0\}$

79. $\{4\} \in \{\{3\}, \{4\}, \{5\}\}$

80. $4 \in \{\{3\}, \{4\}, \{5\}\}$

81. $\{x \mid x \text{ is a natural number less than } 3\} = \{1, 2\}$

82. $\{x \mid x \text{ is a natural number greater than } 10\} = \{11, 12, 13, \ldots\}$

Write true *or* false *for each statement.*

Let $A = \{2, 4, 6, 8, 10, 12\}$, $B = \{2, 4, 8, 10\}$, *and* $C = \{4, 10, 12\}$.

83. $4 \in A$

84. $8 \in B$

85. $4 \notin C$

86. $8 \notin B$

87. Every element of C is also an element of A.

88. Every element of C is also an element of B.

89. This section opened with the statement, "The human mind likes to create collections." Why do you suppose this is so? In your explanation, use one or more particular "collections," mathematical or otherwise.

90. Explain the difference between a well defined set and a not well defined set. Give examples and use terms introduced in this section.

*Two sets are **equal** if they contain identical elements. However, two sets are **equivalent** if they contain the same number of elements (but not necessarily the same elements). For each condition, give an example or explain why it is impossible.*

91. two sets that are neither equal nor equivalent

92. two sets that are equal but not equivalent

93. two sets that are equivalent but not equal

94. two sets that are both equal and equivalent

95. *Volumes of Stocks* The table lists the ten most active stocks on the New York Stock Exchange in 2004.

MOST ACTIVE STOCKS ON NYSE

2004 Rank	Company name (symbol)	2004 share volume (in millions)
1.	Lucent Technologies, Inc. (LU)	5811.0
2.	Nortel Networks Corporation (NT)	4808.5
3.	Pfizer, Inc. (PFE)	4430.4
4.	General Electric Company (GE)	4118.5
5.	Motorola, Inc. (MOT)	2862.5
6.	Time Warner, Inc. (TWX)	2712.8
7.	Citigroup, Inc. (C)	2649.8
8.	Texas Instruments, Inc. (TXN)	2559.7
9.	EMC Corporation (EMC)	2506.7
10.	AT&T Wireless Services, Inc. (AWE)	2350.0

Source: www.info-please.com

(a) List the set of issues that had a share volume of at least 4118.5 million.

(b) List the set of issues that had a share volume of at most 4118.5 million.

96. *Burning Calories* Alexis Cotten is health conscious, but she does like a certain chocolate bar, each of which contains 220 calories. To burn off unwanted calories, Alexis participates in her favorite activities, shown below, in increments of 1 hour and never repeats a given activity on a given day.

Activity	Symbol	Calories Burned per Hour
Volleyball	*v*	160
Golf	*g*	260
Canoeing	*c*	340
Swimming	*s*	410
Running	*r*	680

(a) On Monday, Alexis has time for no more than two hours of activities. List all possible sets of activities that would burn off at least the number of calories obtained from three chocolate bars.

(b) Assume that Alexis can afford up to three hours of time for activities on Saturday. List all sets of activities that would burn off at least the number of calories in five chocolate bars.

2.2 Venn Diagrams and Subsets

Venn Diagrams • Complement of a Set • Subsets of a Set • Proper Subsets • Counting Subsets

Venn Diagrams In the statement of a problem, there is either a stated or implied **universe of discourse.** The universe of discourse includes all things under discussion at a given time. For example, in studying reactions to a proposal that a certain campus raise the minimum age of individuals to whom beer may be sold, the universe of discourse might be all the students at the school, the nearby members of the public, the board of trustees of the school, or perhaps all these groups of people.

In set theory, the universe of discourse is called the **universal set,** typically designated by the letter **U.** The universal set might change from problem to problem.

In set theory, we commonly use **Venn diagrams,** developed by the logician John Venn (1834–1923). In these diagrams, the universal set is represented by a rectangle, and other sets of interest within the universal set are depicted by circular regions. In the Venn diagram of Figure 1, the entire region bounded by the rectangle represents the universal set U, while the portion bounded by the circle represents set A.

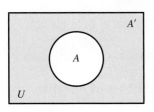

FIGURE 1

Complement of a Set
The colored region inside U and outside the circle in Figure 1 is labeled A' (read **"A prime"**). This set, called the *complement* of A, contains all elements that are contained in U but not contained in A.

> **The Complement of a Set**
>
> For any set A within the universal set U, the **complement** of A, written A', is the set of elements of U that are not elements of A. That is,
>
> $$A' = \{x \mid x \in U \text{ and } x \notin A\}.$$

EXAMPLE 1 Finding Complements

Find each of the following sets.

Let $U = \{a, b, c, d, e, f, g, h\}$, $M = \{a, b, e, f\}$,   and $N = \{b, d, e, g, h\}$.

(a) M' **(b)** N'

SOLUTION

(a) Set M' contains all the elements of set U that are not in set M. Because set M contains the elements a, b, e, and f, these elements will be disqualified from belonging to set M', and consequently set M' will contain c, d, g, and h, or $M' = \{c, d, g, h\}$.

(b) Set N' contains all the elements of U that are not in set N, so $N' = \{a, c, f\}$. ■

Consider the complement of the universal set, U'. The set U' is found by selecting all the elements of U that do not belong to U. There are no such elements, so there can be no elements in set U'. This means that for any universal set U, $U' = \emptyset$.

Now consider the complement of the empty set, $\emptyset'$. Because $\emptyset' = \{x \mid x \in U$ and $x \notin \emptyset\}$ and set $\emptyset$ contains no elements, every member of the universal set U satisfies this description. Therefore, for any universal set U, $\emptyset' = U$.

Subsets of a Set
Suppose that we are given the universal set $U = \{1, 2, 3, 4, 5\}$, while $A = \{1, 2, 3\}$. Every element of set A is also an element of set U. Because of this, set A is called a *subset* of set U, written

$$A \subseteq U.$$

("A is not a subset of set U" would be written $A \nsubseteq U$.)

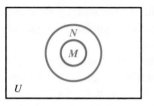

FIGURE 2

A Venn diagram showing that set M is a subset of set N is shown in Figure 2.

Subset of a Set

Set A is a **subset** of set B if every element of A is also an element of B. In symbols this is written $A \subseteq B$.

EXAMPLE 2 Determining Whether One Set is a Subset of Another

Write $\subseteq$ or $\nsubseteq$ in each blank to make a true statement.

(a) $\{3, 4, 5, 6\}$ _____ $\{3, 4, 5, 6, 8\}$ **(b)** $\{1, 2, 6\}$ _____ $\{2, 4, 6, 8\}$
(c) $\{5, 6, 7, 8\}$ _____ $\{5, 6, 7, 8\}$

SOLUTION

(a) Because every element of $\{3, 4, 5, 6\}$ is also an element of $\{3, 4, 5, 6, 8\}$, the first set is a subset of the second, so $\subseteq$ goes in the blank:

$$\{3, 4, 5, 6\} \subseteq \{3, 4, 5, 6, 8\}.$$

(b) The element 1 belongs to $\{1, 2, 6\}$ but not to $\{2, 4, 6, 8\}$. Place $\nsubseteq$ in the blank.
(c) Every element of $\{5, 6, 7, 8\}$ is also an element of $\{5, 6, 7, 8\}$. Place $\subseteq$ in the blank. ■

As Example 2(c) suggests, every set is a subset of itself:

$$B \subseteq B, \quad \text{for any set } B.$$

The statement of set equality in Section 2.1 can be formally presented using subset terminology.

Set Equality (Alternative definition)

Suppose A and B are sets. Then $A = B$ if $A \subseteq B$ and $B \subseteq A$ are both true.

Proper Subsets   When studying subsets of a set B, it is common to look at subsets other than set B itself. Suppose that $B = \{5, 6, 7, 8\}$ and $A = \{6, 7\}$. A is a subset of B, but A is not all of B; there is at least one element in B that is not in A. (Actually, in this case there are two such elements, 5 and 8.) In this situation, A is called a *proper subset* of B. To indicate that A is a proper subset of B, write $A \subset B$.

Notice the similarity of the subset symbols, $\subset$ and $\subseteq$, to the inequality symbols from algebra, $<$ and $\leq$.

Proper Subset of a Set

Set A is a **proper subset** of set B if $A \subseteq B$ and $A \neq B$. In symbols, this is written $A \subset B$.

EXAMPLE 3 Determining Subset and Proper Subset Relationships

Decide whether $\subset$, $\subseteq$, or both could be placed in each blank to make a true statement.

(a) $\{5, 6, 7\}$ _____ $\{5, 6, 7, 8\}$ **(b)** $\{a, b, c\}$ _____ $\{a, b, c\}$

SOLUTION

(a) Every element of {5, 6, 7} is contained in {5, 6, 7, 8}, so ⊆ could be placed in the blank. Also, the element 8 belongs to {5, 6, 7, 8} but not to {5, 6, 7}, making {5, 6, 7} a proper subset of {5, 6, 7, 8}. This means that ⊂ could also be placed in the blank.

(b) The set {a, b, c} is a subset of {a, b, c}. Because the two sets are equal, {a, b, c} is not a proper subset of {a, b, c}. Only ⊆ may be placed in the blank.

Set A is a subset of set B if every element of set A is also an element of set B. This definition can be reworded by saying that set A is a subset of set B if there are no elements of A that are not also elements of B. This second form of the definition shows that the empty set is a subset of any set, or

$$\emptyset \subseteq B, \quad \text{for any set } B.$$

This is true because it is not possible to find any elements of $\emptyset$ that are not also in B. (There are no elements in $\emptyset$.) The empty set $\emptyset$ is a proper subset of every set except itself:

$$\emptyset \subset B \quad \text{if } B \text{ is any set other than } \emptyset.$$

Every set (except $\emptyset$) has at least two subsets, $\emptyset$ and the set itself.

EXAMPLE 4 Listing All Subsets of a Set

Find all possible subsets of each set.

(a) {7, 8} **(b)** {a, b, c}

SOLUTION

(a) By trial and error, the set {7, 8} has four subsets: $\emptyset$, {7}, {8}, {7, 8}.

(b) Here, trial and error leads to eight subsets for {a, b, c}:

$$\emptyset, \{a\}, \{b\}, \{c\}, \{a, b\}, \{a, c\}, \{b, c\}, \{a, b, c\}.$$

Counting Subsets
In Example 4, the subsets of {7, 8} and the subsets of {a, b, c} were found by trial and error. An alternative method involves drawing a **tree diagram,** a systematic way of listing all the subsets of a given set. Figures 3(a) and (b) show tree diagrams for {7, 8} and {a, b, c}.

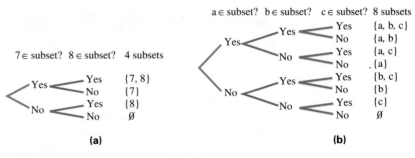

(a) **(b)**

FIGURE 3

Powers of 2

$2^0 = 1$

$2^1 = 2$

$2^2 = 2 \times 2 = 4$

$2^3 = 2 \times 2 \times 2 = 8$

$2^4 = 2 \times 2 \times 2 \times 2 = 16$

$2^5 = 32$

$2^6 = 64$

$2^7 = 128$

$2^8 = 256$

$2^9 = 512$

$2^{10} = 1024$

$2^{11} = 2048$

$2^{12} = 4096$

$2^{15} = 32{,}768$

$2^{20} = 1{,}048{,}576$

$2^{25} = 33{,}554{,}432$

$2^{30} = 1{,}073{,}741{,}824$

In Example 4, we determined the number of subsets of a given set by making a list of all such subsets and then counting them. The tree diagram method also produced a list of all possible subsets. In many applications, we don't need to display all the subsets but simply determine how many there are. Furthermore, the trial and error method and the tree diagram method would both involve far too much work if the original set had a very large number of elements. For these reasons, it is desirable to have a formula for the number of subsets. To obtain such a formula, we use inductive reasoning. That is, we observe particular cases to try to discover a general pattern.

Begin with the set containing the least number of elements possible—the empty set. This set, $\emptyset$, has only one subset, $\emptyset$ itself. Next, a set with one element has only two subsets, itself and $\emptyset$. These facts, together with those obtained above for sets with two and three elements, are summarized here.

Number of elements	0	1	2	3
Number of subsets	1	2	4	8

This chart suggests that as the number of elements of the set increases by one, the number of subsets doubles. This suggests that the number of subsets in each case might be a power of 2. Every number in the second row of the chart is indeed a power of 2. Add this information to the chart.

Number of elements	0	1	2	3
Number of subsets	$1 = 2^0$	$2 = 2^1$	$4 = 2^2$	$8 = 2^3$

This chart shows that the number of elements in each case is the same as the exponent on the base 2. Inductive reasoning gives the following generalization.

Number of Subsets

The number of subsets of a set with n elements is 2^n.

Because the value 2^n includes the set itself, we must subtract 1 from this value to obtain the number of proper subsets of a set containing n elements.

Number of Proper Subsets

The number of proper subsets of a set with n elements is $2^n - 1$.

As shown in Chapter 1, although inductive reasoning is a good way of *discovering* principles or arriving at a *conjecture,* it does not provide a proof that the conjecture is true in general. A proof must be provided by other means. The two formulas above are true, by observation, for $n = 0, 1, 2,$ or 3. (For a general proof, see Exercise 71 at the end of this section.)

> **EXAMPLE 5** **Finding the Numbers of Subsets and Proper Subsets**

Find the number of subsets and the number of proper subsets of each set.

(a) $\{3, 4, 5, 6, 7\}$ **(b)** $\{1, 2, 3, 4, 5, 9, 12, 14\}$

SOLUTION

(a) This set has 5 elements and $2^5 = 2 \cdot 2 \cdot 2 \cdot 2 \cdot 2 = 32$ subsets. Of these, $2^5 - 1 = 32 - 1 = 31$ are proper subsets.

(b) This set has 8 elements. There are $2^8 = 256$ subsets and 255 proper subsets. ∎

2.2 EXERCISES

Match each set or sets in Column I with the appropriate description in Column II.

I

1. $\{p\}, \{q\}, \{p, q\}, \emptyset$

2. $\{p\}, \{q\}, \emptyset$

3. $\{a, b\}$

4. $\emptyset$

5. U

6. $\{a\}$

II

A. the complement of $\emptyset$

B. the proper subsets of $\{p, q\}$

C. the complement of $\{c, d\}$, if $U = \{a, b, c, d\}$

D. the complement of U

E. the complement of $\{b\}$, if $U = \{a, b\}$

F. the subsets of $\{p, q\}$

Insert $\subseteq$ or $\nsubseteq$ in each blank so that the resulting statement is true.

7. $\{-2, 0, 2\}$ _____ $\{-2, -1, 1, 2\}$ **8.** $\{M, W, F\}$ _____ $\{S, M, T, W, Th\}$

9. $\{2, 5\}$ _____ $\{0, 1, 5, 3, 4, 2\}$ **10.** $\{a, n, d\}$ _____ $\{r, a, n, d, y\}$

11. $\emptyset$ _____ $\{a, b, c, d, e\}$ **12.** $\emptyset$ _____ $\emptyset$

13. $\{-7, 4, 9\}$ _____ $\{x \mid x \text{ is an odd integer}\}$ **14.** $\left\{2, \dfrac{1}{3}, \dfrac{5}{9}\right\}$ _____ the set of rational numbers

Decide whether $\subset, \subseteq$, both, or neither can be placed in each blank to make the statement true.

15. $\{B, C, D\}$ _____ $\{B, C, D, F\}$ **16.** $\{red, blue, yellow\}$ _____ $\{yellow, blue, red\}$

17. $\{9, 1, 7, 3, 5\}$ _____ $\{1, 3, 5, 7, 9\}$ **18.** $\{S, M, T, W, Th\}$ _____ $\{M, W, Th, S\}$

19. $\emptyset$ _____ $\{0\}$ **20.** $\emptyset$ _____ $\emptyset$

21. $\{-1, 0, 1, 2, 3\}$ _____ $\{0, 1, 2, 3, 4\}$ **22.** $\left\{\dfrac{5}{6}, \dfrac{9}{8}\right\}$ _____ $\left\{\dfrac{6}{5}, \dfrac{8}{9}\right\}$

For Exercises 23–42, tell whether each statement is true *or* false.

    Let $U = \{a, b, c, d, e, f, g\}$, $A = \{a, e\}$, $B = \{a, b, e, f, g\}$, $C = \{b, f, g\}$, *and* $D = \{d, e\}$.

23. $A \subset U$ **24.** $C \subset U$ **25.** $D \subseteq B$ **26.** $D \subseteq A$

27. $A \subset B$ **28.** $B \subseteq C$ **29.** $\emptyset \subset A$ **30.** $\emptyset \subseteq D$

31. $\emptyset \subseteq \emptyset$ **32.** $D \subset B$ **33.** $D \nsubseteq B$ **34.** $A \nsubseteq B$

35. There are exactly 6 subsets of C.

36. There are exactly 31 subsets of B.

37. There are exactly 3 subsets of A.

38. There are exactly 4 subsets of D.

39. There is exactly 1 subset of $\emptyset$.

40. There are exactly 127 proper subsets of U.

41. The Venn diagram below correctly represents the relationship among sets A, C, and U.

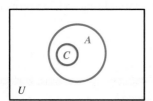

42. The Venn diagram below correctly represents the relationship among sets B, C, and U.

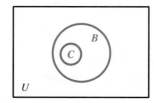

Find **(a)** *the number of subsets and* **(b)** *the number of proper subsets of each set.*

43. $\{1, 5, 10\}$

44. $\{8, 6, 4, 2\}$

45. $\{a, b, c, d, e, f\}$

46. the set of days of the week

47. $\{x \mid x$ is an odd integer between -7 and $4\}$

48. $\{x \mid x$ is an odd whole number less than $4\}$

Let $U = \{1, 2, 3, 4, 5, 6, 7, 8, 9, 10\}$ *and find the complement of each set.*

49. $\{1, 4, 6, 8\}$ **50.** $\{2, 5, 7, 9, 10\}$ **51.** $\{1, 3, 4, 5, 6, 7, 8, 9, 10\}$

52. $\{1, 2, 3, 4, 6, 7, 8, 9, 10\}$ **53.** $\emptyset$ **54.** U

Vacationing in Orlando, FL. Terry McGinnis is planning to take her two sons to Orlando, FL, during their Thanksgiving vacation. In weighing her options concerning whether to fly or drive from their home in Iowa, she has listed the following characteristics.

Fly to Orlando	Drive to Orlando
Higher cost	Lower cost
Educational	Educational
More time to see the sights	Less time to see the sights
Cannot visit relatives along the way	Can visit relatives along the way

Refer to these characteristics in Exercises 55–60.

55. Find the smallest universal set U that contains all listed characteristics of both options.

Let F *represent the set of characteristics of the flying option and let* D *represent the set of characteristics of the driving option. Use the universal set from Exercise 55.*

56. Give the set F'.   **57.** Give the set D'.

Find the set of elements common to both sets in Exercises 58–60.

58. F and D **59.** F' and D'

60. F and D'

Meeting in a Hospitality Suite Allen Wells, Bonnie Garrett, Cathie Ducote, David Bondy, and Eleanor André plan to meet at the hospitality suite after the CEO makes his speech at the January sales meeting of their publishing company. Denoting these five people by A, B, C, D, and E, list all the possible sets of this group in which the given number of them can gather.

61. five people   **62.** four people   **63.** three people

64. two people   **65.** one person   **66.** no people

67. Find the total number of ways that members of this group can gather in the suite. (*Hint:* Find the total number of sets in your answers to Exercises 61–66.)

68. How does your answer in Exercise 67 compare with the number of subsets of a set of five elements? How can you interpret the answer to Exercise 67 in terms of subsets?

69. *Selecting Bills from a Wallet* Suppose that in your wallet you have the bills shown here.
   (a) If you must select at least one bill, and you may select up to all of the bills, how many different sums of money could you make?
   (b) In part (a), remove the condition "you must select at least one bill." Now, how many sums are possible?

70. *Selecting Coins* The photo shows a group of obsolete U.S. coins, consisting of one each of the penny, nickel, dime, quarter, and half dollar. Repeat Exercise 69, replacing "bill(s)" with "coin(s)."

71. In discovering the expression (2^n) for finding the number of subsets of a set with n elements, we observed that for the first few values of n, increasing the number of elements by one doubles the number of subsets. Here, you can prove the formula in general by showing that the same is true for any value of n. Assume set A has n elements and s subsets. Now add one additional element, say e, to the set A. (We now have a new set, say B, with $n + 1$ elements.) Divide the subsets of B into those that do not contain e and those that do.
   (a) How many subsets of B do not contain e? (*Hint:* Each of these is a subset of the original set A.)
   (b) How many subsets of B do contain e? (*Hint:* Each of these would be a subset of the original set A, with the element e inserted.)
   (c) What is the total number of subsets of B?
   (d) What do you conclude?

72. Explain why $\{\emptyset\}$ has $\emptyset$ as a subset and also has $\emptyset$ as an element.

2.3 | Set Operations and Cartesian Products

Intersection of Sets • Union of Sets • Difference of Sets • Ordered Pairs • Cartesian Product of Sets • Venn Diagrams • De Morgan's Laws

Intersection of Sets Two candidates, Mary Lynn Brumfield and J.D. Patin, are running for a seat on the city council. A voter deciding for whom she should vote recalled the following campaign promises made by the candidates. Each promise is given a code letter.

Honest Mary Lynn Brumfield	Determined J.D. Patin
Spend less money, m	Spend less money, m
Emphasize traffic law enforcement, t	Crack down on crooked politicians, p
Increase service to suburban areas, s	Increase service to the city, c

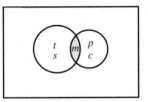

FIGURE 4

The only promise common to both candidates is promise m, to spend less money. Suppose we take each candidate's promises to be a set. The promises of Brumfield give the set $\{m, t, s\}$, while the promises of Patin give $\{m, p, c\}$. The only element common to both sets is m; this element belongs to the *intersection* of the two sets $\{m, t, s\}$ and $\{m, p, c\}$, as shown in color in the Venn diagram in Figure 4. In symbols,

$$\{m, t, s\} \cap \{m, p, c\} = \{m\},$$

where the cap-shaped symbol $\cap$ represents intersection. Notice that the intersection of two sets is itself a set.

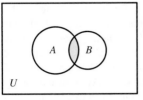

$A \cap B$

FIGURE 5

Intersection of Sets

The **intersection** of sets A and B, written $A \cap B$, is the set of elements common to both A and B, or

$$A \cap B = \{x \mid x \in A \text{ and } x \in B\}.$$

Form the intersection of sets A and B by taking all the elements included in *both* sets, as shown in color in Figure 5.

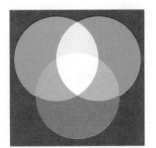

White light can be viewed as the intersection of the three primary colors.

EXAMPLE 1 Finding Intersections

Find each intersection.

(a) $\{3, 4, 5, 6, 7\} \cap \{4, 6, 8, 10\}$
(b) $\{9, 14, 25, 30\} \cap \{10, 17, 19, 38, 52\}$
(c) $\{5, 9, 11\} \cap \varnothing$

SOLUTION

(a) Because the elements common to both sets are 4 and 6,

$$\{3, 4, 5, 6, 7\} \cap \{4, 6, 8, 10\} = \{4, 6\}.$$

(b) These two sets have no elements in common, so

$$\{9, 14, 25, 30\} \cap \{10, 17, 19, 38, 52\} = \varnothing.$$

(c) There are no elements in $\varnothing$, so there can be no elements belonging to both $\{5, 9, 11\}$ and $\varnothing$. Because of this,

$$\{5, 9, 11\} \cap \varnothing = \varnothing. \qquad ▨$$

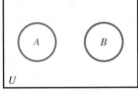

Disjoint sets

FIGURE 6

Examples 1(b) and 1(c) show two sets that have no elements in common. Sets with no elements in common are called **disjoint sets.** A set of dogs and a set of cats would be disjoint sets. In mathematical language, sets A and B are disjoint if $A \cap B = \varnothing$. Two disjoint sets A and B are shown in Figure 6.

Union of Sets   We began this section with lists of campaign promises of two candidates running for city council. Suppose a pollster wants to summarize the types of promises made by candidates for the office. The pollster would need to study *all* the promises made by *either* candidate, or the set

$$\{m, t, s, p, c\},$$

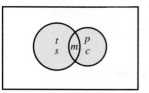

FIGURE 7

the *union* of the sets of promises made by the two candidates, as shown in color in the Venn diagram in Figure 7. In symbols,

$$\{m, t, s\} \cup \{m, p, c\} = \{m, t, s, p, c\},$$

where the cup-shaped symbol $\cup$ denotes set union. Be careful not to confuse this symbol with the universal set U. Again, the union of two sets is a set.

Union of Sets

The **union** of sets A and B, written $A \cup B$, is the set of all elements belonging to either of the sets, or

$$A \cup B = \{x \mid x \in A \text{ or } x \in B\}.$$

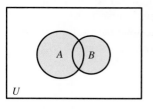

$A \cup B$

FIGURE 8

Form the union of sets A and B by taking all the elements of set A and then including the elements of set B that are not already listed. See Figure 8.

EXAMPLE 2   Finding Unions

Find each union.

(a) $\{2, 4, 6\} \cup \{4, 6, 8, 10, 12\}$
(b) $\{a, b, d, f, g, h\} \cup \{c, f, g, h, k\}$
(c) $\{3, 4, 5\} \cup \emptyset$

SOLUTION

(a) Start by listing all the elements from the first set, 2, 4, and 6. Then list all the elements from the second set that are not in the first set, 8, 10, and 12. The union is made up of *all* these elements, written

$$\{2, 4, 6\} \cup \{4, 6, 8, 10, 12\} = \{2, 4, 6, 8, 10, 12\}.$$

(b) The union of these sets is

$$\{a, b, d, f, g, h\} \cup \{c, f, g, h, k\} = \{a, b, c, d, f, g, h, k\}.$$

(c) Because there are no elements in $\emptyset$, the union of $\{3, 4, 5\}$ and $\emptyset$ contains only the elements 3, 4, and 5, written

$$\{3, 4, 5\} \cup \emptyset = \{3, 4, 5\}.$$

For Further Thought

Comparing Properties

The arithmetic operations of addition and multiplication, when applied to numbers, have some familiar properties. If a, b, and c are *real numbers*, then the **commutative property of addition** says that the order of the numbers being added makes no difference: $a + b = b + a$. (Is there a **commutative property of multiplication**?) The **associative property of addition** says that when three numbers are added, the grouping used makes no difference: $(a + b) + c = a + (b + c)$. (Is there an **associative property of multiplication**?) The number 0 is called the **identity element for addition** since adding it to any number does not change that number: $a + 0 = a$. (What is the **identity element for multiplication**?) Finally, the **distributive property of multiplication over addition** says

that $a(b + c) = ab + ac$. (Is there a distributive property of addition over multiplication?)

For Group Discussion or Individual Investigation

Now consider the operations of union and intersection, applied to sets. By recalling definitions, or by trying examples, answer the following questions.

1. Is set union commutative? How about set intersection?
2. Is set union associative? How about set intersection?
3. Is there an identity element for set union? If so, what is it? How about set intersection?
4. Is set intersection distributive over set union? Is set union distributive over set intersection?

Recall from the previous section that A' represents the *complement* of set A. Set A' is formed by taking all the elements of the universal set U that are not in A.

EXAMPLE 3 Finding Intersections and Unions of Complements

Find each set. Let

$$U = \{1, 2, 3, 4, 5, 6, 9\}, \ A = \{1, 2, 3, 4\}, \ B = \{2, 4, 6\}, \ \text{and} \ C = \{1, 3, 6, 9\}.$$

(a) $A' \cap B$ **(b)** $B' \cup C'$ **(c)** $A \cap (B \cup C')$ **(d)** $(A' \cup C') \cap B'$

SOLUTION

(a) First identify the elements of set A', the elements of U that are not in set A:

$$A' = \{5, 6, 9\}.$$

Now, find $A' \cap B$, the set of elements belonging both to A' and to B:

$$A' \cap B = \{5, 6, 9\} \cap \{2, 4, 6\} = \{6\}.$$

(b) $B' \cup C' = \{1, 3, 5, 9\} \cup \{2, 4, 5\} = \{1, 2, 3, 4, 5, 9\}.$
(c) First find the set inside the parentheses:

$$B \cup C' = \{2, 4, 6\} \cup \{2, 4, 5\} = \{2, 4, 5, 6\}.$$

Now, find the intersection of this set with A.

$$A \cap (B \cup C') = A \cap \{2, 4, 5, 6\}$$
$$= \{1, 2, 3, 4\} \cap \{2, 4, 5, 6\}$$
$$= \{2, 4\}$$

(d) $A' = \{5, 6, 9\}$ and $C' = \{2, 4, 5\}$, so

$$A' \cup C' = \{5, 6, 9\} \cup \{2, 4, 5\} = \{2, 4, 5, 6, 9\}.$$

$B' = \{1, 3, 5, 9\}$, so

$$(A' \cup C') \cap B' = \{2, 4, 5, 6, 9\} \cap \{1, 3, 5, 9\} = \{5, 9\}.$$ ▪

It is often said that mathematics is a "language." As such, it has the advantage of concise symbolism. For example, the set $(A \cap B)' \cup C$ is less easily expressed in words. One attempt is the following: "The set of all elements that are not in both A and B, or are in C."

EXAMPLE 4 Describing Sets in Words

Describe each of the following sets in words.

(a) $A \cap (B \cup C')$ **(b)** $(A' \cup C') \cap B'$

SOLUTION

(a) This set might be described as "the set of all elements that are in A, and also are in B or not in C."
(b) One possibility is "the set of all elements that are not in A or not in C, and also are not in B." ▪

Difference of Sets We now consider the *difference* of two sets. Suppose that $A = \{1, 2, 3, \ldots, 10\}$ and $B = \{2, 4, 6, 8, 10\}$. If the elements of B are excluded (or taken away) from A, the set $C = \{1, 3, 5, 7, 9\}$ is obtained. C is called the difference of sets A and B.

Difference of Sets

The **difference** of sets A and B, written $A - B$, is the set of all elements belonging to set A and not to set B, or

$$A - B = \{x \mid x \in A \text{ and } x \notin B\}.$$

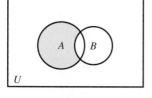

$A - B$

FIGURE 9

Because $x \notin B$ has the same meaning as $x \in B'$ the set difference $A - B$ can also be described as $\{x \mid x \in A \text{ and } x \in B'\}$, or $A \cap B'$. Figure 9 illustrates the idea of set difference. The region in color represents $A - B$.

EXAMPLE 5 Finding Set Differences

Find each set.

Let $U = \{1, 2, 3, 4, 5, 6, 7\}$, $A = \{1, 2, 3, 4, 5, 6\}$, $B = \{2, 3, 6\}$, and $C = \{3, 5, 7\}$.

(a) $A - B$ **(b)** $B - A$ **(c)** $(A - B) \cup C'$

SOLUTION

(a) Begin with set A and exclude any elements found also in set B. So,

$$A - B = \{1, 2, 3, 4, 5, 6\} - \{2, 3, 6\} = \{1, 4, 5\}.$$

(b) To be in $B - A$, an element must be in set B and not in set A. But all elements of B are also in A. Thus, $B - A = \emptyset$.

(c) From part (a), $A - B = \{1, 4, 5\}$. Also, $C' = \{1, 2, 4, 6\}$, so

$$(A - B) \cup C' = \{1, 2, 4, 5, 6\}.$$ ▪

The results in Examples 5(a) and 5(b) illustrate that, in general,

$$A - B \neq B - A.$$

Ordered Pairs

When writing a set that contains several elements, the order in which the elements appear is not relevant. For example, $\{1, 5\} = \{5, 1\}$. However, there are many instances in mathematics where, when two objects are paired, the order in which the objects are written is important. This leads to the idea of the *ordered pair*. When writing ordered pairs, use parentheses rather than braces, which are reserved for writing sets.

Ordered Pairs

In the **ordered pair** (a, b), a is called the **first component** and b is called the **second component.** In general, $(a, b) \neq (b, a)$.

Two ordered pairs (a, b) and (c, d) are **equal** provided that their first components are equal and their second components are equal; that is, $(a, b) = (c, d)$ if and only if $a = c$ and $b = d$.

EXAMPLE 6 Determining Equality of Sets and of Ordered Pairs

Decide whether each statement is *true* or *false*.

(a) $(3, 4) = (5 - 2, 1 + 3)$ **(b)** $\{3, 4\} \neq \{4, 3\}$ **(c)** $(7, 4) = (4, 7)$

SOLUTION

(a) Because $3 = 5 - 2$ and $4 = 1 + 3$, the ordered pairs are equal. The statement is true.

(b) Because these are sets and not ordered pairs, the order in which the elements are listed is not important. Because these sets are equal, the statement is false.

(c) These ordered pairs are not equal because they do not satisfy the requirements for equality of ordered pairs. The statement is false. ▪

Cartesian Product of Sets

A set may contain ordered pairs as elements. If A and B are sets, then each element of A can be paired with each element of B, and the results can be written as ordered pairs. The set of all such ordered pairs is called the *Cartesian product* of A and B, written $A \times B$ and read "A cross B." The name comes from that of the French mathematician René Descartes.

Cartesian Product of Sets

The **Cartesian product** of sets A and B, written $A \times B$, is

$$A \times B = \{(a, b) \mid a \in A \text{ and } b \in B\}.$$

EXAMPLE 7 Finding Cartesian Products

Let $A = \{1, 5, 9\}$ and $B = \{6, 7\}$. Find each set.

(a) $A \times B$ **(b)** $B \times A$

SOLUTION

(a) Pair each element of A with each element of B. Write the results as ordered pairs, with the element of A written first and the element of B written second. Write as a set.

$$A \times B = \{(1, 6), (1, 7), (5, 6), (5, 7), (9, 6), (9, 7)\}$$

(b) Because B is listed first, this set will consist of ordered pairs that have their components interchanged when compared to those in part (a).

$$B \times A = \{(6, 1), (7, 1), (6, 5), (7, 5), (6, 9), (7, 9)\}$$

It should be noted that the order in which the ordered pairs themselves are listed is not important. For example, another way to write $B \times A$ in Example 7 would be

$$\{(6, 1), (6, 5), (6, 9), (7, 1), (7, 5), (7, 9)\}.$$

EXAMPLE 8 Finding the Cartesian Product of a Set with Itself

Let $A = \{1, 2, 3, 4, 5, 6\}$. Find $A \times A$.

SOLUTION

By pairing 1 with each element in the set, 2 with each element, and so on, we obtain the following set.

$$\begin{aligned}
A \times A = \{&(1, 1), (1, 2), (1, 3), (1, 4), (1, 5), (1, 6), \\
&(2, 1), (2, 2), (2, 3), (2, 4), (2, 5), (2, 6), \\
&(3, 1), (3, 2), (3, 3), (3, 4), (3, 5), (3, 6), \\
&(4, 1), (4, 2), (4, 3), (4, 4), (4, 5), (4, 6), \\
&(5, 1), (5, 2), (5, 3), (5, 4), (5, 5), (5, 6), \\
&(6, 1), (6, 2), (6, 3), (6, 4), (6, 5), (6, 6)\}
\end{aligned}$$

It is not unusual to take the Cartesian product of a set with itself, as in Example 8. The Cartesian product in Example 8 represents all possible results that are obtained when two distinguishable dice are rolled. This Cartesian product is important when studying certain problems in counting techniques and probability.

From Example 7 it can be seen that, in general, $A \times B \neq B \times A$, because they do not contain exactly the same ordered pairs. However, each set contains the same number of elements, six. Furthermore, $n(A) = 3$, $n(B) = 2$, and $n(A \times B) = n(B \times A) = 6$. Because $3 \cdot 2 = 6$, one might conclude that the cardinal number of the Cartesian product of two sets is equal to the product of the cardinal numbers of the sets. In general, this conclusion is correct.

Cardinal Number of a Cartesian Product

If $n(A) = a$ and $n(B) = b$, then

$$n(A \times B) = n(B \times A) = n(A) \cdot n(B) = n(B) \cdot n(A) = ab = ba.$$

EXAMPLE 9 Finding Cardinal Numbers of Cartesian Products

Find $n(A \times B)$ and $n(B \times A)$ from the given information.

(a) $A = \{a, b, c, d, e, f, g\}$ and $B = \{2, 4, 6\}$ **(b)** $n(A) = 24$ and $n(B) = 5$

SOLUTION

(a) Because $n(A) = 7$ and $n(B) = 3$, $n(A \times B)$ and $n(B \times A)$ both equal $7 \cdot 3$, or 21.

(b) $n(A \times B) = n(B \times A) = 24 \cdot 5 = 5 \cdot 24 = 120$ ■

Finding intersections, unions, differences, Cartesian products, and complements of sets are examples of *set operations*. An **operation** is a rule or procedure by which one or more objects are used to obtain another object. The most common operations on sets are summarized below, along with their Venn diagrams.

Set Operations

Let A and B be any sets, with U the universal set.

The **complement** of A, written A', is

$$A' = \{x \mid x \in U \text{ and } x \notin A\}.$$

The **intersection** of A and B is

$$A \cap B = \{x \mid x \in A \text{ and } x \in B\}.$$

The **union** of A and B is

$$A \cup B = \{x \mid x \in A \text{ or } x \in B\}.$$

The **difference** of A and B is

$$A - B = \{x \mid x \in A \text{ and } x \notin B\}.$$

The **Cartesian product** of A and B is

$$A \times B = \{(x, y) \mid x \in A \text{ and } y \in B\}.$$

FIGURE 10

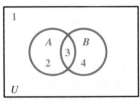

Numbering is arbitrary. The numbers indicate four regions, not cardinal numbers or elements.

FIGURE 11

Venn Diagrams When dealing with a single set, we can use a Venn diagram as seen in Figure 10. The universal set U is divided into two regions, one representing set A and the other representing set A'. Two sets A and B within the universal set suggest a Venn diagram as seen in Figure 11, where the four resulting regions have been numbered to provide a convenient way to refer to them. (The numbering is arbitrary.) Region 1 includes those elements outside of both set A and set B. Region 2 includes the elements belonging to A but not to B. Region 3 includes those elements belonging to both A and B. How would you describe the elements of region 4?

EXAMPLE 10 Shading Venn Diagrams to Represent Sets

Draw a Venn diagram similar to Figure 11 and shade the region or regions representing the following sets.

(a) $A' \cap B$ **(b)** $A' \cup B'$

SOLUTION

(a) Refer to Figure 11. Set A' contains all the elements outside of set A—in other words, the elements in regions 1 and 4. Set B is made up of the elements in regions 3 and 4. The intersection of sets A' and B is made up of the elements in the region common to (1 and 4) and (3 and 4), which is region 4. Thus, $A' \cap B$ is represented by region 4, shown in color in Figure 12. This region can also be described as $B - A$.

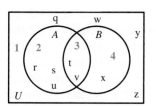

FIGURE 14

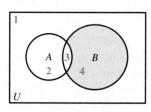

FIGURE 12

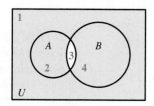

FIGURE 13

(b) Again, set A' is represented by regions 1 and 4, while B' is made up of regions 1 and 2. The union of A' and B', the set $A' \cup B'$, is made up of the elements belonging to the union of regions 1, 2, and 4, which are in color in Figure 13. ■

EXAMPLE 11 Locating Elements in a Venn Diagram

Place the elements of the sets in their proper locations in a Venn diagram.

Let $U = \{q, r, s, t, u, v, w, x, y, z\}$, $A = \{r, s, t, u, v\}$, and $B = \{t, v, x\}$.

SOLUTION

Because $A \cap B = \{t, v\}$, elements t and v are placed in region 3 in Figure 14. The remaining elements of A, that is r, s, and u, go in region 2. The figure shows the proper placement of all other elements. ■

To include three sets A, B, and C in a universal set, draw a Venn diagram as in Figure 15, where again an arbitrary numbering of the regions is shown.

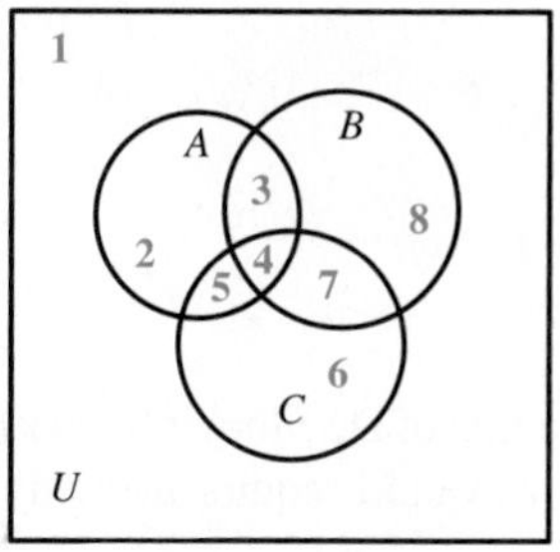

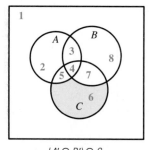

Numbering is arbitrary. The numbers indicate regions, not cardinal numbers or elements.

FIGURE 15

EXAMPLE 12 Shading a Set in a Venn Diagram

Shade the set $(A' \cap B') \cap C$ in a Venn diagram similar to the one in Figure 15.

SOLUTION

Work first inside the parentheses. As shown in Figure 16, set A' is made up of the regions outside set A, or regions 1, 6, 7, and 8. Set B' is made up of regions 1, 2, 5, and 6. The intersection of these sets is given by the overlap of regions 1, 6, 7, 8 and 1, 2, 5, 6, or regions 1 and 6. For the final Venn diagram, find the intersection of regions 1 and 6 with set C. As seen in Figure 16, set C is made up of regions 4, 5, 6, and 7. The overlap of regions 1, 6 and 4, 5, 6, 7 is region 6, the region in color in Figure 16. ■

$(A' \cap B') \cap C$

FIGURE 16

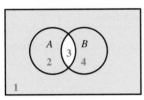

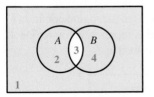

$(A \cap B)'$ is shaded.

(a)

$A' \cup B'$ is shaded.

(b)

FIGURE 17

EXAMPLE 13 Verifying a Statement Using a Venn Diagram

Is the statement $(A \cap B)' = A' \cup B'$ true for every choice of sets A and B?

SOLUTION

To help decide, use the regions labeled in Figure 11. Set $A \cap B$ is made up of region 3, so that $(A \cap B)'$ is made up of regions 1, 2, and 4. These regions are in color in Figure 17(a).

To find a Venn diagram for set $A' \cup B'$, first check that A' is made up of regions 1 and 4, while set B' includes regions 1 and 2. Finally, $A' \cup B'$ is made up of regions 1 and 4, or 1 and 2, that is, regions 1, 2, and 4. These regions are in color in Figure 17(b).

The fact that the same regions are in color in both Venn diagrams suggests that

$$(A \cap B)' = A' \cup B'.$$

De Morgan's Laws The result of Example 13 can be stated in words as follows: ***The complement of the intersection of two sets is equal to the union of the complements of the two sets.*** As a result, it is natural to ask ourselves whether it is true that the complement of the *union* of two sets is equal to the *intersection* of the complements of the two sets (where the words "intersection" and "union" are substituted for each other). It turns out that this was investigated by the British logician Augustus De Morgan (1806–1871) and was found to be true. (See the margin note on page 23.) DeMorgan's two laws for sets follow.

De Morgan's Laws

For any sets A and B,

$$(A \cap B)' = A' \cup B' \quad \text{and} \quad (A \cup B)' = A' \cap B'.$$

The Venn diagrams in Figure 17 strongly suggest the truth of the first of De Morgan's laws. They provide a *conjecture*. Actual proofs of De Morgan's laws would require methods used in more advanced courses on set theory.

EXAMPLE 14 Describing Regions in Venn Diagrams Using Symbols

For the Venn diagrams, write a symbolic description of the region in color, using A, B, C, $\cap$, $\cup$, $-$, and $'$ as necessary.

(a)

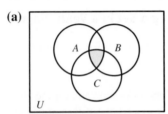

(b)

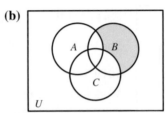

(c) Refer to the figure in part (b) and give two additional ways of describing the region in color.

SOLUTION

(a) The region in color belongs to all three sets, A and B and C. Therefore, the region corresponds to

$$A \cap B \cap C.$$

(b) The region in color is in set B and is not in A and is not in C. Because it is not in A, it is in A', and similarly it is in C'. The region is, therefore, in B and in A' and in C', and corresponds to

$$B \cap A' \cap C'.$$

(c) The region in color includes all of B, except for the regions belonging to either A or C. This suggests the idea of set difference. The region may be described as

$$B - (A \cup C), \quad \text{or equivalently,} \quad B \cap (A \cup C)'.$$

2.3 EXERCISES

Match each term in Column I with its proper designation in Column II. Assume that A and B are sets.

I

1. the intersection of A and B

2. the union of A and B

3. the difference of A and B

4. the complement of A

5. the Cartesian product of A and B

6. the difference of B and A

II

A. the set of elements in A that are not in B

B. the set of elements common to both A and B

C. the set of elements in the universe that are not in A

D. the set of elements in B that are not in A

E. the set of ordered pairs such that each first element is from A and each second element is from B, with every element of A paired with every element of B

F. the set of elements that are in A or in B or in both A and B

Perform the indicated operations.

Let $U = \{a, b, c, d, e, f, g\}$, $X = \{a, c, e, g\}$, $Y = \{a, b, c\}$,   *and* $Z = \{b, c, d, e, f\}$.

7. $X \cap Y$

8. $X \cup Y$

9. $Y \cup Z$

10. $Y \cap Z$

11. $X \cup U$

12. $Y \cap U$

13. X'

14. Y'

15. $X' \cap Y'$

16. $X' \cap Z$

17. $X \cup (Y \cap Z)$

18. $Y \cap (X \cup Z)$

19. $(Y \cap Z') \cup X$

20. $(X' \cup Y') \cup Z$

21. $(Z \cup X')' \cap Y$

22. $(Y \cap X')' \cup Z'$

23. $X - Y$

24. $Y - X$

25. $X \cap (X - Y)$

26. $Y \cup (Y - X)$

27. $X' - Y$

28. $Y' - X$

29. $(X \cap Y') \cup (Y \cap X')$

30. $(X \cap Y') \cap (Y \cap X')$

Describe each set in words.

31. $A \cup (B' \cap C')$

32. $(A \cap B') \cup (B \cap A')$

33. $(C - B) \cup A$

34. $B \cap (A' - C)$

35. $(A - C) \cup (B - C)$

36. $(A' \cap B') \cup C'$

Adverse Effects of Alcohol and Tobacco *The table lists some common adverse effects of prolonged tobacco and alcohol use.*

Tobacco	Alcohol
Emphysema, e	Liver damage, l
Heart damage, h	Brain damage, b
Cancer, c	Heart damage, h

Let T be the set of listed effects of tobacco and A be the set of listed effects of alcohol. Find each set.

37. the smallest possible universal set U that includes all the effects listed

38. A' **39.** T' **40.** $T \cap A$ **41.** $T \cup A$ **42.** $T \cap A'$

Describe in words each set in Exercises 43–48.

Let $U =$ the set of all tax returns,
   $A =$ the set of all tax returns with itemized deductions,
   $B =$ the set of all tax returns showing business income,
   $C =$ the set of all tax returns filed in 2005,
   $D =$ the set of all tax returns selected for audit.

43. $B \cup C$

44. $A \cap D$

45. $C - A$

46. $D \cup A'$

47. $(A \cup B) - D$

48. $(C \cap A) \cap B'$

Assuming that A and B represent any two sets, identify each statement as either always true *or* not always true.

49. $A \subseteq (A \cup B)$

50. $A \subseteq (A \cap B)$

51. $(A \cap B) \subseteq A$

52. $(A \cup B) \subseteq A$

53. $n(A \cup B) = n(A) + n(B)$

54. $n(A \cup B) = n(A) + n(B) - n(A \cap B)$

For Exercises 55–60, use your results in parts (a) and (b) to answer part (c).

Let $U = \{1, 2, 3, 4, 5\}$, $X = \{1, 3, 5\}$, $Y = \{1, 2, 3\}$, and $Z = \{3, 4, 5\}$.

55. (a) Find $X \cup Y$.
 (b) Find $Y \cup X$.
 (c) State a conjecture.

56. (a) Find $X \cap Y$.
 (b) Find $Y \cap X$.
 (c) State a conjecture.

57. (a) Find $X \cup (Y \cup Z)$.
 (b) Find $(X \cup Y) \cup Z$.
 (c) State a conjecture.

58. (a) Find $X \cap (Y \cap Z)$.
 (b) Find $(X \cap Y) \cap Z$.
 (c) State a conjecture.

59. (a) Find $(X \cup Y)'$.
 (b) Find $X' \cap Y'$.
 (c) State a conjecture.

60. (a) Find $(X \cap Y)'$.
 (b) Find $X' \cup Y'$.
 (c) State a conjecture.

In Exercises 61 and 62, let set X equal the different letters in your last name.

61. Find $X \cup \emptyset$ and state a conjecture.

62. Find $X \cap \emptyset$ and state a conjecture.

Decide whether each statement is true or false.

63. $(3, 2) = (5 - 2, 1 + 1)$

64. $(10, 4) = (7 + 3, 5 - 1)$

65. $(6, 3) = (3, 6)$

66. $(2, 13) = (13, 2)$

67. $\{6, 3\} = \{3, 6\}$

68. $\{2, 13\} = \{13, 2\}$

69. $\{(1, 2), (3, 4)\} = \{(3, 4), (1, 2)\}$

70. $\{(5, 9), (4, 8), (4, 2)\} = \{(4, 8), (5, 9), (4, 2)\}$

Find $A \times B$ and $B \times A$, for A and B defined as follows.

71. $A = \{2, 8, 12\}$, $B = \{4, 9\}$

72. $A = \{3, 6, 9, 12\}$, $B = \{6, 8\}$

73. $A = \{d, o, g\}$, $B = \{p, i, g\}$

74. $A = \{b, l, u, e\}$, $B = \{r, e, d\}$

For the sets specified in Exercises 75–78, use the given information to find $n(A \times B)$ and $n(B \times A)$.

75. the sets in Exercise 71

76. the sets in Exercise 73

77. $n(A) = 35$ and $n(B) = 6$

78. $n(A) = 13$ and $n(B) = 5$

Find the cardinal number specified.

79. If $n(A \times B) = 72$ and $n(A) = 12$, find $n(B)$.

80. If $n(A \times B) = 300$ and $n(B) = 30$, find $n(A)$.

Place the elements of these sets in the proper locations on the given Venn diagram.

81. Let $U = \{a, b, c, d, e, f, g\}$,
 $A = \{b, d, f, g\}$,
 $B = \{a, b, d, e, g\}$.

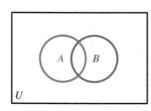

82. Let $U = \{5, 6, 7, 8, 9, 10, 11, 12, 13\}$,
 $M = \{5, 8, 10, 11\}$,
 $N = \{5, 6, 7, 9, 10\}$.

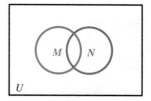

Use a Venn diagram similar to the one shown here to shade each set.

83. $B \cap A'$

84. $A \cup B$

85. $A' \cup B$

86. $A' \cap B'$

87. $B' \cup A$

88. $A' \cup A$

89. $B' \cap B$

90. $A \cap B'$

91. $B' \cup (A' \cap B')$

92. $(A \cap B) \cup B$

93. U'

94. $\emptyset'$

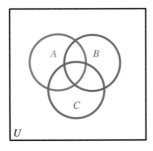

95. Let $U = \{m, n, o, p, q, r, s, t, u, v, w\}$,
  $A = \{m, n, p, q, r, t\}$,
  $B = \{m, o, p, q, s, u\}$,
  $C = \{m, o, p, r, s, t, u, v\}$.

Place the elements of these sets in the proper location on a Venn diagram similar to the one shown at the right.

96. Let $U = \{1, 2, 3, 4, 5, 6, 7, 8, 9\}$,
  $A = \{1, 3, 5, 7\}$,
  $B = \{1, 3, 4, 6, 8\}$,
  $C = \{1, 4, 5, 6, 7, 9\}$.

Place the elements of these sets in the proper location on a Venn diagram.

Use a Venn diagram to shade each set.

97. $(A \cap B) \cap C$

98. $(A \cap C') \cup B$

99. $(A \cap B) \cup C'$

100. $(A' \cap B) \cap C$

101. $(A' \cap B') \cap C$

102. $(A \cup B) \cup C$

103. $(A \cap B') \cup C$

104. $(A \cap C') \cap B$

105. $(A \cap B') \cap C'$

106. $(A' \cap B') \cup C$

107. $(A' \cap B') \cup C'$

108. $(A \cap B)' \cup C$

Write a description of each shaded area. Use the symbols A, B, C, $\cap$, $\cup$, $-$, and $'$ as necessary. More than one answer may be possible.

109.

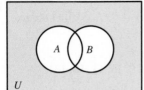

110.

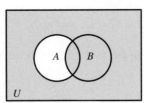

111.

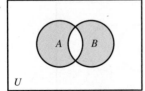

112.

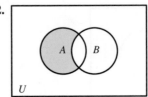

113.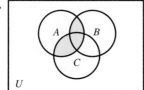

114.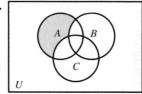

115.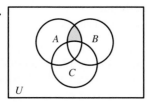

116.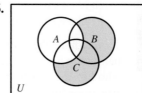

Suppose A and B are sets. Describe the conditions under which each statement would be true.

117. $A = A - B$

118. $A = B - A$

119. $A = A - \emptyset$

120. $A = \emptyset - A$

121. $A \cup \emptyset = \emptyset$

122. $A \cap \emptyset = \emptyset$

123. $A \cap \emptyset = A$

124. $A \cup \emptyset = A$

125. $A \cup A = \emptyset$

126. $A \cap A = \emptyset$

127. $A \cup B = A$

128. $A \cap B = B$

For Exercises 129–135, draw two appropriate Venn diagrams to decide whether the given statement is always true *or* not always true.

129. $A \cap A' = \emptyset$

130. $A \cup A' = U$

131. $(A \cap B) \subseteq A$

132. $(A \cup B) \subseteq A$

133. If $A \subseteq B$, then $A \cup B = A$.

134. If $A \subseteq B$, then $A \cap B = B$.

135. $(A \cup B)' = A' \cap B'$ (De Morgan's second law)

 136. Give examples of how a language such as English, Spanish, Arabic, or Vietnamese can have an advantage over the symbolic language of mathematics.

137. If A and B are sets, is it necessarily true that $n(A - B) = n(A) - n(B)$?

138. If $Q = \{x \mid x$ is a rational number$\}$ and $H = \{x \mid x$ is an irrational number$\}$, describe each set.
(a) $Q \cup H$
(b) $Q \cap H$

2.4 Surveys and Cardinal Numbers

Surveys • Cardinal Number Formula

Surveys Problems involving sets of people (or other objects) sometimes require analyzing known information about certain subsets to obtain cardinal numbers of other subsets. In this section, we apply three problem-solving techniques

to such problems: Venn diagrams, cardinal number formulas, and tables. The "known information" is quite often (although not always) obtained by administering a survey.

Suppose a group of students on a college campus are questioned about some selected musical performers, and the following information is produced.

33 like Kenny Chesney.	15 like Kenny and Carrie.
32 like Beyoncé.	14 like Beyoncé and Carrie.
28 like Carrie Underwood.	5 like all three performers.
11 like Kenny and Beyoncé.	7 like none of these performers.

To determine the total number of students surveyed, we cannot just add the eight numbers above because there is some overlapping. For example, in Figure 18, the 33 students who like Kenny Chesney should not be positioned in region *b* but should be distributed among regions *b*, *c*, *d*, and *e*, in a way that is consistent with all of the given data. (Region *b* actually contains those students who like Kenny but do not like Beyoncé and do not like Carrie.)

Because, at the start, we do not know how to distribute the 33 who like Kenny, we look first for some more manageable data. The smallest total listed, the 5 students who like all three singers, can be placed in region *d* (the intersection of the three sets). The 7 who like none of the three must go into region *a*. Then, the 11 who like Kenny and Beyoncé must go into regions *d* and *e*. Because region *d* already contains 5 students, we must place $11 - 5 = 6$ in region *e*. Because 15 like Kenny and Carrie (regions *c* and *d*), we place $15 - 5 = 10$ in region *c*. Now that regions *c*, *d*, and *e* contain 10, 5, and 6 students respectively, region *b* receives $33 - 10 - 5 - 6 = 12$. By similar reasoning, all regions are assigned their correct numbers, as shown in Figure 19.

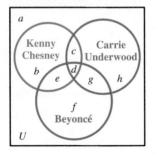

FIGURE 18

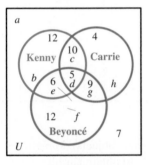

FIGURE 19

EXAMPLE 1 Analyzing a Survey

Using the survey data on student preferences for performers, as summarized in Figure 19, answer the following questions.

(a) How many students like Carrie Underwood only?
(b) How many students like exactly two performers?
(c) How many students were surveyed?

SOLUTION

(a) A student who likes Carrie only does not like Kenny and does not like Beyoncé. These students are inside the regions for Carrie and outside the regions for Kenny and Beyoncé. Region *h* is the appropriate region in Figure 19, and we see that four students like Carrie only.

(b) The students in regions *c*, *e*, and *g* like exactly two performers. The total number of such students is

$$10 + 6 + 9 = 25.$$

(c) Because each student surveyed has been placed in exactly one region of Figure 19, the total number surveyed is the sum of the numbers in all eight regions:

$$7 + 12 + 10 + 5 + 6 + 12 + 9 + 4 = 65.$$

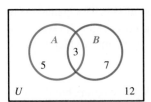

FIGURE 20

Cardinal Number Formula If the numbers shown in Figure 20 are the cardinal numbers of the individual regions, then $n(A) = 5 + 3 = 8$, $n(B) = 3 + 7 = 10$, $n(A \cap B) = 3$, and $n(A \cup B) = 5 + 3 + 7 = 15$. Notice that $n(A \cup B) = n(A) + n(B) - n(A \cap B)$ because $15 = 8 + 10 - 3$. This relationship is true for any two sets A and B.

Cardinal Number Formula

For any two sets A and B,

$$n(A \cup B) = n(A) + n(B) - n(A \cap B).$$

This formula can be rearranged to find any one of its four terms when the others are known.

EXAMPLE 2 **Applying the Cardinal Number Formula**

Find $n(A)$ if $n(A \cup B) = 22$, $n(A \cap B) = 8$, and $n(B) = 12$.

SOLUTION

The formula above can be rearranged. Thus,

$$n(A) = n(A \cup B) - n(B) + n(A \cap B)$$
$$= 22 - 12 + 8$$
$$= 18.$$

Sometimes, even when information is presented as in Example 2, it is more convenient to fit that information into a Venn diagram as in Example 1.

EXAMPLE 3 **Analyzing Data in a Report**

Robert Hurst is a section chief for an electric utility company. Hurst recently submitted the following report to the management of the utility.

My section includes 100 employees, with

$T = $ the set of employees who can cut tall trees,

$P = $ the set of employees who can climb poles,

$W = $ the set of employees who can splice wire.

$n(T) = 45$	$n(T \cap P) = 28$	$n(T \cap P \cap W) = 11$
$n(P) = 50$	$n(P \cap W) = 20$	$n(T' \cap P' \cap W') = 9$
$n(W) = 57$	$n(T \cap W) = 25$	

Is this a valid report? If not, why?

SOLUTION

The data supplied by Hurst are reflected in Figure 21. The sum of the numbers in the diagram gives the total number of employees in the section:

$$9 + 3 + 14 + 23 + 11 + 9 + 17 + 13 = 99.$$

FIGURE 21

Hurst claimed to have 100 employees, but his data indicate only 99. The management decided that this error meant that Hurst did not qualify as section chief. He was reassigned as night-shift information operator at the North Pole. (The moral: Hurst should have taken this course.) ▨

Sometimes information appears in a table rather than a Venn diagram, but the basic ideas of union and intersection still apply.

▉ EXAMPLE 4   Analyzing Data in a Table

The officer in charge of the cafeteria on a North Carolina military base wanted to know if the beverage that enlisted men and women preferred with lunch depended on their ages. On a given day, she categorized her lunch patrons according to age and preferred beverage, recording the results in a table.

		Beverage			
		Cola (C)	**Iced Tea (I)**	**Sweet Tea (S)**	**Totals**
Age	**18–25 (Y)**	45	10	35	90
	26–33 (M)	20	25	30	75
	Over 33 (O)	5	30	20	55
	Totals	70	65	85	220

Using the letters in the table, find the number of people in each of the following sets.

(a) $Y \cap C$ **(b)** $O' \cup I$

SOLUTION

(a) The set Y includes all personnel represented across the top row of the table (90 in all), while C includes the 70 down the left column. The intersection of these two sets is just the upper left entry: 45 people.

(b) The set O' excludes the bottom row, so it includes the first and second rows. The set I includes the middle column only. The union of the two sets represents

$$45 + 10 + 35 + 20 + 25 + 30 + 30 = 195 \text{ people.}$$ ▨

2.4 EXERCISES

Use the numerals representing cardinalities in the Venn diagrams to give the cardinality of each set specified.

1.

(a) $A \cap B$ **(b)** $A \cup B$ **(c)** $A \cap B'$
(d) $A' \cap B$ **(e)** $A' \cap B'$

2.

(a) $A \cap B$ **(b)** $A \cup B$ **(c)** $A \cap B'$
(d) $A' \cap B$ **(e)** $A' \cap B'$

3.

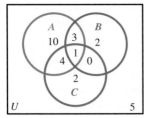

(a) $A \cap B \cap C$ (b) $A \cap B \cap C'$
(c) $A \cap B' \cap C$ (d) $A' \cap B \cap C$
(e) $A' \cap B' \cap C$ (f) $A \cap B' \cap C'$
(g) $A' \cap B \cap C'$ (h) $A' \cap B' \cap C'$

4.

(a) $A \cap B \cap C$ (b) $A \cap B \cap C'$
(c) $A \cap B' \cap C$ (d) $A' \cap B \cap C$
(e) $A' \cap B' \cap C$ (f) $A \cap B' \cap C'$
(g) $A' \cap B \cap C'$ (h) $A' \cap B' \cap C'$

In Exercises 5–10, make use of an appropriate formula.

5. Find the value of $n(A \cup B)$ if $n(A) = 8$, $n(B) = 14$, and $n(A \cap B) = 5$.

6. Find the value of $n(A \cup B)$ if $n(A) = 16$, $n(B) = 28$, and $n(A \cap B) = 9$.

7. Find the value of $n(A \cap B)$ if $n(A) = 15$, $n(B) = 12$, and $n(A \cup B) = 25$.

8. Find the value of $n(A \cap B)$ if $n(A) = 20$, $n(B) = 14$, and $n(A \cup B) = 30$.

9. Find the value of $n(A)$ if $n(B) = 35$, $n(A \cap B) = 15$, and $n(A \cup B) = 55$.

10. Find the value of $n(B)$ if $n(A) = 20$, $n(A \cap B) = 6$, and $n(A \cup B) = 30$.

To prepare for the survey problems that follow later in this exercise set, draw an appropriate Venn diagram and use the given information to fill in the number of elements in each region.

11. $n(A) = 19$, $n(B) = 13$, $n(A \cup B) = 25$, $n(A') = 11$

12. $n(U) = 43$, $n(A) = 25$, $n(A \cap B) = 5$, $n(B') = 30$

13. $n(A') = 25$, $n(B) = 28$, $n(A' \cup B') = 40$, $n(A \cap B) = 10$

14. $n(A \cup B) = 15$, $n(A \cap B) = 8$, $n(A) = 13$, $n(A' \cup B') = 11$

15. $n(A) = 57$, $n(A \cap B) = 35$, $n(A \cup B) = 81$, $n(A \cap B \cap C) = 15$, $n(A \cap C) = 21$, $n(B \cap C) = 25$, $n(C) = 49$, $n(B') = 52$

16. $n(A) = 24$, $n(B) = 24$, $n(C) = 26$, $n(A \cap B) = 10$, $n(B \cap C) = 8$, $n(A \cap C) = 15$, $n(A \cap B \cap C) = 6$, $n(U) = 50$

17. $n(A) = 15$, $n(A \cap B \cap C) = 5$, $n(A \cap C) = 13$, $n(A \cap B') = 9$, $n(B \cap C) = 8$, $n(A' \cap B' \cap C') = 21$, $n(B \cap C') = 3$, $n(B \cup C) = 32$

18. $n(A \cap B) = 21$, $n(A \cap B \cap C) = 6$, $n(A \cap C) = 26$, $n(B \cap C) = 7$, $n(A \cap C') = 20$, $n(B \cap C') = 25$, $n(C) = 40$, $n(A' \cap B' \cap C') = 2$

Use Venn diagrams to work each problem.

19. *Writing and Producing Music* Joe Long writes and produces albums for musicians. Last year, he worked on 10 such projects.

    He wrote and produced 2 projects.
    He wrote a total of 5 projects.
    He produced a total of 7 projects.

(a) How many projects did he write but not produce?
(b) How many projects did he produce but not write?

Joe Long, Bob Gaudio, Tommy DeVito, and Frankie Valli
The Four Seasons

20. **Compact Disc Collection** Paula Story is a fan of the music of Paul Simon and Art Garfunkel. In her collection of 22 compact discs, she has the following:

    5 on which both Simon and Garfunkel sing
    8 on which Simon sings
    7 on which Garfunkel sings
    12 on which neither Simon nor Garfunkel sings.

    (a) How many of her compact discs feature only Paul Simon?
    (b) How many of her compact discs feature only Art Garfunkel?
    (c) How many feature at least one of these two artists?

21. **Viewer Response to Movies** Buddy Vosburg, a child psychologist, was planning a study of response to certain aspects of the movies *The Lion King*, *Shrek*, and *Finding Nemo*. Upon surveying a group of 55 children, he determined the following:

    17 had seen *The Lion King*
    17 had seen *Shrek*,
    23 had seen *Finding Nemo*
    6 had seen *The Lion King* and *Shrek*
    8 had seen *The Lion King* and *Finding Nemo*
    10 had seen *Shrek* and *Finding Nemo*
    2 had seen all three of these movies.

    How many children had seen:
    (a) exactly two of these movies?
    (b) exactly one of these movies?
    (c) none of these movies?
    (d) *The Lion King* but neither of the others?

22. **Financial Aid for Students** At the University of Louisiana, half of the 48 mathematics majors were receiving federal financial aid as follows:

    5 had Pell Grants
    14 participated in the College Work Study Program
    4 had TOPS scholarships
    2 had TOPS scholarships and participated in Work Study.

    Those with Pell Grants had no other federal aid.

    How many of the 48 math majors had:
    (a) no federal aid?
    (b) more than one of these three forms of aid?

    (c) federal aid other than these three forms?
    (d) a TOPS scholarship or Work Study?

23. **Cooking Habits** Robert Hurst (Example 3 in the text) was again reassigned, this time to the home economics department of the electric utility. He interviewed 140 people in a suburban shopping center to find out some of their cooking habits. He obtained the following results:

    58 use microwave ovens
    63 use electric ranges
    58 use gas ranges
    19 use microwave ovens and electric ranges
    17 use microwave ovens and gas ranges
    4 use both gas and electric ranges
    1 uses all three
    2 cook only with solar energy.

    There is a job opening in Siberia. Should he be reassigned yet one more time?

24. **Wine Tasting** The following list shows the preferences of 102 people at a fraternity party:

    99 like Spañada
    96 like Ripple
    99 like Boone's Farm Apple Wine
    95 like Spañada and Ripple
    94 like Ripple and Boone's
    96 like Spañada and Boone's
    93 like all three.

    How many people like:
    (a) none of the three?
    (b) Spañada, but not Ripple?
    (c) anything but Boone's Farm?
    (d) only Ripple?
    (e) exactly two of these wines?

25. **Poultry on a Farm** Old MacDonald surveyed her flock with the following results. She has:

    9 fat red roosters   18 thin brown roosters
    2 fat red hens   6 thin red roosters
    26 fat roosters   5 thin red hens
    37 fat chickens   7 thin brown hens.

    Answer the following questions about the flock. (*Hint:* You need a Venn diagram with circles for fat (assuming that thin is not fat), for male (a rooster is a male; a hen is a female), and for red (assume that

brown and red are opposites in the chicken world).)
How many chickens are:
(a) fat?
(b) red?
(c) male?
(d) fat, but not male?
(e) brown, but not fat?
(f) red and fat?

26. **Student Goals** Carol Britz, who sells college textbooks, interviewed freshmen on a community college
campus to find out the main goals of today's students.

Let W = the set of those who want to be wealthy,
F = the set of those who want to raise
a family,
E = the set of those who want to
become experts in their fields.

Carol's findings are summarized here:

$n(W) = 160$ $n(E \cap F) = 90$

$n(F) = 140$ $n(W \cap F \cap E) = 80$

$n(E) = 130$ $n(E') = 95$

$n(W \cap F) = 95$ $n[(W \cup F \cup E)'] = 10.$

Find the total number of students interviewed.

27. **Hospital Patient Symptoms** Suzanne Chustz conducted
a survey among 75 patients admitted to the cardiac unit
of a Santa Fe hospital during a two-week period.

Let B = the set of patients with high blood
pressure
C = the set of patients with high cholesterol
levels,
S = the set of patients who smoke cigarettes.

Suzanne's data are as follows:

$n(B) = 47$ $n(B \cap S) = 33$

$n(C) = 46$ $n(B \cap C) = 31$

$n(S) = 52$ $n(B \cap C \cap S) = 21$

$n[(B \cap C) \cup (B \cap S) \cup (C \cap S)] = 51.$

Find the number of these patients who:
(a) had either high blood pressure or high cholesterol
levels, but not both
(b) had fewer than two of the indications listed
(c) were smokers but had neither high blood pressure
nor high cholesterol levels
(d) did not have exactly two of the indications listed.

28. **Song Themes** It was once said that Country-Western
songs emphasize three basic themes: love, prison, and
trucks. A survey of the local Country-Western radio
station produced the following data:

12 songs about a truck driver who is in love
while in prison
13 about a prisoner in love
28 about a person in love
18 about a truck driver in love
 3 about a truck driver in prison who is not in love
 2 about people in prison who are not in love
and do not drive trucks
 8 about people who are out of prison, are not
in love, and do not drive trucks
16 about truck drivers who are not in prison.

(a) How many songs were surveyed?

Find the number of songs about:
(b) truck drivers
(c) prisoners
(d) truck drivers in prison
(e) people not in prison
(f) people not in love.

29. The figure below shows U divided into 16 regions by
four sets, A, B, C, and D. Find the numbers of the
regions belonging to each set.
(a) $A \cap B \cap C \cap D$
(b) $A \cup B \cup C \cup D$
(c) $(A \cap B) \cup (C \cap D)$
(d) $(A' \cap B') \cap (C \cup D)$

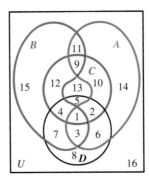

30. *Sports Viewing Habits* A survey of 130 television viewers revealed the following facts:

> 52 watch football
> 56 watch basketball
> 62 watch tennis
> 60 watch golf
> 21 watch football and basketball
> 19 watch football and tennis
> 22 watch basketball and tennis
> 27 watch football and golf
> 30 watch basketball and golf
> 21 watch tennis and golf
> 3 watch football, basketball, and tennis
> 15 watch football, basketball, and golf
> 10 watch football, tennis, and golf
> 10 watch basketball, tennis, and golf
> 3 watch all four of these sports
> 5 don't watch any of these four sports.

Use a diagram like the one in Exercise 29 to answer the following questions.
(a) How many of these viewers watch football, basketball, and tennis, but not golf?
(b) How many watch exactly one of these four sports?
(c) How many watch exactly two of these four sports?

Solve each problem.

31. *Basketball Positions* Dwaine Tomlinson runs a basketball program in California. On the first day of the season, 60 young women showed up and were categorized by age level and by preferred basketball position, as shown in the following table.

		Position		
		Guard (G)	Forward (F)	Center (N)	Totals
Age	**Junior High (J)**	9	6	4	19
	Senior High (S)	12	5	9	26
	College (C)	5	8	2	15
	Totals	26	19	15	60

Using the set labels (letters) in the table, find the number of players in each of the following sets.
(a) $J \cap G$ **(b)** $S \cap N$ **(c)** $N \cup (S \cap F)$

(d) $S' \cap (G \cup N)$ **(e)** $(S \cap N') \cup (C \cap G')$
(f) $N' \cap (S' \cap C')$

32. *Army Housing* A study of U.S. Army housing trends categorized personnel as commissioned officers (C), warrant officers (W), or enlisted (E), and categorized their living facilities as on-base (B), rented off-base (R), or owned off-base (O). One survey yielded the following data.

		Facilities			
		B	**R**	**O**	**Totals**
Personnel	**C**	12	29	54	95
	W	4	5	6	15
	E	374	71	285	730
	Totals	390	105	345	840

Find the number of personnel in each of the following sets.
(a) $W \cap O$ **(b)** $C \cup B$
(c) $R' \cup W'$ **(d)** $(C \cup W) \cap (B \cup R)$
(e) $(C \cap B) \cup (E \cap O)$ **(f)** $B \cap (W \cup R)'$

33. Could the information of Example 4 have been presented in a Venn diagram similar to those in Examples 1 and 3? If so, construct such a diagram. Otherwise, explain the essential difference of Example 4.

34. Explain how a cardinal number formula can be derived for the case where *three* sets occur. Specifically, give a formula relating $n(A \cup B \cup C)$ to $n(A)$, $n(B)$, $n(C)$, $n(A \cap B)$, $n(A \cap C)$, $n(B \cap C)$, and $n(A \cap B \cap C)$. Illustrate with a Venn diagram.

2.5 Infinite Sets and Their Cardinalities

One-to-One Correspondence and Equivalent Sets • The Cardinal Number $\aleph_0$ • Infinite Sets • Sets That Are Not Countable

The word **paradox** in Greek originally meant "wrong opinion" as opposed to orthodox, which meant "right opinion." Over the years, the word came to mean self-contradiction. An example is the statement "This sentence is false." By assuming it is true, we get a contradiction; likewise, by assuming it is false, we get a contradiction. Thus, it's a paradox.

Before the twentieth century it was considered a paradox that any set could be placed into one-to-one correspondence with a proper subset of itself. This paradox, called **Galileo's paradox** after the sixteenth-century mathematician and scientist **Galileo** (see the picture), is now explained by saying that the ability to make such a correspondence is how we distinguish infinite sets from finite sets. What is true for finite sets is not necessarily true for infinite sets.

One-to-One Correspondence and Equivalent Sets As mentioned at the beginning of this chapter, most of the early work in set theory was done by Georg Cantor. He devoted much of his life to a study of the cardinal numbers of sets. Recall that the *cardinal number*, or *cardinality*, of a finite set is the number of elements that it contains. For example, the set $\{5, 9, 15\}$ contains 3 elements and has a cardinal number of 3. The cardinal number of $\emptyset$ is 0.

Cantor proved many results about the cardinal numbers of infinite sets. The proofs of Cantor are quite different from the type of proofs you may have seen in an algebra or geometry course. Because of the novelty of Cantor's methods, they were not quickly accepted by the mathematicians of his day. (In fact, some other aspects of Cantor's theory lead to paradoxes.) The results discussed here, however, are commonly accepted.

The idea of the cardinal number of an infinite set depends on the idea of one-to-one correspondence. For example, each of the sets $\{1, 2, 3, 4\}$ and $\{9, 10, 11, 12\}$ has four elements. Corresponding elements of the two sets could be paired off in the following manner (among many other ways):

$$\{1, \quad 2, \quad 3, \quad 4\}$$
$$\updownarrow \quad \updownarrow \quad \updownarrow \quad \updownarrow$$
$$\{9, \quad 10, \quad 11, \quad 12\}.$$

Such a pairing is a **one-to-one correspondence** between the two sets. The "one-to-one" refers to the fact that each element of the first set is paired with exactly one element of the second set and similarly each element of the second set is paired with exactly one element of the first set.

Two sets A and B which may be put in a one-to-one correspondence are said to be **equivalent.** Symbolically, this is written $\mathbf{A \sim B.}$ The two sets shown above are equivalent but *not* equal.

The following correspondence between sets is not one-to-one because the elements 8 and 12 from the first set are both paired with the element 11 from the second set. These sets are not equivalent.

$$\{1, \quad 8, \quad 12\}$$
$$\updownarrow \quad \searrow \nearrow$$
$$\{6, \quad 11\}$$

It seems reasonable to say that if two non-empty sets have the same cardinal number, then a one-to-one correspondence can be established between the two sets. Also, if a one-to-one correspondence can be established between two sets, then the two sets must have the same cardinal number. These two facts are fundamental in discussing the cardinal numbers of infinite sets.

The Cardinal Number $\aleph_0$ The basic set used in discussing infinite sets is the set of counting numbers, $\{1, 2, 3, 4, 5, \ldots\}$. The set of counting numbers is said to have the infinite cardinal number $\aleph_0$ (the first Hebrew letter, aleph, with a zero subscript,

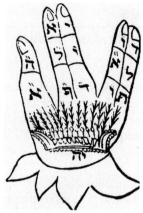

Aleph and other letters of the **Hebrew alphabet** are shown on a Kabbalistic diagram representing one of the ten emanations of God during Creation. Kabbalah, the ultramystical tradition within Judaism, arose in the fifth century and peaked in the sixteenth century in both Palestine and Poland.

Kabbalists believed that the Bible held mysteries that could be discovered in permutations, combinations, and anagrams of its very letters. They also "read" the numerical value of letters in a word by the technique called Gematria (from geometry?). This was possible because each letter in the aleph-bet has a numerical value (aleph = 1), and thus a numeration system exists. The letter Y stands for 10, so 15 should be YH (10 + 5). However, YH is a form of the Holy Name, so instead TW (9 + 6) is the symbol.

read "aleph-null"). Think of $\aleph_0$ as being the "smallest" infinite cardinal number. To the question "How many counting numbers are there?", we answer "There are $\aleph_0$ of them."

From the discussion above, any set that can be placed in a one-to-one correspondence with the counting numbers will have the same cardinal number as the set of counting numbers, or $\aleph_0$. It turns out that many sets of numbers have cardinal number $\aleph_0$.

▎EXAMPLE 1   Showing that {0, 1, 2, 3, ...} Has Cardinal Number $\aleph_0$

Verify that the set of whole numbers {0, 1, 2, 3, ... } has cardinal number $\aleph_0$.

SOLUTION

All we really know about $\aleph_0$ is that it is the cardinal number of the set of counting numbers (by definition). To show that another set, such as the whole numbers, also has $\aleph_0$ as its cardinal number, we must show that set to be equivalent to the set of counting numbers. Equivalence is established by a one-to-one correspondence between the two sets. We exhibit such a correspondence, showing exactly how each counting number is paired with a unique whole number, as follows:

$$\{1, \quad 2, \quad 3, \quad 4, \quad 5, \quad 6, \ldots, \quad n, \quad \ldots\} \quad \text{Counting numbers}$$
$$\updownarrow \quad \updownarrow \quad \updownarrow \quad \updownarrow \quad \updownarrow \quad \updownarrow \qquad \updownarrow \qquad \updownarrow$$
$$\{0, \quad 1, \quad 2, \quad 3, \quad 4, \quad 5, \ldots, \quad n-1, \quad \ldots\}. \quad \text{Whole numbers}$$

The pairing of the counting number n with the whole number $n - 1$ continues indefinitely, with neither set containing any element not used up in the pairing process. Even though the set of whole numbers has an additional element (the number 0) compared to the set of counting numbers, the correspondence proves that both sets have the same cardinal number, $\aleph_0$. ■

Infinite Sets

The result in Example 1 shows that intuition is a poor guide for dealing with infinite sets. Intuitively, it would seem "obvious" that there are more whole numbers than counting numbers. However, because the sets can be placed in a one-to-one correspondence, the two sets have the same cardinal number.

The set {5, 6, 7} is a proper subset of the set {5, 6, 7, 8}, and there is no way to place these two sets in a one-to-one correspondence. However, the set of counting numbers is a proper subset of the set of whole numbers, and Example 1 showed that these two sets *can* be placed in a one-to-one correspondence. This important property is used in the formal definition of an infinite set.

Infinite Set

A set is **infinite** if it can be placed in a one-to-one correspondence with a proper subset of itself.

▎EXAMPLE 2   Showing that {..., −3, −2, −1, 0, 1, 2, 3, ...} Has Cardinal Number $\aleph_0$

Verify that the set of integers {...,−3, −2, −1, 0, 1, 2, 3, ... } has cardinal number $\aleph_0$.

SOLUTION

A one-to-one correspondence can be set up between the set of integers and the set of counting numbers, as follows:

$$\{1, \quad 2, \quad 3, \quad 4, \quad 5, \quad 6, \quad 7, \quad \ldots, \quad 2n, \quad 2n + 1, \quad \ldots\}$$
$$\updownarrow \; \updownarrow \quad \updownarrow \quad \updownarrow \quad \updownarrow \quad \updownarrow \quad \updownarrow \qquad\qquad \updownarrow \qquad \updownarrow$$
$$\{0, \quad 1, \quad -1, \quad 2, \quad -2, \quad 3, \quad -3, \quad \ldots, \quad n, \qquad -n, \quad \ldots\}.$$

Because of this one-to-one correspondence, the cardinal number of the set of integers is the same as the cardinal number of the set of counting numbers, $\aleph_0$.

The one-to-one correspondence of Example 2 proves that the set of integers is infinite; the set was placed in a one-to-one correspondence with a proper subset of itself.

As shown by Example 2, there are just as many integers as there are counting numbers. This result is not at all intuitive. However, the next result is even less intuitive. We know that there is an infinite number of fractions between any two counting numbers. For example, there is an infinite set of fractions $\left\{\frac{1}{2}, \frac{3}{4}, \frac{7}{8}, \frac{15}{16}, \frac{31}{32}, \ldots\right\}$ between the counting numbers 0 and 1. This should imply that there are "more" fractions than counting numbers. However, there are just as many fractions as counting numbers.

EXAMPLE 3 **Showing that the Set of Rational Numbers Has Cardinal Number $\aleph_0$**

Verify that the cardinal number of the set of rational numbers is $\aleph_0$.

SOLUTION

To show that the cardinal number of the set of rational numbers is $\aleph_0$, first show that a one-to-one correspondence may be set up between the set of nonnegative rational numbers and the counting numbers. This is done by the following ingenious scheme, devised by Georg Cantor. Look at Figure 22. The nonnegative rational numbers whose denominators are 1 are written in the first row; those whose denominators are 2 are written in the second row, and so on. Every nonnegative rational number appears in this list sooner or later. For example, $\frac{327}{189}$ is in row 189 and column 327.

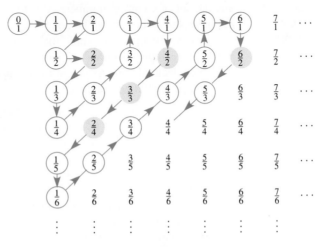

FIGURE 22

To set up a one-to-one correspondence between the set of nonnegative rationals and the set of counting numbers, follow the path drawn in Figure 22. Let $\frac{0}{1}$ correspond to 1, let $\frac{1}{1}$ correspond to 2, $\frac{2}{1}$ to 3, $\frac{1}{2}$ to 4 $\left(\text{skip } \frac{2}{2}, \text{ since } \frac{2}{2} = \frac{1}{1}\right)$, $\frac{1}{3}$ to 5, $\frac{1}{4}$ to 6, and so on. The numbers under the colored disks are omitted because they can be reduced to lower terms, and were thus included earlier in the listing.

This procedure sets up a one-to-one correspondence between the set of nonnegative rationals and the counting numbers, showing that both of these sets have the same cardinal number, $\aleph_0$. Now by using the method of Example 2, (i.e., letting each negative number follow its corresponding positive number), we can extend this correspondence to include negative rational numbers as well. Thus, the set of all rational numbers has cardinal number $\aleph_0$. ■

A set is called **countable** if it is finite or if it has cardinal number $\aleph_0$. All the infinite sets of numbers discussed so far—the counting numbers, the whole numbers, the integers, and the rational numbers—are countable.

Sets That are Not Countable
It would seem that every set is countable. However, the set of real numbers is not countable. That is, its cardinal number is not $\aleph_0$—in fact, it is greater than $\aleph_0$. The next example confirms this fact.

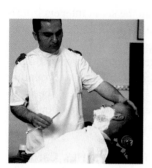

The Barber Paradox is a version of a paradox of set theory that Bertrand Russell proposed in the early twentieth century.

1. The men in a village are of two types: men who do not shave themselves and men who do.

2. The village barber shaves all men who do not shave themselves and he shaves only those men.

But who shaves the barber? The barber cannot shave himself. If he did, he would fall into the category of men who shave themselves. However, (2) above states that the barber does not shave such men.

So the barber does not shave himself. But then he falls into the category of men who do not shave themselves. According to (2), the barber shaves all of these men; hence, the barber shaves himself, too.

We find that the barber cannot shave himself, yet the barber does shave himself—a paradox.

■ **EXAMPLE 4** **Showing that the Set of Real Numbers Does Not Have Cardinal Number $\aleph_0$**

Verify that the set of all real numbers does not have cardinal number $\aleph_0$.

SOLUTION

There are two possibilities:

1. The set of real numbers has cardinal number $\aleph_0$.
2. The set of real numbers does not have cardinal number $\aleph_0$.

Assume for the time being that the first statement is true. If the first statement is true, then a one-to-one correspondence can be set up between the set of real numbers and the set of counting numbers. We do not know what sort of correspondence this might be, but assume it can be done.

In a later chapter, we show that every real number can be written as a decimal number (or simply "decimal"). Thus, in the one-to-one correspondence we are assuming, some decimal corresponds to the counting number 1, some decimal corresponds to 2, and so on. Suppose the correspondence is as follows:

$$1 \leftrightarrow .68458429006\ldots$$
$$2 \leftrightarrow .13479201038\ldots$$
$$3 \leftrightarrow .37291568341\ldots$$
$$4 \leftrightarrow .935223671611\ldots$$

and so on.

Assuming the existence of a one-to-one correspondence between the counting numbers and the real numbers means that every decimal is in the list above. Let's construct a new decimal K as follows. The first decimal in the above list has 6 as its first digit; let K start as $K = .4 \ldots$. We picked 4 because $4 \neq 6$; we could have used any other digit except 6. Because the second digit of the second decimal in the list is 3, we let $K = .45 \ldots$ (because $5 \neq 3$). The third digit of the third decimal is 2, so let $K = .457 \ldots$ (because $7 \neq 2$). The fourth digit of the fourth decimal is 2, so let $K = .4573 \ldots$ (because $3 \neq 2$). Continue defining K in this way.

Is K in the list that we assumed to contain all decimals? The first decimal in the list differs from K in at least the first position (K starts with 4, and the first decimal in the list starts with 6). The second decimal in the list differs from K in at least the second position, and the nth decimal in the list differs from K in at least the nth position. Every decimal in the list differs from K in at least one position, so that K cannot possibly be in the list. In summary:

> We assume every decimal is in the list above.
> The decimal K is not in the list.

Because these statements cannot both be true, the original assumption has led to a contradiction. This forces the acceptance of the only possible alternative to the original assumption: It is not possible to set up a one-to-one correspondence between the set of reals and the set of counting numbers. The cardinal number of the set of reals is not equal to $\aleph_0$. ▪

The set of counting numbers is a proper subset of the set of real numbers. Because of this, it would seem reasonable to say that the cardinal number of the set of reals, commonly written c, is greater than $\aleph_0$. (The letter c here represents *continuum*.) Other, even larger, infinite cardinal numbers can be constructed. For example, the set of all subsets of the set of real numbers has a cardinal number larger than c. Continuing this process of finding cardinal numbers of sets of subsets, more and more, larger and larger infinite cardinal numbers are produced.

The six most important infinite sets of numbers were listed in an earlier section. All of them have been dealt with in this section, except the irrational numbers. The irrationals have decimal representations, so they are all included among the real numbers. Because the irrationals are a subset of the reals, you might guess that the irrationals have cardinal number $\aleph_0$, just like the rationals. However, because the union of the rationals and the irrationals is all the reals, that would imply that the cardinality of the union of two disjoint countable sets is c. But Example 2 showed that this is not the case. A better guess is that the cardinal number of the irrationals is c (the same as that of the reals). This is, in fact, true. The major infinite sets of numbers, with their cardinal numbers, are now summarized.

Zeno's paradox of the Tortoise and Achilles was given in its original form by Zeno of Elea. According to Math Academy Online, it "has inspired many writers and thinkers throughout the ages, notably Lewis Carroll and Douglas Hofstadter." More on Lewis Carroll can be found in Chapter 3.

In the original story, the Tortoise is able to convince Achilles (the Greek hero of Homer's *The Illiad*) that in a race, given a small head start, the Tortoise is always able to defeat Achilles. (See the Chapter Opener and Exercises 51 and 52 in this section.) The resolution of this paradox is discussed on the Website www.mathacademy.com.

Cardinal Numbers of Infinite Number Sets	
Infinite Set	**Cardinal Number**
Natural or counting numbers	$\aleph_0$
Whole numbers	$\aleph_0$
Integers	$\aleph_0$
Rational numbers	$\aleph_0$
Irrational numbers	c
Real numbers	c

2.5 EXERCISES

Match each set in Column I with the set in Column II that has the same cardinality. Give the cardinal number.

I

1. {6}

2. {−16, 14, 3}

3. $\{x \mid x$ is a natural number$\}$

4. $\{x \mid x$ is a real number$\}$

5. $\{x \mid x$ is an integer between 5 and 6$\}$

6. $\{x \mid x$ is an integer that satisfies $x^2 = 100\}$

II

A. $\{x \mid x$ is a rational number$\}$

B. {26}

C. $\{x \mid x$ is an irrational number$\}$

D. {x, y, z}

E. $\{x \mid x$ is a real number that satisfies $x^2 = 25\}$

F. $\{x \mid x$ is an integer that is both even and odd$\}$

Place each pair of sets into a one-to-one correspondence, if possible.

7. {I, II, III} and {x, y, z}

8. {a, b, c, d} and {2, 4, 6}

9. {a, d, d, i, t, i, o, n} and {a, n, s, w, e, r}

10. {Reagan, Clinton, Bush} and {Nancy, Hillary, Laura}

Give the cardinal number of each set.

11. {a, b, c, d, . . . , k}

12. {9, 12, 15, . . . , 36}

13. ∅

14. {0}

15. {300, 400, 500, . . . }

16. {−35, −28, −21, . . . , 56}

17. $\left\{ -\dfrac{1}{4}, -\dfrac{1}{8}, -\dfrac{1}{12}, \cdots \right\}$

18. $\{x \mid x$ is an even integer$\}$

19. $\{x \mid x$ is an odd counting number$\}$

20. {b, a, 1, 1, a, d}

21. {Jan, Feb, Mar, . . . , Dec}

22. {Alabama, Alaska, Arizona, . . . , Wisconsin, Wyoming}

23. Lew Lefton (www.math.gatech.edu/~llefton) has revised the old song "100 Bottles of Beer on the Wall" to illustrate a property of infinite cardinal numbers. Fill in the blank in the first line of Lefton's composition:

> $\aleph_0$ bottles of beer on the wall, $\aleph_0$ bottles of beer, take one down and pass it around, _____ bottles of beer on the wall.

24. Two one-to-one correspondences are considered "different" if some elements are paired differently in one than in the other. For example:

$$\begin{array}{ccc} \{a, & b, & c\} \\ \updownarrow & \updownarrow & \updownarrow \\ \{a, & b, & c\} \end{array} \quad \text{and} \quad \begin{array}{ccc} \{a, & b, & c\} \\ \updownarrow & \updownarrow & \updownarrow \\ \{c, & b, & a\} \end{array} \quad \text{are different,}$$

$$\text{while} \quad \begin{array}{ccc} \{a, & b, & c\} \\ \updownarrow & \updownarrow & \updownarrow \\ \{c, & a, & b\} \end{array} \quad \text{and} \quad \begin{array}{ccc} \{b, & c, & a\} \\ \updownarrow & \updownarrow & \updownarrow \\ \{a, & b, & c\} \end{array} \quad \text{are not.}$$

(a) How many *different* correspondences can be set up between the two sets {Jamie Foxx, Mike Myers, Madonna} and {Austin Powers, Ray Charles, Eva Peron}

(b) Which one of these correspondences pairs each person with the appropriate famous movie role?

Determine whether each pair of sets is equal, equivalent, both, *or* neither.

25. {u, v, w}, {v, u, w}

26. {48, 6}, {4, 86}

27. {X, Y, Z}, {x, y, z}

28. {top}, {pot}

29. $\{x \mid x$ is a positive real number$\}$, $\{x \mid x$ is a negative real number$\}$

30. $\{x \mid x$ is a positive rational number$\}$, $\{x \mid x$ is a negative real number$\}$

Show that each set has cardinal number $\aleph_0$ *by setting up a one-to-one correspondence between the given set and the set of counting numbers.*

31. the set of positive even integers

32. $\{-10, -20, -30, -40, \dots\}$

33. $\{1{,}000{,}000, \quad 2{,}000{,}000, \quad 3{,}000{,}000, \dots\}$

34. the set of odd integers

35. $\{2, 4, 8, 16, 32, \dots\}$ (*Hint:* $4 = 2^2$, $8 = 2^3$, $16 = 2^4$, and so on)

36. $\{-17, -22, -27, -32, \dots\}$

In Exercises 37–40, identify the given statement as always true *or* not always true. *If not always true,* give a counterexample.

37. If A and B are infinite sets, then A is equivalent to B.

38. If set A is an infinite set and set B can be put in a one-to-one correspondence with a proper subset of A, then B must be infinite.

39. If A is an infinite set and A is not equivalent to the set of counting numbers, then $n(A) = c$.

40. If A and B are both countably infinite sets, then $n(A \cup B) = \aleph_0$.

Exercises 41 and 42 are geometric applications of the concept of infinity.

41. The set of real numbers can be represented by an infinite line, extending indefinitely in both directions. Each point on the line corresponds to a unique real number, and each real number corresponds to a unique point on the line.
   (a) Use the figure below, where the line segment between 0 and 1 has been bent into a semicircle and positioned above the line, to prove that

$\{x \mid x$ is a real number between 0 and 1$\}$
is equivalent to $\{x \mid x$ is a real number$\}$.

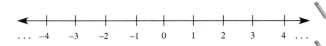

   (b) What fact does part (a) establish about the set of real numbers?

42. Show that the two vertical line segments shown here both have the same number of points.

Show that each set can be placed in a one-to-one correspondence with a proper subset of itself to prove that each set is infinite.

43. $\{3, 6, 9, 12, \dots\}$

44. $\{4, 7, 10, 13, 16, \dots\}$

45. $\left\{\dfrac{3}{4}, \dfrac{3}{8}, \dfrac{3}{12}, \dfrac{3}{16}, \dots\right\}$

46. $\left\{1, \dfrac{4}{3}, \dfrac{5}{3}, 2, \dots\right\}$

47. $\left\{\dfrac{1}{9}, \dfrac{1}{18}, \dfrac{1}{27}, \dfrac{1}{36}, \dots\right\}$

48. $\{-3, -5, -9, -17, \dots\}$

49. Describe the distinction between *equal* and *equivalent* sets.

50. Explain how the correspondence suggested in Example 4 shows that the set of real numbers between 0 and 1 is not countable.

🎥 ***The Paradoxes of Zeno*** *The Chapter Opener discussed the scene in the movie* I.Q. *that deals with Zeno's paradox. Zeno was born about 496 B.C. in southern Italy. Two forms of his paradox are given on the next page.*

What is your explanation for the following two examples of Zeno's paradoxes?

51. Achilles, if he starts out behind a tortoise, can never overtake the tortoise even if he runs faster.

Suppose Tortoise has a head start of one meter and goes one-tenth as fast as Achilles. When Achilles reaches the point where Tortoise started, Tortoise is then one-tenth meter ahead. When Achilles reaches *that* point, Tortoise is one-hundredth meter ahead.

And so on. Achilles gets closer but can never catch up.

52. Motion itself cannot occur.

You cannot travel one meter until after you have first gone a half meter. But you cannot go a half meter until after you have first gone a quarter meter. And so on. Even the tiniest motion cannot occur because a tinier motion would have to occur first.

COLLABORATIVE INVESTIGATION

Surveying the Members of Your Class

This group activity is designed to determine the number of students present in your class without actually counting the members one by one. This will be accomplished by having each member of the class determine one particular set in which he or she belongs, and then finding the sum of the cardinal numbers of the subsets.

For this activity, we designate three sets: X, Y, and Z. Here are their descriptions:

$X = \{$students in the class registered with the Republican party$\}$

$Y = \{$students in the class 24 years of age or younger$\}$

$Z = \{$students who have never been married$\}$

Each student in the class will belong to one of the sets X, X', one of the sets Y, Y', and one of the sets Z, Z'. (Recall that the complement of a set consists of all elements in the universe (class) that are not in the set.)

As an example, suppose that a student is a 23-year-old divorced Democrat. The student belongs to the sets X', Y, and Z'. Joining these with intersection symbols, the set to which the student belongs is

$$X' \cap Y \cap Z'.$$

Now observe the Venn diagram that follows. The eight subsets are identified by lowercase letters (a)

through (h). The final column in the following table will be completed when a survey is made. Each student should now determine to which set he or she belongs. (The student described earlier belongs to (g).)

Region	Description in Terms of Set Notation	Number of Class Members in the Set
(a)	$X \cap Y \cap Z$	
(b)	$X \cap Y \cap Z'$	
(c)	$X \cap Y' \cap Z$	
(d)	$X' \cap Y \cap Z$	
(e)	$X' \cap Y' \cap Z$	
(f)	$X \cap Y' \cap Z'$	
(g)	$X' \cap Y \cap Z'$	
(h)	$X' \cap Y' \cap Z'$	

The instructor will now poll the class to see how many members are in each set. *Remember that each class member will belong to one and only one set.*

After the survey is made, find the sum of the numbers in the final column. They should add up to *exactly* the number of students present. Count the class members individually to verify this.

Topics for Discussion

1. Suppose that the final column entries do not add up to the total number of class members. What might have gone wrong?

2. Why can't a class member be a member of more than one of the eight subsets listed?

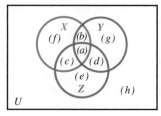

CHAPTER 2 TEST

In Exercises 1–14, let

$$U = \{a, b, c, d, e, f, g, h\}, \quad A = \{a, b, c, d\}, \quad B = \{b, e, a, d\}, \quad and \quad C = \{a, e\}.$$

Find each set.

1. $A \cup C$

2. $B \cap A$

3. B'

4. $A - (B \cap C')$

Identify each statement as true *or* false.

5. $b \in A$

6. $C \subseteq A$

7. $B \subset (A \cup C)$

8. $c \notin C$

9. $n[(A \cup B) - C] = 4$

10. $\emptyset \subset C$

11. $A \cap B'$ is equivalent to $B \cap A'$

12. $(A \cup B)' = A' \cap B'$

Find each of the following.

13. $n(A \times C)$

14. the number of proper subsets of A

Give a word description for each set.

15. $\{-3, -1, 1, 3, 5, 7, 9\}$

16. $\{\text{January, February, March, \dots, December}\}$

Express each set in set-builder notation.

17. $\{-1, -2, -3, -4, \dots\}$

18. $\{24, 32, 40, 48, \dots, 88\}$

Place $\subset, \subseteq$, both, *or* neither *in each blank to make a true statement.*

19. $\emptyset$ _____ $\{x \,|\, x \text{ is a counting number between 20 and 21}\}$

20. $\{4, 9, 16\}$ _____ $\{4, 5, 6, 7, 8, 9, 10\}$

Shade each set in an appropriate Venn diagram.

21. $X \cup Y'$

22. $X' \cap Y'$

23. $(X \cup Y) - Z$

24. $[(X \cap Y) \cup (Y \cap Z) \cup (X \cap Z)] - (X \cap Y \cap Z)$

Facts About Inventions *The following table lists ten inventions, important directly or indirectly in our lives, together with other pertinent data.*

Invention	Date	Inventor	Nation
Adding machine	1642	Pascal	France
Barometer	1643	Torricelli	Italy
Electric razor	1917	Schick	U.S.
Fiber optics	1955	Kapany	England
Geiger counter	1913	Geiger	Germany
Pendulum clock	1657	Huygens	Holland
Radar	1940	Watson-Watt	Scotland
Telegraph	1837	Morse	U.S.
Thermometer	1593	Galileo	Italy
Zipper	1891	Judson	U.S.

Let U = the set of all ten inventions, A = the set of items invented in the United States, and T = the set of items invented in the twentieth century. List the elements of each set.

25. $A \cap T$

26. $(A \cup T)'$

27. $A - T'$

28. State De Morgan's laws for sets in words rather than symbols.

29. The numerals in the Venn diagram indicate the number of elements in each particular subset.

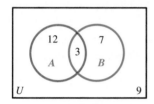

Determine the number of elements in each set.
(a) $A \cup B$ (b) $A \cap B'$ (c) $(A \cap B)'$

***Financial Aid to College Students** In one recent year, financial aid available to college students in the United States was nearly $30 billion. (Much of it went unclaimed, mostly because qualified students were not aware of it, did not know how to obtain or fill out the required applications, or did not feel the results would be worth their effort.) Three major sources of aid are government grants, private scholarships, and the colleges themselves.*

30. Marilyn Cazayoux, Financial Aid Director of a small private Southern college, surveyed the records of 100 sophomores and found the following:

> 49 receive government grants
> 55 receive private scholarships
> 43 receive aid from the college
> 23 receive government grants and private scholarships
> 18 receive government grants and aid from the college
> 28 receive private scholarships and aid from the college
> 8 receive help from all three sources.

How many of the students in the survey:
(a) have government grants only?
(b) have private scholarships but not government grants?
(c) receive financial aid from only one of these sources?
(d) receive aid from exactly two of these sources?
(e) receive no financial aid from any of these sources?
(f) receive no aid from the college or from the government?

3

INTRODUCTION TO LOGIC

The 1959 Oscar-nominated animated short *Donald in Mathmagic Land* was the first Disney cartoon televised in color. After nearly 50 years, it has proved to be a classic, rendering mathematical topics such as geometry, mathematics in music, games, and nature, and the amazing Golden Section in a way that anyone can understand. In one segment, Donald Duck, dressed as Alice from Lewis Carroll's *Through the Looking Glass*, is attacked by a "none-too-friendly group of chess pieces."

Logic (the subject of this chapter) and chess have been paired for centuries. Most scholars agree that chess dates back at least 1500 years, coming from Northern India and Afghanistan following trade routes through Persia. One does not have to have a high I.Q. to excel at chess. In fact, recent studies indicate that chess strategy might rely more on brain activity not usually associated with general intelligence. Good chess players rely on memory, imagination, determination, and inspiration. They are pattern thinkers that use long-established sets of consequences and probabilities resulting from countless hours of studying and playing. In the end, logic does not necessarily dictate the final outcome of any chess game, for if it did, humans would not stand a chance when playing faceless, number-crunching computers.

Sources: www.imdb.com, Walter A. Smart.

3.1 Statements and Quantifiers

Statements • Negations • Symbols • Quantifiers • Sets of Numbers

Gottfried Leibniz (1646–1716) was a wide-ranging philosopher and a universalist who tried to patch up Catholic–Protestant conflicts. He promoted cultural exchange between Europe and the East. Chinese ideograms led him to search for a universal symbolism. He was an early inventor of **symbolic logic**.

Statements This section introduces the study of *symbolic logic,* which uses letters to represent statements, and symbols for words such as *and, or, not.* One of the main applications of logic is in the study of the *truth value* (that is, the truth or falsity) of statements with many parts. The truth value of these statements depends on the components of which they are comprised.

Many kinds of sentences occur in ordinary language, including factual statements, opinions, commands, and questions. Symbolic logic discusses only the first type of sentence, the kind that involves facts. A **statement** is defined as a declarative sentence that is either true or false, but not both simultaneously. For example, both of the following are statements:

$$\left. \begin{array}{l} \text{Electronic mail provides a means of communication.} \\ 11 + 6 = 12. \end{array} \right\} \text{Statements}$$

Each one is either true or false. However, based on this definition, the following sentences are not statements:

Access the file.

Is this a great time, or what?

Luis Pujols is a better baseball player than Johnny Damon.

This sentence is false.

These sentences cannot be identified as being either true or false. The first sentence is a command, and the second is a question. The third is an opinion. "This sentence is false" is a paradox; if we assume it is true, then it is false, and if we assume it is false, then it is true.

A **compound statement** may be formed by combining two or more statements. The statements making up a compound statement are called **component statements.** Various **logical connectives,** or simply **connectives,** can be used in forming compound statements. Words such as *and, or, not,* and *if . . . then* are examples of connectives. (While a statement such as "Today is not Tuesday" does not consist of two component statements, for convenience it is considered compound, because its truth value is determined by noting the truth value of a different statement, "Today is Tuesday.")

▮ EXAMPLE 1 Deciding Whether a Statement Is Compound

Decide whether each statement is compound.

(a) Shakespeare wrote sonnets, and the poem exhibits iambic pentameter.
(b) You can pay me now, or you can pay me later.
(c) If he said it, then it must be true.
(d) My pistol was made by Smith and Wesson.

SOLUTION

(a) This statement is compound, because it is made up of the component statements "Shakespeare wrote sonnets" and "the poem exhibits iambic pentameter." The connective is *and.*

(b) The connective here is *or.* The statement is compound.

(c) The connective here is *if . . . then,* discussed in more detail in a later section. The statement is compound.

(d) While the word "and" is used in this statement, it is not used as a *logical* connective, because it is part of the name of the manufacturer. The statement is not compound.

◼

Negations

The sentence "Greg Chustz has a red truck" is a statement; the **negation** of this statement is "Greg Chustz does not have a red truck." The negation of a true statement is false, and the negation of a false statement is true.

▍ EXAMPLE 2 Forming Negations

Form the negation of each statement.

(a) That state has a governor.   **(b)** The sun is not a star.

SOLUTION

(a) To negate this statement, we introduce *not* into the sentence: "That state does not have a governor."

(b) The negation is "The sun is a star."

◼

One way to detect incorrect negations is to check truth values. A negation must have the opposite truth value from the original statement.

The next example uses some of the inequality symbols in Table 1.

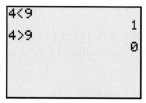

The TEST menu of the TI-83/84 Plus calculator allows the user to test the truth or falsity of statements involving $=$, $\neq$, $>$, $\geq$, $<$, and $\leq$. If a statement is true, it returns a 1; if false, it returns a 0.

TABLE 1

Symbolism	Meaning	Examples	
$a < b$	a is less than b	$4 < 9$	$\frac{1}{2} < \frac{3}{4}$
$a > b$	a is greater than b	$6 > 2$	$-5 > -11$
$a \leq b$	a is less than or equal to b	$8 \leq 10$	$3 \leq 3$
$a \geq b$	a is greater than or equal to b	$-2 \geq -3$	$-5 \geq -5$

▍ EXAMPLE 3 Negating Inequalities

Give a negation of each inequality. Do *not* use a slash symbol.

(a) $p < 9$ **(b)** $7x + 11y \geq 77$

SOLUTION

(a) The negation of "p is less than 9" is "p is *not* less than 9." Because we cannot use "not," which would require writing $p \not< 9$, phrase the negation as "p is greater than or equal to 9," or $p \geq 9$.

(b) The negation, with no slash, is $7x + 11y < 77$.

◼

$4 < 9$ is true, as indicated by the 1.
$4 > 9$ is false, as indicated by the 0.

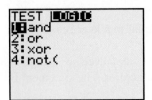

The LOGIC menu of the TI-83/84 Plus calculator allows the user to test truth or falsity of statements involving *and, or, exclusive or* (see Exercise 77 in the next section), and *not.*

Symbols To simplify work with logic, we use symbols. Statements are represented with letters, such as *p, q,* or *r,* while several symbols for connectives are shown in Table 2. The table also names the type of statement having the given connective.

TABLE 2

Connective	Symbol	Type of Statement
and	∧	Conjunction
or	∨	Disjunction
not	∼	Negation

The symbol ∼ represents the connective *not.* If *p* represents the statement "George W. Bush was president in 2005" then ∼*p* represents "George W. Bush was not president in 2005."

EXAMPLE 4 Translating from Symbols to Words

Let *p* represent "It is 80° today," and let *q* represent "It is Tuesday." Write each symbolic statement in words.

(a) $p \lor q$ **(b)** $\sim p \land q$ **(c)** $\sim(p \lor q)$ **(d)** $\sim(p \land q)$

SOLUTION

(a) From the table, ∨ symbolizes *or*; thus, $p \lor q$ represents

It is 80° today or it is Tuesday.

(b) It is not 80° today and it is Tuesday.
(c) It is not the case that it is 80° today or it is Tuesday.
(d) It is not the case that it is 80° today and it is Tuesday.

The statement in Example 4(c) usually is translated as "Neither *p* nor *q.*"

Aristotle, the first to systematize the logic we use in everyday life, appears above in a detail from the painting *The School of Athens,* by Raphael. He is shown debating a point with his teacher **Plato.**

Quantifiers The words *all, each, every,* and *no(ne)* are called **universal quantifiers,** while words and phrases such as *some, there exists,* and *(for) at least one* are called **existential quantifiers.** Quantifiers are used extensively in mathematics to indicate *how many* cases of a particular situation exist. Be careful when forming the negation of a statement involving quantifiers.

The negation of a statement must be false if the given statement is true and must be true if the given statement is false, in all possible cases. Consider the statement

All girls in the group are named Mary.

Many people would write the negation of this statement as "No girls in the group are named Mary" or "All girls in the group are not named Mary." But neither of these is correct. To see why, look at the three groups below:

Group I:	Mary Lynn Brumfield, Mary Smith, Mary Jackson
Group II:	Mary Johnson, Lynne Olinde, Margaret Westmoreland
Group III:	Donna Garbarino, Paula Story, Rhonda Alessi, Kim Falgout.

These groups contain all possibilities that need to be considered. In Group I, *all* girls are named Mary; in Group II, *some* girls are named Mary (and some are not); in Group III, *no* girls are named Mary. Look at the truth values in Table 3 and keep in mind that "some" means "at least one (and possibly all)."

TABLE 3 Truth Value as Applied to:

	Group I	Group II	Group III
(1) All girls in the group are named Mary. **(Given)**	T	F	F
(2) No girls in the group are named Mary. **(Possible negation)**	F	F	T
(3) All girls in the group are not named Mary. **(Possible negation)**	F	F	T
(4) Some girls in the group are not named Mary. **(Possible negation)**	F	T	T

Negation

The negation of the given statement (1) must have opposite truth values in *all* cases. It can be seen that statements (2) and (3) do not satisfy this condition (for Group II), but statement (4) does. It may be concluded that the correct negation for "All girls in the group are named Mary" is "Some girls in the group are not named Mary." Other ways of stating the negation are

Not all girls in the group are named Mary.

It is not the case that all girls in the group are named Mary.

At least one girl in the group is not named Mary.

Table 4 can be used to generalize the method of finding the negation of a statement involving quantifiers.

TABLE 4 Negations of Quantified Statements

Statement	Negation
All do.	Some do not. (Equivalently: Not all do.)
Some do.	None do. (Equivalently: All do not.)

The negation of the negation of a statement is simply the statement itself. For instance, the negations of the statements in the Negation column are simply the corresponding original statements in the Statement column. As an example, the negation of "Some do not" is "All do."

EXAMPLE 5 Forming Negations of Quantified Statements

Form the negation of each statement.

(a) Some cats have fleas.   **(b)** Some cats do not have fleas.

(c) No cats have fleas.

SOLUTION

(a) Because *some* means "at least one," the statement "Some cats have fleas" is really the same as "At least one cat has fleas." The negation of this is "No cat has fleas."

(b) The statement "Some cats do not have fleas" claims that at least one cat, somewhere, does not have fleas. The negation of this is "All cats have fleas."

(c) The negation is "Some cats have fleas." ⟵ Avoid the incorrect answer "All cats have fleas." ▪

Sets of Numbers

Earlier we introduced sets of numbers that are studied in algebra, and they are repeated here.

🎥 The 1997 film *Smilla's Sense of Snow* stars Julia Ormond as a brilliant young scientist who has been displaced from her beloved native Greenland. She has a passion for snow and mathematics. In a conversation, she speaks of her love of **numbers:**

To me, the number system is like human life. First you have the natural numbers, the ones that are whole and positive, like the numbers of a small child. Consciousness expands and a child discovers longing. Do you know the mathematical expression for longing? Negative numbers, the formalization of the feeling that you're missing something. Then the child discovers the in-between spaces, between stones, between people, between numbers, and that produces fractions. But it's like a kind of madness, because it doesn't even stop there. It never stops. There are numbers that we can't even begin to comprehend. Mathematics is a vast, open landscape. You head towards the horizon which is always receding, like Greenland.

Sets of Numbers

Natural or Counting numbers $\{1, 2, 3, 4, \ldots\}$

Whole numbers $\{0, 1, 2, 3, 4, \ldots\}$

Integers $\{\ldots, -3, -2, -1, 0, 1, 2, 3, \ldots\}$

Rational numbers $\left\{\frac{p}{q} \mid p \text{ and } q \text{ are integers, and } q \neq 0\right\}$

(Some examples of rational numbers are $\frac{3}{5}$, $-\frac{7}{5}$, 5, and 0. Any rational number may be expressed as a terminating decimal number, such as .25 or a repeating decimal number, such as .666. . . .)

Real numbers $\{x \mid x \text{ is a number that can be written as a decimal}\}$

Irrational numbers $\{x \mid x \text{ is a real number and } x \text{ cannot be written as a quotient of integers}\}$

(Some examples of irrational numbers are $\sqrt{2}$, $\sqrt[3]{4}$, and π. Decimal representations of irrational numbers never terminate and never repeat.)

EXAMPLE 6 Deciding Whether Quantified Statements Are True or False

Decide whether each of the following statements about sets of numbers involving a quantifier is *true* or *false*.

(a) There exists a whole number that is not a natural number.
(b) Every integer is a natural number.
(c) Every natural number is a rational number.
(d) There exists an irrational number that is not real.

SOLUTION

(a) Because there is such a whole number (it is 0), this statement is true.

(b) This statement is false, because we can find at least one integer that is not a natural number. For example, -1 is an integer but is not a natural number.

(c) Because every natural number can be written as a fraction with denominator 1, this statement is true.

(d) In order to be an irrational number, a number must first be real. Therefore, because we cannot give an irrational number that is not real, this statement is false. (Had we been able to find at least one, the statement would have then been true.) ▪

3.1 EXERCISES

Decide whether each is a statement or is not a statement.

1. September 11, 2001, was a Tuesday.

2. The ZIP code for Manistee, MI, is 49660.

3. Listen, my children, and you shall hear of the midnight ride of Paul Revere.

4. Yield to oncoming traffic.

5. $5 + 8 \neq 13$ and $4 - 3 = 12$

6. $5 + 8 \neq 12$ or $4 - 3 = 5$

7. Some numbers are negative.

8. James Garfield was president of the United States in 1881.

9. Accidents are the main cause of deaths of children under the age of 7.

10. *Shrek 2* was the top-grossing movie of 2004.

11. Where are you going today?

12. Behave yourself and sit down.

13. Kevin "Catfish" McCarthy once took a prolonged continuous shower for 340 hours, 40 minutes.

14. One gallon of milk weighs more than 4 pounds.

Decide whether each statement is compound.

15. I read the *Arizona Republic*, and I read the *Sacramento Bee*.

16. My brother got married in Amsterdam.

17. Tomorrow is Wednesday.

18. Mamie Zwettler is younger than 18 years of age, and so is her friend Emma Lister.

19. Jay Beckenstein's wife loves Ben and Jerry's ice cream.

20. The sign on the back of the car read "Alaska or bust!"

21. If Jane Fleming sells her quota, then Pam Snow will be happy.

22. If Tom is a politician, then Jack is a crook.

Write a negation for each statement.

23. Her aunt's name is Hildegard.

24. The flowers are to be watered.

25. Every dog has its day.

26. No rain fell in southern California today.

27. Some books are longer than this book.

28. All students present will get another chance.

29. No computer repairman can play poker.

30. Some people have all the luck.

31. Everybody loves somebody sometime.

32. Everyone loves a winner.

Give a negation of each inequality. Do not use a slash symbol.

33. $x > 12$ 34. $x < -6$

35. $x \geq 5$ 36. $x \leq 19$

37. Try to negate the sentence "The exact number of words in this sentence is ten" and see what happens. Explain the problem that arises.

38. Explain why the negation of "$x > 5$" is not "$x < 5$."

Let p represent the statement "She has green eyes" and let q represent the statement "He is 56 years old." Translate each symbolic compound statement into words.

39. $\sim p$ 40. $\sim q$ 41. $p \wedge q$

42. $p \vee q$ 43. $\sim p \vee q$ 44. $p \wedge \sim q$

45. $\sim p \vee \sim q$ 46. $\sim p \wedge \sim q$

47. $\sim(\sim p \wedge q)$ 48. $\sim(p \vee \sim q)$

Let p represent the statement "Chris collects DVDs" and let q represent the statement "Jack is an English major." Convert each compound statement into symbols.

49. Chris collects DVDs and Jack is not an English major.

50. Chris does not collect DVDs or Jack is not an English major.

51. Chris does not collect DVDs or Jack is an English major.

52. Jack is an English major and Chris does not collect DVDs.

53. Neither Chris collects DVDs nor Jack is an English major.

54. Either Jack is an English major or Chris collects DVDs, and it is not the case that both Jack is an English major and Chris collects DVDs.

55. Incorrect use of quantifiers often is heard in everyday language. Suppose you hear that a local electronics chain is having a 40% off sale, and the radio advertisement states "All items are not available in all stores." Do you think that, literally translated, the ad really means what it says? What do you think is really meant? Explain your answer.

56. Repeat Exercise 55 for the following: "All people don't have the time to devote to maintaining their vehicles properly."

Refer to the groups of art labeled A, B, *and* C, *and identify by letter the group or groups that are satisfied by the given statements involving quantifiers.*

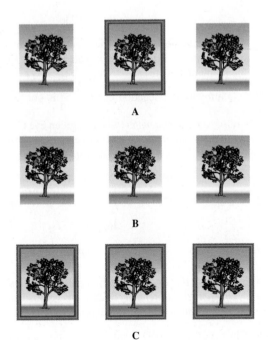

57. All pictures have frames.

58. No picture has a frame.

59. At least one picture does not have a frame.

60. Not every picture has a frame.

61. At least one picture has a frame.

62. No picture does not have a frame.

63. All pictures do not have frames.

64. Not every picture does not have a frame.

Decide whether each statement in Exercises 65–74 involving a quantifier is true *or* false.

65. Every whole number is an integer.

66. Every natural number is an integer.

67. There exists a rational number that is not an integer.

68. There exists an integer that is not a natural number.

69. All rational numbers are real numbers.

70. All irrational numbers are real numbers.

71. Some rational numbers are not integers.

72. Some whole numbers are not rational numbers.

73. Each whole number is a positive number.

74. Each rational number is a positive number.

75. Explain the difference between the following statements:

All students did not pass the test.

Not all students passed the test.

76. The statement "For some real number x, $x^2 \geq 0$" is true. However, your friend does not understand why, because he claims that $x^2 \geq 0$ for *all* real numbers x (and not *some*). How would you explain his misconception to him?

77. Write the following statement using "every": There is no one here who has not done that at one time or another.

78. Only one of the following statements is true. Which one is it?
A. For some real number x, $x \not< 0$.
B. For all real numbers x, $x^3 > 0$.
C. For all real numbers x less than 0, x^2 is also less than 0.
D. For some real number x, $x^2 < 0$.

Truth Tables and Equivalent Statements

**Conjunctions • Disjunctions • Negations • Mathematical Statements
• Truth Tables • Alternative Method for Constructing Truth Tables
• Equivalent Statements and De Morgan's Laws**

Conjunctions   The truth values of component statements are used to find the truth values of compound statements. To begin, let us decide on the truth values of the **conjunction** *p and q*, symbolized *p* ∧ *q*. In everyday language, the connective *and* implies the idea of "both." The statement

  Monday immediately follows Sunday and March immediately follows February

is true, because each component statement is true. On the other hand, the statement

  Monday immediately follows Sunday and March immediately follows January

is false, even though part of the statement (Monday immediately follows Sunday) is true. For the conjunction *p* ∧ *q* to be true, both *p* and *q* must be true. This result is summarized by a table, called a **truth table,** which shows all four of the possible combinations of truth values for the conjunction *p and q*. The truth table for *conjunction* is shown here.

Truth Table for the Conjunction *p* and *q*		
	p and *q*	

p	*q*	*p* ∧ *q*
T	T	T
T	F	F
F	T	F
F	F	F

EXAMPLE 1   Finding the Truth Value of a Conjunction

Let *p* represent "5 > 3" and let *q* represent "6 < 0." Find the truth value of *p* ∧ *q*.

SOLUTION

Here *p* is true and *q* is false. Looking in the second row of the conjunction truth table shows that *p* ∧ *q* is false. ■

In some cases, the logical connective *but* is used in compound statements:

  He wants to go to the mountains but she wants to go to the beach.

Here, *but* is used in place of *and* to give a different sort of emphasis to the statement. In such a case, we consider the statement as we would consider the conjunction using the word *and*. The truth table for the conjunction, given above, would apply.

```
5>3 and 6<0
                 0
```

The calculator returns a "0" for
5 > 3 *and* 6 < 0, indicating that
the statement is false.

Disjunctions In ordinary language, the word *or* can be ambiguous. The expression "this or that" can mean either "this or that or both," or "this or that but not both." For example, the statement

I will paint the wall or I will paint the ceiling

probably has the following meaning: "I will paint the wall or I will paint the ceiling or I will paint both." On the other hand, the statement

I will drive the Saturn or the BMW to the store

probably means "I will drive the Saturn, or I will drive the BMW, but I will not drive both."

The symbol $\vee$ normally represents the first *or* described. That is,

$p \vee q$ means   "*p* or *q* or both."

With this meaning of *or*, $p \vee q$ is called the *inclusive disjunction*, or just the **disjunction** of *p* and *q*. In everyday language, the disjunction implies the idea of "either." For example, the disjunction

I have a quarter or I have a dime

is true whenever I have either a quarter, a dime, or both. The only way this disjunction could be false would be if I had neither coin. A disjunction is false only if both component statements are false. The truth table for *disjunction* follows.

```
5>3 or 6<0
                    1
```

The calculator returns a "1" for $5 > 3$ *or* $6 < 0$, indicating that the statement is true.

Truth Table for the Disjunction *p* or *q*

		p or *q*
p	*q*	*p* $\vee$ *q*
T	T	T
T	F	T
F	T	T
F	F	F

EXAMPLE 2   Finding the Truth Value of a Disjunction

Let *p* represent "$5 > 3$" and let *q* represent "$6 < 0$." Find the truth value of $p \vee q$.

SOLUTION

Here, as in Example 1, *p* is true and *q* is false. The second row of the disjunction truth table shows that $p \vee q$ is true.

TABLE 5

Statement	Reason That It Is True
$8 \geq 8$	$8 = 8$
$3 \geq 1$	$3 > 1$
$-5 \leq -3$	$-5 < -3$
$-4 \leq -4$	$-4 = -4$

The symbol $\geq$ is read "is greater than or equal to," while $\leq$ is read "is less than or equal to." If *a* and *b* are real numbers, then $a \leq b$ is true if $a < b$ or $a = b$. Table 5 in the margin shows several statements and the reasons they are true.

Negations The **negation** of a statement p, symbolized $\sim p$, must have the opposite truth value from the statement p itself. This leads to the truth table for the negation, shown here.

Truth Table for the Negation not p

not p

p	$\sim p$
T	F
F	T

EXAMPLE 3 Finding the Truth Value of a Compound Statement

Suppose p is false, q is true, and r is false. What is the truth value of the compound statement $\sim p \wedge (q \vee \sim r)$?

SOLUTION

Here parentheses are used to group q and $\sim r$ together. Work first inside the parentheses. Because r is false, $\sim r$ will be true. Because $\sim r$ is true and q is true, find the truth value of $q \vee \sim r$ by looking in the first row of the *or* truth table. This row gives the result T. Because p is false, $\sim p$ is true, and the final truth value of $\sim p \wedge (q \vee \sim r)$ is found in the top row of the *and* truth table. From the *and* truth table, when $\sim p$ is true, and $q \vee \sim r$ is true, the statement $\sim p \wedge (q \vee \sim r)$ is true.

The preceding paragraph may be interpreted using a short-cut symbolic method. This method involves replacing the statements with their truth values, letting T represent a true statement and F represent a false statement:

$$\sim p \wedge (q \vee \sim r)$$

Work within parentheses first. ⟶

$$\sim F \wedge (T \vee \sim F)$$
$$T \wedge (T \vee T) \quad \text{\tiny $\sim$F gives T.}$$
$$T \wedge T \quad \text{\tiny T $\vee$ T gives T.}$$
$$T. \quad \text{\tiny T $\wedge$ T gives T.}$$

The T in the final row indicates that the compound statement is true. ■

Mathematical Statements We can use truth tables to determine the truth values of compound mathematical statements.

EXAMPLE 4 Deciding Whether a Compound Mathematical Statement Is True or False

Let p represent the statement $3 > 2$, q represent $5 < 4$, and r represent $3 < 8$. Decide whether each statement is *true* or *false*.

(a) $\sim p \wedge \sim q$ **(b)** $\sim(p \wedge q)$ **(c)** $(\sim p \wedge r) \vee (\sim q \wedge \sim p)$

---

not(3>2) and not
(5<4)
                    0
not((3>2) and (5
<4))
                    1

Example 4(a) explains why
$\sim (3 > 2) \wedge [\sim (5 < 4)]$ is
false. The calculator returns a 0.
For a true statement such as
$\sim [(3 > 2) \wedge (5 < 4)]$, it
returns a 1.

SOLUTION

(a) Because p is true, $\sim p$ is false. By the *and* truth table, if one part of an "and" statement is false, the entire statement is false. This makes $\sim p \wedge \sim q$ false.

(b) For $\sim(p \wedge q)$, first work within the parentheses. Because p is true and q is false, $p \wedge q$ is false by the *and* truth table. Next, apply the negation. The negation of a false statement is true, making $\sim(p \wedge q)$ a true statement.

(c) Here p is true, q is false, and r is true. This makes $\sim p$ false and $\sim q$ true. By the *and* truth table, $\sim p \wedge r$ is false, and $\sim q \wedge \sim p$ is also false. Finally,

$$(\sim p \wedge r) \vee (\sim q \wedge \sim p)$$
$$\downarrow \qquad\qquad \downarrow$$
$$\text{F} \quad \vee \quad \text{F},$$

which is false by the *or* truth table. (Alternatively, see Example 8(b).)

For Further Thought

Beauty or the Beast?

Raymond Smullyan is one of today's foremost writers of logic puzzles. This multitalented professor of mathematics and philosophy at City University of New York has written several books on recreational logic, including *The Lady or the Tiger?, What Is the Name of This Book?,* and *Alice in Puzzleland*. The title of the first of these is taken from the classic Frank Stockton short story, in which a prisoner must make a choice between two doors: behind one is a beautiful lady, and behind the other is a hungry tiger.

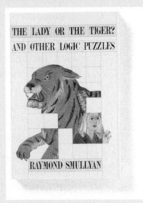

For Group Discussion or Individual Investigation

Smullyan proposes the following: What if each door has a sign, and the man knows that only one sign is true?

The sign on Door 1 reads:

IN THIS ROOM THERE IS A LADY AND
IN THE OTHER ROOM THERE IS A TIGER.

The sign on Door 2 reads:

IN ONE OF THESE ROOMS THERE IS A LADY
AND IN ONE OF THESE ROOMS THERE IS A TIGER.

With this information, the man is able to choose the correct door. Can you? (The answer is on page 110.)

When a quantifier is used with a conjunction or a disjunction, we must be careful in determining the truth value, as shown in the following example.

EXAMPLE 5   Deciding Whether a Quantified Mathematical Statement Is True or False

Decide whether each statement is *true* or *false*.

(a) For some real number x, $x < 5$ and $x > 2$.
(b) For every real number x, $x > 0$ or $x < 1$.
(c) For all real numbers x, $x^2 > 0$.

SOLUTION

(a) Replacing x with 3 (as an example) gives $3 < 5$ and $3 > 2$. Because both $3 < 5$ and $3 > 2$ are true statements, the given statement is true by the *and* truth table. (Remember: *some* means "at least one.")

(b) No matter which real number might be tried as a replacement for x, at least one of the statements $x > 0$ and $x < 1$ will be true. Because an "or" statement is true if one or both component statements are true, the entire statement as given is true.

(c) Because the quantifier is a universal quantifier, we need only find one case in which the inequality is false to make the entire statement false. Can we find a real number whose square is not positive (that is, not greater than 0)? Yes, we can—0 itself is a real number (and the *only* real number) whose square is not positive. Therefore, this statement is false.

George Boole (1815–1864) grew up in poverty. His father, a London tradesman, gave him his first mathematics lessons and taught him to make optical instruments. Boole was largely self-educated. At 16 he worked in an elementary school and by age 20 had opened his own school. He studied mathematics in his spare time. He died of lung disease at age 49.

Boole's ideas have been used in the design of computers and telephone systems.

Truth Tables
In the preceding examples, the truth value for a given statement was found by going back to the basic truth tables. In the long run, it is easier to first create a complete truth table for the given statement itself. Then final truth values can be read directly from this table.

In this book we use the following standard format for listing the possible truth values in compound statements involving two component statements.

p	q	Compound Statement
T	T	
T	F	
F	T	
F	F	

EXAMPLE 6   Constructing a Truth Table

Consider the statement $(\sim p \land q) \lor \sim q$.

(a) Construct a truth table.

(b) Suppose both p and q are true. Find the truth value of this statement.

SOLUTION

(a) Begin by listing all possible combinations of truth values for p and q, as above. Then list the truth values of $\sim p$, which are the opposite of those of p.

p	q	$\sim p$
T	T	F
T	F	F
F	T	T
F	F	T

Use only the "$\sim p$" column and the "q" column, along with the *and* truth table, to find the truth values of $\sim p \land q$. List them in a separate column, as shown on the next page.

p	q	$\sim p$	$\sim p \wedge q$
T	T	F	F
T	F	F	F
F	T	T	T
F	F	T	F

Next include a column for $\sim q$.

p	q	$\sim p$	$\sim p \wedge q$	$\sim q$
T	T	F	F	F
T	F	F	F	T
F	T	T	T	F
F	F	T	F	T

Finally, make a column for the entire compound statement. To find the truth values, use *or* to combine $\sim p \wedge q$ with $\sim q$.

p	q	$\sim p$	$\sim p \wedge q$	$\sim q$	$(\sim p \wedge q) \vee \sim q$
T	T	F	F	F	F
T	F	F	F	T	T
F	T	T	T	F	T
F	F	T	F	T	T

(b) Look in the first row of the final truth table above, where both p and q have truth value T. Read across the row to find that the compound statement is false. ▪

EXAMPLE 7 Constructing a Truth Table

Construct the truth table for $p \wedge (\sim p \vee \sim q)$.

SOLUTION

Proceed as shown.

p	q	$\sim p$	$\sim q$	$\sim p \vee \sim q$	$p \wedge (\sim p \vee \sim q)$
T	T	F	F	F	F
T	F	F	T	T	T
F	T	T	F	T	F
F	F	T	T	T	F

Answer to the Problem of *The Lady or the Tiger?*

The lady is behind Door 2. Suppose that the sign on Door 1 is true. Then the sign on Door 2 would also be true, but this is impossible. So the sign on Door 2 must be true, and the sign on Door 1 must be false. Because the sign on Door 1 says the lady is in Room 1, and this is false, the lady must be behind Door 2.

If a compound statement involves three component statements p, q, and r, we will use the following standard format in setting up the truth table.

p	q	r	Compound Statement
T	T	T	
T	T	F	
T	F	T	
T	F	F	
F	T	T	
F	T	F	
F	F	T	
F	F	F	

Emilie, Marquise du Châtelet
(1706–1749) participated in the scientific activity of the generation after Newton and Leibniz. Educated in science, music, and literature, she was studying mathematics at the time (1733) she began a long intellectual relationship with the philosopher **François Voltaire** (1694–1778). She and Voltaire competed independently in 1738 for a prize offered by the French Academy on the subject of fire. Although du Châtelet did not win, her dissertation was published by the academy in 1744. During the last four years of her life she translated Newton's *Principia* from Latin into French—the only French translation to date.

EXAMPLE 8 Constructing a Truth Table

Consider the statement $(\sim p \wedge r) \vee (\sim q \wedge \sim p)$.

(a) Construct a truth table.
(b) Suppose p is true, q is false, and r is true. Find the truth value of this statement.

SOLUTION

(a) This statement has three component statements, p, q, and r. The truth table thus requires eight rows to list all possible combinations of truth values of p, q, and r. The final truth table, however, can be found in much the same way as the ones above.

p	q	r	$\sim p$	$\sim p \wedge r$	$\sim q$	$\sim q \wedge \sim p$	$(\sim p \wedge r) \vee (\sim q \wedge \sim p)$
T	T	T	F	F	F	F	F
T	T	F	F	F	F	F	F
T	F	T	F	F	T	F	F
T	F	F	F	F	T	F	F
F	T	T	T	T	F	F	T
F	T	F	T	F	F	F	F
F	F	T	T	T	T	T	T
F	F	F	T	F	T	T	T

(b) By the third row of the truth table in part (a), the compound statement is false. (This is an alternative method for working part (c) of Example 4.) ▪

PROBLEM-SOLVING HINT One strategy for problem solving is to notice a pattern and use inductive reasoning. This strategy is applied in the next example.

TABLE 6

Number of Statements	Number of Rows
1	$2 = 2^1$
2	$4 = 2^2$
3	$8 = 2^3$

EXAMPLE 9 Using Inductive Reasoning

If n is a counting number, and a logical statement is composed of n component statements, how many rows will appear in the truth table for the compound statement?

SOLUTION

To answer this question, we examine some of the earlier truth tables in this section. The truth table for the negation has one statement and two rows. The truth tables for the conjunction and the disjunction have two component statements, and each has four rows. The truth table in Example 8(a) has three component statements and eight rows. Summarizing these in Table 6 seen in the margin reveals a pattern encountered earlier. Inductive reasoning leads us to the conjecture that if a logical statement is composed of n component statements, it will have 2^n rows. This can be proved using more advanced concepts. ▪

The result of Example 9 is reminiscent of the formula for the number of subsets of a set having n elements.

Number of Rows in a Truth Table

A logical statement having n component statements will have 2^n rows in its truth table.

Alternative Method for Constructing Truth Tables
After making a reasonable number of truth tables, some people prefer the shortcut method shown in Example 10, which repeats Examples 6 and 8.

EXAMPLE 10 Constructing Truth Tables

Construct the truth table for each statement.

(a) $(\sim p \wedge q) \vee \sim q$ **(b)** $(\sim p \wedge r) \vee (\sim q \wedge \sim p)$

SOLUTION

(a) Start by inserting truth values for $\sim p$ and for q.

p	q	$(\sim p$	$\wedge$	$q)$	$\vee$	$\sim q$
T	T	F				T
T	F	F				F
F	T	T				T
F	F	T				F

Next, use the *and* truth table to obtain the truth values for $\sim p \wedge q$.

p	q	$(\sim p$	$\wedge$	$q)$	$\vee$	$\sim q$
T	T	F	F	T		T
T	F	F	F	F		F
F	T	T	T	T		T
F	F	T	F	F		F

Now disregard the two preliminary columns of truth values for $\sim p$ and for q, and insert truth values for $\sim q$. Finally, use the *or* truth table.

p	q	$(\sim p \wedge q) \vee \sim q$	
T	T	F	F
T	F	F	T
F	T	T	F
F	F	F	T

p	q	$(\sim p \wedge q) \vee \sim q$		
T	T	F	F	F
T	F	F	T	T
F	T	T	T	F
F	F	F	T	T

These steps can be summarized as follows.

p	q	$(\sim p$	$\wedge$	$q)$	$\vee$	$\sim p$
T	T	F	F	T	F	F
T	F	F	F	F	T	T
F	T	T	T	T	T	F
F	F	T	F	F	T	T
		①	②	①	④	③

The circled numbers indicate the order in which the various columns of the truth table were found.

(b) Work as follows.

p	q	r	$(\sim p$	$\wedge$	$r)$	$\vee$	$(\sim q$	$\wedge$	$\sim p)$
T	T	T	F	F	T	F	F	F	F
T	T	F	F	F	F	F	F	F	F
T	F	T	F	F	T	F	T	F	F
T	F	F	F	F	F	F	T	F	F
F	T	T	T	T	T	T	F	F	T
F	T	F	T	F	F	F	F	F	T
F	F	T	T	T	T	T	T	T	T
F	F	F	T	F	F	T	T	T	T
			①	②	①	⑤	③	④	③

The circled numbers indicate the order.

Equivalent Statements and De Morgan's Laws

One application of truth tables is to show that two statements are equivalent. Two statements are **equivalent** if they have the same truth value in *every* possible situation. The columns of each truth table that were the last to be completed will be the same for equivalent statements.

EXAMPLE 11 Deciding Whether Two Statements Are Equivalent

Are the following statements equivalent?

$$\sim p \wedge \sim q \quad \text{and} \quad \sim(p \vee q)$$

SOLUTION

Construct a truth table for each statement.

p	q	$\sim p \wedge \sim q$
T	T	F
T	F	F
F	T	F
F	F	T

p	q	$\sim(p \vee q)$
T	T	F
T	F	F
F	T	F
F	F	T

Because the truth values are the same in all cases, as shown in the columns in color, the statements $\sim p \wedge \sim q$ and $\sim(p \vee q)$ are equivalent. Equivalence is written with a three-bar symbol, $\equiv$. Using this symbol, $\sim p \wedge \sim q \equiv \sim(p \vee q)$. ■

In the same way, the statements $\sim p \vee \sim q$ and $\sim(p \wedge q)$ are equivalent. We call these equivalences *De Morgan's laws*.

De Morgan's Laws

For any statements p and q,

$$\sim(p \vee q) \equiv \sim p \wedge \sim q \quad \text{and} \quad \sim(p \wedge q) \equiv \sim p \vee \sim q.$$

(Compare the logic statements of De Morgan's laws with the set versions.) De Morgan's laws can be used to find the negations of certain compound statements.

EXAMPLE 12   Applying De Morgan's Laws

Find a negation of each statement by applying De Morgan's laws.

(a) I got an A or I got a B.   **(b)** She won't try and he will succeed.
(c) $\sim p \vee (q \wedge \sim p)$

SOLUTION

(a) If p represents "I got an A" and q represents "I got a B," then the compound statement is symbolized $p \vee q$. The negation of $p \vee q$ is $\sim(p \vee q)$; by one of De Morgan's laws, this is equivalent to

$$\sim p \wedge \sim q,$$

or, in words,

I didn't get an A and I didn't get a B.

This negation is reasonable—the original statement says that I got either an A or a B; the negation says that I didn't get *either* grade.

(b) From one of De Morgan's laws, $\sim(p \wedge q) \equiv \sim p \vee \sim q$, so the negation becomes

She will try or he won't succeed.

(c) Negate both component statements and change $\vee$ to $\wedge$.

$$\sim[\sim p \vee (q \wedge \sim p)] \equiv p \wedge \sim(q \wedge \sim p)$$

Now apply De Morgan's law again.

$$p \wedge \sim(q \wedge \sim p) \equiv p \wedge (\sim q \vee \sim(\sim p))$$
$$\equiv p \wedge (\sim q \vee p)$$

A truth table will show that the statements

$$\sim p \vee (q \wedge \sim p) \quad \text{and} \quad p \wedge (\sim q \vee p)$$

are negations.

3.2 EXERCISES

Use the concepts introduced in this section to answer Exercises 1–6.

1. If q is false, what must be the truth value of the statement $(p \wedge \sim q) \wedge q$?

2. If q is true, what must be the truth value of the statement $q \vee (q \wedge \sim p)$?

3. If the statement $p \wedge q$ is true, and p is true, then q must be _____.

4. If the statement $p \vee q$ is false, and p is false, then q must be _____.

5. If $\sim(p \vee q)$ is true, what must be the truth values of the component statements?

6. If $\sim(p \wedge q)$ is false, what must be the truth values of the component statements?

Let p represent a false statement and let q represent a true statement. Find the truth value of the given compound statement.

7. $\sim p$

8. $\sim q$

9. $p \vee q$

10. $p \wedge q$

11. $p \vee \sim q$

12. $\sim p \wedge q$

13. $\sim p \vee \sim q$

14. $p \wedge \sim q$

15. $\sim(p \wedge \sim q)$

16. $\sim(\sim p \vee \sim q)$

17. $\sim[\sim p \wedge (\sim q \vee p)]$

18. $\sim[(\sim p \wedge \sim q) \vee \sim q]$

19. Is the statement $5 \geq 2$ a conjunction or a disjunction? Why?

20. Why is the statement $7 \geq 3$ true? Why is $9 \geq 9$ true?

Let p represent a true statement, and q and r represent false statements. Find the truth value of the given compound statement.

21. $(p \wedge r) \vee \sim q$

22. $(q \vee \sim r) \wedge p$

23. $p \wedge (q \vee r)$

24. $(\sim p \wedge q) \vee \sim r$

25. $\sim(p \wedge q) \wedge (r \vee \sim q)$

26. $(\sim r \wedge \sim q) \vee (\sim r \wedge q)$

27. $\sim[(\sim p \wedge q) \vee r]$

28. $\sim[r \vee (\sim q \wedge \sim p)]$

29. $\sim[\sim q \vee (r \wedge \sim p)]$

30. What is the only possible case in which the statement $(p \wedge \sim q) \wedge \sim r$ is true?

Let p represent the statement $15 < 8$, let q represent the statement $9 \not> 4$, and let r represent the statement $18 \leq 18$. Find the truth value of the given compound statement.

31. $p \wedge r$

32. $p \vee \sim q$

33. $\sim q \vee \sim r$

34. $\sim p \wedge \sim r$

35. $(p \wedge q) \vee r$

36. $\sim p \vee (\sim r \vee \sim q)$

37. $(\sim r \wedge q) \vee \sim p$

38. $\sim(p \vee \sim q) \vee \sim r$

Give the number of rows in the truth table for each compound statement.

39. $p \vee \sim r$

40. $p \wedge (r \wedge \sim s)$

41. $(\sim p \wedge q) \vee (\sim r \vee \sim s) \wedge r$

42. $[(p \vee q) \wedge (r \wedge s)] \wedge (t \vee \sim p)$

43. $[(\sim p \wedge \sim q) \wedge (\sim r \wedge s \wedge \sim t)] \wedge (\sim u \vee \sim v)$

44. $[(\sim p \wedge \sim q) \vee (\sim r \vee \sim s)]$
$\vee [(\sim m \wedge \sim n) \wedge (u \wedge \sim v)]$

45. If the truth table for a certain compound statement has 128 rows, how many distinct component statements does it have?

46. Is it possible for the truth table of a compound statement to have exactly 54 rows? Why or why not?

Construct a truth table for each compound statement.

47. $\sim p \wedge q$

48. $\sim p \vee \sim q$

49. $\sim(p \wedge q)$

50. $p \vee \sim q$

51. $(q \vee \sim p) \vee \sim q$

52. $(p \wedge \sim q) \wedge p$

53. $\sim q \wedge (\sim p \vee q)$

54. $\sim p \vee (\sim q \wedge \sim p)$

55. $(p \vee \sim q) \wedge (p \wedge q)$

56. $(\sim p \wedge \sim q) \vee (\sim p \vee q)$

57. $(\sim p \wedge q) \wedge r$

58. $r \vee (p \wedge \sim q)$

59. $(\sim p \wedge \sim q) \vee (\sim r \vee \sim p)$

60. $(\sim r \vee \sim p) \wedge (\sim p \vee \sim q)$

61. $\sim(\sim p \wedge \sim q) \vee (\sim r \vee \sim s)$

62. $(\sim r \vee s) \wedge (\sim p \wedge q)$

Use one of De Morgan's laws to write the negation of each statement.

63. You can pay me now or you can pay me later.

64. I am not going or she is going.

65. It is summer and there is no snow.

66. $\frac{1}{2}$ is a positive number and -9 is less than zero.

67. I said yes but she said no.

68. Fellman Chutz tried to sell the wine, but he was unable to do so.

69. $5 - 1 = 4$ and $9 + 12 \neq 7$

70. $3 < 10$ or $7 \neq 2$

71. Dasher or Blitzen will lead Santa's sleigh next Christmas.

72. The lawyer and the client appeared in court.

Identify each statement as true *or* false.

73. For every real number x, $x < 13$ or $x > 6$.

74. For every real number x, $x > 9$ or $x < 9$.

75. For some integer n, $n \geq 4$ and $n \leq 4$.

76. There exists an integer n such that $n > 0$ and $n < 0$.

77. Complete the truth table for *exclusive disjunction*. The symbol $\veebar$ represents "one or the other is true, but not both."

78. Attorneys sometimes use the phase "and/or." This phrase corresponds to which usage of the word *or*: inclusive or exclusive disjunction?

p	q	$p \veebar q$
T	T	
T	F	
F	T	
F	F	

Exclusive disjunction

Decide whether each compound statement is true *or* false. *Remember that* ⊻ *is the* exclusive disjunction; *that is, assume* "either *p* or *q* is true, but not both."

79. 3 + 1 = 4 ⊻ 2 + 5 = 7

80. 3 + 1 = 4 ⊻ 2 + 5 = 10

81. 3 + 1 = 6 ⊻ 2 + 5 = 7

82. 3 + 1 = 12 ⊻ 2 + 5 = 10

3.3 The Conditional and Circuits

Conditionals • Negation of a Conditional • Circuits

Conditionals

In his April 21, 1989, five-star review of *Field of Dreams*, the *Chicago Sun-Times* movie critic Roger Ebert gave an explanation of why the movie has become an American classic.

There is a speech in this movie about baseball that is so simple and true that it is heartbreaking. And the whole attitude toward the players reflects that attitude. Why do they come back from the great beyond and play in this cornfield? Not to make any kind of vast, earthshattering statement, but simply to hit a few and field a few, and remind us of a good and innocent time.

"If you build it, he will come."
—The Voice in the movie *Field of Dreams*

Ray Kinsella, an Iowa farmer in the movie *Field of Dreams*, heard a voice from the sky. Ray interpreted it as a promise that if he would build a baseball field in his cornfield, then the ghost of Shoeless Joe Jackson (a baseball star in the early days of the twentieth century) would come to play on it. The promise came in the form of a conditional statement. A **conditional** statement is a compound statement that uses the connective *if . . . then.* For example, here are a few conditional statements:

If I read for too long, *then* I get a headache.

If looks could kill, *then* I would be dead.

If he doesn't get back soon, *then* you should go look for him.

In each of these conditional statements, the component coming after the word *if* gives a condition (but not necessarily the only condition) under which the statement coming after *then* will be true. For example, "If it is over 90°, then I'll go to the mountains" tells one possible condition under which I will go to the mountains—if the temperature is over 90°.

The conditional is written with an arrow, so "if *p*, then *q*" is symbolized

$$p \rightarrow q.$$

We read $p \rightarrow q$ as "*p* implies *q*" or "if *p*, then *q*." In the conditional $p \rightarrow q$, the statement *p* is the **antecedent,** while *q* is the **consequent.**

The conditional connective may not always be explicitly stated. That is, it may be "hidden" in an everyday expression. For example, the statement

Big girls don't cry

can be written in *if . . . then* form as

If you're a big girl, then you don't cry.

As another example, the statement

It is difficult to study when you are distracted

can be written

If you are distracted, then it is difficult to study.

In the quote from the movie *Field of Dreams*, the word "then" is not stated but understood to be there from the context of the statement. In that statement, "you build it" is the antecedent, and "he will come" is the consequent.

$$\frac{2}{3}$$

$$8 > 5$$

$$\neq \qquad |x|$$

$$5.1 \times 10^{-3}$$

$$-2 + 8 = 6$$

$$\leq \qquad \pi$$

$$ax + b = c \qquad (x, y)$$

$$x^2 \qquad \Delta \qquad y = -3$$

The importance of **symbols** was emphasized by the American philosopher-logician **Charles Sanders Peirce** (1839–1914), who asserted the nature of humans as symbol-using or sign-using organisms. Symbolic notation is half of mathematics, Bertrand Russell once said.

The conditional truth table is a little harder to define than the tables in the previous section. To see how to define the conditional truth table, let us analyze a statement made by a politician, Senator Shootie Gosserand:

> If I am elected, then taxes will go down.

As before, there are four possible combinations of truth values for the two component statements. Let p represent "I am elected," and let q represent "Taxes will go down."

As we analyze the four possibilities, it is helpful to think in terms of the following: "Did Senator Gosserand lie?" If she lied, then the conditional statement is considered false; if she did not lie, then the conditional statement is considered true.

Possibility	Elected?	Taxes Go Down?	
1	Yes	Yes	p is T, q is T
2	Yes	No	p is T, q is F
3	No	Yes	p is F, q is T
4	No	No	p is F, q is F

The four possibilities are as follows:

1. In the first case assume that the senator was elected and taxes did go down (p is T, q is T). The senator told the truth, so place T in the first row of the truth table. (We do not claim that taxes went down *because* she was elected; it is possible that she had nothing to do with it at all.)

2. In the second case assume that the senator was elected and taxes did not go down (p is T, q is F). Then the senator did not tell the truth (that is, she lied). So we put F in the second row of the truth table.

3. In the third case assume that the senator was defeated, but taxes went down anyway (p is F, q is T). The senator did not lie; she only promised a tax reduction if she were elected. She said nothing about what would happen if she were not elected. In fact, her campaign promise gives no information about what would happen if she lost. Because we cannot say that the senator lied, place T in the third row of the truth table.

4. In the last case assume that the senator was defeated and taxes did not go down (p is F, q is F). We cannot blame her, because she only promised to reduce taxes if elected. Thus, T goes in the last row of the truth table.

The completed truth table for the conditional is defined as follows.

Truth Table for the Conditional If p, then q

If p, then q

p	q	$p \rightarrow q$
T	T	T
T	F	F
F	T	T
F	F	T

It must be emphasized that the use of the conditional connective in no way implies a cause-and-effect relationship. Any two statements may have an arrow placed between them to create a compound statement. For example,

> If I pass mathematics, then the sun will rise the next day

is true, because the consequent is true. (See the special characteristics following Example 1.) There is, however, no cause-and-effect connection between my passing mathematics and the sun's rising. The sun will rise no matter what grade I get.

EXAMPLE 1 Finding the Truth Value of a Conditional

Given that p, q, and r are all false, find the truth value of the statement

$$(p \rightarrow \sim q) \rightarrow (\sim r \rightarrow q).$$

SOLUTION

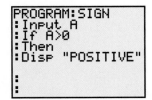

Using the short-cut method explained in Example 3 of the previous section, we can replace p, q, and r with F (since each is false) and proceed as before, using the negation and conditional truth tables as necessary.

$$
\begin{array}{ccl}
(p \rightarrow \sim q) & \rightarrow & (\sim r \rightarrow q) \\
(F \rightarrow \sim F) & \rightarrow & (\sim F \rightarrow F) \\
(F \rightarrow T) & \rightarrow & (T \rightarrow F) \quad \text{\small Use the negation truth table.} \\
T & \rightarrow & F \quad \text{\small Use the conditional truth table.} \\
& F &
\end{array}
$$

The statement $(p \rightarrow \sim q) \rightarrow (\sim r \rightarrow q)$ is false when p, q, and r are all false. ▪

The following observations come from the truth table for $p \rightarrow q$.

Special Characteristics of Conditional Statements

1. $p \rightarrow q$ is false only when the antecedent is *true* and the consequent is *false*.
2. If the antecedent is *false*, then $p \rightarrow q$ is automatically *true*.
3. If the consequent is *true*, then $p \rightarrow q$ is automatically *true*.

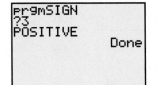

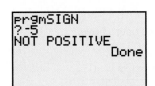

Conditional statements are useful in writing programs. The short program in the first two screens determines whether a number is positive. Notice the lines that begin with *If* and *Then*.

EXAMPLE 2 Determining Whether a Conditional Is True or False

Write *true* or *false* for each statement. Here T represents a true statement, and F represents a false statement.

(a) $T \rightarrow (6 = 3)$ **(b)** $(5 < 2) \rightarrow F$ **(c)** $(3 \neq 2 + 1) \rightarrow T$

SOLUTION

(a) Because the antecedent is true, while the consequent, $6 = 3$, is false, the given statement is false by the first point mentioned above.

(b) The antecedent is false, so the given statement is true by the second observation.

(c) The consequent is true, making the statement true by the third characteristic of conditional statements. ▪

Truth tables for compound statements involving conditionals are found using the techniques described in the previous section.

EXAMPLE 3 Constructing Truth Tables

Construct a truth table for each statement.

(a) $(\sim p \rightarrow \sim q) \rightarrow (\sim p \wedge q)$ **(b)** $(p \rightarrow q) \rightarrow (\sim p \vee q)$

SOLUTION

(a) First insert the truth values of $\sim p$ and of $\sim q$. Then find the truth values of $\sim p \rightarrow \sim q$.

p	q	$\sim p$	$\sim q$	$\sim p \rightarrow \sim q$
T	T	F	F	T
T	F	F	T	T
F	T	T	F	F
F	F	T	T	T

Next use $\sim p$ and q to find the truth values of $\sim p \wedge q$.

p	q	$\sim p$	$\sim q$	$\sim p \rightarrow \sim q$	$\sim p \wedge q$
T	T	F	F	T	F
T	F	F	T	T	F
F	T	T	F	F	T
F	F	T	T	T	F

Now find the truth values of $(\sim p \rightarrow \sim q) \rightarrow (\sim p \wedge q)$.

p	q	$\sim p$	$\sim q$	$\sim p \rightarrow \sim q$	$\sim p \wedge q$	$(\sim p \rightarrow \sim q) \rightarrow (\sim p \wedge q)$
T	T	F	F	T	F	F
T	F	F	T	T	F	F
F	T	T	F	F	T	T
F	F	T	T	T	F	F

(b) For $(p \rightarrow q) \rightarrow (\sim p \vee q)$, go through steps similar to the ones above.

p	q	$p \rightarrow q$	$\sim p$	$\sim p \vee q$	$(p \rightarrow q) \rightarrow (\sim p \vee q)$
T	T	T	F	T	T
T	F	F	F	F	T
F	T	T	T	T	T
F	F	T	T	T	T

As the truth table in Example 3(b) shows, the statement $(p \rightarrow q) \rightarrow (\sim p \vee q)$ is always true, no matter what the truth values of the components. Such a statement is called a **tautology.** Other examples of tautologies (as can be checked by forming truth tables) include $p \vee \sim p, p \rightarrow p, (\sim p \vee \sim q) \rightarrow \sim (q \wedge p)$, and so on. By the way, the truth tables in Example 3 also could have been found by the alternative method shown in the previous section.

Negation of a Conditional

Suppose that someone makes the conditional statement

"If it rains, then I take my umbrella."

When will the person have lied to you? The only case in which you would have been misled is when it rains *and* the person does *not* take the umbrella. Letting p represent "it rains" and q represent "I take my umbrella," you might suspect that the symbolic statement

$$p \wedge \sim q$$

is a candidate for the negation of $p \rightarrow q$. That is,

$$\sim(p \rightarrow q) \equiv p \wedge \sim q.$$

This is indeed the case, as the next truth table indicates.

p	q	$p \rightarrow q$	$\sim(p \rightarrow q)$	$\sim q$	$p \wedge \sim q$
T	T	T	F	F	F
T	F	F	T	T	T
F	T	T	F	F	F
F	F	T	F	T	F

$$\equiv$$

Negation of $p \rightarrow q$

The negation of $p \rightarrow q$ is $p \wedge \sim q$.

Because

$$\sim(p \rightarrow q) \equiv p \wedge \sim q,$$

by negating each expression we have

$$\sim[\sim(p \rightarrow q)] \equiv \sim(p \wedge \sim q).$$

The left side of the above equivalence is $p \rightarrow q$, and one of De Morgan's laws can be applied to the right side:

$$p \rightarrow q \equiv \sim p \vee \sim(\sim q)$$
$$p \rightarrow q \equiv \sim p \vee q.$$

This final row indicates that a conditional may be written as a disjunction.

> **Writing a Conditional as an "or" Statement**
>
> $p \rightarrow q$ is equivalent to $\sim p \lor q$.

EXAMPLE 4   Determining Negations

Determine the negation of each statement.

(a) If you build it, he will come.   **(b)** All dogs have fleas.

SOLUTION

Do not try to negate a conditional with another conditional.

(a) If b represents "you build it" and q represents "he will come," then the given statement can be symbolized by $b \rightarrow q$. The negation of $b \rightarrow q$, as shown earlier, is $b \land \sim q$, so the negation of the statement is

$$\text{You build it and he will not come.}$$

(b) First, we must restate the given statement in *if . . . then* form:

$$\text{If it is a dog, then it has fleas.}$$

Based on our earlier discussion, the negation is

$$\text{It is a dog and it does not have fleas.}$$ ■

As seen in Example 4, the negation of a conditional statement is written as a conjunction.

EXAMPLE 5   Determining Statements Equivalent to Conditionals

Write each conditional as an equivalent statement without using *if . . . then*.

(a) If the Cubs win the pennant, then Gwen will be happy.
(b) If it's Borden's, it's got to be good.

SOLUTION

(a) Because the conditional $p \rightarrow q$ is equivalent to $\sim p \lor q$, let p represent "The Cubs win the pennant" and q represent "Gwen will be happy." Restate the conditional as

$$\text{The Cubs do not win the pennant or Gwen will be happy.}$$

(b) If p represents "it's Borden's" and if q represents "it's got to be good," the conditional may be restated as

$$\text{It's not Borden's or it's got to be good.}$$ ■

FIGURE 1

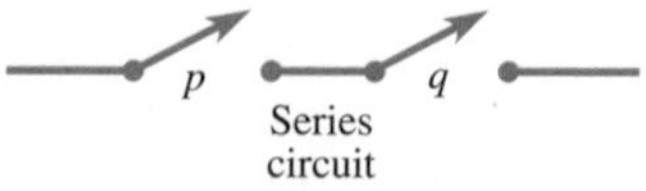

FIGURE 2

Series circuit

Circuits   One of the first nonmathematical applications of symbolic logic was seen in the master's thesis of Claude Shannon in 1937. Shannon showed how logic could be used to design electrical circuits. His work was immediately used by computer designers. Then in the developmental stage, computers could be simplified and built for less money using the ideas of Shannon.

To see how Shannon's ideas work, look at the electrical switch shown in Figure 1. We assume that current will flow through this switch when it is closed and not when it is open.

Figure 2 shows two switches connected in *series;* in such a circuit, current will flow only when both switches are closed. Note how closely a series circuit

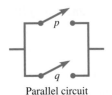

Parallel circuit

FIGURE 3

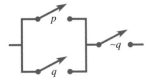

FIGURE 4

corresponds to the conjunction $p \wedge q$. We know that $p \wedge q$ is true only when both p and q are true.

A circuit corresponding to the disjunction $p \vee q$ can be found by drawing a *parallel* circuit, as in Figure 3. Here, current flows if either p *or* q is closed or if both p *and* q are closed.

The circuit in Figure 4 corresponds to the statement $(p \vee q) \wedge \sim q$, which is a compound statement involving both a conjunction and a disjunction.

Simplifying an electrical circuit depends on the idea of equivalent statements from Section 3.2. Recall that two statements are equivalent if they have the same truth table final column. The symbol $\equiv$ is used to indicate that the two statements are equivalent. Some equivalent statements are shown in the following box.

Equivalent Statements Used to Simplify Circuits

$$p \vee (q \wedge r) \equiv (p \vee q) \wedge (p \vee r) \qquad p \vee p \equiv p$$
$$p \wedge (q \vee r) \equiv (p \wedge q) \vee (p \wedge r) \qquad p \wedge p \equiv p$$
$$p \rightarrow q \equiv \sim q \rightarrow \sim p \qquad \sim(p \wedge q) \equiv \sim p \vee \sim q$$
$$p \rightarrow q \equiv \sim p \vee q \qquad \sim(p \vee q) \equiv \sim p \wedge \sim q$$

If T represents any true statement and F represents any false statement, then

$$p \vee T \equiv T \qquad p \vee \sim p \equiv T$$
$$p \wedge F \equiv F \qquad p \wedge \sim p \equiv F.$$

Circuits can be used as models of compound statements, with a closed switch corresponding to T, while an open switch corresponds to F. The method for simplifying circuits is explained in the following example.

EXAMPLE 6 Simplifying a Circuit

Simplify the circuit of Figure 5.

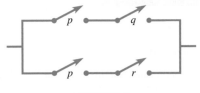

FIGURE 5

SOLUTION

At the top of Figure 5, p and q are connected in series, and at the bottom, p and r are connected in series. These are interpreted as the compound statements $p \wedge q$ and $p \wedge r$, respectively. These two conjunctions are connected in parallel, as indicated by the figure treated as a whole. Write the disjunction of the two conjunctions:

$$(p \wedge q) \vee (p \wedge r).$$

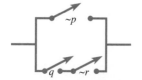

FIGURE 6

(Think of the two switches labeled "*p*" as being controlled by the same lever.) By one of the pairs of equivalent statements in the preceding box,

$$(p \wedge q) \vee (p \wedge r) \equiv p \wedge (q \vee r),$$

which has the circuit of Figure 6. This circuit is logically equivalent to the one in Figure 5, and yet it contains only three switches instead of four—which might well lead to a large savings in manufacturing costs. ▪

EXAMPLE 7 Drawing a Circuit for a Conditional Statement

Draw a circuit for $p \rightarrow (q \wedge \sim r)$.

SOLUTION

From the list of equivalent statements in the box, $p \rightarrow q$ is equivalent to $\sim p \vee q$. This equivalence gives $p \rightarrow (q \wedge \sim r) \equiv \sim p \vee (q \wedge \sim r)$, which has the circuit diagram in Figure 7. ▪

FIGURE 7

3.3 EXERCISES

Rewrite each statement using the if . . . then *connective. Rearrange the wording or add words as necessary.*

1. You can believe it if you see it on the Internet.

2. It must be alive if it is breathing.

3. Garrett Olinde's area code is 225.

4. Lorri Morgan visits Hawaii every summer.

5. All Marines love boot camp.

6. Every picture tells a story.

7. No koalas live in Iowa.

8. No guinea pigs are scholars.

9. An opium eater cannot have self-command.

10. Running Bear loves Little White Dove.

Decide whether each statement is true *or* false.

11. If the consequent of a conditional statement is true, the conditional statement is true.

12. If the antecedent of a conditional statement is false, the conditional statement is true.

13. If *p* is true, then $\sim p \rightarrow (q \vee r)$ is true.

14. If *q* is true, then $(p \wedge q) \rightarrow q$ is true.

15. The statements "If it flies, then it's a bird" and "It does not fly or it's a bird" are logically equivalent.

16. The negation of "If pigs fly, I'll believe it" is "If pigs don't fly, I won't believe it."

17. Given that $\sim p$ is false and *q* is false, the conditional $p \rightarrow q$ is true.

18. Given that $\sim p$ is true and *q* is false, the conditional $p \rightarrow q$ is true.

19. In a few sentences, explain how to determine the truth value of a conditional statement.

20. Explain why the statement "If 3 = 5, then 4 = 6" is true.

Tell whether each conditional is true (T) *or* false (F).

21. $T \rightarrow (6 < 3)$

22. $F \rightarrow (4 \neq 7)$

23. $F \rightarrow (3 \neq 3)$

24. $(6 \geq 6) \rightarrow F$

25. $(4^2 \neq 16) \rightarrow (4 - 4 = 8)$

26. $(4 = 11 - 7) \rightarrow (8 > 0)$

Let s represent "She has a ferret for a pet," *let p represent* "he trains dogs," *and let m represent* "they raise alpacas." *Express each compound statement in words.*

27. $\sim m \rightarrow p$

28. $p \rightarrow \sim m$

29. $s \rightarrow (m \wedge p)$

30. $(s \wedge p) \rightarrow m$

31. $\sim p \rightarrow (\sim m \vee s)$

32. $(\sim s \vee \sim m) \rightarrow \sim p$

Let b represent "I ride my bike," *let r represent* "it rains," *and let p represent* "the concert is cancelled." *Write each compound statement in symbols.*

33. If I ride my bike, then the concert is cancelled.

34. If it rains, then I ride my bike.

35. If the concert is cancelled, then it does not rain.

36. If I do not ride my bike, then it does not rain.

37. The concert is cancelled, and if it rains then I do not ride my bike.

38. I ride my bike, or if the concert is cancelled then it rains.

39. It rains if the concert is cancelled.

40. I'll ride my bike if it doesn't rain.

Find the truth value of each statement. Assume that p and r are false, and q is true.

41. $\sim r \rightarrow q$

42. $\sim p \rightarrow \sim r$

43. $q \rightarrow p$

44. $\sim r \rightarrow p$

45. $p \rightarrow q$

46. $\sim q \rightarrow r$

47. $\sim p \rightarrow (q \wedge r)$

48. $(\sim r \vee p) \rightarrow p$

49. $\sim q \rightarrow (p \wedge r)$

50. $(\sim p \wedge \sim q) \rightarrow (p \wedge \sim r)$

51. $(p \rightarrow \sim q) \rightarrow (\sim p \wedge \sim r)$

52. $(p \rightarrow \sim q) \wedge (p \rightarrow r)$

53. Explain why, if we know that p is true, we also know that

$$[r \vee (p \vee s)] \rightarrow (p \vee q)$$

is true, even if we are not given the truth values of q, r, and s.

54. Construct a true statement involving a conditional, a conjunction, a disjunction, and a negation (not necessarily in that order), that consists of component statements p, q, and r, with all of these component statements false.

Construct a truth table for each statement. Identify any tautologies.

55. $\sim q \rightarrow p$

56. $p \rightarrow \sim q$

57. $(\sim p \rightarrow q) \rightarrow p$

58. $(\sim q \rightarrow \sim p) \rightarrow \sim q$

59. $(p \vee q) \rightarrow (q \vee p)$

60. $(p \wedge q) \rightarrow (p \vee q)$

61. $(\sim p \rightarrow \sim q) \rightarrow (p \wedge q)$

62. $r \rightarrow (p \wedge \sim q)$

63. $[(r \vee p) \wedge \sim q] \rightarrow p$

64. $[(r \wedge p) \wedge (p \wedge q)] \rightarrow p$

65. $(\sim r \rightarrow s) \vee (p \rightarrow \sim q)$

66. $(\sim p \wedge \sim q) \rightarrow (s \rightarrow r)$

67. What is the minimum number of Fs that must appear in the final column of a truth table for us to be assured that the statement is not a tautology?

68. If all truth values in the final column of a truth table are F, how can we easily transform the statement into a tautology?

Write the negation of each statement. Remember that the negation of $p \to q$ *is* $p \wedge \sim q$.

69. If that is an authentic Persian rug, I'll be surprised.

70. If Ella reaches that note, she will shatter glass.

71. If the English measures are not converted to metric measures, then the spacecraft will crash on the surface of Saturn.

72. If you say "I do," then you'll be happy for the rest of your life.

73. "If you want to be happy for the rest of your life, never make a pretty woman your wife." *Jimmy Soul*

74. If loving you is wrong, I don't want to be right.

Write each statement as an equivalent statement that does not use the if . . . then *connective. Remember that* $p \to q$ *is equivalent to* $\sim p \vee q$.

75. If you give your plants tender, loving care, they flourish.

76. If the check is in the mail, I'll be surprised.

77. If she doesn't, he will.

78. If I say "black", she says "white."

79. All residents of Oregon City are residents of Oregon.

80. All men were once boys.

Use truth tables to decide which of the pairs of statements are equivalent.

81. $p \to q$; $\sim p \vee q$

82. $\sim(p \to q)$; $p \wedge \sim q$

83. $p \to q$; $\sim q \to \sim p$

84. $q \to p$; $\sim p \to \sim q$

85. $p \to \sim q$; $\sim p \vee \sim q$

86. $p \to q$; $q \to p$

87. $p \wedge \sim q$; $\sim q \to \sim p$

88. $\sim p \wedge q$; $\sim p \to q$

89. $q \to \sim p$; $p \to \sim q$

90. Explain why the circuit shown will always have exactly one open switch. What does this circuit simplify to?

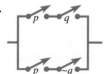

Write a logical statement representing each of the following circuits. Simplify each circuit when possible.

91.

92.

93.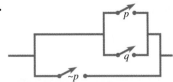

94.

95.

96.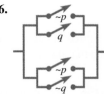

Draw circuits representing the following statements as they are given. Simplify if possible.

97. $p \wedge (q \vee \sim p)$

98. $(\sim p \wedge \sim q) \wedge \sim r$

99. $(p \vee q) \wedge (\sim p \wedge \sim q)$

100. $(\sim q \wedge \sim p) \vee (\sim p \vee q)$

101. $[(p \vee q) \wedge r] \wedge \sim p$

102. $[(\sim p \wedge \sim r) \vee \sim q] \wedge (\sim p \wedge r)$

103. $\sim q \rightarrow (\sim p \rightarrow q)$

104. $\sim p \rightarrow (\sim p \vee \sim q)$

105. Refer to Figures 5 and 6 in Example 6. Suppose the cost of the use of one switch for an hour is $.06. By using the circuit in Figure 6 rather than the circuit in Figure 5, what is the savings for a year of 365 days, assuming that the circuit is in continuous use?

3.4 More on the Conditional

Converse, Inverse, and Contrapositive • Alternative Forms of "If *p*, then *q*" • Biconditionals • Summary of Truth Tables

Converse, Inverse, and Contrapositive   Many mathematical properties and theorems are stated in *if . . . then* form. Because of their usefulness, we expand our consideration of statements of the form $p \rightarrow q$. Any conditional statement is made up of an antecedent and a consequent. If they are interchanged, negated, or both, a new conditional statement is formed. Suppose that we begin with the given conditional statement

If you stay, then I go,

and interchange the antecedent ("you stay") and the consequent ("I go"). We obtain the new conditional statement

If I go, then you stay.

This new conditional is called the **converse** of the given statement.

Alfred North Whitehead
(1861–1947) and Bertrand Russell worked together on *Principia Mathematica*. During that time, Whitehead was teaching mathematics at Cambridge University and had written *Universal Algebra*. In 1910 he went to the University of London, exploring not only the philosophical basis of science but also the "aims of education" (as he called one of his books). It was as a philosopher that he was invited to Harvard University in 1924. Whitehead died at the age of 86 in Cambridge, Massachusetts.

By negating both the antecedent and the consequent, we obtain the **inverse** of the given statement:

> If you do not stay, then I do not go.

If the antecedent and the consequent are both interchanged *and* negated, the **contrapositive** of the given statement is formed:

> If I do not go, then you do not stay.

These three related statements for the conditional $p \rightarrow q$ are summarized below. (Notice that the inverse is the contrapositive of the converse.)

Related Conditional Statements		
Conditional Statement	$p \rightarrow q$	(If p, then q.)
Converse	$q \rightarrow p$	(If q, then p.)
Inverse	$\sim p \rightarrow \sim q$	(If not p, then not q.)
Contrapositive	$\sim q \rightarrow \sim p$	(If not q, then not p.)

EXAMPLE 1 Determining Related Conditional Statements

Given the conditional statement

> If I live in Miami, then I live in Florida,

determine each of the following:

(a) the converse
(b) the inverse
(c) the contrapositive

SOLUTION

(a) Let p represent "I live in Miami" and q represent "I live in Florida." Then the given statement may be written $p \rightarrow q$. The converse, $q \rightarrow p$, is

> If I live in Florida, then I live in Miami.

Notice that for this statement, the converse is not necessarily true, even though the given statement is true.

(b) The inverse of $p \rightarrow q$ is $\sim p \rightarrow \sim q$. For the given conditional statement, the inverse is

> If I don't live in Miami, then I don't live in Florida,

which is again not necessarily true.

(c) The contrapositive, $\sim q \rightarrow \sim p$, is

> If I don't live in Florida, then I don't live in Miami.

The contrapositive, like the given conditional statement, is true. ■

Example 1 shows that the converse and inverse of a true statement need not be true. They *can* be true, but they need not be. The relationships between the truth values of the conditional statement, converse, inverse, and contrapositive are shown in the truth table that follows.

			Equivalent		
				Equivalent	
		Conditional	Converse	Inverse	Contrapositive
p	q	$p \rightarrow q$	$q \rightarrow p$	$\sim p \rightarrow \sim q$	$\sim q \rightarrow \sim p$
T	T	T	T	T	T
T	F	F	T	T	F
F	T	T	F	F	T
F	F	T	T	T	T

As this truth table shows, a conditional statement and its contrapositive always have the same truth values, making it possible to replace any statement with its contrapositive without affecting the logical meaning. Also, the converse and inverse always have the same truth values.

This discussion is summarized as follows.

Equivalences

A conditional statement and its contrapositive are equivalent, and the converse and the inverse are equivalent.

EXAMPLE 2 Determining Related Conditional Statements

For the conditional statement $\sim p \rightarrow q$, write each of the following.
(a) the converse   **(b)** the inverse   **(c)** the contrapositive

SOLUTION
(a) The converse of $\sim p \rightarrow q$ is $q \rightarrow \sim p$.
(b) The inverse is $\sim(\sim p) \rightarrow \sim q$, which simplifies to $p \rightarrow \sim q$.
(c) The contrapositive is $\sim q \rightarrow \sim(\sim p)$, which simplifies to $\sim q \rightarrow p$. ▪

Alternative Forms of "If p, then q"

The conditional statement "if p, then q" can be stated in several other ways in English. For example,

If you go to the shopping center, then you will find a place to park

can also be written

Going to the shopping center is *sufficient* for finding a place to park.

According to this statement, going to the shopping center is enough to guarantee finding a place to park. Going to other places, such as schools or office buildings, *might* also guarantee a place to park, but at least we *know* that going to the shopping center does.

Thus, $p \rightarrow q$ can be written "p is sufficient for q." Knowing that p has occurred is sufficient to guarantee that q will also occur. On the other hand,

Turning on the set is necessary for watching television $\qquad$ (*)

has a different meaning. Here, we are saying that one condition that is necessary for watching television is that you turn on the set. This may not be enough; the set might be broken, for example. The statement labeled (*) could be written as

If you watch television, then you turned on the set.

As this example suggests, $p \rightarrow q$ is the same as "q is necessary for p." In other words, if q doesn't happen, then neither will p. Notice how this idea is closely related to the idea of equivalence between a conditional statement and its contrapositive.

Common Translations of $p \rightarrow q$

The conditional $p \rightarrow q$ can be translated in any of the following ways,

If p, then q.	p is sufficient for q.
If p, q.	q is necessary for p.
p implies q.	All p are q.
p only if q.	q if p.

The translation of $p \rightarrow q$ into these various word forms does not in any way depend on the truth or falsity of $p \rightarrow q$.

For example, the statement

If you are 18, then you can vote

can be written in any of the following alternative ways:

You can vote if you are 18.

You are 18 only if you can vote.

Being able to vote is necessary for you to be 18.

Being 18 is sufficient for being able to vote.

All 18-year-olds can vote.

Being 18 implies that you can vote.

EXAMPLE 3   Rewording Conditional Statements

Write each statement in the form "if p, then q."

(a) You'll be sorry if I go.
(b) Today is Friday only if yesterday was Thursday.
(c) All nurses wear white shoes.

SOLUTION

(a) If I go, then you'll be sorry.
(b) If today is Friday, then yesterday was Thursday.
(c) If you are a nurse, then you wear white shoes.

For Further Thought

A Word to the Wise Is Sufficient

How many times have you heard a wise saying like "A stitch in time saves nine," "A rolling stone gathers no moss," or "Birds of a feather flock together"? In many cases, such proverbial advice can be restated as a conditional in *if . . . then* form. For example, these three statements can be restated as follows:

"If you make a stitch in time, then it will save you nine (stitches)."

"If a stone rolls, then it gathers no moss."

"If they are birds of a feather, then they flock together."

For Group Discussion or Individual Investigation

1. Think of some wise sayings that have been around for a long time, and state them in *if . . . then* form.
2. You have probably heard the saying "All that glitters is not gold." Do you think that what is said here is actually what is meant? If not, restate it as you think it should be stated. (*Hint:* Write the original statement in *if . . . then* form.)

EXAMPLE 4   Translating from Words to Symbols

Let *p* represent "A triangle is equilateral," and let *q* represent "A triangle has three sides of equal length." Write each of the following in symbols.

(a) A triangle is equilateral if it has three sides of equal length.
(b) A triangle is equilateral only if it has three sides of equal length.

SOLUTION

(a) $q \rightarrow p$ **(b)** $p \rightarrow q$

Biconditionals   The compound statement *p if and only if q* (often abbreviated *p iff q*) is called a **biconditional.** It is symbolized $p \leftrightarrow q$, and is interpreted as the conjunction of the two conditionals $p \rightarrow q$ and $q \rightarrow p$. Using symbols, this conjunction is written

$$(q \rightarrow p) \wedge (p \rightarrow q)$$

so that, by definition, $p \leftrightarrow q \equiv (q \rightarrow p) \wedge (p \rightarrow q)$.

The truth table for the biconditional $p \leftrightarrow q$ can be determined using this definition.

Principia Mathematica, the title chosen by Whitehead and Russell, was a deliberate reference to *Philosophiae naturalis principia mathematica,* or "mathematical principles of the philosophy of nature," Isaac Newton's epochal work of 1687. Newton's Principia pictured a kind of "clockwork universe" that ran via his Law of Gravitation. Newton independently invented the calculus, unaware that Leibniz had published his own formulation of it earlier. A controversy over their priority continued into the eighteenth century.

Truth Table for the Biconditional *p* if and only if *q*		
	p if and only if *q*	
p	*q*	$p \leftrightarrow q$
T	T	T
T	F	F
F	T	F
F	F	T

From the truth table, we see that a biconditional is true when both component statements have the same truth value. It is false when they have different truth values.

> ### EXAMPLE 5 Determining Whether Biconditionals Are True or False
>
> Determine whether each biconditional statement is *true* or *false*.
>
> **(a)** $6 + 9 = 15$ if and only if $12 + 4 = 16$ **(b)** $6 = 5$ if and only if $12 \neq 12$
> **(c)** $5 + 2 = 10$ if and only if $17 + 19 = 36$
>
> **SOLUTION**
>
> **(a)** Both $6 + 9 = 15$ and $12 + 4 = 16$ are true. By the truth table for the biconditional, this biconditional is true.
> **(b)** Both component statements are false, so by the last line of the truth table for the biconditional, this biconditional statement is true.
> **(c)** Because the first component $(5 + 2 = 10)$ is false, and the second is true, this biconditional statement is false. ▪

Summary of Truth Tables
In this section and in the previous two sections, truth tables have been derived for several important types of compound statements. The summary that follows describes how these truth tables may be remembered.

> ### Summary of Basic Truth Tables
>
> **1.** $\sim p$, the **negation** of p, has truth value opposite of p.
> **2.** $p \wedge q$, the **conjunction,** is true only when both p and q are true.
> **3.** $p \vee q$, the **disjunction,** is false only when both p and q are false.
> **4.** $p \rightarrow q$, the **conditional,** is false only when p is true and q is false.
> **5.** $p \leftrightarrow q$, the **biconditional,** is true only when p and q have the same truth value.

3.4 EXERCISES

For each given conditional statement (or statement that can be written as a conditional), write **(a)** *the converse,* **(b)** *the inverse, and* **(c)** *the contrapositive in if . . . then form. In some of the exercises, it may be helpful to first restate the given statement in if . . . then form.*

1. If beauty were a minute, then you would be an hour.

2. If you lead, then I will follow.

3. If it ain't broke, don't fix it.

4. If I had a nickel for each time that happened, I would be rich.

5. Walking in front of a moving car is dangerous to your health.

6. Milk contains calcium.

7. Birds of a feather flock together.

8. A rolling stone gathers no moss.

9. If you build it, he will come.

10. Where there's smoke, there's fire.

11. $p \rightarrow \sim q$ **12.** $\sim p \rightarrow q$

13. $\sim p \rightarrow \sim q$ **14.** $\sim q \rightarrow \sim p$

15. $p \rightarrow (q \vee r)$ (*Hint:* Use one of De Morgan's laws as necessary.)

16. $(r \vee \sim q) \rightarrow p$ (*Hint:* Use one of De Morgan's laws as necessary.)

17. Discuss the equivalences that exist among a given conditional statement, its converse, its inverse, and its contrapositive.

18. State the contrapositive of "If the square of a natural number is even, then the natural number is even." The two statements must have the same truth value. Use several examples and inductive reasoning to decide whether both are true or both are false.

Write each statement in the form "if p, then q."

19. If it is muddy, I'll wear my galoshes.

20. If I finish studying, I'll go to the party.

21. "18 is positive" implies that $18 + 1$ is positive.

22. "Today is Tuesday" implies that yesterday was Monday.

23. All integers are rational numbers.

24. All whole numbers are integers.

25. Doing crossword puzzles is sufficient for driving me crazy.

26. Being in Baton Rouge is sufficient for being in Louisiana.

27. A day's growth of beard is necessary for Gerald Guidroz to shave.

28. Being an environmentalist is necessary for being elected.

29. I can go from Park Place to Baltic Avenue only if I pass GO.

30. The principal will hire more teachers only if the school board approves.

31. No whole numbers are not integers.

32. No integers are irrational numbers.

33. The Orioles will win the pennant when their pitching improves.

34. Rush will be a liberal when pigs fly.

35. A rectangle is a parallelogram with a right angle.

36. A parallelogram is a four-sided figure with opposite sides parallel.

37. A triangle with two sides of the same length is isosceles.

38. A square is a rectangle with two adjacent sides equal.

39. The square of a two-digit number whose units digit is 5 will end in 25.

40. An integer whose units digit is 0 or 5 is divisible by 5.

41. One of the following statements is not equivalent to all the others. Which one is it?
A. r only if s.   **B.** r implies s.
C. If r, then s.   **D.** r is necessary for s.

42. Many students have difficulty interpreting *necessary* and *sufficient*. Use the statement "Being in Quebec is sufficient for being in North America" to explain why "p is sufficient for q" translates as "if p, then q."

43. Use the statement "To be an integer, it is necessary that a number be rational" to explain why "p is necessary for q" translates as "if q, then p."

44. Explain why the statement "A week has eight days if and only if October has forty days" is true.

October						
SUNDAY	MONDAY	TUESDAY	WEDNESDAY	THURSDAY	FRIDAY	SATURDAY
1	2	3	4	5	6	7
8	9	10	11	12	13	14
15	16	17	18	19	20	21
22	23	24	25	26	27	28
29	30	31				

Identify each statement as true *or* false.

45. $5 = 9 - 4$ if and only if $8 + 2 = 10$.

46. $3 + 1 \neq 6$ if and only if $8 \neq 8$.

47. $8 + 7 \neq 15$ if and only if $3 \times 5 \neq 9$.

48. $6 \times 2 = 14$ if and only if $9 + 7 \neq 16$.

49. Bill Clinton was president if and only if Jimmy Carter was not president.

50. Burger King sells Big Macs if and only if Apple manufactures Ipods.

Two statements that can both be true about the same object are **consistent.** *For example,* "It is brown" *and* "It weighs 50 pounds" *are consistent statements. Statements that cannot both be true about the same object are called* **contrary;** "It is a Dodge" *and* "It is a Toyota" *are contrary. In Exercises 51–56, label each pair of statements as either* contrary *or* consistent.

51. Elvis is alive. Elvis is dead.

52. George W. Bush is a Democrat. George W. Bush is a Republican.

53. That animal has four legs. That same animal is a dog.

54. That book is nonfiction. That book costs more than $100.

55. This number is an integer. This same number is irrational.

56. This number is positive. This same number is a natural number.

57. Make up two statements that are consistent.

58. Make up two statements that are contrary.

3.5 Analyzing Arguments with Euler Diagrams

Logical Arguments • Arguments with Universal Quantifiers • Arguments with Existential Quantifiers

Leonhard Euler (1707–1783) won the academy prize and edged out du Châtelet and Voltaire. That was a minor achievement, as was the invention of "Euler circles" (which antedated Venn diagrams). Euler was the most prolific mathematician of his generation despite blindness that forced him to dictate from memory.

Logical Arguments With inductive reasoning we observe patterns to solve problems. Now, in this section and the next, we study how deductive reasoning may be used to determine whether logical arguments are valid or invalid. A logical argument is made up of **premises** (assumptions, laws, rules, widely held ideas, or observations) and a **conclusion.** Together, the premises and the conclusion make up the argument. Also recall that *deductive* reasoning involves drawing specific conclusions from given general premises. When reasoning from the premises of an argument to obtain a conclusion, we want the argument to be valid.

> **Valid and Invalid Arguments**
>
> An argument is **valid** if the fact that all the premises are true forces the conclusion to be true. An argument that is not valid is **invalid.** It is called a **fallacy.**

It is very important to note that "valid" and "true" are not the same—an argument can be valid even though the conclusion is false. (See Example 4.)

Arguments with Universal Quantifiers Several techniques can be used to check whether an argument is valid. One of these is the visual technique based on **Euler diagrams,** as shown in Examples 1–4.

EXAMPLE 1 Using an Euler Diagram to Determine Validity

Is the following argument valid?

> All dogs are animals.
>
> Puddles is a dog.
> _____
> Puddles is an animal.

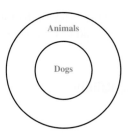

FIGURE 8

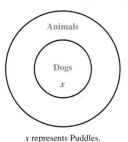

x represents Puddles.

FIGURE 9

SOLUTION

Here we use the common method of placing one premise over another, with the conclusion below a line. To begin, draw regions to represent the first premise. One is the region for "animals." Because all dogs are animals, the region for "dogs" goes inside the region for "animals," as in Figure 8.

The second premise, "Puddles is a dog," suggests that "Puddles" would go inside the region representing "dogs." Let *x* represent "Puddles." Figure 9 shows that "Puddles" is also inside the region for "animals." If both premises are true, the conclusion that Puddles is an animal must be true also. The argument is valid. ▪

EXAMPLE 2 Using an Euler Diagram to Determine Validity

Is the following argument valid?

> All rainy days are cloudy.
> Today is not cloudy. _____
> Today is not rainy.

SOLUTION

In Figure 10, the region for "rainy days" is drawn entirely inside the region for "cloudy days." Since "Today is *not* cloudy," place an *x* for "today" *outside* the region for "cloudy days." See Figure 11. Placing the *x* outside the region for "cloudy days" forces it also to be outside the region for "rainy days." Thus, if the first two premises are true, then it is also true that today is not rainy. The argument is valid.

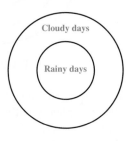
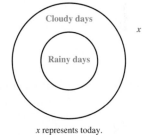

x represents today.

FIGURE 10   **FIGURE 11** ▪

EXAMPLE 3 Using an Euler Diagram to Determine Validity

Is the following argument valid?

> All banana trees have green leaves.
> That plant has green leaves. _____
> That plant is a banana tree.

SOLUTION

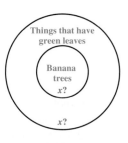

FIGURE 12

The region for "banana trees" goes entirely inside the region for "things that have green leaves." See Figure 12. There is a choice for locating the *x* that represents "that plant." The *x* must go inside the region for "things that have green leaves," but can go either inside or outside the region for "banana trees." Even if the premises are true, we are not forced to accept the conclusion as true. This argument is invalid; it is a fallacy. ▪

As mentioned earlier, the validity of an argument is not the same as the truth of its conclusion. The argument in Example 3 was invalid, but the conclusion "That plant is a banana tree" may or may not be true. We cannot be sure.

EXAMPLE 4   Using an Euler Diagram to Determine Validity

Is the following argument valid?

> All expensive things are desirable.
>
> All desirable things make you feel good.
>
> All things that make you feel good make you live longer.
>
> All expensive things make you live longer.

SOLUTION

A diagram for the argument is given in Figure 13.

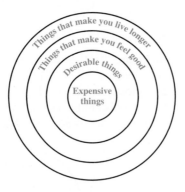

FIGURE 13

If each premise is true, then the conclusion must be true because the region for "expensive things" lies completely within the region for "things that make you live longer." Thus, the argument is valid. (This argument is an example of the fact that a *valid* argument need *not* have a true conclusion.) ■

Arguments with Existential Quantifiers

EXAMPLE 5   Using an Euler Diagram to Determine Validity

Is the following argument valid?

> Some students go to the beach for Spring Break.
>
> I am a student.
>
> I go to the beach for Spring Break.

SOLUTION

The first premise is sketched in Figure 14. As the sketch shows, some (but not necessarily *all*) students go to the beach. There are two possibilities for *I*, as shown in Figure 15.

One possibility is that *I* go to the beach; the other is that *I* don't. Since the truth of the premises does not force the conclusion to be true, the argument is invalid. ■

FIGURE 14

FIGURE 15

3.5 EXERCISES

Decide whether each argument is valid *or* invalid.

1. All amusement parks have thrill rides.
Great America is an amusement park.

Great America has thrill rides.

2. All disc jockeys play music.
Phlash Phelps is a disc jockey.

Phlash Phelps plays music.

3. All politicians lie, cheat, and steal.
That man lies, cheats, and steals.

That man is a politician.

4. All Southerners speak with an accent.
Bill Leonard speaks with an accent.

Bill Leonard is a Southerner.

5. All dogs love to bury bones.
Py does not love to bury bones.

Py is not a dog.

6. All handymen use cell phones.
Lee Guidroz does not use a cell phone.

Lee Guidroz is not a handyman.

7. All residents of Minnesota know how to live in freezing temperatures.
Wendy Rockswold knows how to live in freezing temperatures.

Wendy Rockswold lives in Minnesota.

8. All people who apply for a loan must pay for a title search.
Hilary Langlois paid for a title search.

Hilary Langlois applied for a loan.

9. Some dinosaurs were plant eaters.
Danny was a plant eater.

Danny was a dinosaur.

10. Some philosophers are absent minded.
Loretta Ramagos is a philosopher.

Loretta Ramagos is absent minded.

11. Some nurses wear blue uniforms.
Dee Boyle is a nurse.

Dee Boyle wears a blue uniform.

12. Some trucks have sound systems.
Some trucks have gun racks.

Some trucks with sound systems have gun racks.

13. Refer to Example 3. If the second premise and the conclusion were interchanged, would the argument then be valid?

14. Refer to Example 4. Give a different conclusion than the one given there so that the argument is still valid.

Construct a valid argument based on the Euler diagram shown.

15.

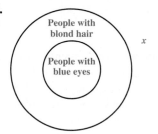

x represents Dinya Norris.

16.

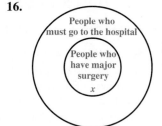

x represents Marty McDonald.

As mentioned in the text, an argument can have a true conclusion yet be invalid. In these exercises, each argument has a true conclusion. Identify each argument as valid *or* invalid.

17. All birds fly.
All planes fly.

A bird is not a plane.

18. All cars have tires.
All tires are rubber.

All cars have rubber.

19. All chickens have beaks.
All hens are chickens.
———————————
All hens have beaks.

20. All chickens have beaks.
All birds have beaks.
———————————
All chickens are birds.

21. Little Rock is northeast of Texarkana.
Little Rock is northeast of Austin.
———————————
Texarkana is northeast of Austin.

22. Veracruz is south of Tampico.
Tampico is south of Monterrey.
———————————
Veracruz is south of Monterrey.

23. No whole numbers are negative.
−4 is negative.
———————————
−4 is not a whole number.

24. A scalene triangle has a longest side.
A scalene triangle has a largest angle.
———————————
The largest angle in a scalene triangle
is opposite the longest side.

In Exercises 25–30, the premises marked A, B, *and* C *are followed by several possible conclusions. Take each conclusion in turn, and check whether the resulting argument is* valid *or* invalid.

  A. *All people who drive contribute to air pollution.*
  B. *All people who contribute to air pollution make life a little worse.*
  C. *Some people who live in a suburb make life a little worse.*

25. Some people who live in a suburb contribute to air pollution.

26. Some people who live in a suburb drive.

27. Suburban residents never drive.

28. Some people who contribute to air pollution live in a suburb.

29. Some people who make life a little worse live in a suburb.

30. All people who drive make life a little worse.

31. Find examples of arguments on television commercials. Check them for validity.

32. Find examples of arguments in magazine ads. Check them for validity.

EXTENSION

Logic Problems and Sudoku

• How to Solve Logic Problems • How to Solve Sudoku

Some people find that logic problems, which appear in periodicals such as *Official's Logic Problems, World-Class Logic Problems* and *England's Best Logic Problems* (both PennyPress), and *Logic Puzzles* (Dell), provide hours of enjoyment. They are based on deductive reasoning, and players answer questions based on clues given. The following explanation on solving such problems appeared in the May 2004 issue of *England's Best Logic Problems*.

How to Solve Logic Problems Solving logic problems is entertaining and challenging. All the information you need to solve a logic problem is given in the introduction and clues, and in illustrations, when provided. If you've never solved a logic problem before, our sample should help you get started. Fill in the Sample Solving

Chart as you follow our explanation. We use a "•" to signify "Yes" and an "X" to signify "No."

Sample Logic Problem

Five couples were married last week, each on a different weekday. From the information provided, determine the woman (one is Cathy) and man (one is Paul) who make up each couple, as well as the day on which each couple was married.

1. Anne was married on Monday, but not to Wally.

2. Stan's wedding was on Wednesday. Rob was married on Friday, but not to Ida.

3. Vern (who married Fran) was married the day after Eve.

Sample Solving Chart:	PAUL	ROB	STAN	VERN	WALLY	MONDAY	TUESDAY	WEDNESDAY	THURSDAY	FRIDAY
ANNE										
CATHY										
EVE										
FRAN										
IDA										
MONDAY										
TUESDAY										
WEDNESDAY										
THURSDAY										
FRIDAY										

1	PAUL	ROB	STAN	VERN	WALLY	MONDAY	TUESDAY	WEDNESDAY	THURSDAY	FRIDAY
ANNE	X	X		X		•	X	X	X	X
CATHY						X				
EVE						X				
FRAN						X				
IDA		X				X				X
MONDAY	X	X								
TUESDAY	X	X								
WEDNESDAY	X	X	•	X	X					
THURSDAY	X	X								
FRIDAY	X	•	X	X	X					

Explanation

Anne was married Mon. (1), so put a "•" at the intersection of Anne and Mon. Put "X"s in all the other days in Anne's row and all the other names in the Mon. column. (Whenever you establish a relationship, as we did here, be sure to place "X"s at the intersections of all relationships that become impossible as a result.) Anne wasn't married to Wally (1), so put an "X" at the intersection of Anne and Wally. Stan's wedding was Wed. (2), so put a "•" at the intersection of Stan and Wed. (Don't forget the "X"s.) Stan didn't marry Anne, who was married Mon., so put an "X" at the intersection of Anne and Stan. Rob was married Fri., but not to Ida (2), so put a "•" at the intersection of Rob and Fri., and "X"s at the intersections of Rob and Ida and Ida and Fri. Rob also didn't marry Anne, who was married Mon., so put an "X" at the intersection of Anne and Rob. Now your chart should look like chart 1.

Vern married Fran (3), so put a "•" at the intersection of Vern and Fran. This leaves Anne's only possible husband as Paul, so put a "•" at the intersection of Anne and Paul and Paul and Mon. Vern and Fran's wedding was the day after Eve's (3), which wasn't Mon. [Anne], so Vern's wasn't Tue. It must have been Thu. [see chart], so Eve's was Wed. (3). Put "•"s at the intersections of Vern and Thu., Fran and Thu., and Eve and Wed. Now your chart should look like chart 2.

(continued)

2	PAUL	ROB	STAN	VERN	WALLY	MONDAY	TUESDAY	WEDNESDAY	THURSDAY	FRIDAY
ANNE	•	×	×	×	×	•	×	×	×	×
CATHY	×		×		×	×		×	×	
EVE	×		×			×	×	•	×	×
FRAN	×	×	×	•	×	×	×	×	•	
IDA	×	×		×			×	×	×	
MONDAY	•	×	×	×	×
TUESDAY	×	×	×	×	
WEDNESDAY	×	×	•	×	×
THURSDAY	×	×	×	•	×
FRIDAY	×	•	×	×	×

3	PAUL	ROB	STAN	VERN	WALLY	MONDAY	TUESDAY	WEDNESDAY	THURSDAY	FRIDAY
ANNE	•	×	×	×	×	•	×	×	×	×
CATHY	×	•	×	×	×	×	×	×	×	•
EVE	×	×	•	×	×	×	×	×	•	×
FRAN	×	×	×	•	×	×	×	×	•	×
IDA	×	×	×	×	•	×	•	×	×	×
MONDAY	•	×	×	×	×
TUESDAY	×	×	×	×	•
WEDNESDAY	×	×	•	×	×
THURSDAY	×	×	×	•	×
FRIDAY	×	•	×	×	×

The chart shows that Cathy was married Fri., Ida was married Tue., and Wally was married Tue. Ida married Wally, and Cathy's wedding was Fri., so she married Rob. After this information is filled in, Eve could only have married Stan. You've completed the puzzle, and your chart should now look like chart 3.

In summary: Anne and Paul, Mon.; Cathy and Rob, Fri.; Eve and Stan, Wed.; Fran and Vern, Thu.; Ida and Wally, Tue.

In some problems, it may be necessary to make a logical guess based on facts you've established. When you do, always look for clues or other facts that disprove it. If you find that your guess is incorrect, eliminate it as a possibility.

How to Solve Sudoku   Sudoku is a simple game that has gained great popularity in the United States during the past few years. It is believed that the game originated as Number Place in the United States over 25 years ago, but gained in popularity only after it became a sensation in Japan, where it was renamed Sudoku, meaning "single number." (*Source: Sudoku #13*, 2005, Platinum Magazine Group.) Today it can be found in daily newspapers, on day-by-day calendars, and in periodical publications on newsstands.

There is only one rule in Sudoku: "Fill in the grid so that every row, every column, and every 3 × 3 box contains the digits 1 through 9." This involves scanning the given digits, marking up the grid, and analyzing. Here is a Sudoku in its original (given) form and in its final (solved) form.

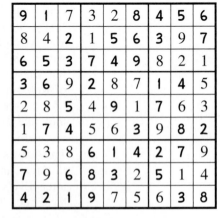

		7	3	2				
8	4		1				9	
						8	2	1
		9		8	7			5
2	8		4		1		6	3
1			5	6		9		
5	3	8						9
	9				2		1	4
				7	5	6		

Given Form

9	1	7	3	2	8	4	5	6
8	4	2	1	5	6	3	9	7
6	5	3	7	4	9	8	2	1
3	6	9	2	8	7	1	4	5
2	8	5	4	9	1	7	6	3
1	7	4	5	6	3	9	8	2
5	3	8	6	1	4	2	7	9
7	9	6	8	3	2	5	1	4
4	2	1	9	7	5	6	3	8

Solved Form

You can find Sudoku puzzles and solving strategies online at www.sudoku.org.

EXTENSION EXERCISES

Follow the guidelines to solve each logic problem, which appeared in the Spring 2004 issue of England's Best Logic Problems, *published by PennyPress.*

1. *A Moving Story*   On the first day of her visit to Russia, British chess prodigy Queenie King, aged 14, played and defeated the adult champions from four different cities. From the clues below, can you work out the full name of her opponent in each game and the city from which he came?

clues below, can you work out the name of the fellow-archaeologist making each offer, which university he is from, what is to be excavated, and where it is?

	Boris	Ivan	Piotr	Yuri	Bishopnik	Knightovich	Pawnchev	Rookov	Corki	Gorki	Porki	Yorki
First												
Second												
Third												
Fourth												
Corki												
Gorki												
Porki												
Yorki												
Bishopnik												
Knightovich												
Pawnchev												
Rookov												

		Universities								Locations			
		Arizona	Berlin	Miami	New York	Fort	Pyramid	Temple	Villa	China	Egypt	Peru	Scotland
	Prof. Azimovic												
	Prof. Katsouris												
	Prof. Partington												
	Prof. Voelkner												
Locations	China												
	Egypt												
	Peru												
	Scotland												
	Fort												
	Pyramid												
	Temple												
	Villa												

Clues:

(a) Boris was from the famous city of Gorki, while the other champions came from cities not so well known.

(b) Mr Rookov, Queenie's second opponent, was not the man from the city of Yorki, centre of the Russian chocolate industry.

(c) Piotr, who was the first Russian to play—and be beaten by—Queenie wasn't Mr Pawnchev.

(d) Mr Bishopnik played Queenie immediately after Ivan and immediately before the man from Corki.

2. *Dig This!*   Professor Rosetta Stone, the eminent British archaeologist, is considering offers to participate in four different "digs" next year. From the

Clues:

(a) Professor Azimovic wants Rosetta to join him for an expedition into the wild highlands of Peru.

(b) The University of New York expedition is being mounted to excavate the site of a two thousand year old temple.

(c) Professor Katsouris isn't organising the expedition that is going to excavate an ancient fort.

(d) The site in the Takla Makan desert of China to be investigated by the University of Arizona expedition is not that of a villa.

(e) Professor Voelkner of the University of Berlin has no connection to the projected expedition to excavate a newly discovered pyramid in Egypt's Nile delta.

3. *Is That a Folk Song?* The traditional answer to the above question, when applied to something that may or may not be a folk song, is "Well, I never heard a cow sing it." None of the singers in this problem are cows, and they only sing folk songs. From the clues below, can you identify each male singer and his female partner, the name they perform under, and the type of folk songs they sing? (*Note:* The only vowels are A, E, I, O, and U.)

4. *Monsieur le Duc* In the 1930s, the Duc de Bauch made a number of profitable business partnerships. The Duc went into business with four heiresses, each of whom had inherited a business from her father. From the clues given below, can you work out each heiress' name, where her family money came from, and the city and year in which she partnered with the Duc?

Logic grid for problem 3 — Men (Ben Ashby, Hans Gruber, Peter Owen, Steven Thorp), song types (American, English, Irish, Own compositions), and duo names (Dirk and Daisy, Merlyns, Rose and Thorn, Starr Twins) cross-referenced against Women (Carol Dodds, Jane Kenny, Nancy O'Hara, Sue Rogers), duo names, and song types (American, English, Irish, Own compositions).

Logic grid for problem 4 — heiresses (Drusilla Camden, Horatia Hampton, Mabelle Oakland, Regina Stamford), years (1932, 1934, 1936, 1938), and cities (Athens, Berlin, Monte Carlo, Paris) cross-referenced against business source (Automobiles, Banking, Mining, Oil), cities (Athens, Berlin, Monte Carlo, Paris), and years (1932, 1934, 1936, 1938).

Clues:

(a) Although he was born in Munich, Hans Gruber and his partner only sing traditional English folk songs.

(b) Nancy O'Hara is the Rose half of Rose and Thorn.

(c) One of the men whose surname begins with a vowel sings with Carol Dodds, while the other performs traditional American material with partner Jane Kenny.

(d) Peter Owen and his partner—who resemble each other not at all—perform as the Starr Twins; Ben Ashby isn't one of the Merlyns.

(e) The male half of the duo who perform folk-type songs of their own composition has a first name with one more letter than that of Sue Rogers' partner.

Clues:

(a) Neither the banking heiress who partnered with the Duc de Bauch in 1938 nor Horatia Hampton, whose father was an oil millionaire, had ever been to Athens.

(b) One partnership was formed in Berlin in 1936.

(c) The Monte Carlo business arrangement was formed earlier than the one with Mabelle Oakland.

(d) The family of Regina Stamford, the Duc's 1934 partner, had no major involvement in the automobile industry.

(e) Drusilla Camden joined forces with the Duc in Paris.

Solve each Sudoku, which appeared in *Sudoku #13*, 2005, *Platinum Magazine Group*. (They are categorized according to difficulty level.)

5. Very Easy

	2	6		9			3	
	4		8				1	7
8				5	2	4		
	8	1	3					9
2	9						8	4
3					7	1	6	
		9	1	3				5
5	3				6		7	
	6			7		8	4	

6. Very Easy

		3				5	8	
8		2			7	6		
7	9		5	6			3	1
	7		3		1	9		
		8				7		
		5	9		2		6	
6	4			5	3		1	2
		1	4			3		9
	2	7				4		

7. Easy

2				8			1	
			5	9		4		7
		9			2			
	4	7			8	1		6
6								3
5		1	6			2	4	
			8			3		
7		2		3	5			
	6			2				4

8. Easy

			2	5			6	
7			6		4	5		8
	6	5			7			
		7				3		9
8								2
9		3				4		
			8			9	2	
2		8	9		5			7
	4			3	2			

9. Medium

1						3	4	
5			8					
	6		2			8		5
4			7			6		
	7			8			2	
		5			3			1
9		1			7		6	
					1			4
	4	3						2

10. Medium

5		6				7		8
	2		1		7		3	
7								4
		1	6	9	3	8		
		9	2	7	5	3		
1								6
	7		8		9		5	
6		3				4		9

11. *Hard*

9		3		4				6
								5
	5	4			1			
1				3				8
		5				3		
3			6					7
			9			1	2	
8								
6				7		5		4

12. *Hard*

7			8					
				5		9		6
	3		2			7		
			5				6	3
		4		7		1		
8	2				3			
		8			5		4	
9		2		1				
					8			1

3.6 Analyzing Arguments with Truth Tables

Truth Tables (Two Premises) • Valid and Invalid Argument Forms • Truth Tables (More Than Two Premises) • Arguments of Lewis Carroll

Truth Tables (Two Premises)   In Section 3.5 we used Euler diagrams to test the validity of arguments. While Euler diagrams often work well for simple arguments, difficulties can develop with more complex ones, because Euler diagrams require a sketch showing every possible case. In complex arguments, it is hard to be sure that all cases have been considered.

In deciding whether to use Euler diagrams to test the validity of an argument, look for quantifiers such as "all," "some," or "no." These words often indicate arguments best tested by Euler diagrams. If these words are absent, it may be better to use truth tables to test the validity of an argument.

As an example of this method, consider the following argument:

> If the floor is dirty, then I must mop it.
>
> The floor is dirty.
> _____
>
> I must mop it.

To test the validity of this argument, we begin by identifying the *component* statements found in the argument. They are "the floor is dirty" and "I must mop it." We assign the letters p and q to represent these statements:

> p represents "the floor is dirty";
>
> q represents "I must mop it."

Now we write the two premises and the conclusion in symbols:

Premise 1: $p \rightarrow q$

Premise 2: p

Conclusion: q .

To decide if this argument is valid, we must determine whether the conjunction of both premises implies the conclusion for all possible cases of truth values for p and q. Therefore, write the conjunction of the premises as the antecedent of a conditional statement, and the conclusion as the consequent.

$$[(p \rightarrow q) \quad \wedge \quad p] \quad \rightarrow \quad q$$

premise and premise implies conclusion

Finally, construct the truth table for this conditional statement, as shown below.

p	q	$p \rightarrow q$	$(p \rightarrow q) \wedge p$	$[(p \rightarrow q) \wedge p] \rightarrow q$
T	T	T	T	T
T	F	F	F	T
F	T	T	F	T
F	F	T	F	T

Because the final column, shown in color, indicates that the conditional statement that represents the argument is true for all possible truth values of p and q, the statement is a tautology. Thus, the argument is valid.

The pattern of the argument in the floor-mopping example,

$$p \rightarrow q$$

$$p$$

$$q \quad ,$$

is a common one, and is called **modus ponens,** or the *law of detachment*.

In summary, to test the validity of an argument using a truth table, follow the steps in the box.

Testing the Validity of an Argument with a Truth Table

Step 1 Assign a letter to represent each component statement in the argument.

Step 2 Express each premise and the conclusion symbolically.

Step 3 Form the symbolic statement of the entire argument by writing the *conjunction* of *all* the premises as the antecedent of a conditional statement, and the conclusion of the argument as the consequent.

Step 4 Complete the truth table for the conditional statement formed in Step 3 above. If it is a tautology, then the argument is valid; otherwise, it is invalid.

EXAMPLE 1   Using a Truth Table to Determine Validity

Determine whether the argument is *valid* or *invalid*.

If my check arrives in time, I'll register for the fall semester.

I've registered for the fall semester.

My check arrived in time.

SOLUTION

Let *p* represent "my check arrives (arrived) in time" and let *q* represent "I'll register (I've registered) for the fall semester." Using these symbols, the argument can be written in the form

$$p \rightarrow q$$

$$q$$

$$p \quad .$$

To test for validity, construct a truth table for the statement $[(p \rightarrow q) \wedge q] \rightarrow p$.

p	*q*	*p → q*	$(p \rightarrow q) \wedge q$	$[(p \rightarrow q) \wedge q] \rightarrow p$
T	T	T	T	T
T	F	F	F	T
F	T	T	T	F
F	F	T	F	T

The third row of the final column of the truth table shows F, and this is enough to conclude that the argument is invalid. ■

If a conditional and its converse were logically equivalent, then an argument of the type found in Example 1 would be valid. Because a conditional and its converse are *not* equivalent, the argument is an example of what is sometimes called the **fallacy of the converse.**

EXAMPLE 2   Using a Truth Table to Determine Validity

Determine whether the argument is *valid* or *invalid*.

If a man could be in two places at one time, I'd be with you.

I am not with you.

A man can't be in two places at one time.

SOLUTION

If *p* represents "a man could be in two places at one time" and *q* represents "I'd be with you," the argument becomes

$$p \rightarrow q$$

$$\sim q$$

$$\sim p \quad .$$

The symbolic statement of the entire argument is

$$[(p \rightarrow q) \land \sim q] \rightarrow \sim p.$$

The truth table for this argument, shown below, indicates a tautology, and the argument is valid.

p	q	$p \rightarrow q$	$\sim q$	$(p \rightarrow q) \land \sim q$	$\sim p$	$[(p \rightarrow q) \land \sim q] \rightarrow \sim p$
T	T	T	F	F	F	T
T	F	F	T	F	F	T
F	T	T	F	F	T	T
F	F	T	T	T	T	T

The pattern of reasoning of this example is called **modus tollens,** or the *law of contraposition,* or *indirect reasoning.* ■

With reasoning similar to that used to name the fallacy of the converse, the fallacy

$$p \rightarrow q$$
$$\underline{\sim p}$$
$$\sim q$$

is called the **fallacy of the inverse.** An example of such a fallacy is "If it rains, I get wet. It doesn't rain. Therefore, I don't get wet."

EXAMPLE 3   Using a Truth Table to Determine Validity

Determine whether the argument is *valid* or *invalid.*

I'll buy a car or I'll take a vacation.

I won't buy a car.

I'll take a vacation.

SOLUTION

If p represents "I'll buy a car" and q represents "I'll take a vacation," the argument becomes

$$p \lor q$$
$$\underline{\sim p}$$
$$q \qquad .$$

We must set up a truth table for the statement $[(p \lor q) \land \sim p] \rightarrow q$.

p	q	$p \lor q$	$\sim p$	$(p \lor q) \land \sim p$	$[(p \lor q) \land \sim p] \rightarrow q$
T	T	T	F	F	T
T	F	T	F	F	T
F	T	T	T	T	T
F	F	F	T	F	T

The statement is a tautology and the argument is valid. Any argument of this form is valid by the law of **disjunctive syllogism.** ■

EXAMPLE 4 Using a Truth Table to Determine Validity

Determine whether the argument is *valid* or *invalid*.

> If it squeaks, then I use WD-40.
>
> If I use WD-40, then I must go to the hardware store.
>
> If it squeaks, then I must go to the hardware store.

SOLUTION

Let p represent "it squeaks," let q represent "I use WD-40," and let r represent "I must go to the hardware store." The argument takes on the general form

$$p \to q$$
$$q \to r$$
$$p \to r.$$

Make a truth table for the following statement:

$$[(p \to q) \land (q \to r)] \to (p \to r).$$

It will require eight rows.

p	q	r	$p \to q$	$q \to r$	$p \to r$	$(p \to q) \land (q \to r)$	$[(p \to q) \land (q \to r)] \to (p \to r)$
T	T	T	T	T	T	T	T
T	T	F	T	F	F	F	T
T	F	T	F	T	T	F	T
T	F	F	F	T	F	F	T
F	T	T	T	T	T	T	T
F	T	F	T	F	T	F	T
F	F	T	T	T	T	T	T
F	F	F	T	T	T	T	T

This argument is valid because the final statement is a tautology. The pattern of argument shown in this example is called **reasoning by transitivity,** or the *law of hypothetical syllogism*.

In a scene near the beginning of the 1974 film *Monty Python and the Holy Grail*, an amazing application of **poor logic** leads to the apparent demise of a supposed witch. A group of peasants have forced a young woman to wear a nose made of wood. The convoluted argument they make is this: Witches and wood are both burned, and because witches are made of wood, and wood floats, and ducks also float, if she weighs the same as a duck, then she is made of wood and therefore is a witch!

So if you're an intellectual midget.

Valid and Invalid Argument Forms
A summary of the valid and invalid forms of argument presented so far follows.

Valid Argument Forms

Modus Ponens	Modus Tollens	Disjunctive Syllogism	Reasoning by Transitivity
$p \to q$	$p \to q$	$p \lor q$	$p \to q$
p	$\sim q$	$\sim p$	$q \to r$
q	$\sim p$	q	$p \to r$

Invalid Argument Forms (Fallacies)

Fallacy of the Converse	Fallacy of the Inverse
$p \rightarrow q$	$p \rightarrow q$
q	$\sim p$
p	$\sim q$

Truth Tables (More Than Two Premises)

When an argument contains more than two premises, it is necessary to determine the truth values of the conjunction of *all* of them. Remember that if *at least one* premise in a conjunction of several premises is false, then the entire conjunction is false.

EXAMPLE 5   Using a Truth Table to Determine Validity

Determine whether the argument is *valid* or *invalid*.

If Eddie goes to town, then Mabel stays at home. If Mabel does not stay at home, then Rita will cook. Rita will not cook. Therefore, Eddie does not go to town.

SOLUTION

In an argument written in this manner, the premises are given first, and the conclusion is the statement that follows the word "Therefore." Let p represent "Eddie goes to town," let q represent "Mabel stays at home," and let r represent "Rita will cook."

$$p \rightarrow q$$
$$\sim q \rightarrow r$$
$$\underline{\sim r}$$
$$\sim p$$

To test validity, set up a truth table for the statement

$$[(p \rightarrow q) \wedge (\sim q \rightarrow r) \wedge \sim r] \rightarrow \sim p.$$

p	q	r	$p \rightarrow q$	$\sim q$	$\sim q \rightarrow r$	$\sim r$	$(p \rightarrow q) \wedge (\sim q \rightarrow r) \wedge \sim r$	$\sim p$	$[(p \rightarrow q) \wedge (\sim q \rightarrow r) \wedge \sim r] \rightarrow \sim p$
T	T	T	T	F	T	F	F	F	T
T	T	F	T	F	T	T	T	F	F
T	F	T	F	T	T	F	F	F	T
T	F	F	F	T	F	T	F	F	T
F	T	T	T	F	T	F	F	T	T
F	T	F	T	F	T	T	T	T	T
F	F	T	T	T	T	F	F	T	T
F	F	F	T	T	F	T	F	T	T

Because the final column does not contain all Ts, the statement is not a tautology. The argument is invalid.

Arguments of Lewis Carroll Consider the following poem, which has been around for many years.

> For want of a nail, the shoe was lost.
> For want of a shoe, the horse was lost.
> For want of a horse, the rider was lost.
> For want of a rider, the battle was lost.
> For want of a battle, the war was lost.
> Therefore, for want of a nail, the war was lost.

Each line of the poem may be written as an *if . . . then* statement. For example, the first line may be restated as "if a nail is lost, then the shoe is lost." The conclusion, "for want of a nail, the war was lost," follows from the premises, because repeated use of the law of transitivity applies. Arguments used by Lewis Carroll often take on a similar form. The next example comes from one of his works.

EXAMPLE 6 Supplying a Conclusion to Assure Validity

Supply a conclusion that yields a valid argument for the following premises.

> Babies are illogical.
>
> Nobody is despised who can manage a crocodile.
>
> Illogical persons are despised.

SOLUTION

First, write each premise in the form *if . . . then*.

> If you are a baby, then you are illogical.
>
> If you can manage a crocodile, then you are not despised.
>
> If you are illogical, then you are despised.

Let p be "you are a baby," let q be "you are logical," let r be "you can manage a crocodile," and let s be "you are despised." With these letters, the statements can be written symbolically as

$$p \rightarrow \sim q$$
$$r \rightarrow \sim s$$
$$\sim q \rightarrow s.$$

Begin with any letter that appears only once. Here p appears only once. Using the contrapositive of $r \rightarrow \sim s$, which is $s \rightarrow \sim r$, rearrange the three statements as follows:

$$p \rightarrow \sim q$$
$$\sim q \rightarrow s$$
$$s \rightarrow \sim r.$$

From the three statements, repeated use of reasoning by transitivity gives the conclusion

$$p \rightarrow \sim r,$$

leading to a valid argument.

In words, the conclusion is "If you are a baby, then you cannot manage a crocodile," or, as Lewis Carroll would have written it, "Babies cannot manage crocodiles." ▪

Tweedlogic "I know what you're thinking about," said Tweedledum, "but it isn't so, nohow." "Contrariwise," continued Tweedledee, "if it was so, it might be; and if it were so, it would be, but as it isn't, it ain't. That's logic."

3.6 EXERCISES

Each argument is either valid by one of the forms of valid arguments discussed in this section, or it is a fallacy by one of the forms of invalid arguments discussed. (See the summary boxes.) Decide whether the argument is valid *or a* fallacy, *and give the form that applies.*

1. If Elton John comes to town, then I will go to the concert.
If I go to the concert, then I'll call in sick for work.

If Elton John comes to town, then I'll call in sick for work.

2. If you use binoculars, then you get a glimpse of the comet.
If you get a glimpse of the comet, then you'll be amazed.

If you use binoculars, then you'll be amazed.

3. If Kim Hobbs works hard enough, she will get a promotion.
Kim Hobbs works hard enough.

She gets a promotion.

4. If Johnny Forbes sells his quota, he'll get a bonus.
Johnny Forbes sells his quota.

He gets a bonus.

5. If he doesn't have to get up at 4:00 A.M., he's ecstatic.
He's ecstatic.

He doesn't have to get up at 4:00 A.M.

6. If she buys another pair of shoes, her closet will overflow.
Her closet will overflow.

She buys another pair of shoes.

7. If Kerry Wood pitches, the Cubs win.
The Cubs do not win.

Kerry Wood does not pitch.

8. If Nelson Dida plays, the opponent gets shut out.
The opponent does not get shut out.

Nelson Dida does not play.

9. "If we evolved a race of Isaac Newtons, that would not be progress." (quote from Aldous Huxley)

We have not evolved a race of Isaac Newtons.

That is progress.

10. "If I have seen farther than others, it is because I stood on the shoulders of giants." (quote from Sir Isaac Newton)

I have not seen farther than others.

I have not stood on the shoulders of giants.

11. She uses e-commerce or she pays by credit card.

She does not pay by credit card.

She uses e-commerce.

12. Mia kicks or Arnold pumps iron.

Arnold does not pump iron.

Mia kicks.

Use a truth table to determine whether the argument is valid *or* invalid.

13. $p \lor q$

p

$\sim q$

14. $p \land \sim q$

p

$\sim q$

15. $\sim p \to \sim q$

q

p

16. $p \lor \sim q$

p

$\sim q$

17. $p \to q$

$q \to p$

$p \land q$

18. $\sim p \to q$

p

$\sim q$

19. $p \to \sim q$

q

$\sim p$

20. $p \to \sim q$

$\sim p$

$\sim q$

21. $(\sim p \lor q) \land (\sim p \to q)$

p

$\sim q$

22. $(p \to q) \land (q \to p)$

p

$p \lor q$

23. $(\sim p \land r) \to (p \lor q)$

$\sim r \to p$

$q \to r$

24. $(r \land p) \to (r \lor q)$

$q \land p$

$r \lor p$

25. Earlier we showed how to analyze arguments using Euler diagrams. Refer to Example 4 in this section, restate each premise and the conclusion using a quantifier, and then draw an Euler diagram to illustrate the relationship.

26. Explain in a few sentences how to determine the statement for which a truth table will be constructed so that the arguments that follow in Exercises 27–36 can be analyzed for validity.

Determine whether each argument is valid *or* invalid.

27. Brian loves to watch movies. If Elayn likes to jog, then Brian does not love to watch movies. If Elayn does not like to jog, then Clay drives a school bus. Therefore, Clay drives a school bus.

28. If Hurricane Katrina hit that grove of trees, then the trees are devastated. People plant trees when disasters strike and the trees are not devastated. Therefore, if people plant trees when disasters strike, then Hurricane Katrina did not hit that grove of trees.

29. If the MP3 personal player craze continues, then downloading music will remain popular. American Girl dolls are favorites or downloading music will remain popular. American Girl dolls are not favorites. Therefore, the MP3 personal player craze does not continue.

30. Ashley Simpson sings or Ashton Kutcher is not a teen idol. If Ashton Kutcher is not a teen idol, then Fantasia does not win a Grammy. Fantasia wins a Grammy. Therefore, Ashley Simpson does not sing.

31. The Steelers will be in the playoffs if and only if Ben leads the league in passing. Bill coaches the Steelers or Ben leads the league in passing. Bill does not coach the Steelers. Therefore, the Steelers will not be in the playoffs.

32. If I've got you under my skin, then you are deep in the heart of me. If you are deep in the heart of me, then you are not really a part of me. You are deep in the heart of me or you are really a part of me. Therefore, if I've got you under my skin, then you are really a part of me.

33. If Dr. Hardy is a department chairman, then he lives in Atlanta. He lives in Atlanta and his first name is Larry. Therefore, if his first name is not Larry, then he is not a department chairman.

34. If I were your woman and you were my man, then I'd never stop loving you. I've stopped loving you. Therefore, I am not your woman or you are not my man.

35. All men are created equal. All people who are created equal are women. Therefore, all men are women.

36. All men are mortal. Socrates is a man. Therefore, Socrates is mortal.

37. Suppose that you ask a stranger for the time and you get the following response:

"If I tell you the time, then we'll start chatting. If we start chatting, then you'll want to meet me at a truck stop. If we meet at a truck stop, then we'll discuss my family. If we discuss my family, then you'll find out that my daughter is available for marriage. If you find out that she is available for marriage, then you'll want to marry her. If you want to marry her, then my life will be miserable since I don't want my daughter married to some fool who can't afford a $10 watch."

Use reasoning by transitivity to draw a valid conclusion.

38. Calandra Davis made the following observation: "If I want to determine whether an argument leading to the statement

$$[(p \rightarrow q) \wedge \sim q] \rightarrow \sim p$$

is valid, I only need to consider the lines of the truth table which lead to T for the column headed $(p \rightarrow q) \wedge \sim q$." Calandra was very perceptive. Can you explain why her observation was correct?

In the arguments used by Lewis Carroll, it is helpful to restate a premise in if . . . then *form in order to more easily identify a valid conclusion. The following premises come from Lewis Carroll. Write each premise in* if . . . then *form.*

39. All my poultry are ducks.

40. None of your sons can do logic.

41. Guinea pigs are hopelessly ignorant of music.

42. No teetotalers are pawnbrokers.

43. No teachable kitten has green eyes.

44. Opium-eaters have no self-command.

45. I have not filed any of them that I can read.

46. All of them written on blue paper are filed.

Exercises 47–52 involve premises from Lewis Carroll. Write each premise in symbols, and then in the final part, give a conclusion that yields a valid argument.

47. Let *p* be "it is a duck," *q* be "it is my poultry," *r* be "one is an officer," and *s* be "one is willing to waltz."

(a) No ducks are willing to waltz.

(b) No officers ever decline to waltz.

(c) All my poultry are ducks.

(d) Give a conclusion that yields a valid argument.

48. Let *p* be "one is able to do logic," *q* be "one is fit to serve on a jury," *r* be "one is sane," and *s* be "he is your son."

(a) Everyone who is sane can do logic.

(b) No lunatics are fit to serve on a jury.

(c) None of your sons can do logic.

(d) Give a conclusion that yields a valid argument.

49. Let *p* be "one is honest," *q* be "one is a pawnbroker," *r* be "one is a promise-breaker," *s* be "one is trustworthy," *t* be "one is very communicative," and *u* be "one is a wine-drinker."

(a) Promise-breakers are untrustworthy.

(b) Wine-drinkers are very communicative.

(c) A person who keeps a promise is honest.

(d) No teetotalers are pawnbrokers. (*Hint:* Assume "teetotaler" is the opposite of "wine-drinker.")

(e) One can always trust a very communicative person.

(f) Give a conclusion that yields a valid argument.

50. Let *p* be "it is a guinea pig," *q* be "it is hopelessly ignorant of music," *r* be "it keeps silent while the

Moonlight Sonata is being played," and *s* be "it appreciates Beethoven."

(a) Nobody who really appreciates Beethoven fails to keep silent while the *Moonlight Sonata* is being played.

(b) Guinea pigs are hopelessly ignorant of music.

(c) No one who is hopelessly ignorant of music ever keeps silent while the *Moonlight Sonata* is being played.

(d) Give a conclusion that yields a valid argument.

51. Let *p* be "it begins with 'Dear Sir'," *q* be "it is crossed," *r* be "it is dated," *s* be "it is filed," *t* be "it is in black ink," *u* be "it is in the third person," *v* be "I can read it," *w* be "it is on blue paper," *x* be "it is on one sheet," and *y* be "it is written by Brown."

(a) All the dated letters are written on blue paper.

(b) None of them are in black ink, except those that are written in the third person.

(c) I have not filed any of them that I can read.

(d) None of them that are written on one sheet are undated.

(e) All of them that are not crossed are in black ink.

(f) All of them written by Brown begin with "Dear Sir."

(g) All of them written on blue paper are filed.

(h) None of them written on more than one sheet are crossed.

(i) None of them that begin with "Dear Sir" are written in the third person.

(j) Give a conclusion that yields a valid argument.

52. Let *p* be "he is going to a party," *q* be "he brushes his hair," *r* be "he has self-command," *s* be "he looks fascinating," *t* be "he is an opium-eater," *u* be "he is tidy," and *v* be "he wears white kid gloves."

(a) No one who is going to a party ever fails to brush his hair.

(b) No one looks fascinating if he is untidy.

(c) Opium-eaters have no self-command.

(d) Everyone who has brushed his hair looks fascinating.

(e) No one wears white kid gloves unless he is going to a party. (*Hint:* "a unless b" ≡ ∼b → a.)

(f) A man is always untidy if he has no self-command.

(g) Give a conclusion that yields a valid argument.

COLLABORATIVE INVESTIGATION

Logic Problems and Sudoku Revisited

The logic problems and Sudoku in the Extension on pages 138–144 are fairly elementary, considering the complexity of some of the other problems found in the magazines mentioned. The problems here require more time and reasoning skills than the ones appearing in the Extension.

They are taken from *England's Best Logic Problems*, May 2004, and *Sudoku #13*, 2005.

The class may wish to divide up into groups and see which group can solve these problems fastest.

EXERCISES

Note: As an exception to our usual style, answers to these Collaborative Investigation Exercises are given in the back of the book.

1. **A Case of Foul Play** At the end of a shelf on a bookcase is a pile of six murder novels published by a book club devoted to such works. From the clues given at the top of the next column, can you work out the titles and authors of the books numbered 1 to 6 in the stack, and work out the colour of its uniform style dust jacket? (*Note*: Women are Dahlia Dagger, Mary Hemlock, and Sandra Bludgeon, and men are Geoffrey Stringer, John Gunn, and Philip G Rott.)

Clues:

(a) *Murder in the Sun* is immediately below the novel by Mary Hemlock but somewhere higher in the pile than the book with the yellow dust jacket.

(b) Dahlia Dagger's contribution to the collection is entitled *Mayhem in Madagascar*; it is two below the green-covered book in the pile.

(c) The blue dust jacket belongs to the novel by Sandra Bludgeon, which occupies an even-numbered position on the shelf.

(d) The book with the red dust jacket is not *Lurking in the Shadows*.

(e) The brown dust jacket belongs to *A Killer Abroad*, which is by a female author.

(f) *The Final Case* occupies position 4 in the stack.

(g) The bottom book in the pile, which was not written by Geoffrey Stringer, has a black dust jacket.

(h) The author of the novel at the very top of the stack is John Gunn.

2. **Very Hard Sudoku**

8		3	7				9	
		6	8					
2								6
	2		1	8				9
				3				
4			6	5		2		
7								3
					1	8		
	5				8	7		1

CHAPTER 3 TEST

Write a negation for each statement.

1. $6 - 3 = 3$

2. All men are created equal.

3. Some members of the class went on the field trip.

4. If that's the way you feel, then I will accept it.

5. She applied and got a FEMA trailer.

Let p represent "You will love me" *and let q represent* "I will love you." *Write each statement in symbols.*

6. If you won't love me, then I will love you.

7. I will love you if you will love me.

8. I won't love you if and only if you won't love me.

Using the same statements as for Exercises 6–8, write each of the following in words.

9. $\sim p \wedge q$

10. $\sim(p \vee \sim q)$

In each of the following, assume that p is true and that q and r are false. Find the truth value of each statement.

11. $\sim q \wedge \sim r$

12. $r \vee (p \wedge \sim q)$

13. $r \rightarrow (s \vee r)$ (The truth value of the statement s is unknown.)

14. $p \leftrightarrow (p \rightarrow q)$

15. Explain in your own words why, if p is a statement, the biconditional $p \leftrightarrow \sim p$ must be false.

16. State the necessary conditions for
 (a) a conditional statement to be false.
 (b) a conjunction to be true.
 (c) a disjunction to be false.

Construct a truth table for each of the following.

17. $p \wedge (\sim p \vee q)$

18. $\sim(p \wedge q) \rightarrow (\sim p \vee \sim q)$

Decide whether each statement is true *or* false.

19. Some negative integers are whole numbers.

20. All irrational numbers are real numbers.

Write each conditional statement in if . . . then form.

21. All integers are rational numbers.

22. Being a rhombus is sufficient for a polygon to be a quadrilateral.

23. Being divisible by 3 is necessary for a number to be divisible by 9.

24. She digs dinosaur bones only if she is a paleontologist.

For each statement, write **(a)** *the converse,* **(b)** *the inverse, and* **(c)** *the contrapositive.*

25. If a picture paints a thousand words, the graph will help me understand it.

26. $\sim p \rightarrow (q \wedge r)$ (Use one of De Morgan's laws as necessary.)

27. Use an Euler diagram to determine whether the argument is *valid* or *invalid*.

All members of that athletic club save money.
Gregory Langlois is a member of that athletic club.

Gregory Langlois saves money.

28. Match each argument in parts (a) – (d) with the law that justifies its validity, or the fallacy of which it is an example, in choices A–F.
 A. Modus ponens
 B. Modus tollens
 C. Reasoning by transitivity
 D. Disjunctive syllogism
 E. Fallacy of the converse
 F. Fallacy of the inverse
 (a) If he eats liver, then he'll eat anything.
 He eats liver.

 He'll eat anything.

(b) If you use your seat belt, you will be safer.
You don't use your seat belt.

You won't be safer.

(c) If I hear *Mr. Bojangles*, I think of her.
If I think of her, I smile.

If I hear *Mr. Bojangles*, I smile.

(d) She sings or she dances.
She does not sing.

She dances.

Use a truth table to determine whether each argument is valid or invalid.

29. If I write a check, it will bounce. If the bank guarantees it, then it does not bounce. The bank guarantees it. Therefore, I don't write a check.

30. $\sim p \rightarrow \sim q$
$q \rightarrow p$

$p \vee q$

4

NUMERATION AND MATHEMATICAL SYSTEMS

Bud Abbott and Lou Costello were probably the best-known comedy team in the United States during the 1940s and 1950s. They made nearly forty movies together, often re-creating their stage comedy acts on film. Their baseball routine "Who's on First," performed in *The Naughty Nineties* (1945), is an American classic and earned them entry into the National Baseball Hall of Fame.

In their 1941 film *In the Navy*, Seaman Pomeroy Watson (Costello) tries to convince Smokey Adams (Abbott) that he can feed seven sailors with a tray of twenty-eight doughnuts so that the sailors will each get thirteen doughnuts. In an amazing misuse of place value and arithmetic algorithms, he shows how 7 divided into 28 is 13. He then multiplies 13 by 7 to get 28, and finally adds 13 seven times to get 28. It is a routine that must be seen to be believed. While Costello's methods were done for laughs, there are algorithms that are unfamiliar to most students that do indeed yield correct answers. Some of them will be discussed in this chapter.

4.1 Historical Numeration Systems

Mathematical and Numeration Systems • Ancient Egyptian Numeration—Simple Grouping • Traditional Chinese Numeration—Multiplicative Grouping • Hindu-Arabic Numeration—Positional

Symbols designed to represent objects or ideas are among the oldest inventions of humans. These Indian symbols in Arizona are several hundred years old.

Mathematical and Numeration Systems Earlier we introduced and studied the concept of a *set,* a collection of elements. A set, in itself, may have no particular structure. But when we introduce *ways of combining the elements* (called *operations*) and *ways of comparing the elements* (called *relations*), we obtain a **mathematical system.**

Mathematical System

A **mathematical system** is made up of three components:

1. a set of elements;
2. one or more operations for combining the elements;
3. one or more relations for comparing the elements.

A familiar example of a mathematical system is the set of whole numbers $\{0, 1, 2, 3, \ldots \}$, along with the operation of addition and the relation of equality.

Historically, the earliest mathematical system to be developed involved the set of counting numbers or at least a limited subset of the first few counting numbers. The various ways of symbolizing and working with the counting numbers are called **numeration systems.** The symbols of a numeration system are called **numerals.**

Numeration systems have developed over many millennia of human history. Ancient documents provide insight into methods used by the early Sumerian peoples, the Egyptians, the Babylonians, the Greeks, the Romans, the Chinese, the Hindus, and the Mayan people.

A practical method of keeping accounts by matching may have developed as humans established permanent settlements and began to grow crops and raise livestock. People might have kept track of the number of sheep in a flock by matching pebbles with the sheep, for example. The pebbles could then be kept as a record of the number of sheep.

A more efficient method is to keep a **tally stick.** With a tally stick, one notch or **tally** is made on a stick for each sheep. Tally sticks and tally marks have been found that appear to be many thousands of years old. Tally marks are still used today: for example, nine items are tallied by writing ⑷⑷ ||||.

Tally sticks like this one were used by the English in about 1400 A.D. to keep track of financial transactions. Each notch stands for one pound sterling.

Ancient Egyptian Numeration—Simple Grouping Early matching and tallying led to the essential feature of all more advanced numeration systems, that of **grouping.** Grouping allows for less repetition of symbols and also makes numerals easier to interpret. Most historical systems, including our own, have used groups of ten, indicating that people commonly learn to count by using their fingers. The size of the groupings (again, usually ten) is called the **base** of the number system. Bases of five, twenty, sixty, and others have also been used historically.

Much of our knowledge of **Egyptian mathematics** comes from the Rhind papyrus, from about 3800 years ago. A small portion of this papyrus, showing methods for finding the area of a triangle, is reproduced here.

The ancient Egyptian system is an example of a **simple grouping** system. It utilized ten as its base, and its various symbols are shown in Table 1. The symbol for 1 (|) is repeated, in a tally scheme, for 2, 3, and so on up to 9. A new symbol is introduced for 10 (∩), and that symbol is repeated for 20, 30, and so on, up to 90. This pattern enabled the Egyptians to express numbers up to 9,999,999 with just the seven symbols shown in the table.

TABLE 1	Early Egyptian Symbols	
Number	**Symbol**	**Description**
1			Stroke
10	∩	Heel bone
100	ͻ	Scroll
1000	⚘	Lotus flower
10,000	⌐	Pointing finger
100,000	⌂	Burbot fish
1,000,000	⚇	Astonished person

The numbers denoted by the seven Egyptian symbols are all *powers* of the base ten:

$$10^0 = 1, \quad 10^1 = 10, \quad 10^2 = 100, \quad 10^3 = 1000, \quad 10^4 = 10,000,$$
$$10^5 = 100,000, \quad \text{and} \quad 10^6 = 1,000,000.$$

These expressions, called *exponential expressions,* were first defined in Section 1.1. In the expression 10^4, for example, 10 is the *base* and 4 is the *exponent*. Recall that the exponent indicates the number of repeated multiples of the base.

EXAMPLE 1 Interpreting an Egyptian Numeral

Write in our system the number below.

⌂⌂⚘⚘⚘⚘⚘ͻͻͻͻ ∩∩∩∩∩|||
                   ∩∩∩∩|||||

An Egyptian tomb painting shows scribes tallying the count of a grain harvest. **Egyptian mathematics** was oriented more to practicality than was Greek or Babylonian mathematics, although the Egyptians did have a formula for finding the volume of a certain portion of a pyramid.

SOLUTION

Refer to Table 1 for the values of the Egyptian symbols. Each ⌂ represents 100,000. Therefore, two ⌂s represent 2 · 100,000, or 200,000. Proceed as shown here.

two	⌂	$2 \cdot 100{,}000 =$	200,000
five	⚘	$5 \cdot 1000 =$	5000
four	ͻ	$4 \cdot 100 =$	400
nine	∩	$9 \cdot 10 =$	90
seven			$7 \cdot 1 =$	7

205,497 ←——— Answer

Number	Symbol
1	I
5	V
10	X
50	L
100	C
500	D
1000	M

Roman numerals still appear today, mostly for decorative purposes: on clock faces, for chapter numbers in books, and so on. The system is essentially base ten, simple grouping, but with separate symbols for the intermediate values 5, 50, and 500, as shown above. If I is positioned left of V or X, it is subtracted rather than added. Likewise for X appearing left of L or C, and for C appearing left of D or M. Thus, for example, whereas CX denotes 110, XC denotes 90.

EXAMPLE 2 Creating an Egyptian Numeral

Write 376,248 in Egyptian symbols.

SOLUTION

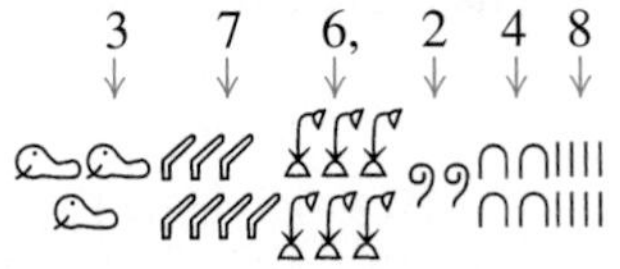

3   7   6,   2   4   8

Refer to Table 1 as needed.

Notice that the position or order of the symbols makes no difference in a simple grouping system. Each of the numbers 99∩∩∩IIII, IIII∩∩99, and II∩∩99∩II would be interpreted as 234. The most common order, however, is that shown in Examples 1 and 2, where like symbols are grouped together and groups of greater-valued symbols are positioned to the left.

A simple grouping system is well suited to the operations of addition and subtraction. For example, to add 99∩∩∩II and 999∩IIIIII in the early Egyptian system, work as shown. Two Is plus six Is is equal to eight Is, and so on.

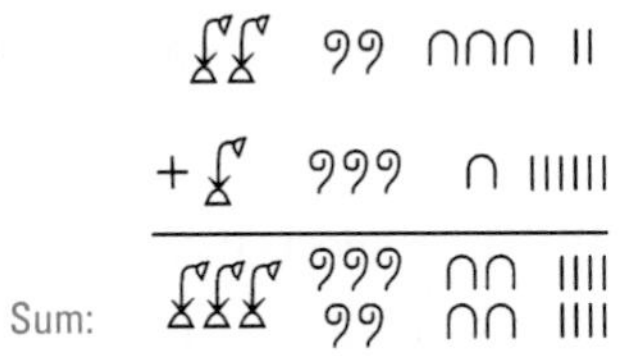

While we used a + sign for convenience and drew a line under the numbers being added, the Egyptians did not do this.

Sometimes regrouping, or "carrying," is needed as in the example below. We get rid of ten heel bones from the tens group by placing an extra scroll in the hundreds group.

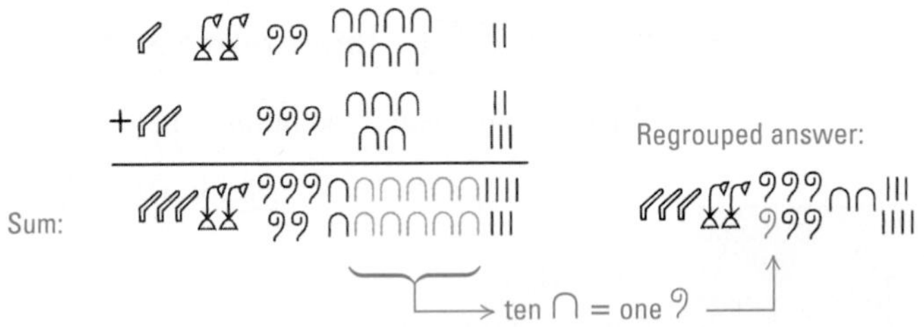

Regrouped answer:

ten ∩ = one 9

Subtraction is done in much the same way, as shown in the next example.

EXAMPLE 3 Subtracting Egyptian Numerals

Work each subtraction problem.

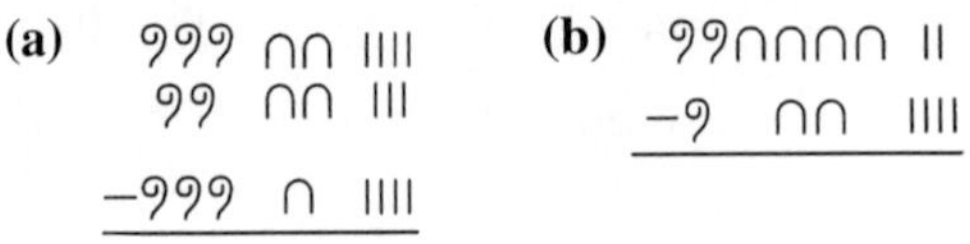

(a)   999 ∩∩ IIII
          99 ∩∩ III
       −999 ∩ IIII

(b)   99∩∩∩∩ II
         −9 ∩∩ IIII

SOLUTION

(a) As with addition, work from right to left and subtract.

$$\begin{array}{r} 999 \;\cap\cap\; |||| \\ 99 \;\cap\cap\; ||| \\ \hline -999 \;\cap\; |||| \\ \end{array}$$

Difference: $99 \;\cap\cap\cap\; |||$

(b) To subtract four ls from two ls, "borrow" one heel bone, which is equivalent to ten ls. Finish the problem after writing ten additional ls on the right.

Regrouped: $99 \cap\cap\cap \begin{smallmatrix}||||||\\||||||\end{smallmatrix}$ one $\cap$ = ten ls

$$\begin{array}{r} -9 \;\cap\cap\; |||| \\ \hline 9 \;\cap\; |||||||| \end{array}$$

Difference:

A procedure such as those described above is called an **algorithm:** a rule or method for working a problem. The Egyptians used an interesting algorithm for multiplication that requires only an ability to add and to double numbers, as shown in Example 4. For convenience, this example uses our symbols rather than theirs.

EXAMPLE 4 Using the Egyptian Multiplication Algorithm

A rectangular room in an archaeological excavation measures 19 cubits by 70 cubits. (A cubit, based on the length of the forearm, from the elbow to the tip of the middle finger, was approximately 18 inches.) Find the area of the room.

SOLUTION

Multiply the width and length to find the area of a rectangle. Build two columns of numbers as shown below. Start the first column with 1, the second with 70. Each column is built downward by doubling the number above. Keep going until the first column contains numbers that can be added to equal 19. Then add the corresponding numbers from the second column.

$$
\begin{array}{rrcl}
\rightarrow & 1 & 70 \leftarrow & \\
\rightarrow & 2 & 140 \leftarrow & \\
1 + 2 + 16 = 19 \qquad & 4 & 280 & \quad 70 + 140 + 1120 = 1330 \\
& 8 & 560 & \\
\rightarrow & 16 & 1120 \leftarrow &
\end{array}
$$

Thus $19 \cdot 70 = 1330$, and the area of the given room is 1330 square cubits.

Traditional Chinese Numeration—Multiplicative Grouping

Examples 1 through 3 above show that simple grouping, although an improvement over tallying, still requires considerable repetition of symbols. To denote 90, for example, the ancient Egyptian system must utilize nine $\cap$s: $\begin{smallmatrix}\cap\cap\cap\cap\cap\\\cap\cap\cap\cap\end{smallmatrix}$. If an additional symbol (a "multiplier") was introduced to represent nine, say "9," then 90 could be denoted 9 $\cap$. All possible numbers of repetitions of powers of the base could be handled by introducing a separate multiplier symbol for each counting number less than the base.

Greek Numerals

1	α	60	ξ
2	β	70	o
3	γ	80	π
4	δ	90	φ
5	ϵ	100	ρ
6	ς	200	σ
7	ζ	300	τ
8	η	400	υ
9	θ	500	ϕ
10	ι	600	χ
20	κ	700	ψ
30	λ	800	ω
40	μ	900	χ
50	ν		

Classical Greeks used letters of their alphabet as numerical symbols. The base of the system was the number 10, and numbers 1 through 9 were symbolized by the first nine letters of the alphabet. Rather than using repetition or multiplication, they assigned nine more letters to multiples of 10 (through 90) and more letters to multiples of 100 (through 900). This is called a **ciphered system,** and it sufficed for small numbers. For example, 57 would be $\nu\zeta$; 573 would be $\phi o\gamma$; and 803 would be $\omega\gamma$. A small stroke was used with a units symbol for multiples of 1000 (up to 9000); thus 1000 would be $,\alpha$ or $'\alpha$. Often M would indicate tens of thousands (M for myriad = 10,000) with the multiples written above M.

TABLE 2

Number	Symbol
1	―
2	⼆
3	三
4	囜
5	五
6	六
7	七
8	八
9	ん
10	十
100	百
1000	千
0	零

Just such a system was developed many years ago in China. It was later adopted, for the most part, by the Japanese, with several versions occurring over the years. Here we show the predominant Chinese version, which used the symbols shown in Table 2. We call this type of system a **multiplicative grouping** system. In general, such a system would involve pairs of symbols, each pair containing a multiplier (with some counting number value less than the base) and then a power of the base. The Chinese numerals are read from top to bottom rather than from left to right.

Three features distinguish this system from a strictly pure multiplicative grouping system. First, the number of 1s is indicated using a single symbol rather than a pair. In effect, the multiplier $(1, 2, 3, \ldots, 9)$ is written but the power of the base (10^0) is not. (See Examples 5(a), (b), and (c).) Second, in the pair indicating 10s, if the multiplier is 1, then that multiplier is omitted. Just the symbol for 10 is written. (See Example 6(a).) Third, when a given power of the base is totally missing in a particular number, this omission is shown by the inclusion of the special zero symbol shown at the bottom of Table 2. (See Examples 5(b) and 6(b).) If two or more consecutive powers are missing, just one zero symbol serves to note the total omission. (See Example 5(c).) The omission of 1s and 10s, and any other powers occurring at the extreme bottom of a numeral need not be noted with a zero symbol. (See Example 5(d).) Note that, for clarification in the following examples, we have emphasized the grouping into pairs by spacing and by using braces. These features are *not* part of the actual numeral.

EXAMPLE 5 Interpreting Chinese Numerals

Interpret each Chinese numeral.

(a) (b) (c) (d)

SOLUTION

(a) $\left.\begin{array}{c} 三 \\ 千 \end{array}\right\}$ $3 \cdot 1000 = 3000$ (b) $\left.\begin{array}{c} 七 \\ 百 \end{array}\right\}$ $7 \cdot 100 = 700$

$\left.\begin{array}{c} ― \\ 百 \end{array}\right\}$ $1 \cdot \quad 100 = \quad 100$ $\left.\begin{array}{c} 零 \end{array}\right.$ $0(\cdot \ 10) = \quad 00$

$\left.\begin{array}{c} 六 \\ 十 \end{array}\right\}$ $6 \cdot \quad 10 = \quad 60$ $三$ $\quad 3(\cdot \ 1) = \quad 3$

$\left.\begin{array}{c} 囜 \end{array}\right.$ $4(\cdot \ 1) = \quad \underline{\quad 4}$ Total: $\overline{703}$

Total: $\overline{3164}$

(c) $\left.\begin{array}{c} 五 \\ 千 \end{array}\right\}$ $5 \cdot 1000 = 5000$ (d) $\left.\begin{array}{c} 囜 \\ 千 \end{array}\right\}$ $4 \cdot 1000 = 4000$

$\left.\begin{array}{c} 零 \end{array}\right\}$ $\begin{array}{l} 0(\cdot \ 100) = \quad 000 \\ 0(\cdot \ 10) = \quad 00 \end{array}$ $\left.\begin{array}{c} ⼆ \\ 百 \end{array}\right\}$ $2 \cdot 100 = \quad \underline{\quad 200}$

$ん$ $\quad 9(\cdot \ 1) = \quad \underline{\quad 9}$ Total: $\overline{4200}$

Total: $\overline{5009}$

This photo is of a **quipu**. In
*Ethnomathematics: A
Multicultural View of
Mathematical Ideas,* Marcia
Ascher writes:

*A quipu is an assemblage of
colored knotted cotton cords.
Used to construct bridges, in
ceremonies, for tribute, and in
every phase of the life cycle
from birth to death, cotton
cordage and cloth were of
unparalleled importance in
Inca culture. The colors of the
cords, the way the cords are
connected, the relative placement of the cords, the spaces
between the cords, the types
of knots on the individual
cords, and the relative placement of the knots are all part of
the logical-numerical recording.*

EXAMPLE 6 Creating Chinese Numerals

Write a Chinese numeral for each number.

(a) 614   **(b)** 5090

SOLUTION

(a) The number 614 is made up of six 100s, one 10,
and one 4, as depicted at the right.

$$6 \cdot 100: \begin{cases} 六 \\ 百 \end{cases}$$
$$(1 \cdot)10: \quad 十$$
$$4(\cdot 1): \quad 囙$$

(b) The number 5090 consists of five 1000s,
no 100s, and nine 10s (no 1s).

$$5 \cdot 1000: \begin{cases} 五 \\ 千 \end{cases}$$
$$(0 \cdot)100: \quad 零$$
$$9(\cdot 10): \begin{cases} 九 \\ 十 \end{cases}$$

Hindu-Arabic Numeration—Positional

A simple grouping system
relies on repetition of symbols to denote the number of each power of the base. A multiplicative grouping system uses multipliers in place of repetition, which is more
efficient. The ultimate in efficiency is attained with a **positional** system in which only
multipliers are used. The various powers of the base require no separate symbols,
because the power associated with each multiplier can be understood by the position
that the multiplier occupies in the numeral. If the Chinese system had evolved into a
positional system, then the numeral for 7482 could be written

rather than

The lowest symbol is understood to represent two 1s (10^0), the next one up denotes
eight 10s (10^1), then four 100s (10^2), and finally seven 1000s (10^3). Each symbol in a
numeral now has both a *face value,* associated with that particular symbol (the multiplier value), and a *place value* (a power of the base), associated with the place, or
position, occupied by the symbol.

Positional Numeration

In a positional numeral, each symbol (called a **digit**) conveys two things:

1. **face value**—the inherent value of the symbol
2. **place value**—the power of the base which is associated with the position
   that the digit occupies in the numeral.

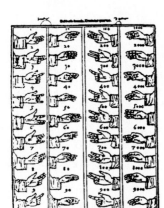

There is much evidence that early humans (in various cultures) used their fingers to represent numbers. As calculations became more complicated, finger reckoning, as shown in this sketch, became popular. The Romans became adept at this sort of calculating, carrying it to 10,000 or perhaps higher.

Number	Symbol
1	▼
10	◄

Babylonian numeration was positional, base sixty. But the face values within the positions were base ten simple grouping numerals, formed with the two symbols shown above. (These symbols resulted from the Babylonian method of writing on clay with a wedge-shaped stylus.) The numeral

◄◄▼▼▼◄◄◄◄▼

denotes 1421 (23 · 60 + 41 · 1).

The place values in a Hindu-Arabic numeral, from right to left, are 1, 10, 100, 1000, and so on. The three 4s in the number 46,424 all have the same face value but different place values. The first 4, on the left, denotes four 10,000s, the next one denotes four 100s, and the one on the right denotes four 1s. Place values (in base ten) are named as shown here.

This numeral is read as eight billion, three hundred twenty-one million, four hundred fifty-six thousand, seven hundred ninety-five.

To work successfully, a positional system must have a symbol for zero to serve as a **placeholder** in case one or more powers of the base are not needed. Because of this requirement, some early numeration systems took a long time to evolve to a positional form, or never did. Although the traditional Chinese system does utilize a zero symbol, it never did incorporate all the features of a positional system, but remained essentially a multiplicative grouping system.

The one numeration system that did achieve the maximum efficiency of positional form is our own system, the **Hindu-Arabic** system. It was developed over many centuries. Its symbols have been traced to the Hindus of 200 B.C. They were picked up by the Arabs and eventually transmitted to Spain, where a late tenth-century version appeared like this:

$$I\ Z\ 7\ \chi\ \mathcal{Y}\ 6\ 7\ 8\ \mathcal{9}.$$

The earliest stages of the system evolved under the influence of navigational, trade, engineering, and military requirements. And in early modern times, the advance of astronomy and other sciences led to a structure well suited to fast and accurate computation. The purely positional form that the system finally assumed was introduced to the West by Leonardo Fibonacci of Pisa (1170–1250) early in the thirteenth century, but widespread acceptance of standardized symbols and form was not achieved until the invention of printing during the fifteenth century. Since that time, no better system of numeration has been devised, and the positional base ten Hindu-Arabic system is commonly used around the world today.

4.1 EXERCISES

Convert each Egyptian numeral to Hindu-Arabic form.

1. ⌒𝄛𝄛𝄛∩∩∩IIIIII

2. 𝄛𝄛9999∩II

3. 𝔛𝔛𝔛𝔛 ⌓⌓⌓ ⌒⌒⌒ 999 ∩∩ IIIII
   𝔛𝔛𝔛 ⌓⌓⌓ 9999 IIII

4. 𝔛𝔛𝔛 𝄛𝄛𝄛𝄛𝄛99∩∩∩I

Convert each Hindu-Arabic numeral to Egyptian form.

5. 23,145   **6.** 427   **7.** 8,657,000   **8.** 306,090

Chapter 1 of the book of Numbers in the Bible describes a census of the draft-eligible men of Israel after Moses led them out of Egypt into the Desert of Sinai, about 1450 B.C. Write an Egyptian numeral for the number of available men from each tribe listed.

9. 59,300 from the tribe of Simeon   **10.** 46,500 from the tribe of Reuben

11. 74,600 from the tribe of Judah   **12.** 45,650 from the tribe of Gad

13. 62,700 from the tribe of Dan   **14.** 54,400 from the tribe of Issachar

Convert each Chinese numeral to Hindu-Arabic form.

15.   **16.**   **17.**   **18.**

Convert each Hindu-Arabic numeral to Chinese.

19. 960   **20.** 63   **21.** 7012   **22.** 2416

Though Chinese art forms began before written history, their highest development was achieved during four particular dynasties. Write traditional Chinese numerals for the beginning and ending dates of each dynasty listed.

23. Ming (1368 to 1644)   **24.** Sung (960 to 1279)

25. T'ang (618 to 907)   **26.** Han (202 B.C. to A.D. 220)

Work each addition or subtraction problem, using regrouping as necessary. Convert each answer to Hindu-Arabic form.

27.   **28.**   **29.**

30.   **31.**   **32.**

33.   **34.**

Use the Egyptian algorithm to find each product.

35. 26 · 53   **36.** 33 · 81   **37.** 58 · 103   **38.** 67 · 115

In Exercises 39 and 40, convert all numbers to Egyptian numerals. Multiply using the Egyptian algorithm, and add using the Egyptian symbols. Give the final answer using a Hindu-Arabic numeral.

39. *Value of a Biblical Treasure* The book of Ezra in the Bible describes the return of the exiles to Jerusalem. When they rebuilt the temple, the King of Persia gave them the following items: thirty golden basins, a thousand silver basins, four hundred ten silver bowls, and thirty golden bowls. Find the total value of this treasure, if each gold basin is worth 3000 shekels, each silver basin is worth 500 shekels, each silver bowl is worth 50 shekels, and each golden bowl is worth 400 shekels.

40. *Total Bill for King Solomon* King Solomon told the King of Tyre (now Lebanon) that Solomon needed the best cedar for his temple, and that he would "pay you for your men whatever sum you fix." Find the total bill to Solomon if the King of Tyre used the following numbers of men: 5500 tree cutters at two shekels per week each, for a total of seven weeks; 4600 sawers of wood at three shekels per week each, for a total of 32 weeks; and 900 sailors at one shekel per week each, for a total of 16 weeks.

Explain why each step would be an improvement in the development of numeration systems.

41. progressing from carrying groups of pebbles to making tally marks on a stick

42. progressing from tallying to simple grouping

43. progressing from simple grouping to multiplicative grouping

44. progressing from multiplicative grouping to positional numeration

Recall that the ancient Egyptian system described in this section was simple grouping, used a base of ten, and contained seven distinct symbols. The largest number expressible in that system is 9,999,999. Identify the largest number expressible in each of the following simple grouping systems. (In Exercises 49–52, d can be any counting number.)

45. base ten, five distinct symbols

46. base ten, ten distinct symbols

47. base five, five distinct symbols

48. base five, ten distinct symbols

49. base ten, *d* distinct symbols

50. base five, *d* distinct symbols

51. base seven, *d* distinct symbols

52. base *b, d* distinct symbols (where *b* is any counting number 2 or greater)

The Hindu-Arabic system is positional and uses ten as the base. Describe any advantages or disadvantages that may have resulted in each case.

53. Suppose the base had been larger, say twelve or twenty for example.

54. Suppose the base had been smaller, maybe eight or five.

4.2 | Arithmetic in the Hindu-Arabic System

Expanded Form • Historical Calculation Devices

Expanded Form The historical development of numeration culminated in positional systems. The most successful of these is the Hindu-Arabic system, which has base ten and, therefore, has place values that are powers of 10.

We now review exponential expressions, or powers (defined in Section 1.1), because they are the basis of expanded form in a positional system.

This Iranian stamp should remind us that counting on fingers (and toes) is an age-old practice. In fact, our word **digit,** referring to the numerals 0–9, comes from a Latin word for "finger" (or "toe"). Aristotle first noted the relationships between fingers and base ten in Greek numeration. Anthropologists go along with the notion. Some cultures, however, have used two, three, or four as number bases, for example, counting on the joints of the fingers or the spaces between them.

EXAMPLE 1   Evaluating Powers

Find each power.

(a) 10^3 **(b)** 7^2 **(c)** 5^4

SOLUTION

(a) $10^3 = 10 \cdot 10 \cdot 10 = 1000$
(10^3 is read "10 cubed," or "10 to the third power.")

(b) $7^2 = 7 \cdot 7 = 49$
(7^2 is read "7 squared," or "7 to the second power.")

(c) $5^4 = 5 \cdot 5 \cdot 5 \cdot 5 = 625$
(5^4 is read "5 to the fourth power.")

To simplify work with exponents, it is agreed that

$$a^0 = 1$$

for any nonzero number a. Thus, $7^0 = 1$, $52^0 = 1$, and so on. At the same time,

$$a^1 = a$$

for any number a. For example, $8^1 = 8$, and $25^1 = 25$. The exponent 1 is usually omitted.

By using exponents, numbers can be written in **expanded form** in which the value of the digit in each position is made clear. For example, write 924 in expanded form by thinking of 924 as nine 100s plus two 10s plus four 1s, or

$$924 = 900 + 20 + 4$$
$$= (9 \cdot 100) + (2 \cdot 10) + (4 \cdot 1)$$
$$= (9 \cdot 10^2) + (2 \cdot 10^1) + (4 \cdot 10^0). \quad \text{100} = 10^2, 10 = 10^1, \text{and } 1 = 10^0.$$

EXAMPLE 2   Writing Numbers in Expanded Form

Write each number in expanded form.

(a) 1906   **(b)** 46,424

SOLUTION

(a) $1906 = (1 \cdot 10^3) + (9 \cdot 10^2) + (0 \cdot 10^1) + (6 \cdot 10^0)$
Because $0 \cdot 10^1 = 0$, this term could be omitted, but the form is clearer with it included.

(b) $46,424 = (4 \cdot 10^4) + (6 \cdot 10^3) + (4 \cdot 10^2) + (2 \cdot 10^1) + (4 \cdot 10^0)$

EXAMPLE 3   Simplifying Expanded Numbers

Simplify each expansion.

(a) $(3 \cdot 10^5) + (2 \cdot 10^4) + (6 \cdot 10^3) + (8 \cdot 10^2) + (7 \cdot 10^1) + (9 \cdot 10^0)$
(b) $(2 \cdot 10^1) + (8 \cdot 10^0)$

SOLUTION

(a) $(3 \cdot 10^5) + (2 \cdot 10^4) + (6 \cdot 10^3) + (8 \cdot 10^2) + (7 \cdot 10^1) + (9 \cdot 10^0) = 326,879$
(b) $(2 \cdot 10^1) + (8 \cdot 10^0) = 28$

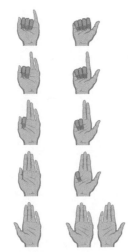

Finger Counting The first digits many people used for counting were their fingers. In Africa the Zulu used the method shown here to count to ten. They started on the left hand with palm up and fist closed. The Zulu finger positions for 1–5 are shown above on the left. The Zulu finger positions for 6–10 are shown on the right.

Expanded notation can be used to see why standard algorithms for addition and subtraction really work. The key idea behind these algorithms is based on the **distributive property,** which will be discussed more fully later in this chapter and also in Chapter 6. It can be written in one form as follows.

Distributive Property

For all real numbers a, b, and c,

$$(b \cdot a) + (c \cdot a) = (b + c) \cdot a.$$

For example, $\quad (3 \cdot 10^4) + (2 \cdot 10^4) = (3 + 2) \cdot 10^4$
$$= 5 \cdot 10^4.$$

EXAMPLE 4 Adding Expanded Forms

Use expanded notation to add 23 and 64.

SOLUTION

$$
\begin{aligned}
23 &= (2 \cdot 10^1) + (3 \cdot 10^0) \\
+\ 64 &= (6 \cdot 10^1) + (4 \cdot 10^0) \\
\hline
&\ \ (8 \cdot 10^1) + (7 \cdot 10^0) = 87 \quad \text{Sum}
\end{aligned}
$$

Subtraction works in much the same way.

EXAMPLE 5 Subtracting Expanded Forms

Use expanded notation to find $695 - 254$.

SOLUTION

$$
\begin{aligned}
695 &= (6 \cdot 10^2) + (9 \cdot 10^1) + (5 \cdot 10^0) \\
-254 &= (2 \cdot 10^2) + (5 \cdot 10^1) + (4 \cdot 10^0) \\
\hline
&\ \ (4 \cdot 10^2) + (4 \cdot 10^1) + (1 \cdot 10^0) = 441 \quad \text{Difference}
\end{aligned}
$$

Expanded notation and the distributive property can also be used to show how to solve addition problems that involve carrying and subtraction problems that involve borrowing.

EXAMPLE 6 Carrying in Expanded Form

Use expanded notation to add 75 and 48.

SOLUTION

$$
\begin{aligned}
75 &= (7 \cdot 10^1) + (5 \cdot 10^0) \\
+\ 48 &= (4 \cdot 10^1) + (8 \cdot 10^0) \\
\hline
&\ \ (11 \cdot 10^1) + (13 \cdot 10^0)
\end{aligned}
$$

The ***Carmen de Algorismo***
(opening verses shown here) by
Alexander de Villa Dei, thirteenth
century, popularized the new art of
"algorismus":

*. . . from these twice five figures
0 9 8 7 6 5 4 3 2 1 of the Indians
we benefit . . .*

The *Carmen* related that Algor, an
Indian king, invented the art. But
actually, "algorism" (or "algorithm")
comes in a roundabout way from
the name Muhammad ibn Musa
al-Khorârizmi, an Arabian
mathematician of the ninth century,
whose arithmetic book was
translated into Latin. Furthermore,
this Muhammad's book on
equations, *Hisab al-jabr
w'almuqâbalah,* yielded the term
"algebra" in a similar way.

Because the units position (10^0) has room for only one digit, $13 \cdot 10^0$ must be modified:

$$13 \cdot 10^0 = (10 \cdot 10^0) + (3 \cdot 10^0)$$
$$= (1 \cdot 10^1) + (3 \cdot 10^0). \quad \text{Distributive property}$$

In effect, the 1 from 13 moved to the left (carried) from the units position to the tens position. Now our sum is

$$\underbrace{(11 \cdot 10^1) + (1 \cdot 10^1)} + (3 \cdot 10^0)$$
$$= (12 \cdot 10^1) + (3 \cdot 10^0) \qquad \text{Distributive property}$$
$$= (10 \cdot 10^1) + (2 \cdot 10^1) + (3 \cdot 10^0) \quad \text{Modify } 12 \cdot 10^1.$$
$$= (1 \cdot 10^2) + (2 \cdot 10^1) + (3 \cdot 10^0)$$
$$= 123. \qquad\qquad\qquad\qquad \text{Sum} \quad ∎$$

EXAMPLE 7 Borrowing in Expanded Form

Use expanded notation to subtract 186 from 364.

SOLUTION

$$364 = (3 \cdot 10^2) + (6 \cdot 10^1) + (4 \cdot 10^0)$$
$$\underline{-186 = (1 \cdot 10^2) + (8 \cdot 10^1) + (6 \cdot 10^0)}$$

Because, in the units position, we cannot subtract 6 from 4, we modify the top expansion as follows (the units position borrows from the tens position):

$$(3 \cdot 10^2) + \overbrace{(6 \cdot 10^1)} + (4 \cdot 10^0)$$
$$= (3 \cdot 10^2) + (5 \cdot 10^1) + \underbrace{(1 \cdot 10^1) + (4 \cdot 10^0)} \quad \text{Distributive property}$$
$$= (3 \cdot 10^2) + (5 \cdot 10^1) + \underbrace{(10 \cdot 10^0) + (4 \cdot 10^0)}$$
$$= (3 \cdot 10^2) + (5 \cdot 10^1) + (14 \cdot 10^0) \qquad \text{Distributive property}$$

We can now subtract 6 from 14 in the units position, but cannot take 8 from 5 in the tens position, so we continue the modification, borrowing from the hundreds to the tens position.

$$\overbrace{(3 \cdot 10^2) + (5 \cdot 10^1)} + (14 \cdot 10^0)$$
$$= (2 \cdot 10^2) + (1 \cdot 10^2) + (5 \cdot 10^1) + (14 \cdot 10^0) \quad \text{Distributive property}$$
$$= (2 \cdot 10^2) + \underbrace{(10 \cdot 10^1) + (5 \cdot 10^1)} + (14 \cdot 10^0)$$
$$= (2 \cdot 10^2) + (15 \cdot 10^1) + (14 \cdot 10^0) \qquad \text{Distributive property}$$

Now we can complete the subtraction.

$$(2 \cdot 10^2) + (15 \cdot 10^1) + (14 \cdot 10^0)$$
$$\underline{- (1 \cdot 10^2) + (8 \cdot 10^1) + (6 \cdot 10^0)}$$
$$(1 \cdot 10^2) + (7 \cdot 10^1) + (8 \cdot 10^0) = 178 \qquad \text{Difference} \quad ∎$$

Examples 4 through 7 used expanded notation and the distributive property to clarify our usual addition and subtraction methods. In practice, our actual work for these four problems would appear as follows:

$$
\begin{array}{cccc}
& & \overset{1}{} & \overset{2\ 15}{} \\
23 & 695 & 75 & 3\ \cancel{6}^1 4 \\
+\ 64 & -\ 254 & +\ 48 & -\ 1\ 8\ 6 \\
\hline
87 & 441 & 123 & 1\ 7\ 8.
\end{array}
$$

The procedures seen in this section also work for positional systems with bases other than ten.

Historical Calculation Devices

Because our numeration system is based on powers of ten, it is often called the **decimal system,** from the Latin word *decem,* meaning ten.* Over the years, many methods have been devised for speeding calculations in the decimal system. One of the oldest is the **abacus,** a device made with a series of rods with sliding beads and a dividing bar. Reading from right to left, the rods have values of 1, 10, 100, 1000, and so on. The bead above the bar has five times the value of those below. Beads moved *toward* the bar are in the "active" position, and those toward the frame are ignored. In our illustrations of abaci (plural form of abacus), such as in Figure 1, the activated beads are shown in black for emphasis.

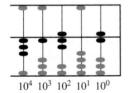

$10^4 \ 10^3 \ 10^2 \ 10^1 \ 10^0$

FIGURE 1

EXAMPLE 8   Reading an Abacus

What number is shown on the abacus in Figure 1?

SOLUTION

Find the number as follows:

$$(3 \cdot 10{,}000) + (1 \cdot 1000) + [(1 \cdot 500) + (2 \cdot 100)] + 0 \cdot 10 + [(1 \cdot 5) + (1 \cdot 1)]$$

$$= 30{,}000 + 1000 + 500 + 200 + 0 + 5 + 1$$

$$= 31{,}706.$$

Beads above the bar have five times the value.

As paper became more readily available, people gradually switched from devices like the abacus (though these still are commonly used in some areas) to paper-and-pencil methods of calculation. One early scheme, used both in India and Persia, was the **lattice method,** which arranged products of single digits into a diagonalized lattice, as shown in the following example.

December was the tenth month in an old form of the calendar. It is interesting to note that *decem* became *dix* in the French language; a ten-dollar bill, called a "dixie," was in use in New Orleans before the Civil War. "Dixie Land" was a nickname for that city before Dixie came to refer to all the Southern states, as in Daniel D. Emmett's song, written in 1859.

> **EXAMPLE 9** **Using the Lattice Method for Products**

Find the product 38 · 794 by the lattice method.

SOLUTION

Step 1 Write the problem, with one number at the side and one across the top.

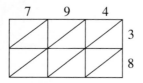

Step 2 Within the lattice, write the products of all pairs of digits from the top and side.

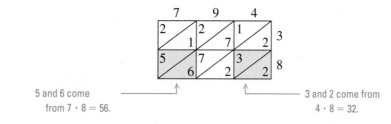

5 and 6 come from 7 · 8 = 56.   3 and 2 come from 4 · 8 = 32.

Step 3 Starting at the right of the lattice add diagonally, carrying as necessary.

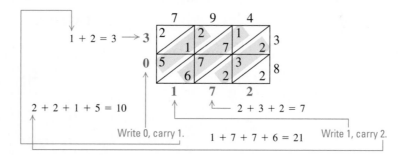

1 + 2 = 3

2 + 2 + 1 + 5 = 10   2 + 3 + 2 = 7

Write 0, carry 1.   1 + 7 + 7 + 6 = 21   Write 1, carry 2.

Step 4 Read the answer around the left side and bottom: 38 · 794 = **30,172**.   ■

John Napier's most significant mathematical contribution, developed over a period of at least 20 years, was the concept of **logarithms,** which, among other things, allow multiplication and division to be accomplished with addition and subtraction. It was a great computational advantage given the state of mathematics at the time (1614).

Napier himself regarded his interest in mathematics as a recreation, his main involvements being political and religious. A supporter of John Knox and James I, he published a widely read anti-Catholic work that analyzed the Biblical book of Revelation. He concluded that the Pope was the Antichrist and that the Creator would end the world between 1688 and 1700. Napier was one of many who, over the years, have miscalculated the end of the world.

The Scottish mathematician John Napier (1550–1617) introduced a significant calculating tool called **Napier's rods,** or **Napier's bones.** Napier's invention, based on the lattice method of multiplication, is widely acknowledged as a very early forerunner of modern computers. It consisted of a set of strips, several for each digit 0 through 9, on which multiples of each digit appeared in a sort of lattice column. See Figure 2 on the next page.

An additional strip, called the *index,* could be laid beside any of the others to indicate the multiplier at each level. Napier's rods were used for mechanically multiplying, dividing, and taking square roots. Figure 3 on the next page shows how to multiply 2806 by 7. Select the rods for 2, 8, 0, and 6, placing them side by side. Then using the index, locate the level for a multiplier of 7. The resulting lattice, shown at the bottom of the figure, gives the product 19,642.

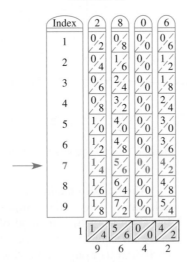

FIGURE 2

FIGURE 3

EXAMPLE 10 Multiplying with Napier's Rods

Use Napier's rods to find the product of 723 and 4198.

SOLUTION

We line up the rods for 4, 1, 9, and 8 next to the index as in Figure 4.

For a way to include a little magic with your calculations, check out http://trunks.secondfoundation. org/files/psychic.swf, and also http://digicc.com/fido.

The product $3 \cdot 4198$ is found as described in Example 9 and written at the bottom of the figure. Then $2 \cdot 4198$ is found similarly and written below, shifted one place to the left. (Why?) Finally, the product $7 \cdot 4198$ is written shifted two places to the left.

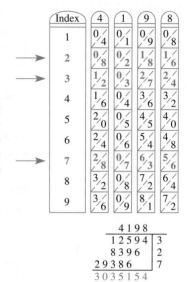

FIGURE 4

The final answer is found by addition to obtain $723 \cdot 4198 = 3{,}035{,}154.$ ▪

One other paper-and-pencil method of multiplication is the **Russian peasant method,** which is similar to the Egyptian method of doubling explained in the previous section. (In fact, both of these methods work, in effect, by expanding one of the numbers to be multiplied, but in base two rather than in base ten. Base two numerals are discussed in the next section.) To multiply 37 and 42 by the Russian peasant method, make two columns headed by 37 and 42. Form the first column by dividing 37 by 2 again and again, ignoring any remainders. Stop when 1 is obtained. Form the second column by doubling each number down the column.

Divide by 2, ignoring remainders.

37	42	Double each number.
18	84	
9	168	
4	336	
2	672	
1	1344	

Now add up only the second column numbers that correspond to odd numbers in the first column. Omit those corresponding to even numbers in the first column.

	37	42	
	18	84	Add
Identify odd numbers.	9	168	← these numbers.
	4	336	
	2	672	
	1	1344	

Finally, $37 \cdot 42 = 42 + 168 + 1344 = 1554.$ ←——— Answer

Most people use standard algorithms for adding and subtracting, carrying or borrowing when appropriate, as illustrated following Example 7. An interesting alternative is the **nines complement method** for subtracting. To use this method, we first agree that the nines complement of a digit n is $9 - n$. For example, the nines complement of 0 is 9, of 1 is 8, of 2 is 7, and so on, up to the nines complement of 9, which is 0.

To carry out the method, complete the following steps:

Step 1 Align the digits as in the standard subtraction algorithm.

Step 2 Add leading zeros, if necessary, in the subtrahend so that both numbers have the same number of digits.

Step 3 Replace each digit in the subtrahend with its nines complement, and then add.

Step 4 Finally, delete the leading digit (1), and add 1 to the remaining part of the sum.

� EXAMPLE 11   Using the Nines Complement Method

Use the nines complement method to subtract $2803 - 647$.

SOLUTION

	Step 1	Step 2	Step 3	Step 4
	2803	2803	2803	2155
	$-\,647$	$-\,0647$	$+\,9352$	$+\,1$
			12,155	2156 Difference

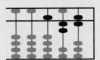
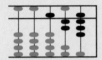
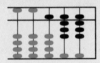
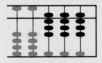

4.2 EXERCISES

Write each number in expanded form.

1. 73   **2.** 925   **3.** 3774   **4.** 12,398

5. four thousand, nine hundred twenty-four

6. fifty-two thousand, one hundred eighteen

7. fourteen million, two hundred six thousand, forty

8. two hundred twelve million, eleven thousand, nine hundred sixteen

Simplify each expansion.

9. $(4 \cdot 10^1) + (2 \cdot 10^0)$

10. $(3 \cdot 10^2) + (5 \cdot 10^1) + (0 \cdot 10^0)$

11. $(6 \cdot 10^3) + (2 \cdot 10^2) + (0 \cdot 10^1) + (9 \cdot 10^0)$

12. $(5 \cdot 10^5) + (0 \cdot 10^4) + (3 \cdot 10^3) + (5 \cdot 10^2) + (6 \cdot 10^1) + (8 \cdot 10^0)$

13. $(7 \cdot 10^7) + (4 \cdot 10^5) + (1 \cdot 10^3) + (9 \cdot 10^0)$

14. $(3 \cdot 10^8) + (8 \cdot 10^7) + (2 \cdot 10^2) + (3 \cdot 10^0)$

In each of the following, add in expanded notation.

15. 54 + 35   **16.** 782 + 413

In each of the following, subtract in expanded notation.

17. 85 − 53   **18.** 784 − 523

Perform each addition using expanded notation.

19. 75 + 34   **20.** 537 + 278   **21.** 434 + 299   **22.** 6755 + 4827

Perform each subtraction using expanded notation.

23. 54 − 48   **24.** 364 − 59   **25.** 645 − 439   **26.** 816 − 335

Identify the number represented on each abacus.

27. 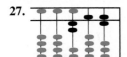   **28.** 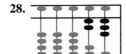   **29.** 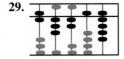   **30.**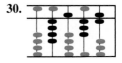

Sketch an abacus to show each number.

31. 38   **32.** 183   **33.** 2547   **34.** 70,163

Use the lattice method to find each product.

35. 65 · 29   **36.** 32 · 741   **37.** 525 · 73   **38.** 912 · 483

Refer to Example 10 where Napier's rods were used to find the product of 723 and 4198. Then complete Exercises 39 and 40.

39. Find the product of 723 and 4198 by completing the lattice process shown here.

40. Explain how Napier's rods could have been used in Example 10 to set up one complete lattice product rather than adding three individual (shifted) lattice products. Illustrate with a sketch.

Use Napier's rods (Figure 2) to find each product.

41. 8 · 62

42. 32 · 73

43. 26 · 8354

44. 526 · 4863

Perform each subtraction using the nines complement method.

45. 283 − 41

46. 536 − 425

47. 50,000 − 199

48. 40,002 − 4846

Use the Russian peasant method to find each product.

49. 5 · 92

50. 41 · 53

51. 62 · 529

52. 145 · 63

Conversion Between Number Bases

General Base Conversions • Computer Mathematics

General Base Conversions   Bases other than ten have occurred historically. For example, the ancient Babylonians used 60 as their base. The Mayan Indians of Central America and Mexico used 20. In this section we consider bases other than ten, but we use the familiar Hindu-Arabic symbols. We will consistently indicate bases other than ten with a spelled-out subscript, as in the numeral 43_{five}. Whenever a number appears without a subscript, it is to be assumed that the intended base is ten. Be careful how you read (or verbalize) numerals here. The numeral 43_{five} is read "four three base five." (Do *not* read it as "forty-three," as that terminology implies base ten and names a totally different number.)

For reference in doing number expansions and base conversions, Table 3 gives the first several powers of some numbers used as alternative bases in this section.

TABLE 3   Selected Powers of Some Alternative Number Bases

	Fourth Power	Third Power	Second Power	First Power	Zero Power
Base two	16	8	4	2	1
Base five	625	125	25	5	1
Base seven	2401	343	49	7	1
Base eight	4096	512	64	8	1
Base sixteen	65,536	4096	256	16	1

TABLE 4	
Base Ten	**Base Five**
0	0
1	1
2	2
3	3
4	4
5	10
6	11
7	12
8	13
9	14
10	20
11	21
12	22
13	23
14	24
15	30
16	31
17	32
18	33
19	34
20	40
21	41
22	42
23	43
24	44
25	100
26	101
27	102
28	103
29	104
30	110

For example, the base two row of Table 3 indicates that

$$2^4 = 16, \quad 2^3 = 8, \quad 2^2 = 4, \ 2^1 = 2, \quad \text{and} \quad 2^0 = 1.$$

We begin with the base five system, which requires just five distinct symbols, 0, 1, 2, 3, and 4. Table 4 compares base five and decimal (base ten) numerals for the whole numbers 0 through 30. Notice that because only the symbols 0, 1, 2, 3, and 4 are used in base five, we must use two digits in base five when we get to 5_ten. The number 5_ten is expressed as one 5 and no 1s, that is as 10_five. Then 6_ten becomes 11_five (one 5 and one 1). Try to predict, without help, the smallest base ten numeral that would require three digits in base five. Is your answer consistent with Table 4? While base five uses fewer distinct symbols than base ten (an apparent advantage because there are few symbols to learn), it often requires more digits than base ten to denote the same number (a disadvantage because more symbols must be written).

You will find that in any base, if you denote the base "b," then the base itself will be 10_b, just as occurred in base five. For example,

$$7_\text{ten} = 10_\text{seven}, \quad 16_\text{ten} = 10_\text{sixteen}, \quad \text{and} \quad \text{so on.}$$

EXAMPLE 1   Converting from Base Five to Base Ten

Convert 1342_five to decimal form.

SOLUTION

Referring to the powers of five in Table 3, we see that this number has one 125, three 25s, four 5s, and two 1s, so

$$\begin{aligned}
1342_\text{five} &= (1 \cdot 125) + (3 \cdot 25) + (4 \cdot 5) + (2 \cdot 1) \\
&= 125 + 75 + 20 + 2 \\
&= 222.
\end{aligned}$$

A shortcut for converting from base five to decimal form, which is *particularly useful when you use a calculator,* can be derived as follows:

$$\begin{aligned}
1342_\text{five} &= (1 \cdot 5^3) + (3 \cdot 5^2) + (4 \cdot 5) + 2 && \text{Factor 5 out of the three quantities in} \\
&= ((1 \cdot 5^2) + (3 \cdot 5) + 4) \cdot 5 + 2 && \text{parentheses.} \\
&= (((1 \cdot 5) + 3) \cdot 5 + 4) \cdot 5 + 2. && \text{Factor 5 out of the two "inner" quantities.}
\end{aligned}$$

The inner parentheses around $1 \cdot 5$ are not needed because the product would be automatically done before the 3 is added. Therefore, we can write

$$1342_\text{five} = ((1 \cdot 5 + 3) \cdot 5 + 4) \cdot 5 + 2.$$

This series of products and sums is easily done as an uninterrupted sequence of operations on a calculator, with no intermediate results written down. The same method works for converting to base ten from any other base.

This procedure is summarized as follows.

Calculator Shortcut for Base Conversion

To convert from another base to decimal form: Start with the first digit on the left and multiply by the base. Then add the next digit, multiply again by the base, and so on. The last step is to add the last digit on the right. Do *not* multiply it by the base.

The binary (base two) symbols of the *I Ching,* a 2000-year-old Chinese classic, permute into 8 elemental trigrams; 64 hexagrams are interpreted in casting oracles.

The basic symbol here is the ancient Chinese **"yin-yang,"** in which the black and the white enfold each other, each containing a part of the other. A kind of duality is conveyed between destructive (yin) and beneficial (yang) aspects. Leibniz (1646–1716) studied Chinese ideograms in search of a universal symbolic language and promoted East–West cultural contact. He saw parallels between the trigrams and his binary arithmetic.

Niels Bohr (1885–1962), famous Danish Nobel laureate in physics (atomic theory), adopted the yin-yang symbol in his coat of arms to depict his principle of *complementarity,* which he believed was fundamental to reality at the deepest levels. Bohr also pushed for East–West cooperation.

In its 1992 edition, *The World Book Dictionary* first judged "yin-yang" to have been used enough to become a permanent part of our ever changing language, assigning it the definition, "made up of opposites."

Exactly how you accomplish these steps depends on the type of calculator you use. With some models, only the digits, the multiplications, and the additions need to be entered, in order. With others, you may need to press the ☐ key following each addition of a digit. If you handle grouped expressions on your calculator by actually entering parentheses, then enter the expression just as illustrated above and in the following example. (The number of left parentheses to start with will be two fewer than the number of digits in the original numeral.)

EXAMPLE 2   Using the Calculator Shortcut

Use the calculator shortcut to convert 244314_{five} to decimal form.

SOLUTION

$$244314_{\text{five}} = ((((2 \cdot 5 + 4) \cdot 5 + 4) \cdot 5 + 3) \cdot 5 + 1) \cdot 5 + 4$$
$$= 9334$$

Note the four left parentheses for a six-digit numeral.

EXAMPLE 3   Converting from Base Ten to Base Five

Convert 497 from decimal form to base five.

SOLUTION

The base five place values, starting from the right, are 1, 5, 25, 125, 625, and so on. Because 497 is between 125 and 625, it will require no 625s, but some 125s, as well as possibly some 25s, 5s, and 1s. Dividing 497 by 125 determines the proper number of 125s. The quotient is 3, with remainder 122. So we need three 125s. Next, the remainder, 122, is divided by 25 (the next place value) to find the proper number of 25s. The quotient is 4, with remainder 22, so we need four 25s. Dividing 22 by 5 yields 4, with remainder 2. So we need four 5s. Dividing 2 by 1 yields 2 (with remainder 0), so we need two 1s. Finally, we see that 497 consists of three 125s, four 25s, four 5s, and two 1s, so $497 = 3442_{\text{five}}$.

More concisely, this process can be written as follows.

$$497 \div 125 = 3 \qquad \text{Remainder 122}$$
$$122 \div 25 = 4 \qquad \text{Remainder 22}$$
$$22 \div 5 = 4 \qquad \text{Remainder 2}$$
$$2 \div 1 = 2 \qquad \text{Remainder 0}$$
$$497 = 3442_{\text{five}}$$

Check: $3442_{\text{five}} = (3 \cdot 125) + (4 \cdot 25) + (4 \cdot 5) + (2 \cdot 1)$
$= 375 + 100 + 20 + 2$
$= 497$

The calculator shortcut for converting from another base to decimal form involved repeated *multiplications* by the other base. (See Example 2.) A shortcut for converting from decimal form to another base makes use of repeated *divisions* by the other base. Just divide the original decimal numeral, and the resulting quotients in turn, by the desired base until the quotient 0 appears.

EXAMPLE 4 Using a Shortcut to Convert from Base Ten to Another Base

Repeat Example 3 using the shortcut just described.

SOLUTION

Remainder

$$
\begin{array}{r|l}
5 & 497 \\
5 & 99 \leftarrow 2 \\
5 & 19 \leftarrow 4 \\
5 & 3 \leftarrow 4 \\
& 0 \leftarrow 3
\end{array}
$$

Read the answer from the remainder column, reading from the bottom up:

$$497 = 3442_{\text{five}}.$$

To see why this shortcut works, notice the following:

The first division shows that four hundred ninety-seven 1s are equivalent to ninety-nine 5s and two 1s. (The two 1s are set aside and account for the last digit of the answer.)

The second division shows that ninety-nine 5s are equivalent to nineteen 25s and four 5s. (The four 5s account for the next digit of the answer.)

The third division shows that nineteen 25s are equivalent to three 125s and four 25s. (The four 25s account for the next digit of the answer.)

The fourth (and final) division shows that the three 125s are equivalent to no 625s and three 125s. The remainders, as they are obtained *from top to bottom*, give the number of 1s, then 5s, then 25s, then 125s.

The methods for converting between bases ten and five, including the shortcuts, can be adapted for conversions between base ten and any other base.

EXAMPLE 5 Converting from Base Seven to Base Ten

Convert 6343_{seven} to decimal form, by expanding in powers, and by using the calculator shortcut.

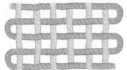

Woven fabric is a binary system of threads going lengthwise (warp threads—tan in the diagram above) and threads going crosswise (weft or woof). At any point in a fabric, either warp or weft is on top, and the variation creates the pattern.

Nineteenth-century looms for weaving operated using punched cards, "programmed" for pattern. The looms were set up with hooked needles, the hooks holding the warp. Where there were holes in cards, the needles moved, the warp lifted, and the weft passed under. Where no holes were, the warp did not lift, and the weft was on top. The system parallels the on–off system in calculators and computers. In fact, these looms were models in the development of modern calculating machinery.

Joseph Marie Jacquard (1752–1823) is credited with improving the mechanical loom so that mass production of fabric was feasible.

SOLUTION

$$6343_{\text{seven}} = (6 \cdot 7^3) + (3 \cdot 7^2) + (4 \cdot 7^1) + (3 \cdot 7^0)$$
$$= (6 \cdot 343) + (3 \cdot 49) + (4 \cdot 7) + (3 \cdot 1)$$
$$= 2058 + 147 + 28 + 3$$
$$= 2236$$

Calculator shortcut: $6343_{\text{seven}} = ((6 \cdot 7 + 3) \cdot 7 + 4) \cdot 7 + 3 = 2236.$ ◼

EXAMPLE 6 Converting from Base Ten to Base Seven

Convert 7508 to base seven.

SOLUTION

Divide 7508 by 7, then divide the resulting quotient by 7, until a quotient of 0 results.

Remainder

```
7 | 7508
7 | 1072  ←  4
7 |  153  ←  1
7 |   21  ←  6
7 |    3  ←  0
        0  ←  3
```

From the remainders, reading bottom to top, $7508 = 30614_{\text{seven}}$. ◼

Because we are accustomed to doing arithmetic in base ten, most of us would handle conversions between arbitrary bases (where neither is ten) by going from the given base to base ten and then to the desired base, as illustrated in the next example.

EXAMPLE 7 Converting Between Two Bases Other Than Ten

Convert 3164_{seven} to base five.

SOLUTION

First convert to decimal form.

$$3164_{\text{seven}} = (3 \cdot 7^3) + (1 \cdot 7^2) + (6 \cdot 7^1) + (4 \cdot 7^0)$$
$$= (3 \cdot 343) + (1 \cdot 49) + (6 \cdot 7) + (4 \cdot 1)$$
$$= 1029 + 49 + 42 + 4$$
$$= 1124$$

Next convert this decimal result to base five.

Remainder

```
5 | 1124
5 |  224  ←  4
5 |   44  ←  4
5 |    8  ←  4
5 |    1  ←  3
        0  ←  1
```

From the remainders, $3164_{\text{seven}} = 13444_{\text{five}}$. ◼

TABLE 5	
Base Ten (decimal)	**Base Two (binary)**
0	0
1	1
2	10
3	11
4	100
5	101
6	110
7	111
8	1000
9	1001
10	1010
11	1011
12	1100
13	1101
14	1110
15	1111
16	10000
17	10001
18	10010
19	10011
20	10100

Computer Mathematics There are three alternative base systems that are most useful in computer applications. These are the **binary** (base two), **octal** (base eight), and **hexadecimal** (base sixteen) systems. Computers and handheld calculators actually use the binary system for their internal calculations because that system consists of only two symbols, 0 and 1. All numbers can then be represented by electronic "switches," of one kind or another, where "on" indicates 1 and "off" indicates 0. The octal and hexadecimal systems have been used extensively by programmers who work with internal computer codes and for communication between the CPU (central processing unit) and a printer or other output device.

The binary system is extreme in that it has only two available symbols (0 and 1); because of this, representing numbers in binary form requires more digits than in any other base. Table 5 shows the whole numbers up to 20 expressed in binary form.

Conversions between any of these three special base systems (binary, octal, and hexadecimal) and the decimal system can be done by the methods already discussed.

◼ **EXAMPLE 8 Converting from Binary to Decimal**

Convert 110101_{two} to decimal form, by expanding in powers, and by using the calculator shortcut.

SOLUTION

$$110101_{two} = (1 \cdot 2^5) + (1 \cdot 2^4) + (0 \cdot 2^3) + (1 \cdot 2^2) + (0 \cdot 2^1) + (1 \cdot 2^0)$$
$$= (1 \cdot 32) + (1 \cdot 16) + (0 \cdot 8) + (1 \cdot 4) + (0 \cdot 2) + (1 \cdot 1)$$
$$= 32 + 16 + 0 + 4 + 0 + 1$$
$$= 53$$

Calculator shortcut:

$$110101_{two} = ((((1 \cdot 2 + 1) \cdot 2 + 0) \cdot 2 + 1) \cdot 2 + 0) \cdot 2 + 1$$
$$= 53. \quad \text{Note the four left parentheses for a six-digit numeral.}$$

◼ **EXAMPLE 9 Converting from Decimal to Octal**

Convert 9583 to octal form.

SOLUTION

Divide repeatedly by 8, writing the remainders at the side.

```
                              Remainder
        8 ⌋ 9 583
          8 ⌋ 1 197   ←   7
            8 ⌋ 149   ←   5
              8 ⌋ 18  ←   5
                8 ⌋ 2 ←   2
                  0   ←   2
```

From the remainders, $9583 = 22557_{eight}$.

Trick or Tree? The octal number 31 is equal to the decimal number 25. This may be written as

31 OCT = 25 DEC

Does this mean that Halloween and Christmas fall on the same day of the year?

The hexadecimal system, having base 16, which is greater than 10, presents a new problem. Because distinct symbols are needed for all whole numbers from 0 up to one

Converting Calculators A number of scientific calculators are available that will convert between decimal, binary, octal, and hexadecimal, and will also do calculations directly in all of these separate modes.

less than the base, base sixteen requires more symbols than are normally used in our decimal system. Computer programmers commonly use the letters A, B, C, D, E, and F as hexadecimal digits for the numbers ten through fifteen, respectively.

EXAMPLE 10 Converting from Hexadecimal to Decimal

Convert $FA5_{sixteen}$ to decimal form.

SOLUTION

The hexadecimal digits F and A represent 15 and 10, respectively.

$$FA5_{sixteen} = (15 \cdot 16^2) + (10 \cdot 16^1) + (5 \cdot 16^0)$$
$$= 3840 + 160 + 5$$
$$= 4005$$

EXAMPLE 11 Converting from Decimal to Hexadecimal

Convert 748 from decimal form to hexadecimal form.

SOLUTION

Use repeated division by 16.

$$
\begin{array}{r}
16\overline{)748} \\
16\overline{)46} \\
16\overline{)2} \\
0
\end{array}
\qquad
\begin{array}{ccc}
 & \text{Remainder} & \begin{array}{c}\text{Hexadecimal}\\ \text{notation}\end{array} \\
\longleftarrow & 12 & \longleftarrow \quad C \\
\longleftarrow & 14 & \longleftarrow \quad E \\
\longleftarrow & 2 & \longleftarrow \quad 2
\end{array}
$$

From the remainders at the right, $748 = 2EC_{sixteen}$.

The decimal whole numbers 0 through 17 are shown in Table 6 on the next page along with their equivalents in the common computer-oriented bases (two, eight, and sixteen). Conversions among binary, octal, and hexadecimal systems can generally be accomplished by the shortcuts explained below.

The binary system is the natural one for internal computer workings because of its compatibility with the two-state electronic switches. It is very cumbersome, however, for human use, because so many digits occur even in the numerals for relatively small numbers. The octal and hexadecimal systems are the choices of computer programmers mainly because of their close relationship with the binary system. *Both eight and sixteen are powers of two.* When conversions involve one base that is a power of the other, there is a quick conversion shortcut available. For example, because $8 = 2^3$, every octal digit (0 through 7) can be expressed as a 3-digit binary numeral. See Table 7 on the next page.

EXAMPLE 12 Converting from Octal to Binary

Convert 473_{eight} to binary form.

SOLUTION

Replace each octal digit with its 3-digit binary equivalent. (Leading zeros can be omitted only when they occur in the leftmost group.) Then combine all the binary equivalents into a single binary numeral.

A T-shirt is currently being marketed with the following message printed on the front. "There are 10 kinds of people in the world: those who understand binary and those who don't." Do YOU understand this message?

$$
\begin{array}{ccc}
4 & 7 & 3_{\text{eight}} \\
\downarrow & \downarrow & \downarrow \\
100 & 111 & 011_{\text{two}}
\end{array}
$$

By this method, $473_{\text{eight}} = 100111011_{\text{two}}$.

TABLE 6 Some Decimal Equivalents in the Common Computer-Oriented Bases

Decimal (Base Ten)	Hexadecimal (Base Sixteen)	Octal (Base Eight)	Binary (Base Two)
0	0	0	0
1	1	1	1
2	2	2	10
3	3	3	11
4	4	4	100
5	5	5	101
6	6	6	110
7	7	7	111
8	8	10	1000
9	9	11	1001
10	A	12	1010
11	B	13	1011
12	C	14	1100
13	D	15	1101
14	E	16	1110
15	F	17	1111
16	10	20	10000
17	11	21	10001

TABLE 7

Octal	Binary
0	000
1	001
2	010
3	011
4	100
5	101
6	110
7	111

EXAMPLE 13 **Converting from Binary to Octal**

Convert 10011110_{two} to octal form.

SOLUTION

Start at the right and break the digits into groups of three. Then convert the groups to their octal equivalents.

$$
\begin{array}{ccc}
10 & 011 & 110_{\text{two}} \\
\downarrow & \downarrow & \downarrow \\
2 & 3 & 6_{\text{eight}}
\end{array}
$$

Finally, $10011110_{\text{two}} = 236_{\text{eight}}$.

TABLE 8

Hexadecimal	Binary
0	0000
1	0001
2	0010
3	0011
4	0100
5	0101
6	0110
7	0111
8	1000
9	1001
A	1010
B	1011
C	1100
D	1101
E	1110
F	1111

Because $16 = 2^4$, every hexadecimal digit can be equated to a 4-digit binary numeral (see Table 8), and conversions between binary and hexadecimal forms can be done in a manner similar to that used in Examples 12 and 13.

EXAMPLE 14 Converting from Hexadecimal to Binary

Convert $8B4F_{sixteen}$ to binary form.

SOLUTION

Each hexadecimal digit yields a 4-digit binary equivalent.

$$
\begin{array}{cccc}
8 & B & 4 & F_{sixteen} \\
\downarrow & \downarrow & \downarrow & \downarrow \\
1000 & 1011 & 0100 & 1111_{two}
\end{array}
$$

Combining these groups of digits, we see that

$$8B4F_{sixteen} = 1000101101001111_{two}.$$

Several games and tricks are based on the binary system. For example, Table 9 can be used to find the age of a person 31 years old or younger. The person need only tell you the columns that contain his or her age. For example, suppose Kellen Dawson says that her age appears in columns B, C, and D. To find her age, add the numbers from the top row of these columns:

Kellen is $2 + 4 + 8 = 14$ years old.

Do you see how this trick works? (See Exercises 69–72.)

Several years ago, the Kellogg Company featured a **Magic Trick Age Detector** activity on specially marked packages of *Kellogg's* ® *Rice Krispies* ® cereal. The trick is simply an extension of the discussion in the text.

Kellogg's ® *Rice Krispies* ® and characters *Snap!* ® *Crackle!* ® and *Pop!* ® are registered trademarks of Kellogg Company.

TABLE 9

A	B	C	D	E
1	2	4	8	16
3	3	5	9	17
5	6	6	10	18
7	7	7	11	19
9	10	12	12	20
11	11	13	13	21
13	14	14	14	22
15	15	15	15	23
17	18	20	24	24
19	19	21	25	25
21	22	22	26	26
23	23	23	27	27
25	26	28	28	28
27	27	29	29	29
29	30	30	30	30
31	31	31	31	31

4.3 EXERCISES

List the first twenty counting numbers in each base.

1. seven (Only digits 0 through 6 are used in base seven.)

2. eight (Only digits 0 through 7 are used.)

3. nine (Only digits 0 through 8 are used.)

4. sixteen (The digits $0, 1, 2, \ldots, 9, A, B, C, D, E, F$ are used in base sixteen.)

Write (in the same base) the counting numbers just before and just after the given number. (Do not convert to base ten.)

5. 14_{five}

6. 555_{six}

7. $B6F_{\text{sixteen}}$

8. 10111_{two}

Determine the number of distinct symbols needed in each of the following positional systems.

9. base three

10. base seven

11. base eleven

12. base sixteen

Determine, in each base, the least and greatest four-digit numbers and their decimal equivalents.

13. three

14. sixteen

Convert each number to decimal form by expanding in powers and by using the calculator shortcut.

15. 24_{five}

16. 62_{seven}

17. 1011_{two}

18. 35_{eight}

19. $3BC_{\text{sixteen}}$

20. 34432_{five}

21. 2366_{seven}

22. 101101110_{two}

23. 70266_{eight}

24. $ABCD_{\text{sixteen}}$

25. 2023_{four}

26. 6185_{nine}

27. 41533_{six}

28. 88703_{nine}

Convert each number from decimal form to the given base.

29. 86 to base five

30. 65 to base seven

31. 19 to base two

32. 935 to base eight

33. 147 to base sixteen

34. 2730 to base sixteen

35. 36401 to base five

36. 70893 to base seven

37. 586 to base two

38. 12888 to base eight

39. 8407 to base three

40. 11028 to base four

41. 9346 to base six

42. 99999 to base nine

Make each conversion as indicated.

43. 43_{five} to base seven

44. 27_{eight} to base five

45. 6748_{nine} to base four

46. $C02_{\text{sixteen}}$ to base seven

Convert each number from octal form to binary form.

47. 367_{eight}

48. 2406_{eight}

Convert each number from binary form to octal form.

49. 100110111_{two}

50. 11010111101_{two}

Make each conversion as indicated.

51. $DC_{sixteen}$ to binary

52. $F111_{sixteen}$ to binary

53. 101101_{two} to hexadecimal

54. 101111011101000_{two} to hexadecimal

Identify the greatest number from each list.

55. 42_{seven}, 37_{eight}, $1D_{sixteen}$

56. 1101110_{two}, 414_{five}, $6F_{sixteen}$

There is a theory that twelve would be a better base than ten for general use. This is mainly because twelve has more divisors (1, 2, 3, 4, 6, 12) than ten (1, 2, 5, 10), which makes fractions easier in base twelve. The base twelve system is called the **duodecimal system.** *In the decimal system we speak of a one, a ten, and a hundred (and so on); in the duodecimal system we say a one, a dozen (twelve), and a gross (twelve squared, or one hundred forty-four).*

57. Otis Taylor's clients ordered 9 gross, 10 dozen, and 11 copies of *The Minnie Minoso Story* during 2002. How many copies was that in base ten?

58. Which amount is larger: 3 gross, 6 dozen or 2 gross, 19 dozen?

One common method of converting symbols into binary digits for computer processing is called ASCII (American Standard Code of Information Interchange). The uppercase letters A through Z are assigned the numbers 65 through 90, so A has binary code 1000001 and Z has code 1011010. Lowercase letters a through z have codes 97 through 122 (that is, 1100001 through 1111010). ASCII codes, as well as other numerical computer output, normally appear without commas.

Write the binary code for each letter.

59. C

60. X

61. k

62. q

Break each code into groups of seven digits and write as letters.

63. 1001000100010110011001010000

64. 1000011100100010101011000011001011

Translate each word into an ASCII string of binary digits. (Be sure to distinguish uppercase and lowercase letters.)

65. New

66. Orleans

67. Explain why the octal and hexadecimal systems are convenient for people who code for computers.

68. There are thirty-seven counting numbers whose base eight numerals contain two digits but whose base three numerals contain four digits. Find the least and greatest of these numbers.

Refer to Table 9 for Exercises 69–72.

69. After observing the binary forms of the numbers 1–31, identify a common property of all Table 9 numbers in each of the following columns.
  (a) Column A
  (b) Column B
  (c) Column C
  (d) Column D
  (e) Column E

70. Explain how the "trick" of Table 9 works.

71. How many columns would be needed for Table 9 to include all ages up to 63?

72. How many columns would be needed for Table 9 to include all numbers up to 127?

In our decimal system, we distinguish odd and even numbers by looking at their ones (or units) digits. If the ones digit is even (0, 2, 4, 6, or 8), the number is even. If the ones digit is odd (1, 3, 5, 7, or 9), the number is odd. For Exercises 73–80, determine whether this same criterion works for numbers expressed in the given bases.

73. two   **74.** three   **75.** four   **76.** five

77. six   **78.** seven   **79.** eight   **80.** nine

81. Consider all even bases. If the above criterion works for all, explain why. If not, find a criterion that does work for all even bases.

82. Consider all odd bases. If the above criterion works for all, explain why. If not, find a criterion that does work for all odd bases.

Determine whether the given base five numeral represents one that is divisible by five.

83. 3204_{five} **84.** 200_{five} **85.** 2310_{five} **86.** 342_{five}

Recall that conversions between binary and octal are simplified because eight is a power of 2: $8 = 2^3$. (See Examples 12 and 13.) The same is true of conversions between binary and hexadecimal, because $16 = 2^4$. (See Example 14.) Direct conversion between octal and hexadecimal does not work the same way, because 16 is not a power of 8. Explain how to carry out each conversion without using base ten, and give an example.

87. hexadecimal to octal   **88.** octal to hexadecimal

Devise a method (similar to the one for conversions between binary, octal, and hexadecimal) for converting between base three and base nine, and use it to carry out each conversion.

89. 6504_{nine} to base three   **90.** 81170_{nine} to base three

91. 212201221_{three} to base nine   **92.** 200121021_{three} to base nine

4.4   Clock Arithmetic and Modular Systems

Finite Systems and Clock Arithmetic • Modular Systems

Finite Systems and Clock Arithmetic   At the beginning of this chapter we described a "mathematical system" as

1. a set of elements along with
2. one or more operations for combining those elements, and
3. one or more relations for comparing those elements.

The numeration systems studied in the first three sections mainly involved the set of whole numbers. The operations were mostly addition and multiplication, and the relation was that of equality. Because the set of whole numbers is infinite, that system is an **infinite mathematical system.** In this section, we consider some **finite mathematical systems,** based on finite sets.

The **12-hour clock system** is based on an ordinary clock face, except that 12 is replaced by 0 so that the finite set of the system is {0, 1, 2, 3, 4, 5, 6, 7, 8, 9, 10, 11}. (We will need just one hand on our clock.) See Figure 5.

FIGURE 5

Plus 2 hours

$5 + 2 = 7$

FIGURE 6

As an operation for this clock system, addition is defined as follows: add by moving the hour hand in a *clockwise* direction. For example, to add 5 and 2 on a clock, first move the hand to 5, as in Figure 6. Then, to add 2, move the hand 2 more hours in a clockwise direction. The hand stops at 7, so

$$5 + 2 = 7.$$

This result agrees with traditional addition. However, the sum of two numbers from the 12-hour clock system is not always what might be expected, as the following example shows.

EXAMPLE 1 Finding Clock Sums by Hand Rotations

Find each sum in 12-hour clock arithmetic.

(a) $8 + 9$ **(b)** $11 + 3$

SOLUTION

(a) Move the hand to 8, as in Figure 7. Then advance the hand clockwise through 9 more hours. It stops at 5, so $8 + 9 = 5$.

(b) To find $11 + 3$, proceed as shown in Figure 8. Check that $11 + 3 = 2$. ■

Plus 9 hours

$8 + 9 = 5$

FIGURE 7

Because there are infinitely many whole numbers, it is not possible to write a complete table of addition facts for that set. Such a table, to show the sum of every possible pair of whole numbers, would have infinite numbers of rows and columns, making it impossible to construct.

On the other hand, the 12-hour clock system uses only the whole numbers 0, 1, 2, 3, 4, 5, 6, 7, 8, 9, 10, and 11. In effect, the clock face serves to "reduce" the infinite set of whole numbers to the finite set {0, 1, 2, 3, 4, 5, 6, 7, 8, 9, 10, 11}. No matter how large a whole number results from additions (clockwise motions around the clock), the result is always equivalent, in this system, to one of the numbers 0 through 11. A table of all possible sums for this system requires only 12 rows and 12 columns. The 12-hour clock **addition table** is shown in Table 10 on the following page. The significance of the colored diagonal line will be discussed later.

Plus 3 hours

$11 + 3 = 2$

FIGURE 8

EXAMPLE 2 Finding Clock Sums by Addition Table

Use the 12-hour clock addition table to find each sum.

(a) $7 + 11$ **(b)** $11 + 1$

SOLUTION

(a) Rather than following rotations around the clock face, we simply refer to the table. Find 7 on the left of the addition table and 11 across the top. The intersection of the row headed 7 and the column headed 11 gives the number 6. Thus, $7 + 11 = 6$.

(b) Also from the table, $11 + 1 = 0$. ■

Mathematical systems are characterized by the properties they possess, specifically, the properties of their operations and relations. Five properties that many of the most commonly applied systems have are the *closure, commutative, associative, identity,* and *inverse* properties. We can check whether the 12-hour clock system has these properties.

Plagued by serious maritime mishaps linked to navigational difficulties, several European governments offered prizes for an effective method of determining longitude. The largest prize was 20,000 pounds (equivalent to several million dollars in today's currency) offered by the British Parliament in the Longitude Act of 1714. While famed scientists, academics, and politicians pursued an answer in the stars, **John Harrison,** a clock maker, set about to build a clock that could maintain accuracy at sea. This turned out to be the key, and Harrison's **Chronometer** eventually earned him the prize.

For a fascinating account of this drama and of Harrison's struggle to collect his prize money from the government, see the book *The Illustrated Longitude* by Dava Sobel and William J. H. Andrewes.

TABLE 10 12-Hour Clock Addition

+	0	1	2	3	4	5	6	7	8	9	10	11
0	0	1	2	3	4	5	6	7	8	9	10	11
1	1	2	3	4	5	6	7	8	9	10	11	0
2	2	3	4	5	6	7	8	9	10	11	0	1
3	3	4	5	6	7	8	9	10	11	0	1	2
4	4	5	6	7	8	9	10	11	0	1	2	3
5	5	6	7	8	9	10	11	0	1	2	3	4
6	6	7	8	9	10	11	0	1	2	3	4	5
7	7	8	9	10	11	0	1	2	3	4	5	6
8	8	9	10	11	0	1	2	3	4	5	6	7
9	9	10	11	0	1	2	3	4	5	6	7	8
10	10	11	0	1	2	3	4	5	6	7	8	9
11	11	0	1	2	3	4	5	6	7	8	9	10

Table 10 shows that the sum of two numbers on a clock face is always a number on the clock face. That is, if a and b are any clock numbers in the set of the system, then $a + b$ is also in the set of the system. Therefore, the system has the **closure property.** (The set of the system is *closed* under clock addition.)

Notice also that in this system $9 + 6$ and $6 + 9$ both yield 3. And the answers, the two 3s, are located in positions that are mirror images of one another with respect to the diagonal line shown. Observe another case—the results for $5 + 8$ and $8 + 5$ are also located symmetrically with respect to the diagonal line, and both results are 1. The entries throughout the entire table occur in equal, diagonally symmetric, pairs. This means that for any clock numbers a and b, $a + b = b + a$. The system, therefore, has the **commutative property.**

The next question is: When any three elements are combined in a given order, say $a + b + c$, does it matter whether the first and second or the second and third are associated initially? In other words, is it true that, for any elements a, b, and c in the 12-hour clock system, $(a + b) + c = a + (b + c)$?

EXAMPLE 3   Checking the Associative Property for Clock Addition

Is 12-hour clock addition associative?

SOLUTION

It would take lots of work to prove that the required relationship *always* holds. But a few examples should either disprove it (by revealing a *counterexample*—a case where it fails to hold), or should make it at least plausible. Using the clock numbers 4, 5, and 9, we see that

$$(4 + 5) + 9 = 9 + 9 \qquad\qquad 4 + (5 + 9) = 4 + 2$$
$$= 6 \qquad\qquad\qquad\qquad\qquad = 6.$$

Thus, $(4 + 5) + 9 = 4 + (5 + 9)$. Try another example:

$$(7 + 6) + 3 = 1 + 3 \qquad\qquad 7 + (6 + 3) = 7 + 9$$
$$= 4 \qquad\qquad\qquad\qquad = 4.$$

So $(7 + 6) + 3 = 7 + (6 + 3)$. Any other examples checked also will work. The 12-hour clock system therefore has the **associative property.** ■

Our next question is whether the clock face contains some element (number) that, when combined with any element (in either order), produces that same element. Such an element (call it e) would satisfy $a + e = a$ and $e + a = a$ for any element a of the system. Notice in Table 10 that $4 + 0 = 0 + 4 = 4$, $6 + 0 = 0 + 6 = 6$, and so on. The number 0 is the required *identity element.* The system has the **identity property.**

Generally, if a finite system has an identity element e, it can be located easily in the operation table. Check the body of Table 10 for a column that is identical to the column at the left side of the table. Because the column under 0 meets this requirement, $a + 0 = a$ holds for all elements a in the system. Thus, 0 is *possibly* the identity. Now locate 0 at the left of the table. Because the corresponding row is identical to the row at the top of the table, $0 + a = a$ also holds for all elements a, which is the other requirement of an identity element. Hence, 0 is *indeed* the identity.

Our 12-hour clock system can be expanded to include operations besides addition. For example, subtraction can be performed on a 12-hour clock. Subtraction may be interpreted on the clock face by a movement in the *counterclockwise* direction. For example, to perform the subtraction $2 - 5$, begin at 2 and move 5 hours counterclockwise, ending at 9, as shown in Figure 9. Therefore, in this system,

$$2 - 5 = 9.$$

In our usual system, subtraction may be checked by addition, and this is also the case in clock arithmetic. To check that $2 - 5 = 9$, simply add $9 + 5$, either by using rotation on the clock face or consulting the addition table. In either case, the result is 2, verifying the accuracy of this subtraction.

The *additive inverse,* $-a$, of an element a in clock arithmetic is the element that satisfies this statement: $a + (-a) = 0$ and $(-a) + a = 0$. Such an element, if it exists, can be determined either on the clock face or by using the addition table, as shown in the next example.

Minus 5 hours

$2 - 5 = 9$

FIGURE 9

EXAMPLE 4   Finding Additive Inverses in Clock Arithmetic

Determine the additive inverse, if it exists, for each number in 12-hour clock arithmetic.

(a) 8   **(b)** 2

SOLUTION

(a) Use the clock face to solve the equation

$$8 + x = 0.$$
$$x = 4 \qquad \text{It is 4 hours from 8 to 0.}$$

The additive inverse of 8 is 4.

A **chess clock** or double clock is used to time chess, backgammon, and Scrabble games. Push one button, and that clock stops—the other begins simultaneously. When a player's allotted time for the game has expired, that player will lose if he or she has not made the required number of moves.

Mathematics and chess both involve structured relationships and demand logical thinking. Emanuel Lasker achieved mastery in both fields. He was best known as a World Chess Champion for 27 years, until 1921. Lasker also was famous in mathematical circles for his work concerning the theory of primary ideals, algebraic analogies of prime numbers. An important result, the Lasker-Noether theorem, bears his name along with that of Emmy Noether. Noether extended Lasker's work. Her father had been Lasker's Ph.D. advisor.

(b) Refer to the addition table to solve the equation

$$2 + x = 0.$$
$$x = 10 \qquad \text{The row headed 2 has 0 in the column headed 10.}$$

The additive inverse of 2 is 10. ▪

The methods used in Example 4 may be used to verify that *every* element of the system has an additive inverse (also in the system). So the system has the **inverse property.**

A simpler way to verify the inverse property, if you have the table, is to make sure the identity element appears exactly once in each row, and that the pair of elements that produces it also produces it in the opposite order. (This last condition is automatically true if the commutative property holds for the system.) For example, note in Table 10 that row 3 contains one 0, under the 9, so $3 + 9 = 0$, and that row 9 contains 0, under the 3, so $9 + 3 = 0$ also. Therefore, 3 and 9 are inverses.

Table 11 lists all the elements and their additive inverses. Notice that one element, 6, is its own inverse for addition.

TABLE 11 Inverses for 12-Hour Clock Addition

Clock value a	0	1	2	3	4	5	6	7	8	9	10	11
Additive inverse $-a$	0	11	10	9	8	7	6	5	4	3	2	1

Using the additive inverse symbol, we can say that in clock arithmetic,

$$-5 = 7, \quad -11 = 1, \quad -10 = 2, \quad \text{and so on.}$$

We have now seen that the 12-hour clock system, with addition, has all five properties that we set out to check: closure, commutative, associative, identity, and inverse. Having discussed additive inverses, we can define subtraction formally. Notice that the definition is the same as for ordinary subtraction of whole numbers.

Subtraction on a Clock

If a and b are elements in clock arithmetic, then the **difference, $a - b$,** is defined as

$$a - b = a + (-b).$$

EXAMPLE 5 **Finding Clock Differences**

Find each difference.

(a) $8 - 5$ **(b)** $6 - 11$

SOLUTION

(a) $8 - 5 = 8 + (-5)$ Use the definition of subtraction.
$$= 8 + 7 \qquad \text{The additive inverse of 5 is 7, from the table of inverses.}$$
$$= 3$$

This result agrees with traditional arithmetic. Check by adding 5 and 3; the sum is 8.

(b) $6 - 11 = 6 + (-11)$

$\qquad = 6 + 1$ The additive inverse of 11 is 1.

$\qquad = 7$

Clock numbers can also be multiplied. For example,

$$5 \cdot 4 = 4 + 4 + 4 + 4 + 4 = 8. \quad \text{Add five 4s.}$$

▌ EXAMPLE 6   Finding Clock Products

Find each product, using clock arithmetic.

(a) $6 \cdot 9$　　**(b)** $3 \cdot 4$　　**(c)** $6 \cdot 0$　　**(d)** $0 \cdot 8$

SOLUTION

(a) $6 \cdot 9 = 9 + 9 + 9 + 9 + 9 + 9 = 6$　　**(b)** $3 \cdot 4 = 4 + 4 + 4 = 0$
(c) $6 \cdot 0 = 0 + 0 + 0 + 0 + 0 + 0 = 0$　　**(d)** $0 \cdot 8 = 0$

Some properties of the system of 12-hour clock numbers with the operation of multiplication will be investigated in Exercises 6–8.

Modular Systems   We now expand the ideas of clock arithmetic to **modular systems** in general. Recall that 12-hour clock arithmetic was set up so that answers were always whole numbers less than 12. For example, $8 + 6 = 2$. The traditional sum, $8 + 6 = 14$, reflects the fact that moving the clock hand forward 8 hours from 0, and then forward another 6 hours, amounts to moving it forward 14 hours total. But because the final position of the clock is at 2, we see that 14 and 2 are, in a sense, equivalent. More formally, we say that 14 and 2 are **congruent modulo** 12 (or **congruent mod** 12), which is written

$$14 \equiv 2 \;(\text{mod } 12) \quad \text{The sign} \equiv \text{indicates congruence.}$$

By observing clock hand movements, you can also see that, for example,

$$26 \equiv 2 \;(\text{mod } 12), \qquad 38 \equiv 2 \;(\text{mod } 12), \qquad \text{and so on.}$$

In each case, the congruence is true because the difference of the two congruent numbers is a multiple of 12:

$$14 - 2 = 12 = 1 \cdot 12, \quad 26 - 2 = 24 = 2 \cdot 12, \quad 38 - 2 = 36 = 3 \cdot 12.$$

This suggests the following definition.

Congruence Modulo *m*

The integers a and b are **congruent modulo** m (where m is a natural number greater than 1 called the **modulus**) if and only if the difference $a - b$ is divisible by m. Symbolically, this congruence is written

$$a \equiv b \;(\textbf{mod } m).$$

Because being divisible by m is the same as being a multiple of m, we can say that

$$a \equiv b \ (\text{mod } m) \text{ if and only if } a - b = km \text{ for some integer } k.$$

EXAMPLE 7   Checking the Truth of Modular Equations

Decide whether each statement is *true* or *false*.

(a) $16 \equiv 10 \ (\text{mod } 2)$ **(b)** $49 \equiv 32 \ (\text{mod } 5)$ **(c)** $30 \equiv 345 \ (\text{mod } 7)$

SOLUTION

(a) The difference $16 - 10 = 6$ is divisible by 2, so $16 \equiv 10 \ (\text{mod } 2)$ is true.
(b) The statement $49 \equiv 32 \ (\text{mod } 5)$ is false, because $49 - 32 = 17$, which is not divisible by 5.
(c) The statement $30 \equiv 345 \ (\text{mod } 7)$ is true, because $30 - 345 = -315$ is divisible by 7. (It doesn't matter if we find $30 - 345$ or $345 - 30$.) ■

There is another method of determining if two numbers, a and b, are congruent modulo m.

Criterion for Congruence

$a \equiv b \ (\text{mod } m)$ if and only if the same remainder is obtained when a and b are divided by m.

For example, we know that $27 \equiv 9 \ (\text{mod } 6)$ because $27 - 9 = 18$, which is divisible by 6. Now, if 27 is divided by 6, the quotient is 4 and the remainder is 3. Also, if 9 is divided by 6, the quotient is 1 and the remainder is 3. According to the criterion above, $27 \equiv 9 \ (\text{mod } 6)$ since both remainders are the same.

Addition, subtraction, and multiplication can be performed in any modular system just as with clock numbers. Because final answers should be whole numbers less than the modulus, we can first find an answer using ordinary arithmetic. Then, as long as the answer is nonnegative, simply divide it by the modulus and keep the remainder. This produces the smallest nonnegative integer that is congruent (modulo m) to the ordinary answer.

EXAMPLE 8   Performing Modular Arithmetic

Find each sum, difference, or product.

(a) $(9 + 14) \ (\text{mod } 3)$ **(b)** $(27 - 5) \ (\text{mod } 6)$ **(c)** $(50 + 34) \ (\text{mod } 7)$
(d) $(8 \cdot 9) \ (\text{mod } 10)$ **(e)** $(12 \cdot 10) \ (\text{mod } 5)$

SOLUTION

(a) First add 9 and 14 to get 23. Then divide 23 by 3. The remainder is 2, so we obtain $23 \equiv 2 \ (\text{mod } 3)$ and

$$(9 + 14) \equiv 2 \ (\text{mod } 3).$$

(b) $27 - 5 = 22$. Divide 22 by 6, obtaining 4 as a remainder:

$$(27 - 5) \equiv 4 \ (\text{mod } 6).$$

(c) $50 + 34 = 84$. When 84 is divided by 7, a remainder of 0 is found:

$$(50 + 34) \equiv 0 \ (\text{mod } 7).$$

(d) Since $8 \cdot 9 = 72$, and 72 leaves a remainder of 2 when divided by 10,

$$(8 \cdot 9) \equiv 2 \ (\text{mod } 10).$$

(e) $(12 \cdot 10) \ (\text{mod } 5) = 120 \equiv 0 \ (\text{mod } 5)$ ▨

PROBLEM-SOLVING HINT Modular systems can often be applied to questions involving cyclical changes. For example, our method of dividing time into weeks causes the days to repeatedly cycle through the same pattern of seven. Suppose today is Sunday and we want to know what day of the week it will be 45 days from now. Because we don't care how many weeks will pass between now and then, we can discard the largest whole number of weeks in 45 days and keep the remainder. (We are finding the smallest nonnegative integer that is congruent to 45 modulo 7.) Dividing 45 by 7 leaves remainder 3, so the desired day of the week is 3 days past Sunday, or *Wednesday.*

EXAMPLE 9 **Using Modular Methods to Find the Day of the Week**

If today is Thursday, November 12, and *next* year is a leap year, what day of the week will it be one year from today?

SOLUTION

A modulo 7 system applies here, but we need to know the number of days between today and one year from today. Today's date, November 12, is unimportant except that it shows we are later in the year than the end of February and therefore the next year (starting today) will contain 366 days. (This would not be so if today were, say, January 12.) Now dividing 366 by 7 produces 52 with remainder 2. Two days past Thursday is our answer. That is, one year from today will be a Saturday. ▨

PROBLEM-SOLVING HINT A modular system (mod m) allows only a fixed set of remainder values, $0, 1, 2, \ldots, m - 1$. One practical approach to solving modular equations, at least when m is reasonably small, is to simply try all these integers. For each solution found in this way, others can be found by adding multiples of the modulus to it.

███ **EXAMPLE 10** **Solving Modular Equations**

Solve each modular equation for whole number solutions.

(a) $(3 + x) \equiv 5 \pmod 7$ **(b)** $5x \equiv 4 \pmod 9$

(c) $6x \equiv 3 \pmod 8$ **(d)** $8x \equiv 8 \pmod 8$

SOLUTION

(a) Because dividing 5 by 7 yields remainder 5, the criterion for congruence is that the given equation is true only if dividing $3 + x$ by 7 also yields remainder 5. Try replacing x, in turn, by 0, 1, 2, 3, 4, 5, and 6.

$$x = 0: \quad (3 + 0) \equiv 5 \pmod 7 \text{ is false.} \quad \text{The remainder is 3.}$$
$$x = 1: \quad (3 + 1) \equiv 5 \pmod 7 \text{ is false.} \quad \text{The remainder is 4.}$$
$$x = 2: \quad (3 + 2) \equiv 5 \pmod 7 \text{ is true.} \quad \text{The remainder is 5.}$$

Try $x = 3$, $x = 4$, $x = 5$, and $x = 6$ to see that none work. Of the integers from 0 through 6, only 2 is a solution of the equation $(3 + x) \equiv 5 \pmod 7$.

Because 2 is a solution, find other solutions to this mod 7 equation by repeatedly adding 7:

$$2 + 7 = 9, \quad 9 + 7 = 16, \quad 16 + 7 = 23, \quad \text{and so on.}$$

The set of all nonnegative solutions of $(3 + x) \equiv 5 \pmod 7$ is

$$\{2, 9, 16, 23, 30, 37, \dots\}.$$

(b) Dividing 4 by 9 yields remainder 4. Because the modulus is 9, check the remainders when $5x$ is divided by 9 for $x = 0, 1, 2, 3, 4, 5, 6, 7,$ and 8.

$$x = 0: \quad 5 \cdot 0 \equiv 4 \pmod 9 \text{ is false.} \quad \text{The remainder is 0.}$$
$$x = 1: \quad 5 \cdot 1 \equiv 4 \pmod 9 \text{ is false.} \quad \text{The remainder is 5.}$$

Continue trying numbers. Only $x = 8$ works:

$$5 \cdot 8 = 40 \equiv 4 \pmod 9. \quad \text{The remainder is 4.}$$

The set of all nonnegative solutions to the equation $5x \equiv 4 \pmod 9$ is

$$\{8, 8 + 9, 8 + 9 + 9, 8 + 9 + 9 + 9, \dots\} \quad \text{or} \quad \{8, 17, 26, 35, 44, 53, \dots\}.$$

(c) To solve $6x \equiv 3 \pmod 8$, try the numbers 0, 1, 2, 3, 4, 5, 6, and 7. None work. Therefore, the equation $6x \equiv 3 \pmod 8$ has no solutions. Write the set of all solutions as the empty set, $\emptyset$.

This result is reasonable because $6x$ will always be even, no matter which whole number is used for x. Because $6x$ is even and 3 is odd, the difference $6x - 3$ will be odd and therefore not divisible by 8.

(d) To solve $8x \equiv 8 \pmod 8$, trying the integers 0, 1, 2, 3, 4, 5, 6, and 7. *Any* replacement will work. The solution set is $\{0, 1, 2, 3, \dots\}$. ███

Some problems can be solved by writing down two or more modular equations and finding their common solutions. The next example illustrates the process.

▌ **EXAMPLE 11** **Finding the Number of Discs in a CD Collection**

Julio wants to arrange his CD collection in equal size stacks, but after trying stacks of 4, stacks of 5, and stacks of 6, he finds that there is always 1 disc left over. Assuming Julio owns more than one CD, what is the least possible number of discs in his collection?

SOLUTION

The given information leads to three modular equations,

$$x \equiv 1 \text{ (mod 4)}, \quad x \equiv 1 \text{ (mod 5)}, \quad \text{and} \quad x \equiv 1 \text{ (mod 6)}.$$

For the first equation, try $x = 0$, $x = 1$, $x = 2$, and $x = 3$. The value 1 works, as it does for the other two equations as well. So the solution sets are, respectively,

$$\{1, 5, 9, 13, 17, 21, 25, 29, 33, 37, 41, 45, 49, 53, 57, \mathbf{61}, 65, 69.\ldots\},$$
$$\{1, 6, 11, 16, 21, 26, 31, 36, 41, 46, 51, 56, \mathbf{61}, 66, 71, 76, \ldots\},$$
and $\{1, 7, 13, 19, 25, 31, 37, 43, 49, 55, \mathbf{61}, \ldots\}.$

The least common solution greater than 1 is 61, so the least possible number of discs in the collection is 61.

▌ **EXAMPLE 12** **Applying Congruences to a Construction Problem**

A dry-wall contractor is ordering materials to finish a 17-foot-by-45-foot room. The wallboard panels come in 4-foot widths. Show that, after uncut panels are applied, all four walls will require additional partial strips of the same width.

SOLUTION

The width of any partial strip needed will be the remainder when the wall length is divided by 4 (the panel width). In terms of congruence, we must show that $17 \equiv 45$ (mod 4). By the criterion for congruence, we see that this is true because both 17 and 45 give the same remainder (namely 1) when divided by 4. A 1-foot partial strip will be required for each wall. (In this case four 1-foot strips can be cut from a single panel, so there will be no waste.)

For Further Thought

A Card Trick

Many card "tricks" that have been around for years are really not illusions at all but are based on mathematical properties that allow anyone to do them with no special conjuring abilities. One of them is based on mod 14 arithmetic.

In this trick, suits play no role. Each card has a numerical value: 1 for ace, 2 for two, . . . , 11 for jack, 12 for queen, and 13 for king. The deck is shuffled and given to a spectator, who is instructed to place the deck of cards face up on a table and is told to follow the procedure described: The top card is removed from the deck and laid on the table with its face up. (We shall call it the "starter" card.) The starter card will be at the bottom of a pile. In order to form a pile, note

(continued)

the value of the starter card, and then add cards on top of it while counting up to 13. For example, if the starter card is a six, pile up seven cards on top of it. If it is a jack, add two cards to it, and so on.

When the first pile is completed, it is picked up and placed face down. The next card from the deck becomes the starter card for the next pile, and the process is repeated. This continues until all cards are used or until there are not enough cards to complete the last pile. Any cards that are left over are put aside, face down, for later use. We will refer to these as "leftovers."

The performer then requests that a spectator choose three piles at random. The remaining piles are added to the leftovers. The spectator is then instructed to turn over any two top cards from the piles. The performer is then able to determine the value of the third top card.

The secret to the trick is that the performer adds the values of the two top cards that were turned over, and then adds 10 to this sum. The performer then counts off this number of cards from the leftovers. The number of cards remaining in the leftovers is the value of the remaining top card!

For Group Discussion or Individual Investigation

1. Obtain a deck of playing cards and perform the "trick" as described above. (As with many activities, you'll find that doing it is simpler than describing it.) Does it work?
2. Explain why this procedure works. (If you want to see how someone else explained it, using modulo 14 arithmetic, see "An Old Card Trick Revisited," by Barry C. Felps, in the December 1976 issue of the journal *The Mathematics Teacher*.)

4.4 EXERCISES

Find each difference on the 12-hour clock.

1. $8 - 3$ **2.** $4 - 9$ **3.** $2 - 8$ **4.** $0 - 3$

5. Complete the 12-hour clock multiplication table below. You can use repeated addition and the addition table (for example, $3 \cdot 7 = 7 + 7 + 7 = 2 + 7 = 9$) or use mod 12 multiplication techniques, as in Example 8, parts (d) and (e).

·	0	1	2	3	4	5	6	7	8	9	10	11
0	0	0	0	0	0	0	0	0	0	0	0	0
1	0	1	2	3	4	5	6	7	8	9	10	11
2	0	2	4	6	8	10		2	4		8	
3	0	3	6	9	0	3	6			3	6	
4	0	4	8			8		4			4	8
5	0	5	10	3	8		6	11	4			
6	0	6	0		0	6	0	6		6		6
7	0	7	2	9				1			10	
8	0	8	4	0				8	4		8	4
9	0	9			0		6		0			
10	0	10	8			2						2
11	0	11										1

By referring to your table in Exercise 5, determine which properties hold for the system of 12-hour clock numbers with the operation of multiplication.

6. closure   **7.** commutative

8. identity (If so, what is the identity element?)

A 5-hour clock system utilizes the set {0, 1, 2, 3, 4}, and relates to the clock face shown here.

9. Complete this 5-hour clock addition table.

5-hour clock

+	0	1	2	3	4
0	0	1	2	3	4
1	1	2	3	4	
2	2	3	4		1
3	3	4			
4	4			3	

Which properties are satisfied by the system of 5-hour clock numbers with the operation of addition?

10. closure

11. commutative

12. identity (If so, what is the identity element?)

13. inverse (If so, name the inverse of each element.)

14. Complete this 5-hour clock multiplication table.

·	0	1	2	3	4
0	0	0	0	0	0
1	0	1	2	3	4
2	0	2	4		
3	0	3			
4	0	4			

Determine which properties hold for the system of 5-hour clock numbers with the operation of multiplication.

15. closure   **16.** commutative

17. identity (If so, what is the identity element?)

In clock arithmetic, as in ordinary arithmetic, $a - b = d$ is true if and only if $b + d = a$. Similarly, $a \div b = q$ if and only if $b \cdot q = a$.

Use the idea above and your 5-hour clock multiplication table of Exercise 14 to find each quotient on a 5-hour clock.

18. $1 \div 3$ **19.** $3 \div 1$

20. $2 \div 3$ **21.** $3 \div 2$

22. Is division commutative on a 5-hour clock? Explain.

23. Is there an answer for $4 \div 0$ on a 5-hour clock? Find it or explain why not.

The military uses a 24-hour clock to avoid the problems of "A.M." and "P.M." For example, 1100 hours is 11 A.M., while 2100 hours is 9 P.M. (12 noon + 9 hours). In these designations, the last two digits represent minutes, and the digits before that represent hours. Find each sum in the 24-hour clock system.

24. $1400 + 500$ **25.** $1300 + 1800$

26. $0750 + 1630$ **27.** $1545 + 0815$

28. Explain how the following three statements can *all* be true. (*Hint:* Think of clocks.)

$$1145 + 1135 = 2280$$
$$1145 + 1135 = 1120$$
$$1145 + 1135 = 2320$$

Answer true or false for each statement.

29. $5 \equiv 19 \pmod 3$ **30.** $35 \equiv 8 \pmod 9$

31. $5445 \equiv 0 \pmod 3$ **32.** $7021 \equiv 4202 \pmod 6$

Work each modular arithmetic problem.

33. $(12 + 7)(\bmod 4)$ **34.** $(62 + 95)(\bmod 9)$

35. $(35 - 22)(\bmod 5)$ **36.** $(82 - 45)(\bmod 3)$

37. $(5 \cdot 8)(\bmod 3)$ **38.** $(32 \cdot 21)(\bmod 8)$

39. $[4 \cdot (13 + 6)](\bmod 11)$

40. $[(10 + 7) \cdot (5 + 3)](\bmod 10)$

41. The text described how to do arithmetic mod *m* when the ordinary answer comes out nonnegative. Explain what to do when the ordinary answer is negative.

Work each modular arithmetic problem.

42. $(3 - 27)(\bmod 5)$ **43.** $(16 - 60)(\bmod 7)$

44. $[(-8) \cdot 11](\text{mod } 3)$ **45.** $[2 \cdot (-23)](\text{mod } 5)$

In Exercises 46 and 47:
(a) *Complete the given addition table.*
(b) *Decide whether the closure, commutative, identity, and inverse properties are satisfied.*
(c) *If the inverse property is satisfied, give the inverse of each number.*

46. mod 4

+	0	1	2	3
0	0	1	2	3
1				
2				
3				

47. mod 7

+	0	1	2	3	4	5	6
0	0	1	2	3	4	5	6
1	1	2	3	4	5	6	
2							
3							
4							
5							
6							

In Exercises 48–51:
(a) *Complete the given multiplication table.*
(b) *Decide whether the closure, commutative, identity, and inverse properties are satisfied.*
(c) *Give the inverse of each nonzero number that has an inverse.*

48. mod 2

·	0	1
0	0	0
1	0	

49. mod 3

·	0	1	2
0	0	0	0
1	0	1	2
2	0	2	

50. mod 4

·	0	1	2	3
0	0	0	0	0
1	0	1	2	3
2	0	2		
3	0	3		

51. mod 9

·	0	1	2	3	4	5	6	7	8
0	0	0	0	0	0	0	0	0	0
1	0	1	2	3	4	5	6	7	8
2	0	2	4	6	8			5	
3	0	3	6	0		6		3	6
4	0	4	8		7		6		5
5	0	5	1		2		3	8	
6	0	6	3	0	6	3	0	6	3
7	0	7	5			8			2
8	0	8	7		4	3			1

52. Explain why a modular system containing the number 0 cannot satisfy the inverse property for multiplication.

Find all nonnegative solutions for each equation.

53. $x \equiv 3 \ (\text{mod } 7)$

54. $(2 + x) \equiv 7 \ (\text{mod } 3)$

55. $6x \equiv 2 \ (\text{mod } 2)$

56. $(5x - 3) \equiv 7 \ (\text{mod } 4)$

Solve each problem.

57. *Odometer Readings* For many years automobile odometers showed five whole number digits and a digit for tenths of a mile. For those odometers showing just five whole number digits, totals are recorded according to what modulus?

58. *Distance Traveled by a Car* If a car's five-digit whole number odometer shows a reading of 29,306, *in theory* how many miles might the car have traveled?

59. *Determining Day of the Week* Refer to Example 9 in the text. (Recall that *next* year is a leap year.) Assuming today was Thursday, January 12, answer the following questions.
(a) How many days would the next year (starting today) contain?
(b) What day of the week would occur one year from today?

60. *Silver Spoon Collection* Roxanna Parker has a collection of silver spoons from all over the world. She finds that she can arrange her spoons in sets of 7 with 6 left over, sets of 8 with 1 left over, or sets of 15 with 3 left over. If Roxanna has fewer than 200 spoons, how many are there?

61. *Piles of Ticket Stubs* Lawrence Rosenthal finds that whether he sorts his White Sox ticket stubs into piles of 10, piles of 15, or piles of 20, there are always 2 left over. What is the least number of stubs he could have (assuming he has more than 2)?

62. *Determining a Range of Dates* Assume again, as in Example 9, that *next* year is a leap year. If the next year (starting today) does *not* contain 366 days, what is the range of possible dates for today?

63. *Flight Attendant Schedules* Robin Strang and Kristyn Wasag, flight attendants for two different airlines, are close friends and like to get together as often as possible. Robin flies a 21-day schedule (including days off), which then repeats, while Kristyn has a repeating 30-day schedule. Both of their routines include layovers in Chicago, New Orleans, and San Francisco. The table below shows which days of each of their individual schedules they are in these cities. (Assume the first day of a cycle is day number 1.)

	Days in Chicago	Days in New Orleans	Days in San Francisco
Robin	1, 2, 8	5, 12	6, 18, 19
Kristyn	23, 29, 30	5, 6, 17	8, 10, 15, 20, 25

If today is July 1 and both are starting their schedules today (day 1), list the days during July and August that they will be able to see each other in each of the three cities.

The following formula can be used to find the day of the week on which a given year begins. Here y represents the year (which must be after 1582, when our current calendar began). First calculate*

$$a = y + [(y - 1)/4] - [(y - 1)/100]$$
$$+ [(y - 1)/400],$$

where $[x]$ represents the greatest integer less than or equal to x. (For example, $[9.2] = 9$, and $[\pi] = 3$.) After finding a, find the smallest nonnegative integer b such that

$$a \equiv b \pmod{7}.$$

*Given in "An Aid to the Superstitious," by G. L. Ritter, S. R. Lowry, H. B. Woodruff, and T. L. Isenhour. *The Mathematics Teacher,* May 1977, pp. 456–457.

Then b gives the day of January 1, with $b = 0$ representing Sunday, $b = 1$ Monday, and so on.

Find the day of the week on which January 1 would occur in each year.

64. 1812

65. 1865

66. 2006

67. 2020

Some people believe that Friday the thirteenth is unlucky. The table* below shows the months that will have a Friday the thirteenth if the first day of the year is known. A year is a leap year if it is divisible by 4. The only exception to this rule is that a century year (1900, for example) is a leap year only when it is divisible by 400.

First Day of Year	Non-leap Year	Leap Year
Sunday	Jan., Oct.	Jan., April, July
Monday	April, July	Sept., Dec.
Tuesday	Sept., Dec.	June
Wednesday	June	March, Nov.
Thursday	Feb., March, Nov.	Feb., Aug.
Friday	August	May
Saturday	May	Oct.

Use the table to determine the months that have a Friday the thirteenth for each year.

68. 2007

69. 2008

70. 2009

71. 2200

72. Modular arithmetic can be used to create **residue designs.** For example, the designs (11, 3) and (65, 3) are shown here.

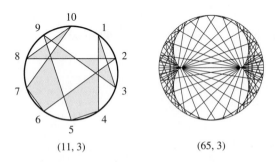

(11, 3)   (65, 3)

To see how such designs are created, construct a new design, (11, 5), by proceeding as follows.

(a) Draw a circle and divide the circumference into 10 equal parts. Label the division points as 1, 2, 3, . . . , 10.

(b) Since $1 \cdot 5 \equiv 5 \pmod{11}$, connect 1 and 5. (We use 5 as a multiplier because we are making an $(11, 5)$ design.)

(c) $2 \cdot 5 \equiv 10 \pmod{11}$

Therefore, connect 2 and _____.

(d) $3 \cdot 5 \equiv$ _____ $\pmod{11}$

Connect 3 and _____.

(e) $4 \cdot 5 \equiv$ _____ $\pmod{11}$

Connect 4 and _____.

(f) $5 \cdot 5 \equiv$ _____ $\pmod{11}$

Connect 5 and _____.

(g) $6 \cdot 5 \equiv$ _____ $\pmod{11}$

Connect 6 and _____.

(h) $7 \cdot 5 \equiv$ _____ $\pmod{11}$

Connect 7 and _____.

(i) $8 \cdot 5 \equiv$ _____ $\pmod{11}$

Connect 8 and _____.

(j) $9 \cdot 5 \equiv$ _____ $\pmod{11}$

Connect 9 and _____.

(k) $10 \cdot 5 \equiv$ _____ $\pmod{11}$

Connect 10 and _____.

(l) You might want to shade some of the regions you have found to make an interesting pattern. For more information, see "Residue Designs," by Phil Locke in *The Mathematics Teacher*, March 1972, pages 260–263.

Identification numbers are used in various ways for many kinds of different products.* Books, for example, are assigned International Standard Book Numbers (ISBNs). Each ISBN is a ten-digit number. It includes a check digit, which is determined on the basis of modular arithmetic. The ISBN for one version of this book is

$$0\text{-}321\text{-}36146\text{-}6.$$

---

*For an interesting general discussion, see "The Mathematics of Identification Numbers," by Joseph A. Gallian in The College Mathematics Journal, *May 1991, p. 194.*

The first digit, 0, identifies the book as being published in an English-speaking country. The next digits, 321, identify the publisher, while 36146 identifies this particular book. The final digit, 6, is a check digit. To find this check digit, start at the left and multiply the digits of the ISBN by 10, 9, 8, 7, 6, 5, 4, 3, and 2, respectively. Then add these products. For this book we get

$$(10 \cdot 0) + (9 \cdot 3) + (8 \cdot 2) + (7 \cdot 1) + (6 \cdot 3)$$
$$+ (5 \cdot 6) + (4 \cdot 1) + (3 \cdot 4) + (2 \cdot 6) = 126.$$

The check digit is the smallest number that must be added to this result to get a multiple of 11. Because $126 + 6 = 132$, a multiple of 11, the check digit is 6. (It is possible to have a check "digit" of 10; the letter X is used instead of 10.)

When an order for this book is received, the ISBN is entered into a computer, and the check digit evaluated. If this result does not match the check digit on the order, the order will not be processed. Does each ISBN have the correct check digit?

73. 0-275-98341-2

74. 0-374-29288-7

Find the appropriate check digit for each ISBN. (Note: The positions of hyphens (or spaces) may vary (or there may be none), but this does not affect the determination of the check digit.)

75. *Man of the Century,* by Jonathan Kwitny, 0-8050-2688- _____

76. *Winning,* by Jack Welch, 0-06-075394- _____

77. *1776,* by David McCullough, 0-7432-2671- _____

78. *The Da Vinci Code,* by Dan Brown, 0-385-50420- _____

4.5 Properties of Mathematical Systems

An Abstract System • Closure Property • Commutative Property • Associative Property • Identity Property • Inverse Property • Distributive Property

An Abstract System   Clock arithmetic and modular systems, discussed in the previous section, were built upon ordinary numbers and involved familiar operations such as addition, subtraction, multiplication, and division. We begin this section by presenting a more abstract system, where the elements and the operations have no implied mathematical significance. This way, we can concentrate on investigating the properties of the system without preconceived notions of what they may be.

TABLE 12

☆	a	b	c	d
a	a	b	c	d
b	b	d	a	c
c	c	a	d	b
d	d	c	b	a

To begin, we introduce a finite mathematical system made up of the set of elements {a, b, c, d} and an operation we will write with the symbol ☆. We define the system in Table 12, an **operation table** that shows how operation ☆ combines any two elements from the set {a, b, c, d}. To use the table to find, say, c ☆ d, first locate c on the left, and d across the top. This row and column intersect at b, so that

$$c \, ☆ \, d = b.$$

As with clock arithmetic, the important properties we shall look for in this system are the following: *closure, commutative, associative, identity,* and *inverse.*

Closure Property   For this system to be closed under the operation ☆, the answer to any possible combination of elements from the system must be in the set {a, b, c, d}. A glance at Table 12 shows that the answers in the body of the table are all elements of this set. This means that the system is closed. If an element other than a, b, c, or d had appeared in the body of the table, or if any position in the body of the table had contained no entry, the system would not have been closed.

TABLE 13

☆	a	b	c	d
a	a	b	c	d
b	b	d	a	c
c	c	a	d	b
d	d	c	b	a

Commutative Property   In order for the system to have the commutative property, it must be true that Γ ☆ Δ = Δ ☆ Γ, where Γ and Δ stand for any elements from the set {a, b, c, d}. For example,

$$c \, ☆ \, d = b \quad \text{and} \quad d \, ☆ \, c = b, \quad \text{so} \quad c \, ☆ \, d = d \, ☆ \, c.$$

To see that the same is true for *all* choices of Γ and Δ, observe that Table 13 is symmetric with respect to the diagonal line shown. This "diagonal line test" establishes that ☆ is a commutative operation for this system.

Associative Property   The system is associative if (Γ ☆ Δ) ☆ Y = Γ ☆ (Δ ☆ Y), where Γ, Δ, and Y represent any elements from the set {a, b, c, d}. There is no quick way to check a table for the associative property, as there is for the commutative property. All we can do is try some examples. Using the table that defines operation ☆,

$$(a \, ☆ \, d) \, ☆ \, b = d \, ☆ \, b = c, \quad \text{and} \quad a \, ☆ \, (d \, ☆ \, b) = a \, ☆ \, c = c,$$

so that
$$(a \, ☆ \, d) \, ☆ \, b = a \, ☆ \, (d \, ☆ \, b).$$

In the same way,
$$b \, ☆ \, (c \, ☆ \, d) = (b \, ☆ \, c) \, ☆ \, d.$$

In both these examples, changing the location of parentheses did not change the answers. Because the two examples worked, we suspect that the system is associative. We cannot be sure of this, however, unless every possible choice of three letters from the set is checked. (Although we have not completely verified it here, this system does, in fact, satisfy the associative property.)

Identity Property   For the identity property to hold, there must be an element Δ from the set of the system such that Δ ☆ X = X and X ☆ Δ = X, where X represents any element from the set {a, b, c, d}. We can see that a is such an element as follows. In Table 13, the column below a (at the top) is identical to the column at the left, and the row across from a (at the left) is identical to the row at the top. Therefore, a is in fact the identity element of the system. (It is shown in more advanced courses that if a system has an identity element, it has *only* one.)

Bernard Bolzano (1781–1848) was an early exponent of rigor and precision in mathematics. Many early results in such areas as calculus were produced by the masters in the field; these masters knew what they were doing and produced accurate results. However, their sloppy arguments caused trouble in the hands of the less gifted. The work of Bolzano and others helped put mathematics on a strong footing.

Inverse Property   We found earlier that a is the identity element for the system using operation ☆. If there is an inverse in this system for, say, the element b, and if Δ represents the inverse of b, then

$$b \,☆\, \Delta = a \quad \text{and} \quad \Delta \,☆\, b = a \quad \text{(because } a \text{ is the identity element).}$$

Inspecting the table for operation ☆ shows that Δ can be replaced with c:

$$b \,☆\, c = a \quad \text{and} \quad c \,☆\, b = a.$$

So we see that c is the inverse of b.

   We can inspect the table to see if every element of our system has an inverse in the system. We see (in Table 13) that the identity element a appears once in each row, and that, in each case, the pair of elements that produces a also produces it in the opposite order. Therefore, we conclude that the system satisfies the inverse property.

   In summary, the mathematical system made up of the set $\{a, b, c, d\}$ and operation ☆ satisfies the closure, commutative, associative, identity, and inverse properties.

Potential Properties of a Single-Operation System

Here a, b, and c represent elements from the set of any system, and $\circ$ represents the operation of the system.

Closure   The system is closed if for all elements a and b,

$$a \circ b$$

is in the set of the system.

Commutative   The system has the commutative property if

$$a \circ b = b \circ a$$

for all elements a and b of the system.

Associative   The system has the associative property if

$$(a \circ b) \circ c = a \circ (b \circ c)$$

for every choice of three elements a, b, and c of the system.

Identity   The system has the identity property if there exists an identity element e (where e is in the set of the system) such that

$$a \circ e = a \quad \text{and} \quad e \circ a = a$$

for every element a of the system.

Inverse   The system has the inverse property if, for every element a of the system, there is an element x in the system such that

$$a \circ x = e \quad \text{and} \quad x \circ a = e,$$

where e is the identity element of the system.

EXAMPLE 1   Identifying the Properties of a System

Table 14 on the next page defines a system consisting of the set $\{0, 1, 2, 3, 4, 5\}$ under an operation designated $\otimes$. Which properties above are satisfied by this system?

TABLE 14

⊗	0	1	2	3	4	5
0	0	0	0	0	0	0
1	0	1	2	3	4	5
2	0	2	4	0	2	4
3	0	3	0	3	0	3
4	0	4	2	0	4	2
5	0	5	4	3	2	1

SOLUTION

All the numbers in the body of the table come from the set $\{0, 1, 2, 3, 4, 5\}$, so the system is closed. If we draw a line from upper left to lower right, we could fold the table along this line and have the corresponding elements match; the system has the commutative property.

To check for the associative property, try some examples:

$$2 \otimes (3 \otimes 5) = 2 \otimes 3 = 0 \quad \text{and} \quad (2 \otimes 3) \otimes 5 = 0 \otimes 5 = 0,$$

so that

$$2 \otimes (3 \otimes 5) = (2 \otimes 3) \otimes 5.$$

Also,

$$5 \otimes (4 \otimes 2) = (5 \otimes 4) \otimes 2.$$

Any other examples that we might try would also work. The system has the associative property.

Because the column at the left of the operation table is repeated under 1 in the body of the table, 1 is a candidate for the identity element in the system. To be sure that 1 is the identity element here, check that the row corresponding to 1 at the left is identical with the row at the top of the table. Since it is, 1 is indeed the identity element.

To find inverse elements, look for the identity element, 1, in the rows of the table. The identity element appears in the second row, $1 \otimes 1 = 1$; and in the bottom row, $5 \otimes 5 = 1$; so 1 and 5 both are their own inverses. There is no identity element in the rows opposite the numbers 0, 2, 3, and 4, so none of these elements has an inverse.

In summary, the system made up of the set $\{0, 1, 2, 3, 4, 5\}$ under this operation ⊗ satisfies the closure, associative, commutative, and identity properties, but not the inverse property. ■

TABLE 15

⊠	1	2	3	4	5	6
1	1	2	3	4	5	6
2	2	4	6	1	3	5
3	3	6	2	5	1	4
4	4	1	5	2	6	3
5	5	3	1	6	4	2
6	6	5	4	3	2	1

EXAMPLE 2 **Identifying the Properties of a System**

Table 15 defines a system consisting of the set of numbers $\{1, 2, 3, 4, 5, 6\}$ under an operation designated ⊠. Which properties are satisfied by this system?

SOLUTION

Notice here that 0 is not an element of this system. This is perfectly legitimate. Because we are defining the system, we can include (or exclude) whatever we wish. Check that the system satisfies the closure, commutative, associative, and identity properties, with identity element 1. Let us now check for inverses. The element 1 is its own inverse, because $1 \boxtimes 1 = 1$. In row 2, the identity element 1 appears under the number 4, so $2 \boxtimes 4 = 1$ (and $4 \boxtimes 2 = 1$), with 2 and 4 inverses of each other. Also, 3 and 5 are inverses of each other, and 6 is its own inverse. Because each number in the set of the system has an inverse, the system satisfies the inverse property. ■

Distributive Property When a mathematical system has two operations, rather than just one, we can look for the **distributive property.**

Distributive Property

Let ☆ and ∘ be two operations defined for elements in the same set. Then ☆ is distributive over ∘ if

$$a \,☆\, (b \circ c) = (a \,☆\, b) \circ (a \,☆\, c)$$

for every choice of elements a, b, and c from the set.

It is a well-known fact that multiplication is distributive over (or with respect to) addition on the set of real numbers. For example,

$$5 \cdot (8 + 3) = 5 \cdot 11 = 55 \quad \text{and} \quad 5 \cdot 8 + 5 \cdot 3 = 40 + 15 = 55,$$

so
$$5 \cdot (8 + 3) = 5 \cdot 8 + 5 \cdot 3.$$

EXAMPLE 3 Testing for the Distributive Property

Is addition distributive over multiplication on the set of whole numbers?

SOLUTION

To find out, replace ☆ with addition (+) and ∘ with multiplication (·) in the statement of the distributive property at the bottom of the previous page:

$$a + (b \cdot c) = (a + b) \cdot (a + c). \quad \text{Is this true in general?}$$

We need to find out whether this statement is true for *every* choice of three whole numbers that we might make. Try an example. If $a = 3$, $b = 4$, and $c = 5$,

$$a + (b \cdot c) = 3 + (4 \cdot 5) = 3 + 20 = 23,$$

while
$$(a + b) \cdot (a + c) = (3 + 4) \cdot (3 + 5) = 7 \cdot 8 = 56.$$

Since $23 \neq 56$, we have $3 + (4 \cdot 5) \neq (3 + 4) \cdot (3 + 5)$. This false result is a *counterexample* (an example showing that a general statement is false). This counterexample shows that addition is *not* distributive over multiplication on the whole numbers. ∎

The final example illustrates how the distributive property may hold for an abstract finite system.

EXAMPLE 4 Testing for the Distributive Property

Suppose that the set $\{a, b, c, d, e\}$ has two operations ☆ and ∘ defined by Tables 16 and 17. The distributive property of ☆ with respect to ∘ holds in this system. Verify for the following case: $e \,☆\, (d \circ b) = (e \,☆\, d) \circ (e \,☆\, b)$.

SOLUTION

First evaluate the left side of the equation by using the tables.

$$e \,☆\, (d \circ b) = e \,☆\, e \quad \text{Use the } \circ \text{ table.}$$
$$= b \quad \text{Use the } ☆ \text{ table.}$$

Now, evaluate the right side of the equation.

$$(e \,☆\, d) \circ (e \,☆\, b) = c \circ e \quad \text{Use the } ☆ \text{ table twice.}$$
$$= b \quad \text{Use the } \circ \text{ table.}$$

Each time the final result is b; the distributive property is verified for this case. ∎

TABLE 16

☆	a	b	c	d	e
a	a	a	a	a	a
b	a	b	c	d	e
c	a	c	e	b	d
d	a	d	b	e	c
e	a	e	d	c	b

TABLE 17

∘	a	b	c	d	e
a	a	b	c	d	e
b	b	c	d	e	a
c	c	d	e	a	b
d	d	e	a	b	c
e	e	a	b	c	d

4.5 EXERCISES

For each system in Exercises 1–10, decide which of the properties of single-operation systems are satisfied. If the identity property is satisfied, give the identity element. If the inverse property is satisfied, give the inverse of each element. If the identity property is satisfied but the inverse property is not, name the elements that have no inverses.

1. {1, 2}; operation ⊗

⊗	1	2
1	1	2
2	2	1

2. {1, 2, 3, 4}; operation ⊗

⊗	1	2	3	4
1	1	2	3	4
2	2	4	1	3
3	3	1	4	2
4	4	3	2	1

3. {1, 2, 3, 4, 5, 6, 7}; operation ⊠

⊠	1	2	3	4	5	6	7
1	1	2	3	4	5	6	7
2	2	4	6	0	2	4	6
3	3	6	1	4	7	2	5
4	4	0	4	0	4	0	4
5	5	2	7	4	1	6	3
6	6	4	2	0	6	4	2
7	7	6	5	4	3	2	1

4. {1, 2, 3, 4, 5}; operation ⊠

⊠	1	2	3	4	5
1	1	2	3	4	5
2	2	4	0	2	4
3	3	0	3	0	3
4	4	2	0	4	2
5	5	4	3	2	1

5. {1, 3, 5, 7, 9}; operation ☆

☆	1	3	5	7	9
1	1	3	5	7	9
3	3	9	5	1	7
5	5	5	5	5	5
7	7	1	5	9	3
9	9	7	5	3	1

6. {1, 3, 5, 7}; operation ☆

☆	1	3	5	7
1	1	3	5	7
3	3	1	7	5
5	5	7	1	3
7	7	5	3	1

7. {A, B, F}; operation *

*	A	B	F
A	B	F	A
B	F	A	B
F	A	B	F

8. {m, n, p}; operation *J*

J	m	n	p
m	n	p	n
n	p	m	n
p	n	n	m

9. {r, s, t, u}; operation Z

Z	r	s	t	u
r	u	t	r	s
s	t	u	s	r
t	r	s	t	u
u	s	r	u	t

10. {A, J, T, U}; operation #

#	A	J	T	U
A	A	J	T	U
J	J	T	U	A
T	T	U	A	J
U	U	A	J	T

The tables in the finite mathematical systems that we developed in this section can be obtained in a variety of ways. For example, let us begin with a square, as shown in the figure. Let the symbols a, b, c, and d be defined as shown in the figure.

Let *a* represent zero rotation—leave the original square as is.

Let *b* represent rotation of 90° clockwise from original position.

Let *c* represent rotation of 180° clockwise from original position.

Let *d* represent rotation of 270° clockwise from original position.

Define an operation □ for these letters as follows. To evaluate b □ c, for example, first perform b by rotating the square 90°. (See the figure.) Then perform operation c by rotating the square an additional 180°. The net result is the same as if we had performed d only. Thus,

$$b \,\square\, c = d.$$

Start with *a*. Perform *b*. Start with *b*, and perform *c*.

Use this method to find each of the following.

11. $b \,\square\, d$ **12.** $b \,\square\, b$ **13.** $d \,\square\, b$ **14.** $a \,\square\, b$

Solve each problem.

15. Complete the table at the right for the system of square rotations described above.

□	a	b	c	d
a	a	b	c	d
b	b	c		a
c	c		a	
d	d	a		

16. Which of the properties from this section are satisfied by this system?

17. Define a universal set U as the set of counting numbers. Form a new set that contains all possible subsets of U. This new set of subsets together with the operation of set intersection forms a mathematical system. Which of the properties listed in this section are satisfied by this system?

18. Replace the word "intersection" with the word "union" in Exercise 17; then answer the same question.

19. Complete the table at the right so that the result is *not* the same as operation □ of Exercise 15, but so that the five properties listed in this section still hold.

	a	b	c	d
a				
b				
c				
d				

Try examples to help you decide whether each operation, when applied to the integers, satisfies the distributive property.

20. subtraction with respect to multiplication

21. addition with respect to subtraction

22. subtraction with respect to addition

Recall that Example 3 provided a counterexample for the general statement

$$a + (b \cdot c) = (a + b) \cdot (a + c).$$

Thus, addition is not *distributive with respect to multiplication. Now work Exercises 23–26.*

23. Decide if the statement above is true for each of the following sets of values.
(a) $a = 2, b = -5, c = 4$
(b) $a = -7, b = 5, c = 3$
(c) $a = -8, b = 14, c = -5$
(d) $a = 1, b = 6, c = -6$

24. Find another set of a, b, and c values that make the statement true.

25. Under what general conditions will the statement above be true?

26. Explain why, regardless of the results in Exercises 23–25, addition is still *not* distributive with respect to multiplication.

27. Give the conditions under which each equation would be true.
(a) $a + (b - c) = (a + b) - (a + c)$
(b) $a - (b + c) = (a - b) + (a - c)$

28. (a) Find values of a, b and c such that
$$a - (b \cdot c) = (a - b) \cdot (a - c).$$
(b) Does this mean that subtraction is distributive with respect to multiplication? Explain.

Verify for the mathematical system of Example 4, defined by Tables 16 and 17, that the distributive property holds for each case.

29. $c \star (d \circ e) = (c \star d) \circ (c \star e)$

30. $a \star (a \circ b) = (a \star a) \circ (a \star b)$

31. $d \star (e \circ c) = (d \star e) \circ (d \star c)$

32. $b \star (b \circ b) = (b \star b) \circ (b \star b)$

Exercises 33 and 34 are for students who have studied sets.

33. Use Venn diagrams to show that the distributive property for union with respect to intersection holds for sets *A, B,* and *C.* That is,

$$A \cup (B \cap C) = (A \cup B) \cap (A \cup C).$$

34. Use Venn diagrams to show that *another* distributive property holds for sets *A, B,* and *C.* It is the distributive property of intersection with respect to union.

$$A \cap (B \cup C) = (A \cap B) \cup (A \cap C)$$

Exercises 35 and 36 are for students who have studied logic.

35. Use truth tables to show that the following distributive property holds:

$$p \vee (q \wedge r) \equiv (p \vee q) \wedge (p \vee r).$$

36. Use truth tables to show that *another* distributive property holds:

$$p \wedge (q \vee r) \equiv (p \wedge q) \vee (p \wedge r).$$

4.6 Groups

Groups • Symmetry Groups • Permutation Groups

Groups   We have considered some mathematical systems, most of which have satisfied some or all of the closure, associative, commutative, identity, inverse, and distributive properties. Systems are commonly classified according to which properties they satisfy. One important category, when a single operation is considered, is the mathematical *group,* which we define here.

Group

A mathematical system is called a **group** if, under its operation, it satisfies the closure, associative, identity, and inverse properties.

Some sets of numbers, under certain operations, form groups. Others do not.

EXAMPLE 1   Checking the Group Properties

Does the set $\{-1, 1\}$ under the operation of multiplication form a group?

SOLUTION

Check the necessary four properties.

Closure   The given system leads to the multiplication table below. All entries in the body of the table are either -1 or 1; the system is closed.

·	−1	1
−1	1	−1
1	−1	1

Niels Henrik Abel (1802–1829) of Norway was identified in childhood as a mathematical genius but never received in his lifetime the professional recognition his work deserved.

At 16, influenced by a perceptive teacher, he read the works of Newton, Euler, and Lagrange. One of Abel's achievements was the demonstration that a general formula for solving fifth-degree equations does not exist. The quadratic formula (for equations of degree 2) is well known, and formulas do exist for solving third- and fourth-degree equations. Abel's accomplishment ended a search that had lasted for years.

In the study of abstract algebra, groups that have the commutative property are referred to as **abelian groups** in honor of Abel. He died of tuberculosis at age 27.

Associative Try some examples:

$$-1 \cdot (-1 \cdot 1) = -1 \cdot (-1) = 1$$

and

$$[-1 \cdot (-1)] \cdot 1 = 1 \cdot 1 = 1,$$

so

$$-1 \cdot (-1 \cdot 1) = [-1 \cdot (-1)] \cdot 1.$$

Also

$$1 \cdot [(-1) \cdot 1] = 1 \cdot (-1) = -1$$

and

$$[1 \cdot (-1)] \cdot 1 = -1 \cdot 1 = -1,$$

so

$$1 \cdot [(-1) \cdot 1] = [1 \cdot (-1)] \cdot 1.$$

Any other examples likewise will work. This system satisfies the associative property.

Identity The operation table for the system shows that the identity element is 1. (The column under 1 is identical to the column at the left, and the row to the right of 1 is identical to the row at the top.)

Inverse Check in the table that -1 is its own inverse, because $-1 \cdot (-1) = 1$ (the identity element); also, 1 is its own inverse.

All four of the properties are satisfied, so the system is a group. ∎

EXAMPLE 2 Checking the Group Properties

Does the set $\{-1, 1\}$ under the operation of addition form a group?

SOLUTION

The addition table below shows that closure is not satisfied, so there is no need to check further. The system is not a group.

+	−1	1
−1	−2	0
1	0	2

EXAMPLE 3 Checking the Group Properties

Does the set of integers $\{\ldots, -3, -2, -1, 0, 1, 2, 3, \ldots\}$ under the operation of addition form a group?

SOLUTION

Check the required properties.

Closure The sum of any two integers is an integer; the system is closed.

Associative Try some examples:

$$2 + (5 + 8) = 2 + 13 = 15$$

and

$$(2 + 5) + 8 = 7 + 8 = 15,$$

so

$$2 + (5 + 8) = (2 + 5) + 8.$$

Also

$$-4 + (7 + 14) = -4 + 21 = 17$$

and

$$(-4 + 7) + 14 = 3 + 14 = 17,$$

so

$$-4 + (7 + 14) = (-4 + 7) + 14.$$

Apparently, addition of integers is associative.

Amalie ("Emmy") Noether
(1882–1935) was an outstanding mathematician in the field of **abstract algebra.** She studied and worked in Germany at a time when it was very difficult for a woman to do so. At the University of Erlangen in 1900, Noether was one of only two women. Although she could attend classes, professors could and did deny her the right to take the exams for their courses. Not until 1904 was Noether allowed to officially register. She completed her doctorate four years later.

In 1916 Emmy Noether went to Göttingen to work with David Hilbert on the general theory of relativity. But even with Hilbert's backing and prestige, it was three years before the faculty voted to make Noether a *Privatdozent,* the lowest rank in the faculty. In 1922 Noether was made an unofficial professor (or assistant). She received no pay for this post, although she was given a small stipend to lecture in algebra.

Noether's area of interest was abstract algebra, particularly structures called rings and ideals. (Groups are structures, too, with different properties.) One special type of ring bears her name; she was the first to study its properties.

Identity We know that $a + 0 = a$ and $0 + a = a$ for any integer a. The identity element for addition of integers is 0.

Inverse Given any integer a, its additive inverse, $-a$, is also an integer. For example, 5 and -5 are inverses. The system satisfies the inverse property.

Since all four properties are satisfied, this (infinite) system *is* a group. ◼

Symmetry Groups

Groups can be built upon sets of objects other than numbers. An example is the group of **symmetries of a square**, which we now develop. First, cut out a small square, and label it as shown in Figure 10.

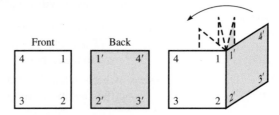

FIGURE 10

Make sure that 1 is in front of $1'$, 2 is in front of $2'$, 3 is in front of $3'$, and 4 is in front of $4'$. Let the letter M represent a clockwise rotation of 90° *about the center of the square* (marked with a dot in Figure 11). Let N represent a rotation of 180°, and so on. A list of the symmetries of a square is given in Figure 11.

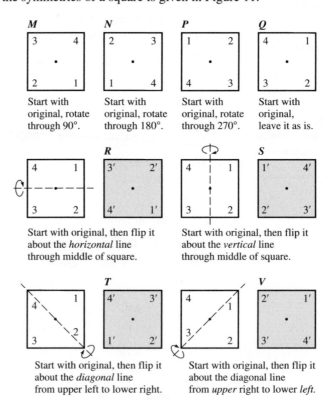

Symmetries of a square

FIGURE 11

Combine symmetries as follows: Let *NP* represent *N* followed by *P*. Performing *N* and then *P* is the same as performing just *M*, so that *NP = M*. See Figure 12.

Évariste Galois (1811–1832), as a young Frenchman, agreed to fight a duel. He had been engaged in profound mathematical research for some time. Now, anticipating the possibility of his death, he summarized the essentials of his discoveries in a letter to a friend. The next day Galois was killed. He was not yet 21 years old when he died.

It was not until 1846 that Galois's theories were published. Mathematicians began to appreciate the importance of Galois's work, which centered on solving equations by using groups. Galois found a way to derive a group that corresponds to each equation. So-called **Galois groups** form an important part of modern abstract algebra.

A 2005 book by Mario Livio, titled *The Equation That Couldn't Be Solved: How Mathematical Genius Discovered the Language of Symmetry,* explores the story of Galois and Abel.

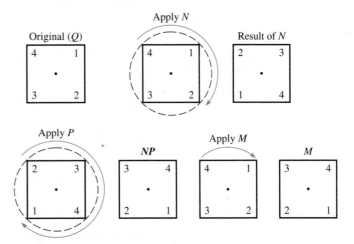

Think of *N* as advancing each corner two quarter turns clockwise. Thus 4 goes from upper left to lower right. To this result apply *P,* which advances each corner three quarter turns. Thus 2 goes from upper left to lower left. The result, *NP,* is the same as advancing each (original) corner one quarter turn, which *M* does. Thus *NP = M.*

FIGURE 12

EXAMPLE 4 Combining Symmetries of a Square

Find *RT* using the symmetries of Figure 11.

SOLUTION

First, perform *R* by flipping the square about a horizontal line through the middle. Then, perform *T* by flipping the result of *R* about a diagonal from upper left to lower right. The result of *RT* is the same as performing only *M*, so that *RT = M*. ◼

The method in Example 4 can be used to complete Table 18 for combining the symmetries of a square.

TABLE 18

□	M	N	P	Q	R	S	T	V
M	N	P	Q	M	V	T	R	S
N	P	Q	M	N	S	R	V	T
P	Q	M	N	P	T	V	S	R
Q	M	N	P	Q	R	S	T	V
R	T	S	V	R	Q	N	M	P
S	V	R	T	S	N	Q	P	M
T	S	V	R	T	P	M	Q	N
V	R	T	S	V	M	P	N	Q

▨ **EXAMPLE 5** **Verifying the Group Properties**

Show that the system made up of the symmetries of a square is a group.

SOLUTION

For the system to be a group, it must satisfy the closure, associative, identity, and inverse properties.

Closure All the entries in the body of Table 18 come from the set {*M, N, P, Q, R, S, T, V*}. Thus, the system is closed.

Associative Try examples:

$$P(MT) = P(R) = T.$$

Also, $$(PM)T = (Q)T = T,$$

so that $$P(MT) = (PM)T.$$

Other similar examples also work. (See Exercises 25–28.) Thus, the system has the associative property.

Identity The column at the left in the table is repeated under *Q*. Check that *Q* is indeed the identity element.

Inverse In the first row, *Q* appears under *P*. Check that *M* and *P* are inverses of each other. In fact, every element in the system has an inverse. (See Exercises 29–34.)

Because all four properties are satisfied, the system is a group. ▨

▨ **EXAMPLE 6** **Verifying that a System Has a Subgroup**

TABLE 19

□	*M*	*N*	*P*	*Q*
M	*N*	*P*	*Q*	*M*
N	*P*	*Q*	*M*	*N*
P	*Q*	*M*	*N*	*P*
Q	*M*	*N*	*P*	*Q*

Form a mathematical system by using only the set {*M, N, P, Q*} from the group of symmetries of a square. Is this new system a group?

SOLUTION

Table 19 for the elements {*M, N, P, Q*} is just one corner of the table for the entire system. Verify that the system represented by this table satisfies all four properties and thus is a group. This new group is a *subgroup* of the original group of the symmetries of a square. ▨

Permutation Groups A very useful example of a group comes from studying the arrangements, or permutations, of a list of numbers. Start with the symbols 1-2-3, in that order.

There are several ways in which the order could be changed—for example, 2-3-1. This rearrangement is written

1-2-3

2-3-1.

Replace 1 with 2, replace 2 with 3, and replace 3 with 1. In the same way,

1-2-3

3-1-2

means replace 1 with 3, 2 with 1, and 3 with 2, while

1-2-3

3-2-1

says to replace 1 with 3, leave the 2 unchanged, and replace 3 with 1. All possible rearrangements of the symbols 1-2-3 are listed below where, for convenience, a name has been given to each rearrangement.

$A*$: 1-2-3	$B*$: 1-2-3	$C*$: 1-2-3	$D*$: 1-2-3	$E*$: 1-2-3	$F*$: 1-2-3
2-3-1	2-1-3	1-2-3	1-3-2	3-1-2	3-2-1

Two rearrangements can be combined as with the symmetries of a square; for example, the symbol $B*F*$ means to first apply $B*$ to 1-2-3 and then apply $F*$ to the result. Rearrangement $B*$ changes 1-2-3 into 2-1-3. Then apply $F*$ to this result: 1 becomes 3, 2 is unchanged, and 3 becomes 1. In summary:

1-2-3

2-1-3   Rearrange according to $B*$.

3   By $F*$, 1 is replaced by 3.

2-3   Next, 2 remains unchanged.

2-3-1.   As a last step, 3 changes into 1.

The net result of $B*F*$ is to change 1-2-3 into 2-3-1, which is exactly what $A*$ does to 1-2-3. Therefore,

$$B*F* = A*.$$

EXAMPLE 7   Combining Rearrangements

Find $D*E*$.

SOLUTION

Use the procedure described above.

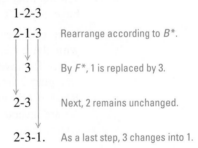

Elie-Joseph Cartan (1869–1951) did extensive work in **group theory.** His 1894 doctoral thesis completely categorized all finite groups known at the time. The classification of *all* finite groups took 150 years and culminated with the monster group (see page 215) constructed in 1980 by Robert Griess, Jr.

Throughout the last half of the twentieth century, physicists were able to apply the structure of some of these groups to improve their understanding of the basic particles of matter and their quantum interactions, thereby enabling them to formulate ever better theories of the fundamental forces of nature.

The result is that D^*E^* converts 1-2-3 into 3-2-1, as does F^*, so

$$D^*E^* = F^*.$$

As further examples, $A^*B^* = D^*$ and $F^*E^* = B^*$.

Once again, we see that we encountered a mathematical system: the set $\{A^*, B^*, C^*, D^*, E^*, F^*\}$ and the operation of the combination of two rearrangements. To see whether this system is a group, check the requirements.

Closure   Combine any two rearrangements and the result is another rearrangement, so the system is closed.

Associative   Try an example:

First $(B^*D^*)A^* = E^*A^* = C^*$.

Also $B^*(D^*A^*) = B^*B^* = C^*$,

so that $(B^*D^*)A^* = B^*(D^*A^*)$.

Because other examples will work out similarly, the system is associative.

Identity   The identity element is C^*. If x is any rearrangement, then we have $xC^* = C^*x = x$.

Inverse   Does each rearrangement have an inverse rearrangement? Begin with the basic order 1-2-3 and then apply, say B^*, resulting in 2-1-3. The inverse of B^* must convert this 2-1-3 back into 1-2-3, by changing 2 into 1 and 1 into 2. But B^* itself will do this. Hence, $B^*B^* = C^*$ and B^* is its own inverse. By the same process, E^* and A^* are inverses of each other. Also, each of C^*, D^*, and F^* is its own inverse.

Because all four requirements are satisfied, the system is a group. Rearrangements are also referred to as *permutations,* so this group is sometimes called the **permutation group on three symbols.** The total number of different permutations of a given number of symbols can be determined by techniques described in the chapter on counting methods.

4.6 EXERCISES

What is wrong with the way in which each question is stated?

1. Do the integers form a group?

2. Does multiplication satisfy all of the group properties?

Decide whether each system is a group. If not a group, identify all properties that are not satisfied. (Recall that any system failing to satisfy the identity property automatically fails to satisfy the inverse property also.) For the finite systems, it may help to construct tables. For infinite systems, try some examples to help you decide.

3. {0}; multiplication

4. {0}; addition

5. {0, 1}; addition

6. {0}; subtraction

7. $\{-1, 1\}$; division

8. $\{0, 1\}$; multiplication

9. $\{-1, 0, 1\}$; multiplication

10. $\{-1, 0, 1\}$; addition

11. integers; subtraction

12. integers; multiplication

13. odd integers; multiplication

14. counting numbers; addition

15. rational numbers; addition

16. even integers; addition

17. prime numbers; addition

18. nonzero rational numbers; multiplication

19. Explain why a *finite* group based on the operation of ordinary addition of numbers cannot contain the element 1.

20. Explain why a group based on the operation of ordinary addition of numbers *must* contain the element 0.

Exercises 21–34 apply to the system of symmetries of a square presented in the text. Find each combination.

21. *RN*

22. *PR*

23. *TV*

24. *VP*

Verify each statement.

25. $N(TR) = (NT)R$

26. $V(PS) = (VP)S$

27. $T(VN) = (TV)N$

28. $S(MR) = (SM)R$

Find the inverse of each element.

29. *N*

30. *Q*

31. *R*

32. *S*

33. *T*

34. *V*

A group that also satisfies the commutative property is called a **commutative group** *(or an* **abelian group,** *after Niels Henrik Abel). Determine whether each group is commutative.*

35. the group of symmetries of a square

36. the subgroup of Example 6

37. the integers under addition

38. the permutation group on three symbols

Give illustrations to support your answers for Exercises 39–42.

39. Produce a mathematical system with two operations which is a group under one operation but not a group under the other operation.

40. Explain what property is gained when the system of counting numbers is extended to the system of whole numbers.

41. Explain what property is gained when the system of whole numbers is extended to the system of integers.

42. Explain what property is gained when the system of integers is extended to the system of rational numbers.

Consider the following set of "actions" (A, B, C, and D) on three symbols (a, b, and c):

A:	a	b	c	B:	a	b	c	C:	a	b	c	D:	a	b	c
	a	b	c		c	b	a		a	-b	c		c	-b	a

(continued)

The resulting system is somewhat similar to the permutation group on three symbols discussed in the text, except that not all possible rearrangements of a, b, and c are included, and two of the actions involve sign changes. The operation of the system is the combination of actions as follows, for example, BD represents B followed by D:

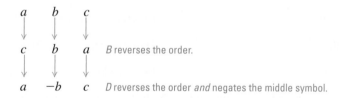

The net result, from beginning to end, is simply to negate the middle symbol, which is exactly what C does. Therefore, BD = C.

43. Verify, for yourself, the entries shown in the following operation table and fill in the missing entries.

	A	*B*	*C*	*D*
A	*A*	*B*	*C*	*D*
B	*B*	*A*		*C*
C	*C*		*A*	
D	*D*			*A*

44. (a) Is there an identity element in this system?
(b) If so, what is it?

45. (a) Is closure satisfied by this system?
(b) Explain.

46. (a) Is this system commutative?
(b) Explain.

47. (a) Is the distributive property satisfied in this system?
(b) Explain.

48. (a) Assuming the associative property is satisfied, is the system a group?
(b) Explain.

COLLABORATIVE INVESTIGATION

A Perpetual Calendar Algorithm

In this chapter we examined some alternative algorithms for arithmetic computations. Algorithms appear in various places in mathematics and computer science, and in each case give us a specified method of carrying out a procedure that produces a desired result. The algorithm that follows allows us to find the day of the week on which a particular date occurred or will occur.

In applying the algorithm, you will need to know whether a particular year is a leap year. In general, if a year is divisible (evenly) by 4, it is a leap year. However, there are exceptions. Century years, such as 1800 and 1900, are not leap years, despite the fact that they are divisible by 4. Furthermore, as an exception to the exception, a century year that is divisible by 400 (such as the year 2000) is a leap year.

In groups of three to five students, read the algorithm and then work the Topics for Discussion.

The Algorithm

This algorithm requires several *key numbers*. Key numbers for the month, day, and century are determined by the following tables.

Month	Key
January	1 (0 if a leap year)
February	4 (3 if a leap year)
March	4
April	0
May	2
June	5
July	0
August	3
September	6
October	1
November	4
December	6

Day	Key
Saturday	0
Sunday	1
Monday	2
Tuesday	3
Wednesday	4
Thursday	5
Friday	6

Century	Key
1700s	4
1800s	2
1900s	0
2000s	6

The algorithm works as follows. (We use October 12, 1949, as an example.)

Step 1 Obtain the following five numbers. Example

1. The number formed by the last two digits of the year — 49
2. The number in Step 1, divided by 4, with the remainder ignored — 12
3. The month key (1 for October in our example) — 1
4. The day of the month (12 for October 12) — 12
5. The century key (0 for the 1900s) — 0

Step 2 Add these five numbers. — 74

Step 3 Divide the sum by 7, and retain the remainder. $\left(\frac{74}{7} = 10, \text{ with remainder } 4\right)$

Step 4 Find this remainder in the day key table. (The number 4 implies that October 12, 1949 was a Wednesday.)

Topics for Discussion

1. Have each person in the group determine the day of the week on which he or she was born.

2. Among the group members, discuss whether the following poem applies. (This is all in good fun, of course.)

   Monday's child is fair of face,
   Tuesday's child is full of grace.
   Wednesday's child is full of woe,
   Thursday's child has far to go.
   Friday's child is loving and giving,
   Saturday's child works hard for a living.
   But the child that is born on the Sabbath
   day is bonny and good, happy and gay.

3. Determine the day of the week on which the following important historical events occurred.
   (a) December 7, 1941 (the bombing of Pearl Harbor)
   (b) November 22, 1963 (the assassination of John F. Kennedy)
   (c) July 4, 1976 (the bicentennial of the United States)
   (d) January 1, 2000 (the "dreaded" Y2K day)
   (e) September 11, 2001 (the terrorist attacks on the United States)

CHAPTER 4 TEST

1. For the numeral 𝄐 𝄐99 ∩∩|||, identify the numeration system, and give the Hindu-Arabic equivalent.

2. Simplify:
   $(7 \cdot 10^3) + (5 \cdot 10^2) + (6 \cdot 10^1) + (1 \cdot 10^0)$.

3. Write in expanded notation: 60,923.

Perform each operation using the alternative algorithm specified.

4. $37 \cdot 54$ (Russian peasant or Egyptian method)

5. $236 \cdot 94$ (Lattice method)

6. $21,325 - 8498$ (Nines complement method)

Convert each number to base ten.

7. 324_{five} **8.** 110010_{two} **9.** $DEAF_{sixteen}$

Convert as indicated.

10. 49 to base two

11. 2930 to base five

12. 10101110_{two} to base eight

13. Find all positive solutions for the equation

$$3x + 1 \equiv 2 \ (\text{mod } 5).$$

14. Find each quantity on the 12-hour-clock.
    (a) $8 + 9$ **(b)** $4 \cdot 10$
    (c) -3 **(d)** $3 - 7$

15. Work each modular arithmetic problem.
    (a) $(7 + 11) \ (\text{mod } 5)$ **(b)** $(8 \cdot 15) \ (\text{mod } 17)$

16. ***Two-Dollar Bill Collection*** Alec has a collection of two-dollar bills which he can arrange in groups of 5 with 3 left over, groups of 7 with 6 left over, or groups of 10 with 8 left over. What is the least number of bills he could have?

Briefly explain each of the following.

17. the advantage of multiplicative grouping over simple grouping

18. the advantage, in a positional numeration system, of a smaller base over a larger base

19. the advantage, in a positional numeration system, of a larger base over a smaller base

Answer the questions in Exercises 20–22.

20. For addition of whole numbers, what is the identity element?

21. For multiplication of rational numbers, what is the inverse of 3?

22. For any whole numbers a, b, and c, $(a + b) + c = (b + a) + c$. What property does this illustrate?

Consider the mathematical system with the set $\{1, 3, 5, 7\}$ and with the operation of multiplication modulo 8.

23. Complete the operation table for the system.

$\circ$	1	3	5	7
1	1	3	5	7
3	3			5
5	5		1	
7	7		3	

24. (a) Is there an identity element in this system?
    (b) If so, what is it?

25. (a) Is closure satisfied by this system?
    (b) Explain.

26. (a) Is this system commutative?
    (b) Explain.

27. (a) Is the distributive property satisfied in this system?
    (b) Explain.

28. (a) Assuming the associative property is satisfied, is the system a group?
    (b) Explain.

5

NUMBER THEORY

The first episode of the animated series *The Simpsons* aired on December 17, 1989 and has since become a pop culture icon, providing humor, social commentary, and even lessons in mathematics. An annual treat for fans is the *Treehouse of Horror* episode, which airs near Halloween. In the sixth installment, this episode featured a segment titled *Homer 3D* in which a two-dimensional Homer Simpson became trapped in the third dimension. Computer graphics portrayed a three-dimensional coordinate system, the Parthenon (an example of the *Golden Ratio*), a cone, a black hole, and several mathematical equations. One such equation was

$$1782^{12} + 1841^{12} = 1922^{12}.$$

In Section 5.2 you will learn that **this equation cannot be true.** It is of the form of an equation of Fermat's Last Theorem, one of the most famous theorems in *number theory*, the topic of this chapter. The theorem was stated by the French mathematician Pierre de Fermat over 400 years ago, but was not proved until 1994. A graphing calculator such as the TI-83/84 Plus will indicate that the equation is true, but only because the calculator is unable to compute powers of this size. Can you explain why it can't be true? (*Hint:* Show that one side is an odd number and the other is an even number.) See page 237 for the complete answer.

5.1 Prime and Composite Numbers

Primes, Composites, and Divisibility • The Fundamental Theorem of Arithmetic • The Infinitude of Primes • The Search for Large Primes

Primes, Composites, and Divisibility

The famous German mathematician Carl Friedrich Gauss once remarked, "Mathematics is the Queen of Science, and number theory is the Queen of Mathematics." This chapter is centered around the study of number theory. **Number theory** is the branch of mathematics devoted to the study of the properties of the natural numbers. In earlier chapters we discussed the set of **natural numbers**, also called the **counting numbers** or the **positive integers**:

$$\{1, 2, 3, \ldots\}.$$

Number theory deals with the study of the properties of this set of numbers, and a key concept of number theory is the idea of *divisibility*. Informally, we say that one counting number is *divisible* by another if the operation of dividing the first by the second leaves a remainder 0. A formal definition follows.

Do not confuse $b \mid a$ with b/a. The expression $b \mid a$ denotes the *statement* "b divides a." For example, 3 | 12 is a true statement, while 5 | 14 is a false statement. On the other hand, b/a denotes the *operation* "b divided by a." For example, 28/4 yields the result 7.

> ### Divisibility
>
> The natural number a is **divisible** by the natural number b if there exists a natural number k such that $a = bk$. If b divides a, then we write $b \mid a$.

Notice that if b divides a, then the quotient a/b or $\frac{a}{b}$ is a natural number. For example, 4 divides 20 because there exists a natural number k such that $20 = 4k$. The value of k here is 5, because $20 = 4 \cdot 5$. The natural number 20 is not divisible by 7, for example, since there is no natural number k satisfying $20 = 7k$. Alternatively, we think "20 divided by 7 gives quotient 2 with remainder 6" and since there is a nonzero remainder, divisibility does not hold. We write $7 \nmid 20$ to indicate that 7 does not divide 20.

If the natural number a is divisible by the natural number b, then b is a **factor** (or **divisor**) of a, and a is a **multiple** of b. For example, 5 is a factor of 30, and 30 is a multiple of 5. Also, 6 is a factor of 30, and 30 is a multiple of 6. The number 30 equals $6 \cdot 5$; this product $6 \cdot 5$ is called a **factorization** of 30. Other factorizations of 30 include $3 \cdot 10$, $2 \cdot 15$, $1 \cdot 30$, and $2 \cdot 3 \cdot 5$.

The ideas of **even** and **odd natural numbers** are based on the concept of divisibility. A natural number is even if it is divisible by 2 and odd if it is not. Every even number can be written in the form $2k$ (for some natural number k), while every odd number can be written in the form $2k + 1$. Another way to say the same thing: 2 divides every even number but fails to divide every odd number. (If a is even, then $2 \mid a$, whereas if a is odd, then $2 \nmid a$.)

EXAMPLE 1 Checking Divisibility

Decide whether the first number is divisible by the second.

(a) 45; 9   **(b)** 60; 7   **(c)** 19; 19   **(d)** 26; 1

SOLUTION

(a) Is there a natural number k that satisfies $45 = 9k$? The answer is yes, because $45 = 9 \cdot 5$, and 5 is a natural number. Therefore, 9 divides 45, written $9 \mid 45$.

(b) Because the quotient $60 \div 7$ is not a natural number, 60 is not divisible by 7, written $7 \nmid 60$.

(c) The quotient $19 \div 19$ is the natural number 1, so 19 is divisible by 19. (In fact, any natural number is divisible by itself.)

(d) The quotient $26 \div 1$ is the natural number 26, so 26 is divisible by 1. (In fact, any natural number is divisible by 1.)

For any natural number a, it is true that $a \mid a$, and also that $1 \mid a$.

EXAMPLE 2 Finding Factors

Find all the natural number factors of each number.

(a) 36   **(b)** 50   **(c)** 11

SOLUTION

(a) To find the factors of 36, try to divide 36 by 1, 2, 3, 4, 5, 6, and so on. Doing this gives the following list of natural number factors of 36:

$$1, 2, 3, 4, 6, 9, 12, 18, \text{ and } 36.$$

(b) The factors of 50 are 1, 2, 5, 10, 25, and 50.

(c) The only natural number factors of 11 are 11 and 1.

Like the number 19 in Example 1(c), the number 11 has only two natural number factors, itself and 1. Such a natural number is called a *prime number*.

Prime and Composite Numbers

A natural number greater than 1 that has only itself and 1 as factors is called a **prime number.** A natural number greater than 1 that is not prime is called **composite.**

The 1997 movie *Contact*, based on the Carl Sagan novel of the same name, portrays Jodie Foster as scientist Ellie Arroway. After years of searching, Ellie makes contact with intelligent life in outer space. Her contact is verified after receiving radio signals that indicate **prime numbers:** 2, 3, 5, 7, 11, and so on. Her superiors are not convinced, asking why the aliens don't just speak English. Ellie's response:

Well, maybe because 70% of the planet speaks other languages. Mathematics is the only true universal language, Senator. It's no coincidence that they're using primes . . . Prime numbers—that would be integers that are divisible only by themselves and 1.

Mathematicians agree that the natural number 1 is neither prime nor composite. The following alternative definition of a prime number clarifies that 1 is not a prime.

Alternative Definition of a Prime Number

A **prime number** is a natural number that has *exactly* two different natural number factors.

There is a systematic method for identifying prime numbers in a list of numbers: 2, 3, . . . , n. The method, known as the **Sieve of Eratosthenes,** is named after the Greek geographer, poet, astronomer, and mathematician, who lived from about 276 to 192 B.C. To construct such a sieve, list all the natural numbers from 2 through some given natural number n, such as 100. The number 2 is prime, but all other multiples of 2 (4, 6, 8, 10, and so on) are composite. Circle the prime 2, and cross out all other multiples of 2. The next number not crossed out and not circled is 3, the next prime. Circle the 3, and cross out all other multiples of 3 (6, 9, 12, 15, and so on) that are not already crossed out. Circle the next prime, 5, and cross out all other multiples of 5 not already crossed out. Continue this process for all primes less than or equal to the square root of the last number in the list. For this list, we may stop with 7, because the next prime, 11, is greater than the square root of 100, which is 10. At this stage, simply circle all remaining numbers that are not crossed out.

Table 1 shows the Sieve of Eratosthenes for 2, 3, 4, . . . , 100, identifying the 25 primes in that range. Theoretically, such a sieve can be constructed for any value of *n*.

TABLE 1 Sieve of Eratosthenes

②	③	4̶	⑤	6̶	⑦	8̶	9̶	1̶0̶	⑪	1̶2̶	⑬	1̶4̶
1̶5̶	1̶6̶	⑰	1̶8̶	⑲	2̶0̶	2̶1̶	2̶2̶	㉓	2̶4̶	2̶5̶	2̶6̶	2̶7̶	2̶8̶
㉙	3̶0̶	㉛	3̶2̶	3̶3̶	3̶4̶	3̶5̶	3̶6̶	㊲	3̶8̶	3̶9̶	4̶0̶	㊶	4̶2̶
㊸	4̶4̶	4̶5̶	4̶6̶	㊷	4̶8̶	4̶9̶	5̶0̶	5̶1̶	5̶2̶	㊼	5̶4̶	5̶5̶	5̶6̶
5̶7̶	5̶8̶	㊾	6̶0̶	㊿	6̶2̶	6̶3̶	6̶4̶	6̶5̶	6̶6̶	67	6̶8̶	6̶9̶	7̶0̶
71	7̶2̶	73	7̶4̶	7̶5̶	7̶6̶	7̶7̶	7̶8̶	79	8̶0̶	8̶1̶	8̶2̶	83	8̶4̶
8̶5̶	8̶6̶	8̶7̶	8̶8̶	89	9̶0̶	9̶1̶	9̶2̶	9̶3̶	9̶4̶	9̶5̶	9̶6̶	97	9̶8̶
9̶9̶	1̶0̶0̶											

EXAMPLE 3 **Identifying Prime and Composite Numbers**

Decide whether each number is prime or composite.

(a) 97   **(b)** 59,872   **(c)** 697

SOLUTION

(a) Because 97 is circled in Table 1, it is prime. If 97 had a smaller prime factor, 97 would have been crossed out as a multiple of that factor.

(b) The number 59,872 is even, so it is divisible by 2. It is composite. (There is only one even prime, the number 2 itself.)

(c) For 697 to be composite, there must be a number other than 697 and 1 that divides into it with remainder 0. Start by trying 2, and then 3. Neither works. There is no need to try 4. (If 4 divides with remainder 0 into a number, then 2 will also.) Try 5. There is no need to try 6 or any succeeding even number. (Why?) Try 7. Try 11. (Why not try 9?) Try 13. Keep trying numbers until one works, or until a number is tried whose square exceeds the given number, 697. Try 17:

$$697 \div 17 = 41.$$

The number 697 is composite: $697 = 17 \cdot 41$.   ∎

An aid in determining whether a natural number is divisible by another natural number is called a **divisibility test.** Some simple divisibility tests exist for small natural numbers, and they are given in Table 2 on the next page. Divisibility tests for 7 and 11 are a bit involved, and they are discussed in the exercises for this section. Each test in the table is both a necessary and a sufficient condition. If the test statement is true, then divisibility occurs. If the test statement is not true, then divisibility does not occur.

How to Use Up Lots of Chalk
In 1903, the mathematician F. N. Cole presented before a meeting of the American Mathematical Society his discovery of a factorization of the number

$$2^{67} - 1.$$

He walked up to the chalk-board, raised 2 to the 67th power, and then subtracted 1. Then he moved over to another part of the board and multiplied out

193,707,721
   × 761,838,257,287.

The two calculations agreed, and Cole received a standing ovation for a presentation that did not include a single word.

Writing in the October 1, 1994 issue of *Science News*, Ivars Peterson gives a fascinating account of the recent discovery of a 75-year-old **factoring machine** ("Cranking Out Primes: Tracking Down a Long-lost Factoring Machine"). In 1989, Jeffrey Shallit of the University of Waterloo in Ontario came across an article in an obscure 1920 French journal, in which the author, Eugene Olivier Carissan, reported his invention of the factoring apparatus. Shallit and two colleagues embarked on a search for the machine. They contacted all telephone subscribers in France named Carissan and received a reply from Eugene Carissan's daughter. The machine was still in existence and in working condition, stored in a drawer at an astronomical observatory in Floirac, near Bordeaux.

Peterson explains in the article how the apparatus works. Using the machine, Carissan took just ten minutes to prove that 708,158,977 is a prime number, and he was able to factor a 13-digit number. While this cannot compare to what technology can accomplish today, it was a significant achievement for Carissan's day.

TABLE 2	Divisibility Tests	
Divisible By	**Test**	**Example**
2	Number ends in 0, 2, 4, 6, or 8. (The last digit is even.)	9,489,994 ends in 4; it is divisible by 2.
3	Sum of the digits is divisible by 3.	897,432 is divisible by 3, since $8 + 9 + 7 + 4 + 3 + 2 = 33$ is divisible by 3.
4	Last two digits form a number divisible by 4.	7,693,432 is divisible by 4, since 32 is divisible by 4.
5	Number ends in 0 or 5.	890 and 7635 are divisible by 5.
6	Number is divisible by both 2 and 3.	27,342 is divisible by 6 since it is divisible by both 2 and 3.
8	Last three digits form a number divisible by 8.	1,437,816 is divisible by 8, since 816 is divisible by 8.
9	Sum of the digits is divisible by 9.	428,376,105 is divisible by 9 since sum of digits is 36, which is divisible by 9.
10	The last digit is 0.	897,463,940 is divisible by 10.
12	Number is divisible by both 4 and 3.	376,984,032 is divisible by 12.

EXAMPLE 4   Applying Divisibility Tests

In each case, decide whether the first number is divisible by the second.

(a) 2,984,094;   4   **(b)** 4,119,806,514;   9

SOLUTION

(a) The last two digits form the number 94. Since 94 is not divisible by 4, the given number is not divisible by 4.

(b) The sum of the digits is $4 + 1 + 1 + 9 + 8 + 0 + 6 + 5 + 1 + 4 = 39$, which is not divisible by 9. The given number is therefore not divisible by 9. ■

The Fundamental Theorem of Arithmetic

A *composite* number can be thought of as "composed" of smaller factors. For example, 42 is composite: $42 = 6 \cdot 7$. If the smaller factors are all primes, then we have a *prime factorization*. For example, $42 = 2 \cdot 3 \cdot 7$. An important theorem in mathematics states that there is only one possible way to write the prime factorization of a given composite natural number. A form of this theorem was known to the ancient Greeks.[*]

---

[*]A theorem is a statement that can be proved true from other statements. For a proof of this theorem, see *What Is Mathematics?* by Richard Courant and Herbert Robbins (Oxford University Press, 1941), p. 23.

The following program, written by Charles W. Gantner and provided courtesy of Texas Instruments, can be used on the TI-83/84 Plus calculator to list all primes less than or equal to a given natural number N.

```
PROGRAM: PRIMES
: Disp "INPUT N ≥ 2"
: Disp "TO GET"
: Disp "PRIMES ≤ N"
: Input N
: 2 → T
: Disp T
: 1 → A
: Lbl 1
: A + 2 → A
: 3 → B
: If A > N
: Stop
: Lbl 2
: If B ≤ √(A)
: Goto 3
: Disp A
: Pause
: Goto 1
: Lbl 3
: If A/B ≤ int (A/B)
: Goto 1
: B + 2 → B
: Goto 2
```

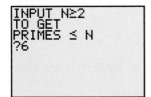

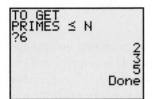

The display indicates that the primes less than or equal to 6 are 2, 3, and 5.

The Fundamental Theorem of Arithmetic

Every natural number can be expressed in one and only one way as a product of primes (if the order of the factors is disregarded). This unique product of primes is called the **prime factorization** of the natural number.

Because a prime natural number is not composed of smaller factors, its prime factorization is simply itself. For example, $17 = 17$ (or $17 = 1 \cdot 17$).

The following example shows two ways to factor a composite number into primes: (1) using a "factor tree" and (2) using repeated division.

EXAMPLE 5 Finding the Unique Prime Factorization of a Composite Number

Find the prime factorization of the number 504.

SOLUTION

The factor tree can start with $504 = 2 \cdot 252$, as shown below on the left. Then $252 = 2 \cdot 126$, and so on, until every branch of the tree ends with a prime. All the resulting prime factors are shown circled in the diagram.

Alternatively, the same factorization is obtained by repeated division by primes, as shown on the right. (In general, you would divide by the primes 2, 3, 5, 7, 11, and so on, each as many times as possible, until the answer is no longer composite.)

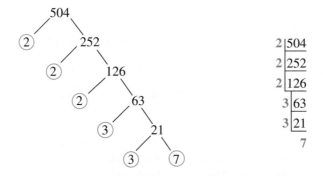

By either method, the prime factorization, in exponential form, is

$$504 = 2^3 \cdot 3^2 \cdot 7. \quad 2 \cdot 2 \cdot 2 = 2^3; 3 \cdot 3 = 3^2$$

The Infinitude of Primes

Mathematicians (amateur as well as professional) have sought for thousands of years to learn as much as possible about prime numbers. One important basic result was proved by Euclid around 300 B.C., namely that there are infinitely many primes. This means that no matter how large a prime we identify, there are always others even larger. Euclid's proof remains today as one of the most elegant proofs in all of mathematics. (An *elegant* mathematical proof is one that demonstrates the desired result in a most direct, concise manner. Mathematicians strive for elegance in their proofs.) It is called a **proof by contradiction.**

The Riemann Hypothesis is an insightful conjecture stated in the mid-1800s by Georg Friedrich Bernhard Riemann (profiled on page 601). It concerns how the prime numbers are distributed on the number line and is undoubtedly the most important unproven claim in all of mathematics. Thousands of other "theorems" are built upon the assumption of its truth. If it were ever disproved, those results would fall apart. A proof, on the other hand, may provide sufficient understanding of the primes to demolish public key cryptography, upon which rests the security of all Internet commerce (among other things).

Two excellent books on the Riemann Hypothesis, and the mathematicians at the forefront of its study over the years, both published in 2003, are *Prime Obsession*, by John Derbyshire, and *The Music of the Primes*, by Marcus du Sautoy.

A statement can be proved by contradiction as follows: We assume that the negation of the statement is true. The assumption that the negation is true is used to produce some sort of contradiction, or absurdity. The fact that the negation of the original statement leads to a contradiction means that the original statement must be true.

In order to better understand a particular part of the proof that there are infinitely many primes, it is helpful to examine the following argument.

Suppose that $M = 2 \cdot 3 \cdot 5 \cdot 7 + 1 = 211$. Now M is the product of the first four prime numbers, plus 1. If we divide 211 by each of the primes 2, 3, 5, and 7, the remainder is always 1.

$$
\begin{array}{cccc}
105 & 70 & 42 & 30 \\
2\overline{)211} & 3\overline{)211} & 5\overline{)211} & 7\overline{)211} \\
\underline{105} & \underline{210} & \underline{210} & \underline{210} \\
1 & 1 & 1 & 1
\end{array}
$$

All remainders are 1.

So 211 is not divisible by any of the primes 2, 3, 5, and 7.

Now we are ready to prove that there are infinitely many primes. If it can be shown that *there is no largest prime number*, then there must be infinitely many primes.

▌ THEOREM

Statement: There is no largest prime number.

Proof: Suppose that there is a largest prime number and call it P. Now form the number M such that

$$M = p_1 \cdot p_2 \cdot p_3 \cdots P + 1,$$

where $p_1, p_2, p_3, \ldots, P$ represent all the primes less than or equal to P. Now the number M must be either prime or composite.

1. Suppose that M is prime.
   M is obviously larger than P, so if M is prime, it is larger than the assumed largest prime P. We have reached a *contradiction*.

2. Suppose that M is composite.
   If M is composite, it must have a prime factor. But none of $p_1, p_2, p_3, \ldots, P$ are factors of M, because division by each will leave a remainder of 1. (Recall the above argument.) So if M has a prime factor, it must be greater than P. But this is a *contradiction*, because P is the assumed largest prime.

In either case 1 or 2, we reach a contradiction. The whole argument was based upon the assumption that a largest prime exists, but as this leads to contradictions, there must be no largest prime, or equivalently, there are infinitely many primes. ◼

The Search for Large Primes

Identifying larger and larger prime numbers and factoring large composite numbers into their prime components is of great practical importance today, because it is the basis of modern **cryptography systems,** or secret codes. Various codes have been used for centuries in military applications. Today the security of vast amounts of industrial, business, and personal data also depend upon the theory of prime numbers. See the Extension following Section 5.3.

🎥 During the first season of the CBS television series *NUMB3RS,* the episode *Prime Suspect* was based on the premise that a mathematician was very close to proving the Riemann Hypothesis (which later proved to be erroneous). His daughter was kidnapped by people who were hoping to exchange her for the results in order to unlock financial security codes.

At one time, $2^{11,213} - 1$ was the largest known **Mersenne prime**. To honor its discovery, the Urbana, Illinois, post office used the cancellation picture above.

As mathematicians continue to search for larger and larger primes, a formula for generating all the primes would be nice (something similar, for example, to the formula $2n$, which generates all even counting numbers for $n = 1, 2, 3, \ldots$, or the formula n^2, which generates all the perfect squares). Numbers generated by the formula $M_n = 2^n - 1$ are called **Mersenne numbers** to honor the French monk Marin Mersenne (1588–1648). It was long known that a *composite* value of n would always generate a composite Mersenne number. (See Exercises 83–88.) And some early mathematicians believed (incorrectly) that a *prime* value of n would always generate a prime Mersenne number. That is, they believed that, starting with any known prime number n, one could always produce another, larger prime number $2^n - 1$. (Although "always generate a prime" is not the same as "generate all primes," at least it would have been an unending source of guaranteed primes.)

EXAMPLE 6   Finding Mersenne Numbers

Find each Mersenne number M_n for $n = 2, 3,$ and 5.

SOLUTION

$$M_2 = 2^2 - 1 = 3 \qquad 2^2 = 2 \cdot 2 = 4$$
$$M_3 = 2^3 - 1 = 7 \qquad 2^3 = 2 \cdot 2 \cdot 2 = 8$$
$$M_5 = 2^5 - 1 = 31 \qquad 2^5 = 2 \cdot 2 \cdot 2 \cdot 2 \cdot 2 = 32$$

Note that all three values, 3, 7, and 31, are indeed primes.   ▪

It turns out that M_7 is also a prime (see Exercise 26), but it was discovered in 1536 that $M_{11} = 2^{11} - 1 = 2047$ is not prime (since it is $23 \cdot 89$). So prime values of n do *not* always produce prime M_n. The question then became which prime values of n do produce prime Mersenne numbers (the so-called **Mersenne primes**). Since no way was ever found to identify, in general, which prime values of n result in Mersenne primes, it became a matter of checking out each prime n value individually—not an easy task given that the Mersenne numbers rapidly become very large.

We can summarize the discussion of Mersenne numbers, up to this point, as follows.

Marin Mersenne (1588–1648), in his *Cogitata Physico-Mathematica* (1644), claimed that M_n was prime for $n = 2, 3, 5, 7, 13, 17, 19, 31, 67, 127,$ and $257,$ and composite for all other prime numbers n less than 257. Other mathematicians at the time knew that Mersenne could not have actually tested all these values, but no one else could prove or disprove them either. It was more then 300 years later before all primes up to 257 were legitimately checked out, and Mersenne was finally revealed to have made five errors:

M_{61} is prime.
M_{67} is composite.
M_{89} is prime.
M_{107} is prime.
M_{257} is composite.

Mersenne Numbers and Mersenne Primes

For $n = 1, 2, 3, \ldots,$ the **Mersenne numbers** are those generated by the formula

$$M_n = 2^n - 1.$$

(1) If n is composite, then M_n is also composite.
(2) If n is prime, then M_n may be either prime or composite.

The prime values of M_n are called the **Mersenne primes.** Large primes being verified currently (though at a rather gradual pace) are commonly Mersenne primes.

The Mersenne prime search yielded results slowly. By about 1600, M_n had been verified as prime for all prime n up to 19 (except for 11, as mentioned above). The next one was M_{31}, verified by Euler in 1732. In 1876, French mathematician Edouard Lucas used a clever test he had developed to show that M_{127} (a 39-digit number) is prime. In the 1930s Lucas's method was further simplified by D. H. Lehmer, and the testing of Mersenne numbers for primality has been done ever since with the Lucas–Lehmer test. In 1952 an early computer verified that M_{521}, M_{607}, M_{1279}, M_{2203}, and M_{2281} are primes.

Over the last half century, most new record-breaking primes have been identified by computer algorithms devised and implemented by mathematicians and programmers. In 1996, the **Great Internet Mersenne Prime Search (GIMPS)** was launched. Since then, many thousands of individuals have signed on, receiving free software and source code to run during slack time on personal computers throughout the world. The nine largest record Mersenne primes have been found by GIMPS.

As of early 2006, the record largest prime (discovered on December 15, 2005) was

$$M_{30,402,457} = 2^{30,402,457} - 1,$$

a number with 9,152,052 digits. It was the 43rd known Mersenne prime.

During the same general period that Mersenne was thinking about prime numbers, Pierre de Fermat (about 1601–1665) conjectured that the formula

$$2^{2^n} + 1$$

would always produce a prime, for any whole number value of n. Table 3 shows how this formula generates the first four **Fermat numbers,** which are all primes. The fifth Fermat number (from $n = 4$) is likewise prime. Fermat had verified these first five by around 1630. But the sixth Fermat number (from $n = 5$) turns out to be 4,294,967,297, which is *not* prime. (See Exercises 75 and 76.) To date, no more primes have been found among the Fermat numbers.

TABLE 3	The Generation of Fermat Numbers		
n	2^n	2^{2^n}	$2^{2^n} + 1$
0	1	2	3
1	2	4	5
2	4	16	17
3	8	256	257

Of historical note are a couple of polynomial formulas that produce primes. (A *polynomial* in a given variable involves adding or subtracting integer multiples of whole number powers of the variable. Polynomials are among the most basic mathematical functions. They are discussed in Section 7.6.) In 1732, Leonhard Euler offered the formula $n^2 - n + 41$, which generates primes for n up to 40 and fails at $n = 41$. In 1879, E. B. Escott produced more primes with the formula $n^2 - 79n + 1601$, which first fails at $n = 80$.

▌ EXAMPLE 7 Finding Numbers Using Euler's and Escott's Formulas

Find the first five numbers produced by each of the polynomial formulas of Euler and Escott.

SOLUTION

Table 4 on the next page shows the required numbers.

	Euler formula	Escott formula
TABLE 4	A Few Polynomial-Generated Prime Numbers	
n	$n^2 - n + 41$	$n^2 - 79n + 1601$
1	41	1523
2	43	1447
3	47	1373
4	53	1301
5	61	1231

All values found here are primes. (Use Table 1 to verify the Euler values.)

Actually, it is not hard to prove that there can be no polynomial that will consistently generate primes. More complicated mathematical formulas exist for generating primes, but none produced so far can be practically applied in a reasonable amount of time, even using the fastest computers.

5.1 EXERCISES

Decide whether each statement is true *or* false.

1. Every natural number is divisible by 1.

2. No natural number is both prime and composite.

3. There are no even prime numbers.

4. If n is a natural number and $9|n$, then $3|n$.

5. If n is a natural number and $5|n$, then $10|n$.

6. 1 is the least prime number.

7. Every natural number is both a factor and a multiple of itself.

8. If 16 divides a natural number, then 2, 4, and 8 must also divide that natural number.

9. The composite number 50 has exactly two prime factorizations.

10. The prime number 53 has exactly two natural number factors.

11. The number $2^{11} - 1$ is an example of a Mersenne prime.

12. As of early 2006, only five Fermat primes had ever been found.

Find all natural number factors of each number.

13. 12

14. 18

15. 20

16. 28

17. 120

18. 172

Use divisibility tests to decide whether the given number is divisible by each number.

(a) 2   (b) 3   (c) 4   (d) 5   (e) 6   (f) 8
(g) 9   (h) 10   (i) 12

19. 315

20. 630

21. 25,025

22. 45,815

23. 123,456,789

24. 987,654,321

25. (a) In constructing the Sieve of Eratosthenes for 2 through 100, we said that any composite in that range had to be a multiple of some prime less than or equal to 7 (since the next prime, 11, is greater than the square root of 100). Explain.

(b) To extend the Sieve of Eratosthenes to 200, what is the largest prime whose multiples would have to be considered?

(c) Complete this statement: In seeking prime factors of a given number, we need only consider all primes up to and including the _____ _____ of that number, since a prime factor greater than the _____ _____ can only occur if there is at least one other prime factor less than the _____ _____.

(d) Complete this statement: If no prime less than or equal to $\sqrt{n}$ divides n, then n is a _____ number.

26. (a) Continue the Sieve of Eratosthenes in Table 1 from 101 to 200 and list the primes between 100 and 200. How many are there?

(b) From your list in part (a), verify that the Mersenne number M_7 is indeed prime.

27. List two primes that are consecutive natural numbers. Can there be any others?

28. Can there be three primes that are consecutive natural numbers? Explain.

29. For a natural number to be divisible by both 2 and 5, what must be true about its last digit?

30. Consider the divisibility tests for 2, 4, and 8 (all powers of 2). Use inductive reasoning to predict the divisibility test for 16. Then, use the test to show that 456,882,320 is divisible by 16.

31. Redraw the factor tree of Example 5, assuming that you first observe that $504 = 12 \cdot 42$, then that $12 = 3 \cdot 4$ and $42 = 6 \cdot 7$. Complete the process and give the resulting prime factorization.

32. Explain how your result in Exercise 31 verifies the fundamental theorem of arithmetic.

Find the prime factorization of each composite number.

33. 240   34. 300

35. 360   36. 425

37. 663   38. 885

Here is a divisibility test for 7.

(a) *Double the last digit of the given number, and subtract this value from the given number with the last digit omitted.*

(b) *Repeat the process of part* (a) *as many times as necessary until the number obtained can easily be divided by* 7.

(c) *If the final number obtained is divisible by* 7, *then the given number also is divisible by* 7. *If the final number is not divisible by* 7, *then neither is the given number.*

Use this divisibility test to determine whether each number is divisible by 7.

39. 142,891   40. 409,311

41. 458,485   42. 287,824

Here is a divisibility test for 11.

(a) *Starting at the left of the given number, add together every other digit.*

(b) *Add together the remaining digits.*

(c) *Subtract the smaller of the two sums from the larger. (If they are the same, the difference is* 0.)

(d) *If the final number obtained is divisible by* 11, *then the given number also is divisible by* 11. *If the final number is not divisible by* 11, *then neither is the given number.*

Use this divisibility test to determine whether each number is divisible by 11.

43. 8,493,969   44. 847,667,942

45. 453,896,248   46. 552,749,913

47. Consider the divisibility test for the composite number 6, and make a conjecture for the divisibility test for the composite number 15.

48. Explain what is meant by a "proof by contradiction."

49. Give two factorizations of the number 75 that are not prime factorizations.

50. Explain, in general, when a factorization is a prime factorization.

Determine all possible digit replacements for x so that the first number is divisible by the second. For example, 37,58x *is divisible by* 2 *if*

$$x = 0, 2, 4, 6, or\ 8.$$

51. 398,87x; 2   52. 2,45x,765; 3

53. 64,537,84x; 4   54. 2,143,89x; 5

55. 985,23x; 6   56. 7,643,24x; 8

57. 4,329,7x5; 9   58. 23,x54,470; 10

There is a method to determine the **number of divisors** *of a composite number. To do this, write the composite number in its prime factored form, using exponents. Add* 1 *to each exponent and multiply these numbers. Their product gives the number of divisors of the composite number. For example,*

$$24 = 2^3 \cdot 3 = 2^3 \cdot 3^1.$$

Now add 1 *to each exponent:*

$$3 + 1 = 4, 1 + 1 = 2.$$

Multiply $4 \cdot 2$ *to get* 8. *There are* 8 *divisors of* 24. *(Because* 24 *is rather small, this can be verified easily. The divisors are* 1, 2, 3, 4, 6, 8, 12, *and* 24, *a total of eight as predicted.)*

(*continued*)

Find the number of divisors of each composite number.

59. 48

60. 144

61. $2^8 \cdot 3^2$

62. $2^4 \cdot 3^4 \cdot 5^2$

Leap years occur when the year number is divisible by 4. An exception to this occurs when the year number is divisible by 100 (that is, it ends in two zeros). In such a case, the number must be divisible by 400 in order for the year to be a leap year. Determine which years are leap years.

63. 1776

64. 1894

65. 2400

66. 1800

67. Why is the following *not* a valid divisibility test for 8? "A number is divisible by 8 if it is divisible by both 4 and 2." Support your answer with an example.

68. Choose any three consecutive natural numbers, multiply them together, and divide the product by 6. Repeat this several times, using different choices of three consecutive numbers. Make a conjecture concerning the result.

69. Explain why the product of three consecutive natural numbers must be divisible by 6.

70. Choose any 6-digit number consisting of three digits followed by the same three digits in the same order (for example, 467,467). Divide by 13. Divide by 11. Divide by 7. What do you notice? Why do you think this happens?

71. Verify that Euler's polynomial prime-generating formula

$$n^2 - n + 41$$

fails to produce a prime for $n = 41$.

72. Evaluate Euler's polynomial formula for **(a)** $n = 42$, and **(b)** $n = 43$.

73. Choose the correct completion: For $n > 41$, Euler's formula produces a prime
A. never. **B.** sometimes. **C.** always.
(*Hint:* If no prime less than or equal to $\sqrt{n}$ divides n, then n is prime.)

74. Recall that Escott's formula, $n^2 - 79n + 1601$, fails to produce a prime for $n = 80$. Evaluate this formula for $n = 81$ and $n = 82$ and then complete the following statement: For $n > 80$, Escott's formula produces a prime
A. never. **B.** sometimes. **C.** always.

75. **(a)** Evaluate the Fermat number $2^{2^n} + 1$ for $n = 4$.
(b) In seeking possible prime factors of the Fermat number of part (a), what is the largest potential prime factor that one would have to try? (As stated in the text, this "fifth" Fermat number is in fact prime.)

76. **(a)** Verify the value given in the text for the "sixth" Fermat number (i.e., $2^{2^5} + 1$).
(b) Divide this Fermat number by 641. (Euler discovered this factorization in 1732, proving that the sixth Fermat number is not prime.)

77. Write a short report on the Great Internet Mersenne Prime Search (GIMPS).

78. Write a short report identifying the 40th, 41st, and 42nd known Mersenne primes and how, when, and by whom they were found.

79. The Mersenne margin note on page 228 cites a 1644 claim that was not totally resolved for some 300 years. Find out when, and by whom, Mersenne's five errors were demonstrated. (*Hint:* One was mentioned in the margin note on page 224.)

80. In Euclid's proof that there is no largest prime, we formed a number M by taking the product of primes and adding 1. Observe the pattern below.

$M = 2 + 1 = 3$	(3 is prime)
$M = 2 \cdot 3 + 1 = 7$	(7 is prime)
$M = 2 \cdot 3 \cdot 5 + 1 = 31$	(31 is prime)
$M = 2 \cdot 3 \cdot 5 \cdot 7 + 1 = 211$	(211 is prime)
$M = 2 \cdot 3 \cdot 5 \cdot 7 \cdot 11 + 1 = 2311$	(2311 is prime)

It seems as though this pattern will always yield a prime number. Now evaluate

$$M = 2 \cdot 3 \cdot 5 \cdot 7 \cdot 11 \cdot 13 + 1.$$

81. Is M prime or composite? If composite, give its prime factorization.

82. Explain in your own words the proof by Euclid that there is no largest prime.

The text stated that the Mersenne number M_n is composite whenever n is composite. Exercises 83–86 on the next page develop one way you can always find a factor of such a Mersenne number.

83. For the composite number $n = 6$, find

$$M_n = 2^n - 1.$$

84. Notice that $p = 3$ is a prime factor of $n = 6$. Find $2^p - 1$ for $p = 3$. Is $2^p - 1$ a factor of $2^n - 1$?

85. Complete this statement: If p is a prime factor of n, then _____ is a factor of the Mersenne number $2^n - 1$.

86. Find $M_n = 2^n - 1$ for $n = 10$.

87. Use the statement of Exercise 85 to find two distinct factors of M_{10}.

88. Do you think this procedure will always produce *prime* factors of M_n for composite n? (*Hint:* Consider $n = 22$ and its prime factor $p = 11$, and recall the statement following Example 6.) Explain.

5.2 Selected Topics from Number Theory

Perfect Numbers • Deficient and Abundant Numbers • Amicable (Friendly) Numbers • Goldbach's Conjecture • Twin Primes • Fermat's Last Theorem

The mathematician **Albert Wilansky,** when phoning his brother-in-law, Mr. Smith, noticed an interesting property concerning Smith's phone number (493–7775). The number 4,937,775 is composite, and its prime factorization is 3 · 5 · 5 · 65,837. When the digits of the phone number are added, the result, 42, is equal to the sum of the digits in the prime factors: 3 + 5 + 5 + 6 + 5 + 8 + 3 + 7 = 42. Wilansky termed such a number a **Smith number.** In 1985 it was proved that there are infinitely many Smith numbers, but there still are many unanswered questions about them.

Perfect Numbers In an earlier chapter we introduced figurate numbers, a topic investigated by the Pythagoreans. This group of Greek mathematicians and musicians held their meetings in secret, and were led by Pythagoras. In this section we examine some of the other special numbers that fascinated the Pythagoreans and are still studied by mathematicians today.

Divisors of a natural number were covered in Section 5.1. The **proper divisors** of a natural number include all divisors of the number except the number itself. For example, the proper divisors of 8 are 1, 2, and 4. (8 is *not* a proper divisor of 8.)

> **Perfect Numbers**
>
> A natural number is said to be **perfect** if it is equal to the sum of its proper divisors.

Is 8 perfect? No, because $1 + 2 + 4 = 7$, and $7 \neq 8$. The least perfect number is 6, because the proper divisors of 6 are 1, 2, and 3, and

$$1 + 2 + 3 = 6. \quad \text{6 is perfect.}$$

EXAMPLE 1 Verifying a Perfect Number

Show that 28 is a perfect number.

SOLUTION

The proper divisors of 28 are 1, 2, 4, 7, and 14. The sum of these is 28:

$$1 + 2 + 4 + 7 + 14 = 28.$$

By the definition, 28 is perfect. ▪

The numbers 6 and 28 are the two least perfect numbers. The next two are 496 and 8128. The pattern of these first four perfect numbers led early writers to conjecture that

1. The nth perfect number contains exactly n digits.
2. The even perfect numbers end in the digits 6 and 8, alternately. } Conjectures

(Exercises 41–43 will help you evaluate these conjectures.)

There still are many unanswered questions about perfect numbers. Euclid showed that if $2^n - 1$ is prime, then $2^{n-1}(2^n - 1)$ is perfect, and conversely. Because the prime values of $2^n - 1$ are the Mersenne primes (discussed in the previous section), this means that for every new Mersenne prime discovered, another perfect number is automatically revealed. (Hence, as of early 2006, there were also 43 known perfect numbers.) It is also known that all even perfect numbers must take the form $2^{n-1}(2^n - 1)$ and it is strongly suspected that no odd perfect numbers exist. (Any odd one would have at least eight different prime factors and would have at least 300 decimal digits.) Therefore, Euclid and the early Greeks most likely identified the form of all perfect numbers.

Deficient and Abundant Numbers   Earlier we saw that 8 is not perfect because it is not equal to the sum of its proper divisors ($8 \neq 7$). Next we define two alternative categories for natural numbers that are *not* perfect.

A number is said to be a **weird number** if it is abundant without being equal to the sum of any set of its own proper divisors. For example, 70 is weird because it is abundant ($1 + 2 + 5 + 7 + 10 + 14 + 35 = 74 > 70$), but no set of the factors 1, 2, 5, 7, 10, 14, 35 adds up to 70.

Deficient and Abundant Numbers

A natural number is **deficient** if it is greater than the sum of its proper divisors. It is **abundant** if it is less than the sum of its proper divisors.

Based on this definition, a *deficient number* is one with proper divisors that add up to less than the number itself, while an *abundant number* is one with proper divisors that add up to more than the number itself. For example, because the proper divisors of 8 (1, 2, and 4) add up to 7, which is less than 8, the number 8 is deficient.

EXAMPLE 2   Identifying Deficient and Abundant Numbers

Decide whether each number is deficient or abundant.

(a) 12   (b) 10

SOLUTION

(a) The proper divisors of 12 are 1, 2, 3, 4, and 6. The sum of these divisors is 16. Because $16 > 12$, the number 12 is abundant.
(b) The proper divisors of 10 are 1, 2, and 5. Since $1 + 2 + 5 = 8$, and $8 < 10$, the number 10 is deficient. ▪

Amicable (Friendly) Numbers   Suppose that we add the proper divisors of 284:

$$1 + 2 + 4 + 71 + 142 = 220.$$

Their sum is 220. Now, add the proper divisors of 220:

$$1 + 2 + 4 + 5 + 10 + 11 + 20 + 22 + 44 + 55 + 110 = 284.$$

An extension of the idea of amicable numbers results in **sociable numbers.** In a chain of sociable numbers, the sum of the proper divisors of each number is the next number in the chain, and the sum of the proper divisors of the last number in the chain is the first number. Here is a 5-link chain of sociable numbers:

> 12,496
> 14,288
> 15,472
> 14,536
> 14,264.

The number 14,316 starts a 28-link chain of sociable numbers.

A Dull Number? The Indian mathematician **Srinivasa Ramanujan** (1887–1920) developed many ideas in number theory. His friend and collaborator on occasion was G. H. Hardy, also a number theorist and professor at Cambridge University in England.

A story has been told about Ramanujan that illustrates his genius. Hardy once mentioned to Ramanujan that he had just taken a taxicab with a rather dull number: 1729. Ramanujan countered by saying that this number isn't dull at all; it is the smallest natural number that can be expressed as the sum of two cubes in two different ways:

$$1^3 + 12^3 = 1729$$
and $$9^3 + 10^3 = 1729.$$

Show that 85 can be written as the sum of two squares in two ways.

Notice that the sum of the proper divisors of 220 is 284, while the sum of the proper divisors of 284 is 220. Number pairs such as these are said to be *amicable,* or *friendly*.

Amicable or Friendly Numbers

The natural numbers a and b are **amicable,** or **friendly,** if the sum of the proper divisors of a is b, and the sum of the proper divisors of b is a.

The smallest pair of amicable numbers, 220 and 284, was known to the Pythagoreans, but it was not until more than 1000 years later that the next pair, 17,296 and 18,416, was discovered. Many more pairs were found over the next few decades, but it took a 16-year-old Italian boy named Nicolo Paganini to discover in the year 1866 that the pair of amicable numbers 1184 and 1210 had been overlooked for centuries!

Today, powerful computers continually extend the lists of known amicable pairs. The last time we checked, over ten million pairs were known. It still is unknown, however, if there are infinitely many such pairs. Finally, no one has found an amicable pair without prime factors in common, but the possibility of such a pair has not been eliminated.

Goldbach's Conjecture   One of the most famous unsolved problems in mathematics is Goldbach's conjecture. The mathematician Christian Goldbach (1690–1764) stated the following conjecture (guess).

Goldbach's Conjecture (Not Proved)

Every even number greater than 2 can be written as the sum of two prime numbers.
Examples: $8 = 5 + 3$
$$10 = 5 + 5 \text{ (or } 10 = 7 + 3)$$

Mathematicians have tried to prove the conjecture but have not been successful. However, the conjecture has been verified (as of early 2006) for numbers up to 2×10^{17}.

EXAMPLE 3   Expressing Numbers as Sums of Primes

Write each even number as the sum of two primes.

(a) 18   **(b)** 60

SOLUTION

(a) $18 = 5 + 13$. Another way of writing it is $7 + 11$. Notice that $1 + 17$ is *not* valid because by definition 1 is not a prime number.

(b) $60 = 7 + 53$. Can you find other ways? Why is $3 + 57$ not valid?   ▪

Mathematics professor Gregory Larkin, played by Jeff Bridges, woos colleague Rose Morgan (Barbra Streisand) in the 1996 film *The Mirror Has Two Faces.* Larkin's research and book focus on the **twin prime conjecture,** which he correctly states in a dinner scene. He is amazed that his nonmathematician friend actually understands what he is talking about.

Twin Primes Prime numbers that differ by 2 are called **twin primes.** Some twin primes are 3 and 5, 5 and 7, 11 and 13, and so on. Like Goldbach's conjecture, the following conjecture about twin primes has never been proved, although significant progress toward a proof was announced in 2005.

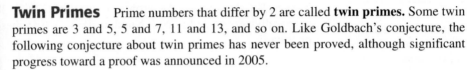

Twin Prime Conjecture (Not Proved)

There are infinitely many pairs of twin primes.

You may wish to verify that there are eight such pairs less than 100, using the Sieve of Eratosthenes in Table 1. As of early 2006, the largest known twin primes were

$$16{,}869{,}987{,}339{,}975 \cdot 2^{171{,}960} \pm 1.$$

Each contains 51,779 digits.

Recall from Section 5.1 that Euclid's proof of the infinitude of primes used numbers of the form $p_1 \cdot p_2 \cdot p_3 \ldots p_n + 1$, where all the ps are prime. It may seem that any such number must be prime, but that is not so. (See Exercise 80 of Section 5.1.) However, this form often does produce primes (as does the same form with the plus replaced by a minus). When *all* the primes up to p_n are included, the resulting numbers, if prime, are called **primorial primes.** They are denoted

$$p\# \pm 1.$$

For example, $5\# + 1 = 2 \cdot 3 \cdot 5 + 1 = 31$ is a primorial prime. (In late 2005, the largest known primorial prime was $392{,}113\# + 1$, a number with 169,966 digits.) The primorial primes are a popular place to look for twin primes.

Sophie Germain (1776–1831) studied at the École Polytechnique in Paris in a day when female students were not admitted. A **Sophie Germain prime** is an odd prime p for which $2p + 1$ also is prime. Lately, large Sophie Germain primes have been discovered at the rate of several per year. As of early 2006, the largest one known was $137{,}211{,}941{,}292{,}195 \cdot 2^{171{,}960} - 1$, which has 51,780 digits.

Source: www.utm.edu/research/primes

EXAMPLE 4 Verifying Twin Primes

Verify that the primorial formula $p\# \pm 1$ produces twin prime pairs for both **(a)** $p = 3$ and **(b)** $p = 5$.

SOLUTION

(a) $3\# \pm 1 = 2 \cdot 3 \pm 1 = 6 \pm 1 = 5$ and 7   Twin primes

Multiply, then add and subtract.

(b) $5\# \pm 1 = 2 \cdot 3 \cdot 5 \pm 1 = 30 \pm 1 = 29$ and 31   Twin primes

Fermat's Last Theorem In any right triangle with shorter sides a and b, and longest side (hypotenuse) c, the equation $a^2 + b^2 = c^2$ will hold true. This is the famous Pythagorean theorem. For example,

$$3^2 + 4^2 = 5^2 \quad a = 3, b = 4, c = 5$$
$$9 + 16 = 25$$
$$25 = 25.$$

It is known that there are infinitely many such triples (a, b, c) that satisfy the equation

$$a^2 + b^2 = c^2.$$

Is something similar true of the equation

$$a^n + b^n = c^n$$

for natural numbers $n \geq 3$? Pierre de Fermat, profiled in a margin note on page 241, thought that not only were there not infinitely many such triples, but that there were, in fact, none. He made the following claim in the 1600s.

Fermat's Last Theorem (Proved in the 1990s)

For *any* natural number $n \geq 3$, there are *no* triples (a, b, c) that satisfy the equation

$$a^n + b^n = c^n.$$

Fermat wrote in the margin of a book that he had "a truly wonderful proof" for this, but that the margin was "too small to contain it." Did he indeed have a proof, or did he have an incorrect proof?

Whatever the case, Fermat's assertion was the object of some 350 years of attempts by mathematicians to provide a suitable proof. While it was verified for many specific cases (Fermat himself proved it for $n = 3$), a proof of the general case could not be found until the Princeton mathematician Andrew Wiles announced a proof in the spring of 1993. Although some flaws were discovered in his argument, Wiles was able, by the fall of 1994, to repair and even improve the proof.

There were probably about 100 mathematicians around the world qualified to understand the Wiles proof. Many of these examined and approved it. Today Fermat's Last Theorem finally is regarded by the mathematics community as officially proved.

The solution to the Chapter Opener problem is as follows.

The first term on the left side, 1782^{12}, must be an even number, because raising an even number to any power yields an even number. The second term on the left side, 1841^{12}, must be odd, because raising an odd number to any power yields an odd number (in this case, we know that it must have 1 as units digit as well). The sum on the left side must be odd, because even + odd = odd.

The right side must be an even number using the earlier reasoning. So the equation indicates that an odd number is equal to an even number, which is impossible.

EXAMPLE 5   Using a Theorem Proved by Fermat

One of the theorems legitimately proved by Fermat is as follows:

Every odd prime can be expressed as the difference of two squares in one and only one way.

Express each odd prime as the difference of two squares.

(a) 3   **(b)** 7

SOLUTION

(a) $3 = 4 - 1 = 2^2 - 1^2$
(b) $7 = 16 - 9 = 4^2 - 3^2$

For Further Thought

Curious and Interesting

One of the most remarkable books on number theory is *The Penguin Dictionary of Curious and Interesting Numbers* (1986) by David Wells. This book contains fascinating numbers and their properties, including the following.

- There are only three sets of three digits that form prime numbers in all possible arrangements: $\{1, 1, 3\}$, $\{1, 9, 9\}$, $\{3, 3, 7\}$.
- Find the sum of the cubes of the digits of 136: $1^3 + 3^3 + 6^3 = 244$. Repeat the process with the digits of 244: $2^3 + 4^3 + 4^3 = 136$. We're back to where we started.
- 635,318,657 is the least number that can be expressed as the sum of two fourth powers in two ways:

$$635{,}318{,}657 = 59^4 + 158^4 = 133^4 + 134^4.$$

- The number 24,678,050 has an interesting property:

$$24{,}678{,}050 = 2^8 + 4^8 + 6^8 + 7^8 + 8^8 + 0^8$$
$$+ \, 5^8 + 0^8.$$

- The number 54,748 has a similar interesting property:

$$54{,}748 = 5^5 + 4^5 + 7^5 + 4^5 + 8^5.$$

- The number 3435 has this property:

$$3435 = 3^3 + 4^4 + 3^3 + 5^5.$$

For anyone whose curiosity is piqued by such facts, this book is for you!

For Group Discussion or Individual Investigation

Have each student in the class choose a three-digit number that is a multiple of 3. Add the cubes of the digits. Repeat the process until the same number is obtained over and over. Then, have the students compare their results. What is curious and interesting about this process?

5.2 EXERCISES

Decide whether each statement in Exercises 1–10 is true *or* false.

1. There are infinitely many prime numbers.

2. The prime numbers 2 and 3 are twin primes.

3. There is no perfect number between 496 and 8128.

4. $2^n - 1$ is prime if and only if $2^{n-1}(2^n - 1)$ is perfect.

5. Any prime number must be deficient.

6. The equation $17 + 51 = 68$ verifies Goldbach's conjecture for the number 68.

7. There are more Mersenne primes known than there are perfect numbers.

8. The number 31 cannot be represented as the difference of two squares.

9. The number $2^6(2^7 - 1)$ is perfect.

10. A natural number greater than 1 will be one and only one of the following: perfect, deficient, or abundant.

11. The proper divisors of 496 are 1, 2, 4, 8, 16, 31, 62, 124, and 248. Use this information to verify that 496 is perfect.

12. The proper divisors of 8128 are 1, 2, 4, 8, 16, 32, 64, 127, 254, 508, 1016, 2032, and 4064. Use this information to verify that 8128 is perfect.

13. As mentioned in the text, when $2^n - 1$ is prime, $2^{n-1}(2^n - 1)$ is perfect. By letting $n = 2, 3, 5,$ and 7, we obtain the first four perfect numbers. Show that $2^n - 1$ is prime for $n = 13$, and then find the decimal digit representation for the fifth perfect number.

14. At the end of 2005, the largest known prime number was $2^{30,402,457} - 1$. Use the formula in Exercise 13 to

write an expression for the perfect number generated by this prime number.

15. It has been proved that the reciprocals of *all* the positive divisors of a perfect number have a sum of 2. Verify this for the perfect number 6.

16. Consider the following equations.

$$6 = 1 + 2 + 3$$
$$28 = 1 + 2 + 3 + 4 + 5 + 6 + 7$$

Show that a similar equation is valid for the third perfect number, 496.

Determine whether each number is abundant *or* deficient.

17. 36   **18.** 30

19. 75   **20.** 95

21. There are four abundant numbers between 1 and 25. Find them. (*Hint:* They are all even, and no prime number is abundant.)

22. Explain why a prime number must be deficient.

23. The first odd abundant number is 945. Its proper divisors are 1, 3, 5, 7, 9, 15, 21, 27, 35, 45, 63, 105, 135, 189, and 315. Use this information to verify that 945 is abundant.

24. Explain in your own words the terms *perfect number,* *abundant number,* and *deficient number.*

25. Nicolo Paganini's numbers 1184 and 1210 are amicable. The proper divisors of 1184 are 1, 2, 4, 8, 16, 32, 37, 74, 148, 296, and 592. The proper divisors of 1210 are 1, 2, 5, 10, 11, 22, 55, 110, 121, 242, and 605. Use the definition of amicable (friendly) numbers to show that they are indeed amicable.

26. An Arabian mathematician of the ninth century stated the following.
     If the three numbers

$$x = 3 \cdot 2^{n-1} - 1,$$
$$y = 3 \cdot 2^n - 1,$$
and $$z = 9 \cdot 2^{2n-1} - 1$$

are all prime and $n \geq 2$, then $2^n xy$ and $2^n z$ are amicable numbers.
   (a) Use $n = 2$, and show that the result is the least pair of amicable numbers, namely 220 and 284.

   (b) Use $n = 4$ to obtain another pair of amicable numbers.

Write each even number as the sum of two primes. (There may be more than one way to do this.)

27. 14   **28.** 22

29. 26   **30.** 32

31. Joseph Louis Lagrange (1736–1813) conjectured that every odd natural number greater than 5 can be written as a sum $a + 2b$, where a and b are both primes. Verify this for the odd natural number 11.

32. Another unproved conjecture in number theory states that every natural number multiple of 6 can be written as the difference of two primes. Verify this for 6, 12, and 18.

Find one pair of twin primes between the two numbers given.

33. 65, 80

34. 85, 105

35. 125, 140

While Pierre de Fermat probably is best known for his now famous "last theorem," he did provide proofs of many other theorems in number theory. Exercises 36–40 investigate some of these theorems.

36. If p is prime and the natural numbers a and p have no common factor except 1, then $a^{p-1} - 1$ is divisible by p.
   (a) Verify this for $p = 5$ and $a = 3$.
   (b) Verify this for $p = 7$ and $a = 2$.

37. Every odd prime can be expressed as the difference of two squares in one and only one way.
   (a) Find this one way for the prime number 5.
   (b) Find this one way for the prime number 11.

38. A prime number of the form $4k + 1$ can be represented as the sum of two squares.
   (a) The prime number 5 satisfies the conditions of the theorem, with $k = 1$. Verify this theorem for 5.
   (b) Verify this theorem for 13 (here, $k = 3$).

39. There is only one solution in natural numbers for $a^2 + 2 = b^3$, and it is $a = 5$, $b = 3$. Verify this solution.

40. There are only two solutions in integers for $a^2 + 4 = b^3$. One solution is $a = 2$, $b = 2$. Find the other solution.

The first four perfect numbers were identified in the text: 6, 28, 496, and 8128. The next two are 33,550,336 and 8,589,869,056. Use this information about perfect numbers to work Exercises 41–43.

41. Verify that each of these six perfect numbers ends in either 6 or 28. (In fact, this is true of all even perfect numbers.)

42. Is conjecture (1) in the text (that the *n*th perfect number contains exactly *n* digits) true or false? Explain.

43. Is conjecture (2) in the text (that the even perfect numbers end in the digits 6 and 8, alternately) true or false? Explain.

According to the Web site www.shyamsundergupta.com/ amicable.htm, a natural number is happy if the process of repeatedly summing the squares of its decimal digits finally ends in 1. For example, the least natural number (greater than 1) that is happy is 7, as shown here.

$$7^2 = 49, \quad 4^2 + 9^2 = 97, \quad 9^2 + 7^2 = 130,$$
$$1^2 + 3^2 + 0^2 = 10, \quad 1^2 + 0^2 = 1.$$

*An amicable pair is a **happy amicable pair** if and only if both members of the pair are happy numbers. (The first 5000 amicable pairs include only 111 that are happy amicable pairs.) For each amicable pair, determine whether neither, one, or both of the members are happy, and whether the pair is a happy amicable pair.*

44. 220 and 284

45. 1184 and 1210

46. 10,572,550 and 10,854,650

47. 35,361,326 and 40,117,714

48. If the early Greeks knew the form of all even perfect numbers, namely $2^{n-1}(2^n - 1)$, then why did they not discover all the ones that are known today?

49. Explain why the primorial formula $p\# \pm 1$ does not result in a pair of twin primes for the prime value $p = 2$.

50. (a) What two numbers does the primorial formula produce for $p = 7$?
　　(b) Which, if either, of these numbers is prime?

51. Choose the correct completion: The primorial formula produces twin primes
　　A. never.　　**B.** sometimes.　　**C.** always.

See the margin note (on page 236) defining a Sophie Germain prime, and complete this table.

	p	$2p + 1$	Is p a Sophie Germain prime?
52.	2	_____	_____
53.	3	_____	_____
54.	5	_____	_____
55.	7	_____	_____
56.	11	_____	_____
57.	13	_____	_____

Factorial primes *are of the form n! $\pm$ 1 for natural numbers n. (n! denotes "n factorial," the product of all natural numbers up to n, not just the primes as in the primorial primes. For example, 4! = 1 · 2 · 3 · 4 = 24.) As of early 2006, the largest verified factorial prime was 34,790! − 1, which has 142,891 digits. Find the missing entries in this table.*

n	$n!$	$n! - 1$	$n! + 1$	Is $n! - 1$ prime?	Is $n! + 1$ prime?
2	2	1	3	no	yes
58. 3	_____	_____	_____	_____	_____
59. 4	_____	_____	_____	_____	_____
60. 5	_____	_____	_____	_____	_____

61. Explain why the factorial prime formula does not give twin primes for $n = 2$.

Based on the preceding table, complete each statement with one of the following: **A.** *never,* **B.** *sometimes, or* **C.** *always. When applied to particular values of n, the factorial formula n! $\pm$ 1 produces*

62. no primes _____　　　　**63.** exactly one prime _____　　　　**64.** twin primes _____

5.3 Greatest Common Factor and Least Common Multiple

Greatest Common Factor • Least Common Multiple

Greatest Common Factor The **greatest common factor** is defined as follows.

Pierre de Fermat (about 1601–1665), a government official who did not interest himself in mathematics until he was past 30, devoted leisure time to its study. He was a worthy scholar, best known for his work in number theory. His other major contributions involved certain applications in geometry and his original work in probability.

Much of Fermat's best work survived only on loose sheets or jotted, without proof, in the margins of works that he read. Mathematicians of subsequent generations have not always had an easy time verifying some of those results, though their truth has generally not been doubted.

> **Greatest Common Factor**
>
> The **greatest common factor (GCF)** of a group of natural numbers is the largest natural number that is a factor of all the numbers in the group.
>
> *Examples:* 18 is the GCF of 36 and 54, because 18 is the largest natural number that divides both 36 and 54.
>
> 1 is the GCF of 7 and 16.

Greatest common factors can be found by using prime factorizations. To verify the GCF of 36 and 54, first write the prime factorization of each number (perhaps by using factor trees or repeated division):

$$36 = 2^2 \cdot 3^2 \quad \text{and} \quad 54 = 2^1 \cdot 3^3.$$

The GCF is the product of the primes common to the factorizations, with each prime raised to the power indicated by the *least* exponent that it has in any factorization. Here, the prime 2 has 1 as the smallest exponent (in $54 = 2^1 \cdot 3^3$), while the prime 3 has 2 as the least exponent (in $36 = 2^2 \cdot 3^2$). The GCF of 36 and 54 is

$$2^1 \cdot 3^2 = 2 \cdot 9 = 18,$$

as stated earlier. We summarize as follows.

> **Finding the Greatest Common Factor (Prime Factors Method)**
>
> *Step 1* Write the prime factorization of each number.
>
> *Step 2* Choose all primes common to *all* factorizations, with each prime raised to the *least* exponent that it has in any factorization.
>
> *Step 3* Form the product of all the numbers in Step 2; this product is the greatest common factor.

■ **EXAMPLE 1** **Finding the Greatest Common Factor by the Prime Factors Method**

Find the greatest common factor of 360 and 2700.

SOLUTION

Write the prime factorization of each number:

$$360 = 2^3 \cdot 3^2 \cdot 5 \quad \text{and} \quad 2700 = 2^2 \cdot 3^3 \cdot 5^2.$$

Now find the primes common to both factorizations, with each prime having as its exponent the *least* exponent from either product: 2^2, 3^2, 5. Then form the product of these numbers.

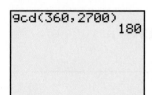

The calculator shows that the greatest common divisor (factor) of 360 and 2700 is 180. Compare with Example 1.

$$\text{GCF} = 2^2 \cdot 3^2 \cdot 5 = 180 \quad \text{Use the smallest exponents.}$$

The greatest common factor of 360 and 2700 is 180.

EXAMPLE 2   Finding the Greatest Common Factor by the Prime Factors Method

Find the greatest common factor of 720, 1000, and 1800.

SOLUTION

Write the prime factorization for each number:

$$720 = 2^4 \cdot 3^2 \cdot 5, \qquad 1000 = 2^3 \cdot 5^3, \qquad \text{and} \qquad 1800 = 2^3 \cdot 3^2 \cdot 5^2.$$

Use the smallest exponent on each prime common to the factorizations:

$$\text{GCF} = 2^3 \cdot 5 = 40.$$

(The prime 3 is not used in the greatest common factor because it does not appear in the prime factorization of 1000.)

EXAMPLE 3   Finding the Greatest Common Factor by the Prime Factors Method

Find the greatest common factor of 80 and 63.

SOLUTION

Start with

$$80 = 2^4 \cdot 5 \quad \text{and} \quad 63 = 3^2 \cdot 7.$$

There are no primes in common here, so the GCF is 1. The number 1 is the largest number that will divide into both 80 and 63.

Two numbers, such as 80 and 63, with a greatest common factor of 1 are called **relatively prime numbers**—that is, they are prime *relative* to one another. (They have no common factors other than 1.)

Another method of finding the greatest common factor involves dividing the numbers by common prime factors.

Finding the Greatest Common Factor (Dividing by Prime Factors Method)

Step 1   Write the numbers in a row.

Step 2   Divide each of the numbers by a common prime factor. Try 2, then try 3, and so on.

Step 3   Divide the quotients by a common prime factor. Continue until no prime will divide into all the quotients.

Step 4   The product of the primes in Steps 2 and 3 is the greatest common factor.

EXAMPLE 4   Finding the Greatest Common Factor by Dividing by Prime Factors

Find the greatest common factor of 12, 18, and 60.

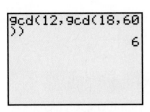

This screen uses the fact that gcd $(a, b, c) = $ gcd $(a,$ gcd$(b, c))$. Compare with Example 4.

SOLUTION

Write the numbers in a row and divide by 2.

$$2\underline{|12 \quad 18 \quad 60}$$
$$6 \quad 9 \quad 30$$

The numbers 6, 9, and 30 are not all divisible by 2, but they are divisible by 3.

$$2\underline{|12 \quad 18 \quad 60}$$
$$3\underline{|6 \quad 9 \quad 30}$$
$$2 \quad 3 \quad 10$$

No prime divides into 2, 3, and 10, so the greatest common factor of the numbers 12, 18, and 60 is given by the product of the primes on the left, 2 and 3.

$$2\underline{|12 \quad 18 \quad 60}$$
$$3\underline{|6 \quad 9 \quad 30}$$
$$2 \quad 3 \quad 10$$
$$2 \cdot 3 = 6$$

The GCF of 12, 18, and 60 is 6.

There is yet another method of finding the greatest common factor of two numbers (but not more than two) that does not require factoring into primes or successively dividing by primes. It is called the **Euclidean algorithm,*** and it is illustrated in the next example.

▦ **EXAMPLE 5   Finding the Greatest Common Factor Using the Euclidean Algorithm**

Use the Euclidean algorithm to find the greatest common factor of 90 and 168.

SOLUTION

Step 1   Begin by dividing the larger, 168, by the smaller, 90. Disregard the quotient, but note the remainder.

$$\begin{array}{r} 1 \\ 90\overline{)168} \\ \underline{90} \\ 78 \end{array}$$

Step 2   Divide the smaller of the two numbers by the remainder obtained in Step 1. Once again, note the remainder.

$$\begin{array}{r} 1 \\ 78\overline{)90} \\ \underline{78} \\ 12 \end{array}$$

Step 3   Continue dividing the successive remainders, as many times as necessary to obtain a remainder of 0.

$$\begin{array}{r} 6 \\ 12\overline{)78} \\ \underline{72} \\ 6 \end{array}$$

Greatest common factor

Step 4   The *last positive remainder* in this process is the greatest common factor of 90 and 168. It can be seen that their GCF is 6.

$$\begin{array}{r} 2 \\ 6\overline{)12} \\ \underline{12} \\ 0 \end{array}$$

▦

---

*For a proof that this process does indeed give the greatest common factor, see *Elementary Introduction to Number Theory, Second Edition*, by Calvin T. Long, pp. 34–35.

The Euclidean algorithm is particularly useful if the two numbers are difficult to factor into primes. We summarize the algorithm here.

Finding the Greatest Common Factor (Euclidean Algorithm)

To find the greatest common factor of two unequal numbers, divide the larger by the smaller. Note the remainder, and divide the previous divisor by this remainder. Continue the process until a remainder of 0 is obtained. The greatest common factor is the last positive remainder obtained in this process.

Least Common Multiple   Closely related to the idea of the greatest common factor is the concept of the *least common multiple*, which we define as follows.

Least Common Multiple

The **least common multiple (LCM)** of a group of natural numbers is the smallest natural number that is a multiple of all the numbers in the group.

Example: 30 is the LCM of 15 and 10 because 30 is the smallest number that appears in both sets of multiples.

Multiples of 15:   {15, **30,** 45, 60, 75, 90, 105, . . . }
Multiples of 10:   {10, 20, **30,** 40, 50, 60, 70, . . . }

```
lcm(15,10)
              30
```

The least common multiple of 15 and 10 is 30.

The set of natural numbers that are multiples of *both* 15 and 10 form the set of *common multiples:*

$$\{30, 60, 90, 120, \dots \}.$$

While there are infinitely many common multiples, the *least* common multiple is observed to be 30.

A method similar to the first one given for the greatest common factor may be used to find the least common multiple of a group of numbers.

Finding the Least Common Multiple (Prime Factors Method)

Step 1   Write the prime factorization of each number.

Step 2   Choose all primes belonging to *any* factorization, with each prime raised to the power indicated by the *largest* exponent that it has in any factorization.

Step 3   Form the product of all the numbers in Step 2; this product is the least common multiple.

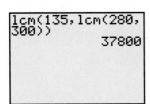

The least common multiple of 135, 280, and 300 is 37,800. Compare with Example 6.

EXAMPLE 6 **Finding the Least Common Multiple by the Prime Factors Method**

Find the least common multiple of 135, 280, and 300.

SOLUTION

Write the prime factorizations:

$$135 = 3^3 \cdot 5, \quad 280 = 2^3 \cdot 5 \cdot 7, \quad \text{and} \quad 300 = 2^2 \cdot 3 \cdot 5^2.$$

Form the product of all the primes that appear in *any* of the factorizations. Use the *largest* exponent from any factorization.

$$\text{LCM} = 2^3 \cdot 3^3 \cdot 5^2 \cdot 7 = 37{,}800 \qquad \textit{Use the largest exponents.}$$

The smallest natural number divisible by 135, 280, and 300 is 37,800.

The least common multiple of a group of numbers can also be found by dividing by prime factors. The process is slightly different than that for finding the GCF.

Finding the Least Common Multiple (Dividing by Prime Factors Method)

Step 1 Write the numbers in a row.

Step 2 Divide each of the numbers by a common prime factor. Try 2, then try 3, and so on.

Step 3 Divide the quotients by a common prime factor. When no prime will divide all quotients, but a prime will divide some of them, divide where possible and bring any nondivisible quotients down. Continue until no prime will divide any two quotients.

Step 4 The product of all prime divisors from Steps 2 and 3 as well as all remaining quotients is the least common multiple.

EXAMPLE 7 **Finding the Least Common Multiple by Dividing by Prime Factors**

Find the least common multiple of 12, 18, and 60.

SOLUTION

Proceed just as in Example 4 to obtain the following.

$$
\begin{array}{r|ccc}
2 & 12 & 18 & 60 \\
3 & 6 & 9 & 30 \\
  & 2 & 3 & 10
\end{array}
$$

Now, even though no prime will divide 2, 3, and 10, the prime 2 will divide 2 and 10. Divide the 2 and the 10 and bring down the 3.

$$
\begin{array}{r|ccc}
2 & 12 & 18 & 60 \\
3 & 6 & 9 & 30 \\
2 & 2 & 3 & 10 \\
  & 1 & 3 & 5
\end{array}
\qquad 2 \cdot 3 \cdot 2 \cdot 1 \cdot 3 \cdot 5 = 180
$$

The LCM of 12, 18, and 60 is 180.

It is shown in more advanced courses that the least common multiple of two numbers *m* and *n* can be obtained by dividing their product by their greatest common factor.

Finding the Least Common Multiple (Formula)

The least common multiple of *m* and *n* is given by

$$LCM = \frac{m \cdot n}{\text{greatest common factor of } m \text{ and } n}.$$

(This method works only for two numbers, not for more than two.)

```
(90*168)/gcd(90,
168)
                 2520
```

This supports the result in Example 8.

EXAMPLE 8 Finding the Least Common Multiple by Formula

Use the formula to find the least common multiple of 90 and 168.

SOLUTION

In Example 5 we used the Euclidean algorithm to find that the greatest common factor of 90 and 168 is 6. Therefore, the formula gives us

$$\text{Least common multiple of 90 and 168} = \frac{90 \cdot 168}{6} = 2520.$$
∎

PROBLEM-SOLVING HINT Problems that deal with questions such as "How many objects will there be in each group if each group contains the same number of objects?" and "When will two events occur at the same time?" can sometimes be solved using the ideas of greatest common factor and least common multiple.

EXAMPLE 9 Finding Common Starting Times of Movie Cycles

The King Theatre and the Star Theatre run movies continuously, and each starts its first feature at 1:00 P.M. If the movie shown at the King lasts 80 minutes and the movie shown at the Star lasts 2 hours, when will the two movies start again at the same time?

SOLUTION

First, convert 2 hours to 120 minutes. The question can be restated as follows: "What is the smallest number of minutes it will take for the two movies to start at the same time again?" This is equivalent to asking, "What is the least common multiple of 80 and 120?" Using any of the methods described in this section, it can be shown that the least common multiple of 80 and 120 is 240. Therefore, it will take 240 minutes, or $\frac{240}{60} = 4$ hours for the movies to start again at the same time. By adding 4 hours to 1:00 P.M., we find that they will start together again at 5:00 P.M. ∎

EXAMPLE 10 Finding the Largest Common Size of Stacks of Cards

Joshua Hornsby has 450 football cards and 840 baseball cards. He wants to place them in stacks on a table so that each stack has the same number of cards, and no stack has different types of cards within it. What is the largest number of cards that he can have in each stack?

SOLUTION

Here, we are looking for the largest number that will divide evenly into 450 and 840. This is, of course, the greatest common factor of 450 and 840. Using any of the methods described in this section, we find that

greatest common factor of 450 and 840 = 30.

Therefore, the largest number of cards he can have in each stack is 30. ▪

5.3 EXERCISES

Decide whether each statement is true *or* false.

1. Two even natural numbers cannot be relatively prime.

2. Two different prime numbers must be relatively prime.

3. If p is a prime number, then the greatest common factor of p and p^2 is p.

4. If p is a prime number, then the least common multiple of p and p^2 is p^3.

5. There is no prime number p such that the greatest common factor of p and 2 is 2.

6. The set of all common multiples of two given natural numbers is finite.

7. Two natural numbers must have at least one common factor.

8. The least common multiple of two different primes is their product.

9. Two composite numbers may be relatively prime.

10. The set of all common factors of two given natural numbers is finite.

Use the prime factors method to find the greatest common factor of each group of numbers.

11. 70 and 120

12. 180 and 300

13. 480 and 1800

14. 168 and 504

15. 28, 35, and 56

16. 252, 308, and 504

Use the method of dividing by prime factors to find the greatest common factor of each group of numbers.

17. 60 and 84

18. 130 and 455

19. 310 and 460

20. 234 and 470

21. 12, 18, and 30

22. 450, 1500, and 432

Use the Euclidean algorithm to find the greatest common factor of each group of numbers.

23. 36 and 60

24. 25 and 70

25. 84 and 180

26. 72 and 120

27. 210 and 560

28. 150 and 480

29. Explain in your own words how to find the greatest common factor of a group of numbers.

30. Explain in your own words how to find the least common multiple of a group of numbers.

Use the prime factors method to find the least common multiple of each group of numbers.

31. 24 and 30

32. 12 and 32

33. 56 and 96

34. 28 and 70

35. 30, 40, and 70

36. 24, 36, and 48

Use the method of dividing by prime factors to find the least common multiple of each group of numbers.

37. 24 and 32

38. 35 and 56

39. 45 and 75

40. 48, 54, and 60

41. 16, 120, and 216

42. 210, 385, and 2310

Use the formula given in the text and the results of Exercises 23–28 to find the least common multiple of each group of numbers.

43. 36 and 60

44. 25 and 70

45. 84 and 180

46. 72 and 120

47. 210 and 560

48. 150 and 480

49. If p, q, and r are different primes, and a, b, and c are natural numbers such that $a > b > c$,
   (a) what is the greatest common factor of $p^a q^c r^b$ and $p^b q^a r^c$?
   (b) what is the least common multiple of $p^b q^a$, $q^b r^c$, and $p^a r^b$?

50. Find **(a)** the greatest common factor and **(b)** the least common multiple of

$$2^{31} \cdot 5^{17} \cdot 7^{21} \quad \text{and} \quad 2^{34} \cdot 5^{22} \cdot 7^{13}.$$

Leave your answers in prime factored form.

It is possible to extend the Euclidean algorithm in order to find the greatest common factor of more than two numbers. For example, if we wish to find the greatest common factor of 150, 210, and 240, we can first use the algorithm to find the greatest common factor of two of these (say, for example, 150 and 210). Then we find the greatest common factor of that result and the third number, 240. The final result is the greatest common factor of the original group of numbers. Use the Euclidean algorithm as described above to find the greatest common factor of each group of numbers.

51. 150, 210, and 240

52. 12, 75, and 120

53. 90, 105, and 315

54. 48, 315, and 450

55. 144, 180, and 192

56. 180, 210, and 630

If we allow repetitions of prime factors, we can use Venn diagrams (Chapter 2) to find the greatest common factor and the least common multiple of two numbers. For example, consider $36 = 2^2 \cdot 3^2$ and $45 = 3^2 \cdot 5$. Their greatest common factor is $3^2 = 9$, and their least common multiple is $2^2 \cdot 3^2 \cdot 5 = 180$.

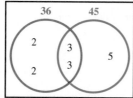

Intersection gives 3, 3.
Union gives 2, 2, 3, 3, 5.

Use this method to find **(a)** *the greatest common factor and* **(b)** *the least common multiple of the two numbers given.*

57. 12 and 18

58. 27 and 36

59. 54 and 72

60. Suppose that the least common multiple of p and q is q. What can we say about p and q?

61. Suppose that the least common multiple of p and q is pq. What can we say about p and q?

62. Suppose that the greatest common factor of p and q is p. What can we say about p and q?

63. Recall some of your early experiences in mathematics (for example, in the elementary grade classroom). What topic involving fractions required the use of the least common multiple? Give an example.

64. Recall some of your experiences in elementary algebra. What topics required the use of the greatest common factor? Give an example.

Refer to Examples 9 and 10 to solve each problem.

65. *Inspecting Calculators* Colleen Jones and Nancy Barre work on an assembly line, inspecting electronic calculators. Colleen inspects the electronics of every sixteenth calculator, while Nancy inspects the workmanship of every thirty-sixth calculator. If they both start working at the same time, which calculator will be the first that they both inspect?

66. *Night Off for Security Guards* Paul Crockett and Cindy Herring work as security guards at a publishing company. Paul has every sixth night off, and Cindy has every tenth night off. If both are off on July 1, what is the next night that they will both be off together?

67. *Stacking Coins* Sheila Abbruzzo has 240 pennies and 288 nickels. She wants to place the pennies and nickels in stacks so that each stack has the same number of coins, and each stack contains only one denomination of coin. What is the largest number of coins that she can place in each stack?

68. *Bicycle Racing* Kathryn Campbell and Tami Dreyfus are in a bicycle race, following a circular track. If they start at the same place and travel in the same direction, and Kathryn completes a revolution every 40 seconds and Tami completes a revolution every 45 seconds, how long will it take them before they reach the starting point again simultaneously?

69. *Selling Books* John Cross sold some books at $24 each, and used the money to buy some concert tickets at $50 each. He had no money left over after buying the tickets. What is the least amount of money he could have earned from selling the books? What is the least number of books he could have sold?

70. *Sawing Lumber* Jill Bos has some pieces of two-by-four lumber. Some are 60 inches long, and some are 72 inches long. She wishes to saw them so as to obtain equal-length pieces. What is the longest such piece she can saw so that no lumber is left over?

EXTENSION

Modern Cryptography

Cryptography involves secret codes, ways of disguising information in order that a "sender" can transmit it to an intended "receiver" so that an "adversary" who somehow intercepts the transmission will be unable to discern its meaning. It has become customary in discussions of cryptography to refer to the sender and receiver (in either order) as Alice and Bob (*A* and *B*) and to the adversary as Eve (*E*). We follow that practice here. Converting a message to disguised form is called **encryption,** and converting it back to original form is called **decryption.**

Cryptography has been employed for thousands of years. It became more crucial as the extent of military, diplomatic, then industrial, and now even personal applications expanded. As the "code makers" became more adept at designing their systems, the "code breakers" became more adept at compromising those systems. If intercepting secret information is very important to an adversary, then vast resources will likely be expended in that effort.

The basis of a cryptography system is normally some mathematical function, the "encryption algorithm," that encrypts (disguises) the message. (*Functions* are used extensively in mathematics. They are discussed in Chapter 8 of this book.). An example of a simple (and very insecure) encryption algorithm is the following:

Replace every letter of the alphabet with the letter that *follows* it.
(Replace z with a.)

(continued)

Then the message "zebra" would be encrypted as "afcsb." Analyzing one or more intercepted messages encrypted using this function, and trying various possibilities, would enable an adversary to quickly determine the function, and its inverse, which would be the following:

> Replace every letter of the alphabet with the letter that *precedes* it. (Replace a with z.)

More advanced systems also use a **key,** which is some additional information needed to perform the algorithm correctly.

By the middle of the twentieth century, state-of-the-art requirements for an effective cryptography system were the following.

Basic Requirements of a Cryptography System

1. A *secret* algorithm (or function) for encrypting and decrypting data
2. A *secret* key that provides additional information necessary for a receiver to carry out the decrypting process

---

The difficulty with requirement number 1 was that all known encryption functions at the time were two-way functions. Once an adversary obtained the encryption algorithm, the inverse (that is, the decryption algorithm) could be deduced mathematically. The difficulty with requirement number 2 was that the security of the key frequently dropped off after a period of use. This meant that Bob and Alice must exchange a new key fairly often so that their communications would continue to be safe. But this measure may be self-defeating, because every key exchange may be vulnerable to interception. This dilemma became known as the **key exchange problem** (or the **key distribution problem** in the case of multiple intended receivers).

The world of cryptography was revolutionized in the 1970s when researchers discovered how to construct a *one-way* function that overcame both difficulties. That *exponential function* is given by

$$C = M^k \;(\text{mod } n),$$

with the calculation carried out modulo n. The practical success of this formula, the achievement of an essentially one-way, rather than two-way, function, is made possible by the theory of large prime numbers (studied earlier in this chapter), the nature of modular arithmetic (introduced in Section 4.4), and the present state of computer hardware and algorithms.

The Diffie-Hellman-Merkle Key Exchange Scheme

First the key exchange problem was solved by the **Diffie-Hellman-Merkle key exchange scheme** (announced in 1976 and named for the Stanford University team of Whitfield Diffie, Martin Hellman, and Ralph Merkle). Basically, it works as follows.

The Diffie-Hellman-Merkle Key Exchange Scheme

Alice and Bob can establish a key (a number) that they both will know, but that Eve cannot find out, even if she observes the communications between Bob and Alice as they set up their key. Alice and Bob can agree to use the function $C = M^k \pmod{n}$ with specific values for M and n. (They can agree to all this by mail, telephone, e-mail, or even casual conversation. It won't matter if Eve finds out.) Then they carry out the following sequence of individual steps.

Alice's Actions	*Bob's Actions*
Step 1 Choose a value of a. (Keep this value secret.)	**Step 1** Choose a value of b. (Keep this value secret.)
Step 2 Compute $\alpha = M^a \pmod{n}$.	**Step 2** Compute $\beta = M^b \pmod{n}$.
Step 3 Send the value of α to Bob.	**Step 3** Send the value of β to Alice.
Step 4 Receive the value of β from Bob.	**Step 4** Receive the value of α from Alice.
Step 5 Compute the key: $$K = \beta^a \pmod{n}.$$	**Step 5** Compute the key: $$K = \alpha^b \pmod{n}.$$

By this procedure, Alice and Bob will arrive at the same key value K because

$$
\begin{aligned}
\beta^a &= (M^b)^a & \beta = M^b \\
&= M^{ba} & \text{Rule of exponents: } (a^m)^n = a^{mn} \\
&= M^{ab} & \text{Commutative property: } ab = ba \\
&= (M^a)^b & \text{Rule of exponents: } (a^m)^n = a^{mn} \\
&= \alpha^b. & \alpha = M^a
\end{aligned}
$$

We illustrate the basic procedures using much smaller numbers than would be used in practice so that our computations can be done on a handheld calculator. (It is not recommended that you try working any of the following examples *without* a calculator.)

One of the essential aspects of the schemes we use here is the nature of modular arithmetic. Given a modulus n, every natural number a is "equivalent" (actually congruent) to the remainder obtained when a is divided by n. This remainder is called the **residue** of a, modulo n. To find the residue can be thought of as to "mod." In Example 1 to follow, for instance, one of the calculations will be to find the residue of 16,807, modulo 13. A quick procedure to accomplish this on a calculator is as follows.

```
16807/13
         1292.846154
Ans-1292
         .8461538462
Ans*13
                  11
```

The display shows that the residue of 16,807, modulo 13, is 11.

Step 1 Divide 16,807 by 13, obtaining 1292.846154.

Step 2 Subtract the integer part of the quotient, obtaining .846154.

Step 3 Multiply by 13, obtaining 11.

So, we see that $16{,}807 \equiv 11 \pmod{13}$. We have shown that $16{,}807 = 1292 \cdot 13 + 11$.

(continued)

(*Note:* In the work that follows, we carry out some lengthy sequences of modular arithmetic. We sometimes use equals signs, $=$, rather than congruence symbols, $\equiv$, and when the modulus is understood, we sometimes omit the designation (mod n).)

This calculator routine can be summarized.

Calculator Routine for Finding the Residue of *a*, Modulo *n*

In a modular system, the residue modulo n for a number a can be found by completing these three steps, in turn.

Step 1 Divide a by the modulus n.

Step 2 Subtract the integer part of the quotient to obtain only the fractional part.

Step 3 Multiply the fractional part of the quotient by n.

The final result is the residue modulo n.

EXAMPLE 1 Using the Diffie-Hellman-Merkle Key Exchange Scheme

Establish a common key for Alice and Bob by using specific values for M, n, a, and b, and completing the steps outlined earlier for the Diffie-Hellman-Merkle key exchange scheme.

SOLUTION

Suppose Alice and Bob agree to use the values $M = 7$ and $n = 13$.

```
11^8
         214358881
Ans/13
         16489144.69
Ans-16489144
         .692308
```

```
Ans*13
         9.000004
```

The display shows the calculation of K in the right column. (Ignore the tiny roundoff error.)

Alice's Actions

Step 1 Choose a value of a, say 5. (Alice keeps this value secret.)

Step 2 $\alpha = M^a$ (mod n)
$= 7^5$ (mod 13)
$= 16{,}807$ (mod 13)
$= 11$

Step 3 Send $\alpha = 11$ to Bob.

Step 4 Receive $\beta = 3$.

Step 5 Compute the key:
$K = \beta^a$ (mod n)
$= 3^5$ (mod 13)
$= 243$ (mod 13)
$= 9.$

Bob's Actions

Step 1 Choose a value of b, say 8. (Bob keeps this value secret.)

Step 2 $\beta = M^b$ (mod n)
$= 7^8$ (mod 13)
$= 5{,}764{,}801$ (mod 13)
$= 3$

Step 3 Send $\beta = 3$ to Alice.

Step 4 Receive $\alpha = 11$.

Step 5 Compute the key:
$K = \alpha^b$ (mod n)
$= 11^8$ (mod 13)
$= 214{,}358{,}881$ (mod 13)
$= 9.$

Both Alice and Bob arrived at the same key value, $K = 9$, which they can use for encrypting future communications to one another. ▪

Suppose, at Step 3 in Example 1, Eve intercepts Bob's transmission of the value $\beta = 3$ to Alice. This will not help her, because she cannot deduce Bob's value of b that generated β. In fact it could have been any of the values

$$8, 20, 32, 44, 56, \ldots,$$

an infinite list of possibilities. Also, Eve does not know what exponent Alice will apply to 3 to obtain the key. The value $a = 5$ is Alice's secret, never communicated to anyone else, not even Bob, so Eve cannot know what key Alice will obtain. The same argument applies if Eve intercepts Alice's transmission to Bob of the value $\alpha = 11$. (She is stymied even if she intercepts both transmissions.)

RSA Public Key Cryptography

At practically the same time that Diffie, Hellman, and Merkle solved the key exchange problem, another team of researchers, Ron Rivest, Adi Shamir, and Leonard Adleman, at MIT, used the same type of mathematical function to provide an even better solution that eliminated the need for key exchange. Their scheme, known as RSA (from their surnames), is called **public key cryptography.** Anyone who wants the capability of receiving encrypted data simply makes known their public key, which anyone else can then use to encrypt messages to them. The beauty of the system is that the receiver possesses another private key, necessary for decrypting but never released to anyone else.

What makes RSA successful is that we have the mathematical understanding to identify very large prime numbers, and to multiply them to obtain a product. But if the prime factors are large enough, it is impossible, given the present state of knowledge, for anyone to determine the two original factors. This is true even using very powerful computers. Large prime factors can be used so that it would take one hundred million personal computers, working together, over a thousand years to break the code. This sort of security is due to the fact that factoring large primes is mathematically much more difficult than multiplying large primes (again, even for computers).

Using RSA, Alice can receive encrypted messages from Bob in such a way that Eve cannot discern their meaning even if she intercepts them (the usual goal of cryptography). Again, we use rather small values in our examples (relative to values used in practice). Although we give examples of specific portions of the process later, we show here a complete outline of all the basic procedures, from setting up the scheme to encrypting and then decrypting a message.

When the **RSA code** was first introduced in 1977, Martin Gardner's "Mathematical Games" column in *Scientific American* challenged researchers to decode a message using an *n* with 129 digits. Some estimated it would take approximately 20,000 years to decipher without any knowledge of *p* or *q*. However, with the aid of number theory, it took 600 mathematicians in 25 different countries only 17 years to factor *n* into 64- and 65-digit prime factors, as shown here

114,381,625,757,888,867,669,235,
779,976,146,612,010,218,296,721,
242,362,562,561,842,935,706,935,
245,733,897,830,597,123,563,958,
705,058,989,075,147,599,290,026,
879,543,541 = 3,490,529,510,847,
650,949,147,849,619,903,898,133,
417,764,638,493,387,843,990,820,
577 × 32,769,132,993,266,709,
549,961,988,190,834,461,413,177,
642,967,992,942,539,798,288,533.

The decoded message said, "The magic words are squeamish ossifrage."

Today, RSA users select much larger values of *p* and *q*, resulting in an *n* of well over 300 digits. It is thought that breaking such an encryption would take all the computers in the world, working together, more time than the age of the universe. So until someone discovers new factoring techniques, or new computer designs, RSA would seem to be safe from attack.

RSA Basics: A Public Key Cryptography Scheme

Alice (the receiver) completes the following steps.

Step 1 Choose two prime numbers, p and q, which she keeps secret.

Step 2 Compute the *modulus n* (which is the product $p \cdot q$).

Step 3 Compute $\ell = (p - 1)(q - 1)$.

Step 4 Choose the *encryption exponent e*, which can be any integer between 1 and ℓ that is relatively prime to ℓ, that is, has no common factors with ℓ.

Step 5 Find her *decryption exponent d*, a number satisfying

$$e \cdot d = 1 \ (\text{mod } \ell).$$

She keeps d secret.

Step 6 Provide Bob with her *public key*, which consists of the modulus n and the encryption exponent e.

(Bob's steps are on the next page.)

(continued)

Now Bob (the sender) completes the following steps. (Recall that the purpose of all this is for Bob to be able to send Alice secure messages.)

Step 7 Convert the message to be sent to Alice into a number M (sometimes called the *plaintext*).

Step 8 Encrypt M, that is, use Alice's public key (n and e) to generate the encrypted message C (sometimes called the *ciphertext*) according to the formula $C = M^e \pmod{n}$.

Step 9 Transmit C to Alice.

When Alice receives C, she completes the final step:

Step 10 Decrypt C, that is, use her private key, consisting of n (also part of her public key) and d, to reproduce the original plaintext message M according to the formula $M = C^d \pmod{n}$.

James Ellis, Clifford Cocks, and Malcolm Williamson all worked for Britain's Government Communications Headquarters in the 1970s. In a strange twist of fate, they actually discovered the mathematics of public key cryptography several years before the work at Stanford and MIT was announced (and subsequently patented). The British work was classified top secret and never came to light until some twenty years later, at approximately the same time that RSA Data Security, the company that had been built on U.S. RSA patents, was sold for $200 million.

EXAMPLE 2 Devising a Public Encryption Key

Use the values $p = 7$ and $q = 13$ (arbitrarily chosen primes) to devise Alice's public key by completing Steps 2–4 of the above outline of RSA basics.

SOLUTION

Step 2 $n = p \cdot q = 7 \cdot 13 = 91$

Step 3 $\ell = (p - 1)(q - 1) = 6 \cdot 12 = 72$

Step 4 There are many choices here, but a prime less than 72 will certainly meet the requirements. We arbitrarily choose $e = 11$.

Alice's public key is $n = 91$, $e = 11$. (Prime factors p and q must be kept secret.) ▪

EXAMPLE 3 Finding a Private Decryption Key

Complete Step 5 of the RSA basics outline to find Alice's private decryption key.

SOLUTION

Step 5 The decryption exponent d must satisfy

$$e \cdot d = 1 \pmod{\ell} \quad \text{or} \quad 11d = 1 \pmod{72}.$$

One way to satisfy this equation is to check the powers of 11 until we find one equal (actually congruent) to 1, modulo 72:

Mod 72 congruences →

$$11^1 = 11, \quad 11^2 = 121 = 49, \quad 11^3 = 1331 = 35,$$
$$11^4 = 14{,}641 = 25, \quad 11^5 = 161{,}051 = 59, \quad 11^6 = 1{,}771{,}561 = 1.$$

(The residues were found using the calculator routine explained before Example 1.) Because we found that $11^6 = 1$, we take $d = 11^5 = 59$. This way,

$$e \cdot d = 11 \cdot 11^5 = 11^6 = 1, \qquad \text{as required.}$$

Alice's private key is $n = 91$, $d = 59$. ▪

EXAMPLE 4 Encrypting a Message for Transmission

Complete Steps 7 and 8 of the RSA basics outline to encrypt the message "HI" for Bob to send Alice. Use Alice's public key found in Example 2: $n = 91$, $e = 11$.

SOLUTION

Step 7 A simple way to convert "HI" to a number is to note that H and I are the 8th and 9th letters of the English alphabet. Simply let the plaintext message be $M = 89$.

Step 8 Now compute the ciphertext C.

$$C = M^e \pmod{n} = 89^{11} \pmod{91}$$

This presents a new difficulty, because 89^{11} is too large to be handled as we did the powers of 11 in Example 3. But we can use a trick here, expressing 11 as $1 + 2 + 8$. (1, 2, and 8 are the unique powers of 2 that sum to 11. So we are doing something like what we did when discussing the binary system in Section 4.3.) Now we can rewrite 89^{11} in terms of smaller powers and then make use of rules of exponents (which are covered in Section 7.5).

$$89^{11} = 89^{1+2+8} \qquad \text{\small $1 + 2 + 8 = 11$}$$
$$= 89^1 \cdot 89^2 \cdot 89^8 \qquad \text{\small Rule of exponents: $a^{n + m} = a^n \cdot a^m$}$$

Now it will help to follow the maxim "mod before you multiply," in other words, compute the residue of individual factors first, then multiply those results. This keeps the numbers we must deal with smaller.

$$89^1 = 89 \qquad \text{\small Definition of first power}$$
$$89^2 = 7921 = 4 \qquad \text{\small Mod}$$
$$89^8 = 3.936588806E15 \qquad \text{\small Calculator result}$$

This last factor is far too large to handle like the others. But because of the way we "split up" the exponent, each subsequent power of 89 can be written as a power of an earlier one, again using rules of exponents. Specifically,

$$89^8 = (89^2)^4 \qquad \text{\small Rule of exponents: $a^{m \cdot n} = (a^m)^n$}$$
$$= 4^4 \qquad \text{\small $89^2 = 4$ from above}$$
$$= 256 \qquad \text{\small Evaluate 4^4.}$$
$$= 74. \qquad \text{\small Mod}$$

Finally we obtain

$$89^{11} = 89 \cdot 4 \cdot 74 \qquad \text{\small Substitute.}$$
$$= 26{,}344 \qquad \text{\small Multiply.}$$
$$= 45. \qquad \text{\small Mod}$$

The plaintext $M = 89$ (for the message "HI") has been converted to the ciphertext $C = 45$. ▪

Now let's see if Alice can successfully decrypt the message 45 when she receives it.

(continued)

EXAMPLE 5 Decrypting a Received Message

Complete Step 10 of the RSA basics outline to decrypt the message $C = 45$ from Example 4. Use Alice's private key, found in Example 3: $d = 59$ (also, $n = 91$).

SOLUTION

Step 10 The decryption formula gives

$$M = C^d \, (\text{mod } n)$$
$$= 45^{59} \, (\text{mod } 91)$$
$$= 45^{1+2+8+16+32} \, (\text{mod } 91)$$
$$= 45 \cdot 45^2 \cdot 45^8 \cdot 45^{16} \cdot 45^{32} \, (\text{mod } 91).$$

Start with the smaller powers and "mod" each factor individually.

$$45^2 = 2025 = 23$$
$$45^8 = (45^2)^4 = 23^4 = 279{,}841 = 16$$
$$45^{16} = (45^8)^2 = 16^2 = 256 = 74$$
$$45^{32} = (45^{16})^2 = 74^2 = 5476 = 16$$

Inserting these values in the product above for M, we get

$$M = 45 \cdot 23 \cdot 16 \cdot 74 \cdot 16$$
$$= 19{,}607{,}040$$
$$= 89.$$

We have correctly decrypted $C = 45$ to obtain

$$M = 89 = \text{HI}.$$

EXTENSION EXERCISES

Find the residue in each case.

1. 45 (mod 6)

2. 67 (mod 10)

3. 225 (mod 13)

4. 418 (mod 15)

5. 5^9 (mod 12)

6. 4^{11} (mod 9)

7. 8^7 (mod 11)

8. 14^5 (mod 13)

9. 8^{27} (mod 17)

10. 45^7 (mod 23)

11. 11^{14} (mod 18)

12. 14^9 (mod 19)

Finding a Common Key *Find Alice and Bob's common key K by using the Diffie-Hellman-Merkle key exchange scheme with the given values of M, n, a, and b.*

	M	n	a	b
13.	5	13	7	6
14.	11	9	5	4
15.	5	11	6	7
16.	17	5	6	3

Apply the RSA scheme to find each missing value.

	p	q	n	ℓ
17.	5	11	___	___
18.	11	3	___	___
19.	5	13	___	___
20.	17	7	___	___

Encrypting Plaintext *Given the modulus n, the encryption exponent e, and the plaintext M, use RSA encryption to find the ciphertext C in each case.*

	n	e	M
21.	55	7	15
22.	33	7	8
23.	65	5	16
24.	119	11	12

Decrypting Ciphertext *Given the prime factors p and q, the encryption exponent e, and the ciphertext C, apply the RSA algorithm to find* **(a)** *the decryption exponent d and* **(b)** *the plaintext message M.*

	p	q	e	C
25.	5	11	3	30
26.	11	3	13	24
27.	5	13	35	17
28.	17	7	5	40

29. Describe the breakthrough represented by Diffie-Hellman-Merkle and RSA as opposed to all earlier forms of cryptography.

30. Explain why RSA would fail if mathematicians could (using computers) factor arbitrarily large numbers.

5.4 The Fibonacci Sequence and the Golden Ratio

The Fibonacci Sequence • The Golden Ratio

The solution of Fibonacci's rabbit problem is examined in Chapter 1, pages 21–22.

The Fibonacci Sequence One of the most famous problems in elementary mathematics comes from the book *Liber Abaci*, written in 1202 by Leonardo of Pisa, a.k.a. Fibonacci. The problem is as follows:

> A man put a pair of rabbits in a cage. During the first month the rabbits produced no offspring, but each month thereafter produced one new pair of rabbits. If each new pair thus produced reproduces in the same manner, how many pairs of rabbits will there be at the end of one year?

The solution of this problem leads to a sequence of numbers known as the **Fibonacci sequence.** Here are the first fifteen terms of the Fibonacci sequence:

$$1, 1, 2, 3, 5, 8, 13, 21, 34, 55, 89, 144, 233, 377, 610.$$

Notice the pattern established in the sequence. After the first two terms (both 1), each term is obtained by adding the two previous terms. For example, the third term is obtained by adding $1 + 1$ to get 2, the fourth term is obtained by adding $1 + 2$ to get 3, and so on. This can be described by a mathematical formula known as a *recursion formula*.

If F_n represents the Fibonacci number in the nth position in the sequence, then

$$F_1 = 1$$
$$F_2 = 1$$
$$F_n = F_{n-2} + F_{n-1}, \quad \text{for } n \geq 3.$$

Using the recursion formula $F_n = F_{n-2} + F_{n-1}$, we obtain

$$F_3 = F_1 + F_2 = 1 + 1 = 2, \quad F_4 = F_2 + F_3 = 1 + 2 = 3, \quad \text{and so on.}$$

The Fibonacci sequence exhibits many interesting patterns, and by inductive reasoning we can make many conjectures about these patterns. However, as we have indicated many times earlier, simply observing a finite number of examples does not provide a proof of a statement. Proofs of the properties of the Fibonacci sequence often involve mathematical induction (covered in college algebra texts). Here we simply observe the patterns and do not attempt to provide such proofs.

As an example of the many interesting properties of the Fibonacci sequence, choose any term of the sequence after the first and square it. Then multiply the terms on either side of it, and subtract the smaller result from the larger. The difference is always 1. For example, choose the sixth term in the sequence, 8. The square of 8 is 64. Now multiply the terms on either side of 8: $5 \cdot 13 = 65$. Subtract 64 from 65 to get $65 - 64 = 1$. This pattern continues throughout the sequence.

The **Fibonacci Association** is a research organization dedicated to investigation into the **Fibonacci sequence** and related topics. Check your library to see if it has the journal *Fibonacci Quarterly*. The first two journals of 1963 contain a basic introduction to the Fibonacci sequence.

EXAMPLE 1 Observing a Pattern of the Fibonacci Numbers

Find the sum of the squares of the first n Fibonacci numbers for $n = 1, 2, 3, 4, 5$, and examine the pattern. Generalize this relationship.

SOLUTION

$$1^2 = 1 = 1 \cdot 1 = F_1 \cdot F_2$$
$$1^2 + 1^2 = 2 = 1 \cdot 2 = F_2 \cdot F_3$$
$$1^2 + 1^2 + 2^2 = 6 = 2 \cdot 3 = F_3 \cdot F_4$$
$$1^2 + 1^2 + 2^2 + 3^2 = 15 = 3 \cdot 5 = F_4 \cdot F_5$$
$$1^2 + 1^2 + 2^2 + 3^2 + 5^2 = 40 = 5 \cdot 8 = F_5 \cdot F_6$$

The sum of the squares of the first n Fibonacci numbers seems to always be the product of F_n and F_{n+1}. This has been proven to be true, in general, using mathematical induction. ∎

The following program for the TI-83/84 Plus utilizes the *Binet form* of the nth Fibonacci number (see Exercises 33–38) to determine its value.

```
PROGRAM: FIB
: Clr Home
: Disp "WHICH TERM"
: Disp "OF THE"
: Disp "SEQUENCE DO"
: Disp "YOU WANT?"
: Input N
:(1 + √(5))/2 → A
:(1 − √(5))/2 → B
:(A^N − B^N)/√(5) → F
: Disp F
```

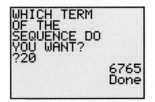

This screen indicates that the twentieth Fibonacci number is 6765.

There are many other patterns similar to the one examined in Example 1, and some of them are discussed in the exercises of this section. An interesting property of the decimal value of the reciprocal of 89, the eleventh Fibonacci number, is examined in the next example.

EXAMPLE 2 Observing the Fibonacci Sequence in a Long Division Problem

Observe the steps of the long division process used to find the first few decimal places for $\frac{1}{89}$.

SOLUTION

$$
\begin{array}{r}
.011235\ldots \\
89\overline{)1.000000} \\
\underline{89} \\
110 \\
\underline{89} \\
210 \\
\underline{178} \\
320 \\
\underline{267} \\
530 \\
\underline{445} \\
850\ldots
\end{array}
$$

Notice that after the 0 in the tenths place, the next five digits are the first five terms of the Fibonacci sequence. In addition, as indicated in color in the process, the digits 1, 1, 2, 3, 5, 8 appear in the division steps. Now, look at the digits next to the ones in color, beginning with the second "1"; they, too, are 1, 1, 2, 3, 5, ...

If the division process is continued past the final step shown above, the pattern seems to stop, since to ten decimal places, $\frac{1}{89} \approx .0112359551$. (The decimal representation actually begins to repeat later in the process, since $\frac{1}{89}$ is a rational number.) However, the sum below indicates how the Fibonacci numbers are actually "hidden" in this decimal.

$$
\begin{array}{r}
.01 \\
.001 \\
.0002 \\
.00003 \\
.000005 \\
.0000008 \\
.00000013 \\
.000000021 \\
.0000000034 \\
.00000000055 \\
\underline{.000000000089} \\
\frac{1}{89} = .0112359550\ldots
\end{array}
$$

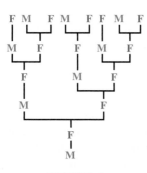

FIGURE 1

Fibonacci patterns have been found in numerous places in nature. For example, male honeybees (drones) hatch from eggs which have not been fertilized, so a male bee has only one parent, a female. On the other hand, female honeybees hatch from fertilized eggs, so a female has two parents, one male and one female. Figure 1 shows several generations of ancestors for a male honeybee.

Notice that in the first generation, starting at the bottom, there is 1 bee, in the second there is 1 bee, in the third there are 2 bees, and so on. These are the terms of the Fibonacci sequence. Furthermore, beginning with the second generation, the numbers of female bees form the sequence, and beginning with the third generation, the numbers of male bees also form the sequence.

Successive terms in the Fibonacci sequence also appear in some plants. For example, the photo (at the left on the next page) shows the double spiraling of a daisy head, with 21 clockwise spirals and 34 counterclockwise spirals. These numbers are successive terms in the sequence. Most pineapples (see the photo on the right) exhibit the Fibonacci sequence in the following way: Count the spirals formed by the "scales" of the cone, first counting from lower left to upper right. Then count the spirals from lower right to upper left. You should find that in one direction you get 8 spirals, and in the other you get 13 spirals, once again successive terms of the Fibonacci sequence. Many pinecones exhibit 5 and 8 spirals, and the cone of the giant sequoia has 3 and 5 spirals.

A fraction such as

$$1 + \cfrac{1}{1 + \cfrac{1}{1 + \cfrac{1}{1 + \cdots}}}$$

is called a **continued fraction.** This continued fraction can be evaluated as follows.

Let $x = 1 + \cfrac{1}{1 + \cfrac{1}{1 + \cdots}}$

Then $x = 1 + \dfrac{1}{x}$

$x^2 = x + 1$

$x^2 - x - 1 = 0.$

By the quadratic formula from algebra,

$$x = \frac{1 \pm \sqrt{1 - 4(1)(-1)}}{2(1)}$$

$$x = \frac{1 \pm \sqrt{5}}{2}.$$

Notice that the positive solution

$$\frac{1 + \sqrt{5}}{2}$$

is the **golden ratio.**

The Golden Ratio If we consider the quotients of successive Fibonacci numbers, a pattern emerges.

$\dfrac{1}{1} = 1$	$\dfrac{13}{8} = 1.625$
$\dfrac{2}{1} = 2$	$\dfrac{21}{13} \approx 1.615384615$
$\dfrac{3}{2} = 1.5$	$\dfrac{34}{21} \approx 1.619047619$
$\dfrac{5}{3} = 1.666\ldots$	$\dfrac{55}{34} \approx 1.617647059$
$\dfrac{8}{5} = 1.6$	$\dfrac{89}{55} = 1.618181818\ldots$

These quotients seem to be approaching some "limiting value" close to 1.618. In fact, as we go farther into the sequence, these quotients approach the number

$$\frac{1 + \sqrt{5}}{2},$$

known as the **golden ratio,** and often symbolized by ϕ, the Greek letter phi.

The golden ratio appears over and over in art, architecture, music, and nature. Its origins go back to the days of the ancient Greeks, who thought that a golden rectangle exhibited the most aesthetically pleasing proportion. A **golden rectangle** is one that can be divided into a square and another (smaller) rectangle the same shape as the original rectangle. (See Figure 2 on the next page.) If we let the smaller rectangle have

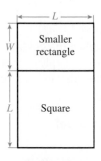

FIGURE 2

length L and width W, as shown in the figure, then we see that the original rectangle has length $L + W$ and width L. Both rectangles (being "golden") have their lengths and widths in the golden ratio, ϕ, given above, so we have

$$\frac{L}{W} = \frac{L + W}{L}$$

$$\frac{L}{W} = \frac{L}{L} + \frac{W}{L} \quad \text{Write the right side as two fractions.}$$

$$\phi = 1 + \frac{1}{\phi} \quad \text{Substitute } \tfrac{L}{W} = \phi, \tfrac{L}{L} = 1, \text{ and } \tfrac{W}{L} = \tfrac{1}{\phi}.$$

$$\phi^2 = \phi + 1 \quad \text{Multiply both sides by } \phi.$$

$$\phi^2 - \phi - 1 = 0. \quad \text{Write in standard quadratic form.}$$

Using the quadratic formula from algebra, the positive solution of this equation is found to be $\frac{1 + \sqrt{5}}{2} \approx 1.618033989$, the golden ratio.

The Parthenon (see the photo), built on the Acropolis in ancient Athens during the fifth century B.C., is an example of architecture exhibiting many distinct golden rectangles.

A Golden Rectangle in Art The rectangle outlining the figure in *St. Jerome* by Leonardo da Vinci is an example of a golden rectangle.

To see an interesting connection between the terms of the Fibonacci sequence, the golden ratio, and a phenomenon of nature, we can start with a rectangle measuring 89 by 55 units. (See Figure 3.)

This is a very close approximation to a golden rectangle. Within this rectangle a square is then constructed, 55 units on a side. The remaining rectangle is also approximately a golden rectangle, measuring 55 units by 34 units. Each time this process is repeated, a square and an approximate golden rectangle are formed. As indicated in the figure, vertices of the square may be joined by a smooth curve known as a *spiral*. This spiral resembles the outline of a cross section of the shell of the chambered nautilus, as shown in the photograph next to Figure 3.

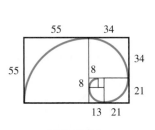

FIGURE 3

For Further Thought

Mathematical Animation

🎥 The 1959 animated film *Donald in Mathmagic Land* has endured for nearly 50 years as a classic. It provides a 25-minute trip with Donald Duck, led by the Spirit of Mathematics, through the world of mathematics. Several minutes of the film are devoted to the golden ratio (or, as it is termed there, the golden section). (*Donald in Mathmagic Land* is also discussed in the opener to Chapter 3 on page 97.)

© The Walt Disney Company

Disney provides animation to explain the golden ratio in a way that the printed word simply cannot do. The golden ratio is seen in architecture, nature, and the human body.

For Group Discussion or Individual Investigation

1. Verify the following Fibonacci pattern in the conifer family. Obtain a pineapple, and count spirals formed by the "scales" of the cone, first counting from lower left to upper right. Then count the spirals from lower right to upper left. What do you find?
2. Two popular sizes of index cards are 3″ by 5″ and 5″ by 8″. Why do you think that these are industry-standard sizes?
3. Divide your height by the height to your navel. Find a class average. What value does this come close to?

5.4 EXERCISES

Answer each question concerning the Fibonacci sequence or the golden ratio.

1. The sixteenth Fibonacci number is 987 and the seventeenth Fibonacci number is 1597. What is the eighteenth Fibonacci number?

2. Recall that F_n represents the Fibonacci number in the nth position in the sequence. What are the only two values of n such that $F_n = n$?

3. $F_{23} = 28,657$ and $F_{25} = 75,025$. What is the value of F_{24}?

4. If two successive terms of the Fibonacci sequence are both odd, is the next term even or odd?

5. What is the exact value of the golden ratio?

6. What is the approximate value of the golden ratio to the nearest thousandth?

In each of Exercises 7–14, a pattern is established involving terms of the Fibonacci sequence. Use inductive reasoning to make a conjecture concerning the next equation in the pattern, and verify it. You may wish to refer to the first few terms of the sequence given in the text.

7. $1 = 2 - 1$
   $1 + 1 = 3 - 1$
   $1 + 1 + 2 = 5 - 1$
   $1 + 1 + 2 + 3 = 8 - 1$
   $1 + 1 + 2 + 3 + 5 = 13 - 1$

8. $1 = 2 - 1$
   $1 + 3 = 5 - 1$
   $1 + 3 + 8 = 13 - 1$
   $1 + 3 + 8 + 21 = 34 - 1$
   $1 + 3 + 8 + 21 + 55 = 89 - 1$

9. $1 = 1$
$1 + 2 = 3$
$1 + 2 + 5 = 8$
$1 + 2 + 5 + 13 = 21$
$1 + 2 + 5 + 13 + 34 = 55$

10. $1^2 + 1^2 = 2$
$1^2 + 2^2 = 5$
$2^2 + 3^2 = 13$
$3^2 + 5^2 = 34$
$5^2 + 8^2 = 89$

11. $2^2 - 1^2 = 3$
$3^2 - 1^2 = 8$
$5^2 - 2^2 = 21$
$8^2 - 3^2 = 55$

12. $2^3 + 1^3 - 1^3 = 8$
$3^3 + 2^3 - 1^3 = 34$
$5^3 + 3^3 - 2^3 = 144$
$8^3 + 5^3 - 3^3 = 610$

13. $1 = 1^2$
$1 - 2 = -1^2$
$1 - 2 + 5 = 2^2$
$1 - 2 + 5 - 13 = -3^2$
$1 - 2 + 5 - 13 + 34 = 5^2$

14. $1 - 1 = -1 + 1$
$1 - 1 + 2 = 1 + 1$
$1 - 1 + 2 - 3 = -2 + 1$
$1 - 1 + 2 - 3 + 5 = 3 + 1$
$1 - 1 + 2 - 3 + 5 - 8 = -5 + 1$

15. Every natural number can be expressed as a sum of Fibonacci numbers, where no number is used more than once. For example, $25 = 21 + 3 + 1$. Express each of the following in this way.
(a) 37   **(b)** 40   **(c)** 52

16. It has been shown that if m divides n, then F_m is a factor of F_n. Show that this is true for the following values of m and n.
(a) $m = 2, n = 6$ **(b)** $m = 3, n = 9$
(c) $m = 4, n = 8$

17. It has been shown that if the greatest common factor of m and n is r, then the greatest common factor of F_m and F_n is F_r. Show that this is true for the following values of m and n.
(a) $m = 10, n = 4$ **(b)** $m = 12, n = 6$
(c) $m = 14, n = 6$

18. For any prime number p except 2 or 5, either F_{p+1} or F_{p-1} is divisible by p. Show that this is true for the following values of p.
(a) $p = 3$ **(b)** $p = 7$ **(c)** $p = 11$

19. Earlier we saw that if a term of the Fibonacci sequence is squared and then the product of the terms on each side of the term is found, there will always be a difference of 1. Follow the steps below, choosing the seventh Fibonacci number, 13.
(a) Square 13. Multiply the terms of the sequence two positions away from 13 (i.e., 5 and 34). Subtract the smaller result from the larger, and record your answer.
(b) Square 13. Multiply the terms of the sequence three positions away from 13. Once again, subtract the smaller result from the larger, and record your answer.
(c) Repeat the process, moving four terms away from 13.
(d) Make a conjecture about what will happen when you repeat the process, moving five terms away. Verify your answer.

20. *A Number Trick* Here is a number trick that you can perform. Ask someone to pick any two numbers at random and to write them down. Ask the person to determine a third number by adding the first and second, a fourth number by adding the second and third, and so on, until ten numbers are determined. Then ask the person to add these ten numbers. You will be able to give the sum before the person even completes the list, because the sum will always be 11 times the seventh number in the list. Verify that this is true, by using x and y as the first two numbers arbitrarily chosen. (*Hint:* Remember the distributive property from algebra.)

Another Fibonacci-type sequence that has been studied by mathematicians is the **Lucas sequence,** *named after a French mathematician of the nineteenth century. The first ten terms of the Lucas sequence are*

$$1, 3, 4, 7, 11, 18, 29, 47, 76, 123.$$

21. What is the eleventh term of the Lucas sequence?

22. Choose any term of the Lucas sequence and square it. Then multiply the terms on either side of the one you chose. Subtract the smaller result from the larger. Repeat this for a different term of the sequence. Do you get the same result? Make a conjecture about this pattern.

23. The first term of the Lucas sequence is 1. Add the first and third terms. Record your answer. Now add the first, third, and fifth terms and record your answer. Continue this pattern, each time adding another term that is in an *odd* position in the sequence. What do you notice about all of your sums?

24. The second term of the Lucas sequence is 3. Add the second and fourth terms. Record your answer. Now add the second, fourth, and sixth terms and record your answer. Continue this pattern, each time adding another term that is in an *even* position of the sequence. What do you notice about all of your sums?

25. Many interesting patterns exist between the terms of the Fibonacci sequence and the Lucas sequence. Make a conjecture about the next equation that would appear in each of the lists and then verify it.

(a) $1 \cdot 1 = 1$
$1 \cdot 3 = 3$
$2 \cdot 4 = 8$
$3 \cdot 7 = 21$
$5 \cdot 11 = 55$

(b) $1 + 2 = 3$
$1 + 3 = 4$
$2 + 5 = 7$
$3 + 8 = 11$
$5 + 13 = 18$

(c) $1 + 1 = 2 \cdot 1$
$1 + 3 = 2 \cdot 2$
$2 + 4 = 2 \cdot 3$
$3 + 7 = 2 \cdot 5$
$5 + 11 = 2 \cdot 8$

26. In the text we illustrate that the quotients of successive terms of the Fibonacci sequence approach the golden ratio. Make a similar observation for the terms of the Lucas sequence; that is, find the decimal approximations for the quotients

$$\frac{3}{1}, \frac{4}{3}, \frac{7}{4}, \frac{11}{7}, \frac{18}{11}, \frac{29}{18},$$

and so on, using a calculator. Then make a conjecture about what seems to be happening.

*Recall the **Pythagorean theorem** from geometry: If a right triangle has legs of lengths a and b and hypotenuse of length c, then*

$$a^2 + b^2 = c^2.$$

*Suppose that we choose any four successive terms of the Fibonacci sequence. Multiply the first and fourth. Double the product of the second and third. Add the squares of the second and third. The three results obtained form a **Pythagorean triple** (three numbers that satisfy the equation $a^2 + b^2 = a^2$). Find the Pythagorean triple obtained this way using the four given successive terms of the Fibonacci sequence.*

27. 1, 1, 2, 3

28. 1, 2, 3, 5

29. 2, 3, 5, 8

30. Look at the values of the hypotenuse (c) in the answers to Exercises 27–29. What do you notice about each of them?

31. The following array of numbers is called **Pascal's triangle.**

$$
\begin{array}{ccccccccccccc}
&&&&&& 1 &&&&&& \\
&&&&& 1 && 1 &&&&& \\
&&&& 1 && 2 && 1 &&&& \\
&&& 1 && 3 && 3 && 1 &&& \\
&& 1 && 4 && 6 && 4 && 1 && \\
& 1 && 5 && 10 && 10 && 5 && 1 & \\
1 && 6 && 15 && 20 && 15 && 6 && 1
\end{array}
$$

This array is important in the study of counting techniques and probability (see later chapters) and appears in algebra in the binomial theorem. If the triangular array is written in a different form, as follows, and the sums along the diagonals as indicated by the dashed lines are found, there is an interesting occurrence. What do you find when the numbers are added?

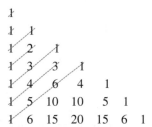

32. Write a paragraph explaining some of the occurrences of the Fibonacci sequence and the golden ratio in your everyday surroundings.

Exercises 33–38 require a scientific calculator.

33. The positive solution of the equation $x^2 - x - 1 = 0$ is $\frac{1 + \sqrt{5}}{2}$, as indicated in the text. The negative solution is $\frac{1 - \sqrt{5}}{2}$. Find the decimal approximations for both. What similarity do you notice between the two decimals?

34. In some cases, writers define the golden ratio to be the *reciprocal* of $\frac{1 + \sqrt{5}}{2}$. Find a decimal approximation for the reciprocal of $\frac{1 + \sqrt{5}}{2}$. What similarity do you notice between the decimals for $\frac{1 + \sqrt{5}}{2}$ and its reciprocal?

A remarkable relationship exists between the two solutions of $x^2 - x - 1 = 0$,

$$\phi = \frac{1 + \sqrt{5}}{2} \quad \text{and} \quad \overline{\phi} = \frac{1 - \sqrt{5}}{2},$$

and the Fibonacci numbers. To find the nth Fibonacci number without using the recursion formula, evaluate

$$\frac{\phi^n - \overline{\phi}^n}{\sqrt{5}}$$

using a calculator. For example, to find the thirteenth Fibonacci number, evaluate

$$\frac{\left(\dfrac{1 + \sqrt{5}}{2}\right)^{13} - \left(\dfrac{1 - \sqrt{5}}{2}\right)^{13}}{\sqrt{5}}$$

This form is known as the **Binet form** of the nth Fibonacci number. Use the Binet form and a calculator to find the nth Fibonacci number for each of the following values of n.

35. $n = 14$ **36.** $n = 20$

37. $n = 22$ **38.** $n = 25$

EXTENSION

Magic Squares

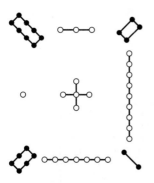

FIGURE 4

8	3	4
1	5	9
6	7	2

FIGURE 5

Legend has it that in about 2200 B.C. the Chinese Emperor Yu discovered on the bank of the Yellow River a tortoise whose shell bore the diagram in Figure 4. This so-called *lo-shu* is an early example of a **magic square.** If the numbers of dots are counted and arranged in a square fashion, the array in Figure 5 is obtained. A magic square is a square array of numbers with the property that the sum along each row, column, and diagonal is the same. This common value is called the "magic sum." The **order** of a magic square is simply the number of rows (and columns) in the square. The magic square of Figure 5 is an order 3 magic square.

By using the formula for the sum of the first *n* terms of an arithmetic sequence, it can be shown that if a magic square of order *n* has entries $1, 2, 3, \ldots, n^2$, then the sum of *all entries* in the square is

$$\frac{n^2(n^2 + 1)}{2}.$$

Because there are *n* rows (and columns), the magic sum of the square may be found by dividing the above expression by *n*. This results in the following formula for finding the magic sum.

Magic Sum Formula

If a magic square of order *n* has entries $1, 2, 3, \ldots, n^2$, then the magic sum MS is given by the formula

$$\text{MS} = \frac{n(n^2 + 1)}{2}.$$

(continued)

Consider blocked

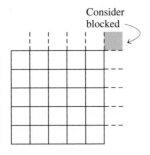

FIGURE 6

FIGURE 7

With $n = 3$ in this formula we find that the magic sum of the square in Figure 5, which may be verified by direct addition, is

$$MS = \frac{3(3^2 + 1)}{2} = 15.$$

There is a method of constructing an odd-order magic square which is attributed to an early French envoy, *de la Loubere,* that is sometimes referred to as the "staircase method." The method is described below for an order 5 square, with entries 1, 2, 3, . . . , 25.

Begin by sketching a square divided into 25 cells into which the numbers 1–25 are to be entered. Proceed as described below, referring to Figures 6 and 7 for clarification.

Step 1 Write 1 in the middle cell of the top row.

Step 2 Always try to enter numbers in sequence in the cells by moving diagonally from lower left to upper right. There are two exceptions to this:

    (a) If you go outside of the magic square, move all the way across the row or down the column to enter the number. Then proceed to move diagonally.

    (b) If you run into a cell which is already occupied (that is, you are "blocked"), drop down one cell from the last entry written and enter the next number there. Then proceed to move diagonally.

Step 3 Your last entry, 25, will be in the middle cell of the bottom row.

Figure 7 shows the completed magic square. Its magic sum is 65.

---

no mechanical invention without geometry. He also thought that mathematical demonstrations are better than academic logic for training the mind to reason with exactness and distinguish truth from falsity even outside of mathematics.

The square shown here is one developed by Franklin. It has a sum of 2056 in each row and diagonal, and, in Franklin's words, has the additional property "that a four-square hole being cut in a piece of paper of such size as to take in and show through it just 16 of the little squares, when laid on the greater square, the sum of the 16 numbers so appearing through the hole, wherever it was placed on the greater square should likewise make 2056." He claimed that it

Benjamin Franklin admitted that he would amuse himself while in the Pennysylvania Assembly with magic squares or circles "or any thing to avoid Weariness." He wrote about the usefulness of mathematics in the *Gazette* in 1735, saying that no employment can be managed without arithmetic,

was "the most magically magic square ever made by any magician."

You might wish to verify the following property of this magic square: The sum of any four numbers that are opposite each other and at equal distances from the center is 514 (which is one-fourth of the magic sum).

EXTENSION EXERCISES

Given a magic square, other magic squares may be obtained by rotating the given one. For example, starting with the magic square in Figure 5, a 90° rotation in a clockwise direction gives the magic square shown here.

6	1	8
7	5	3
2	9	4

Start with Figure 5 and give the magic square obtained by each rotation described.

1. 180° in a clockwise direction

2. 90° in a counterclockwise direction

Start with Figure 7 and give the magic square obtained by each rotation described.

3. 90° in a clockwise direction

4. 180° in a clockwise direction

5. 90° in a counterclockwise direction

6. Try to construct an order 2 magic square containing the entries 1, 2, 3, 4. What happens?

Given a magic square, other magic squares may be obtained by adding or subtracting a constant value to or from each entry, multiplying each entry by a constant value, or dividing each entry by a nonzero constant value. In Exercises 7–10, start with the magic square whose figure number is indicated, and perform the operation described to find a new magic square. Give the new magic sum.

7. Figure 5, multiply by 3

8. Figure 5, add 7

9. Figure 7, divide by 2

10. Figure 7, subtract 10

According to a fanciful story by Charles Trigg in Mathematics Magazine *(September 1976, page 212), the Emperor Charlemagne (742–814) ordered a five-sided fort to be built at an important point in his kingdom. As good-luck charms, he had magic squares placed on all five sides of the fort. He had one restriction for these magic squares: all the numbers in them must be prime.*

Charlemagne's magic squares are given in Exercises 11–15, with one missing entry. Find the missing entry in each square.

11.

	71	257
47	269	491
281	467	59

12.

389		227
107	269	431
311	347	149

13.

389	227	191
71	269	
347	311	149

14.

401	227	179
47	269	491
359		137

15.

401	257	149
17		521
389	281	137

16. Compare the magic sums in Exercises 11–15. Charlemagne had stipulated that each magic sum should be the year in which the fort was built. What was that year?

Find the missing entries in each magic square.

17.

75	68	(a)
(b)	72	(c)
71	76	(d)

18.

1	8	13	(a)
(b)	14	7	2
16	9	4	(c)
(d)	(e)	(f)	15

19.

3	20	(a)	24	11
(b)	14	1	18	10
9	21	13	(c)	17
16	8	25	12	(d)
(e)	2	(f)	(g)	(h)

(continued)

20.

3	36	2	35	31	4
10	12	(a)	26	7	27
21	13	17	14	(b)	22
16	(c)	23	(d)	18	15
28	30	8	(e)	25	9
(f)	1	32	5	6	34

21. Use the "staircase method" to construct a magic square of order 7, containing the entries 1, 2, 3, . . . , 49.

The magic square shown in the photograph is from a woodcut by Albrecht Dürer entitled Melancholia.

The two bottom center numbers give 1514, the date of the woodcut. Refer to this magic square for Exercises 22–30.

16	3	2	13
5	10	11	8
9	6	7	12
4	15	14	1

Dürer's Magic Square

22. What is the magic sum?

23. Verify: The sum of the entries in the four corners is equal to the magic sum.

24. Verify: The sum of the entries in any 2 by 2 square at a corner of the given magic square is equal to the magic sum.

25. Verify: The sum of the entries in the diagonals is equal to the sum of the entries not in the diagonals.

26. Verify: The sum of the squares of the entries in the diagonals is equal to the sum of the squares of the entries not in the diagonals.

27. Verify: The sum of the cubes of the entries in the diagonals is equal to the sum of the cubes of the entries not in the diagonals.

28. Verify: The sum of the squares of the entries in the top two rows is equal to the sum of the squares of the entries in the bottom two rows.

29. Verify: The sum of the squares of the entries in the first and third rows is equal to the sum of the squares of the entries in the second and fourth rows.

30. Find another interesting property of Dürer's magic square and state it.

31. A magic square of order 4 may be constructed as follows. Lightly sketch in the diagonals of the blank magic square. Beginning at the upper left, move across each row from left to right, counting the cells as you go along. If the cell is on a diagonal, count it but do not enter its number. If it is not on a diagonal, enter its number. When this is completed, reverse the procedure, beginning at the bottom right and moving across from right to left. As you count the cells, enter the number if the cell is not occupied. If it is already occupied, count it but do not enter its number. You should obtain a magic square similar to the one given for Exercises 22–30. How do they differ?

With chosen values for a, b, and c, an order 3 magic square can be constructed by substituting these values in the generalized form shown here.

$a + b$	$a - b - c$	$a + c$
$a - b + c$	a	$a + b - c$
$a - c$	$a + b + c$	$a - b$

Use the given values of a, b, and c to construct an order 3 magic square, using this generalized form.

32. $a = 5$, $b = 1$, $c = -3$

33. $a = 16$, $b = 2$, $c = -6$

34. $a = 5$, $b = 4$, $c = -8$

35. It can be shown that if an order n magic square has least entry k, and its entries are consecutive counting numbers, then its magic sum is given by the formula

$$MS = \frac{n(2k + n^2 - 1)}{2}.$$

Construct an order 7 magic square with least entry 10 using the staircase method. Find its magic sum.

36. Use the formula of Exercise 35 to find the missing entries in the following order 4 magic square whose least entry is 24.

(a)	38	37	27
35	(b)	30	32
31	33	(c)	28
(d)	26	25	(e)

In a 1769 letter from Benjamin Franklin to a Mr. Peter Collinson, Franklin exhibited the following semimagic square of order 8. (Note: A square is semimagic if it is magic except that one or both diagonals fail to give the magic sum.)

52	61	4	13	20	29	36	45
14	3	62	51	46	35	30	19
53	60	5	12	21	28	37	44
11	6	59	54	43	38	27	22
55	58	7	10	23	26	39	42
9	8	57	56	41	40	25	24
50	63	2	15	18	31	34	47
16	1	64	49	48	33	32	17

37. What is the magic sum?

Verify the following properties of this semimagic square.

38. The sums in the first half of each row and the second half of each row are both equal to half the magic sum.

39. The four corner entries added to the four center entries is equal to the magic sum.

40. The "bent diagonals" consisting of eight entries, going up four entries from left to right and down four entries from left to right, give the magic sum. (For example, starting with 16, one bent diagonal sum is $16 + 63 + 57 + 10 + 23 + 40 + 34 + 17$.)

If we use a "knight's move" (up two, right one) from chess, a variation of the staircase method gives rise to the magic square shown here. (When blocked, we move to the cell just below the previous entry.)

10	18	1	14	22
11	24	7	20	3
17	5	13	21	9
23	6	19	2	15
4	12	25	8	16

Use a similar process to construct an order 5 magic square, starting with 1 in the cell described.

41. fourth row, second column (up two, right one; when blocked, move to the cell just below the previous entry)

42. third row, third column (up one, right two; when blocked, move to the cell just to the left of the previous entry)

COLLABORATIVE INVESTIGATION

Investigating an Interesting Property of Number Squares

In the Extension at the end of this chapter, we looked at magic squares. Now in this group activity we will investigate another property of squares of numbers. Begin by dividing up the class into groups of three or four students. Each student in the group should prepare a square of numbers like the one that follows:

1	2	3	4	5
6	7	8	9	10
11	12	13	14	15
16	17	18	19	20
21	22	23	24	25

Topics for Discussion

1. Each student should do the following individually:

   Choose any number in the first row. Circle it, and cross out all entries in the column below it. (For example, if you circle 4, cross out 9, 14, 19, and 24.) Now circle any remaining number in the second row, and cross out all entries in the column below it.

   Repeat this procedure for the third and fourth rows, and then circle the final remaining number in the fifth row.

   Now each student in the group should add the circled numbers and compare his or her sum with all others in the group. What do you notice?

2. How does the sum obtained in Exercise 1 compare with the magic sum for an order 5 magic square?

3. Suppose Exercise 1 was done as shown here:

1	②	3	4	5
6	~~7~~	⑧	9	10
11	~~12~~	~~13~~	14	⑮
⑯	~~17~~	~~18~~	19	~~20~~
~~21~~	~~22~~	~~23~~	㉔	~~25~~

   Notice that summing the circled entries is just like summing $1 + 2 + 3 + 4 + 5$, except that

   $$3 \text{ is replaced by } 3 + 5,$$
   $$5 \text{ is replaced by } 5 + 10,$$
   $$1 \text{ is replaced by } 1 + 15,$$
   $$4 \text{ is replaced by } 4 + 20.$$

We can express this as

$$\text{sum} = (1 + 2 + 3 + 4 + 5)$$
$$+ (5 + 10 + 15 + 20)$$
$$= 15 + 50 = 65.$$

4. Explain why, whatever entries you choose to circle in the various rows, the sum is always the same.

5. Prepare a similar square of the natural numbers 1 through 36. Then repeat Exercise 1. Discuss your results. How does the sum compare with the magic sum for an order 6 magic square?

6. As a group, fill in the entries in this equation for the 6 by 6 square.

   $$\text{sum} = (\underline{} + \underline{} + \underline{} + \underline{} + \underline{} + \underline{}) + (\underline{} + \underline{} + \underline{} + \underline{} + \underline{})$$

7. As a group, predict the sum of the circled numbers in a 7 by 7 square by expressing it as follows. (Do not actually construct the square.)

   $$\text{sum} = (\underline{} + \underline{} + \underline{} + \underline{} + \underline{} + \underline{} + \underline{}) + (\underline{} + \underline{} + \underline{} + \underline{} + \underline{} + \underline{})$$

   How does the sum compare with the magic sum for an order 7 magic square?

8. Each individual should now prepare another 5 by 5 square and repeat Exercise 1, except this time start with a number in the first *column* and cross out remaining numbers in *rows*. In your group, discuss and explain what you observe.

CHAPTER 5 TEST

In Exercises 1–5, decide whether each statement is true *or* false.

1. No two prime numbers differ by 1.

2. There are infinitely many prime numbers.

3. If a natural number is divisible by 9, then it must also be divisible by 3.

4. If p and q are different primes, 1 is their greatest common factor and pq is their least common multiple.

5. For all natural numbers n, 1 is a factor of n and n is a multiple of n.

6. Use divisibility tests to determine whether the number

$$331,153,470$$

is divisible by each of the following.
- (a) 2
- (b) 3
- (c) 4
- (d) 5
- (e) 6
- (f) 8
- (g) 9
- (h) 10
- (i) 12

7. Decide whether each number is prime, composite, or neither.
- (a) 93
- (b) 1
- (c) 59

8. Give the prime factorization of 1440.

9. In your own words state the Fundamental Theorem of Arithmetic.

10. Decide whether each number is perfect, deficient, or abundant.
- (a) 17
- (b) 6
- (c) 24

11. Which of the following statements is false?
- **A.** There are no known odd perfect numbers.
- **B.** Every even perfect number must end in 6 or 28.
- **C.** Goldbach's Conjecture for the number 8 is verified by the equation $8 = 7 + 1$.

12. Give a pair of twin primes between 40 and 50.

13. Find the greatest common factor of 270 and 450.

14. Find the least common multiple of 24, 36, and 60.

15. *Day Off for Fast-food Workers* Both Sherrie Firavich and Della Daniel work at a fast-food outlet. Sherrie has every sixth day off and Della has every fourth day off. If they are both off on Wednesday of this week, what will be the day of the week that they are next off together?

16. The twenty-second Fibonacci number is 17,711 and the twenty-third Fibonacci number is 28,657. What is the twenty-fourth Fibonacci number?

17. Make a conjecture about the next equation in the following list, and verify it.

$$8 - (1 + 1 + 2 + 3) = 1$$
$$13 - (1 + 2 + 3 + 5) = 2$$
$$21 - (2 + 3 + 5 + 8) = 3$$
$$34 - (3 + 5 + 8 + 13) = 5$$
$$55 - (5 + 8 + 13 + 21) = 8$$

18. Choose the correct completion of this statement: If p is a prime number, then $2^p - 1$ is prime
- **A.** never
- **B.** sometimes
- **C.** always.

19. (a) Give the first eight terms of a Fibonacci-type sequence with first term 1 and second term 5.

(b) Choose any term after the first in the sequence just formed. Square it. Multiply the two terms on either side of it. Subtract the smaller result from the larger. Now repeat the process with a different term. Make a conjecture about what this process will yield for any term of the sequence.

20. Which one of the following is the *exact* value of the golden ratio?
- **A.** $\dfrac{1 + \sqrt{5}}{2}$
- **B.** $\dfrac{1 - \sqrt{5}}{2}$
- **C.** 1.6
- **D.** 1.618

21. Briefly state what Fermat's Last Theorem says, and describe the circumstances of its proof.

22. Write a brief explanation of the acronym GIMPS. Include a definition and several examples of the term represented by the letters MP.

THE REAL NUMBERS AND THEIR REPRESENTATIONS

The original *Star Trek* series first aired on NBC on September 8, 1966, and spawned an entire generation of science fiction fans. In its second season, the episode "Wolf in the Fold" told the story of an alien entity that had taken over the computer of the starship *Enterprise.* In an effort to drive the entity out of the computer, Captain Kirk suggested the following to Mr. Spock:

KIRK: Spock, don't you have a compulsory scan unit built into the computer banks?

SPOCK: Yes we do, Captain, but with the entity in control. . . .

KIRK: Well aren't there certain mathematical problems which simply cannot be solved?

SPOCK: Indeed. If we can focus the attention of the computer on one of them. . .

KIRK: That ought to do it.

Later, they are able to do just that:

SPOCK: Ready?

KIRK: Implement.

SPOCK: Computer, this is a class "A" compulsory directive. Compute to the last digit the value of pi.

COMPUTER: No, no, no, no, no, . . .

SPOCK (TO KIRK): As we know, the value of pi is a transcendental figure without resolution. The computer banks will work on this problem to the exclusion of all else until we order it to stop.

KIRK: Yes, that should keep that thing busy for a while.

The alien could not comply with the compulsory directive, because pi (π) is an irrational number, and its decimal representation has no last digit. As a result, ingenuity and mathematics saved the *Enterprise.* In this chapter, we study the rational numbers and irrational numbers, which together form the real number system.

6.1 Real Numbers, Order, and Absolute Value

Sets of Real Numbers • Order in the Real Numbers • Additive Inverses and Absolute Value • Applications

The Origins of Zero The Mayan Indians of Mexico and Central America had one of the earliest numeration systems that included a symbol for zero. The very early Babylonians had a positional system, but they placed only a space between "digits" to indicate a missing power. When the Greeks absorbed Babylonian astronomy, they used the letter omicron, o, of their alphabet or ō to represent "no power," or "zero." The Greek numeration system was gradually replaced by the Roman numeration system.

The Roman system was the one most commonly used in Europe from the time of Christ until perhaps 1400 A.D., when the Hindu-Arabic system began to take over. The original Hindu word for zero was *sunya*, meaning "void." The Arabs adopted this word as *sifr*, or "vacant." The word *sifr* passed into Latin as *zephirum*, which over the years became *zevero, zepiro,* and finally, *zero*.

Sets of Real Numbers As mathematics developed, it was discovered that the *counting,* or *natural, numbers* did not satisfy all requirements of mathematicians. Consequently, new, expanded number systems were created. The mathematician Leopold Kronecker (1823–1891) once made the statement, "God made the integers, all the rest is the work of man." The *natural numbers* are those numbers with which we count discrete objects. By including 0 in the set, we obtain the set of *whole numbers*.

Natural Numbers

$\{1, 2, 3, 4, \ldots\}$ is the set of **natural numbers.**

Whole Numbers

$\{0, 1, 2, 3, \ldots\}$ is the set of **whole numbers.**

These numbers, along with many others, can be represented on **number lines** like the one pictured in Figure 1. We draw a number line by locating any point on the line and calling it 0. Choose any point to the right of 0 and call it 1. The distance between 0 and 1 gives a unit of measure used to locate other points, as shown in Figure 1. The points labeled in Figure 1 and those continuing in the same way to the right correspond to the set of whole numbers.

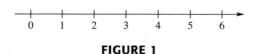

FIGURE 1

All the whole numbers starting with 1 are located to the right of 0 on the number line. But numbers may also be placed to the left of 0. These numbers, written $-1, -2, -3$, and so on, are shown in Figure 2. (The negative sign is used to show that the numbers are located to the *left* of 0.)

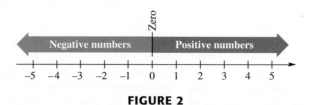

FIGURE 2

The numbers to the *left* of 0 are **negative numbers.** The numbers to the *right* of 0 are **positive numbers.** The number 0 itself is neither positive nor negative. Positive numbers and negative numbers are called **signed numbers.**

The Origins of Negative Numbers Negative numbers can be traced back to the Chinese between 200 B.C. and 220 A.D. Mathematicians at first found negative numbers ugly and unpleasant, even though they kept cropping up in the solutions of problems. For example, an Indian text of about 1150 A.D. gives the solution of an equation as −5 and then makes fun of anything so useless.

Leonardo of Pisa (Fibonacci), while working on a financial problem, was forced to conclude that the solution must be a negative number (that is, a financial loss). In 1545 A.D., the rules governing operations with negative numbers were published by **Girolamo Cardano** in his *Ars Magna* (Great Art).

There are many practical applications of negative numbers. For example, temperatures sometimes fall below zero. The lowest temperature ever recorded in meteorological records was $-128.6°F$ at Vostok, Antarctica, on July 22, 1983. Altitudes below sea level can be represented by negative numbers. The shore surrounding the Dead Sea is 1312 feet below sea level; this can be represented as -1312 feet.

The set of numbers marked on the number line in Figure 2, including positive and negative numbers and zero, is part of the set of *integers*.

Integers

$\{\ldots, -3, -2, -1, 0, 1, 2, 3, \ldots\}$ is the set of **integers.**

Not all numbers are integers. For example, $\frac{1}{2}$ is not; it is a number halfway between the integers 0 and 1. Also, $3\frac{1}{4}$ is not an integer. Several numbers that are not integers are *graphed* in Figure 3. The **graph** of a number is a point on the number line. Think of the graph of a set of numbers as a picture of the set. All the numbers in Figure 3 can be written as quotients of integers. These numbers are examples of *rational numbers.*

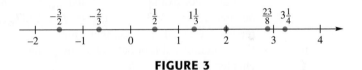

FIGURE 3

Notice that an integer, such as 2, is also a rational number; for example, $2 = \frac{2}{1}$.

Rational Numbers

$\{x \mid x$ is a quotient of two integers, with denominator not equal to 0$\}$ is the set of **rational numbers.**

(Read the part in the braces as "the set of all numbers x such that x is a quotient of two integers, with denominator not equal to 0.")

The set symbolism used in the definition of rational numbers,

$$\{x \mid x \text{ has a certain property}\},$$

is called **set-builder notation.** This notation is convenient to use when it is not possible, or practical, to list all the elements of the set.

Although a great many numbers are rational, not all are. For example, a square that measures one unit on a side has a diagonal whose length is the square root of 2, written $\sqrt{2}$. See Figure 4. It will be shown later that $\sqrt{2}$ cannot be written as a quotient of integers. Because of this, $\sqrt{2}$ is not rational; it is *irrational.*

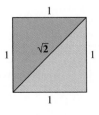

FIGURE 4

Irrational Numbers

$\{x \mid x$ is a number on the number line that is not rational$\}$ is the set of **irrational numbers.**

Examples of irrational numbers include $\sqrt{3}$, $\sqrt{7}$, $-\sqrt{10}$, and π, which is the ratio of the distance around a circle (its *circumference*) to the distance across it (its *diameter*).

All numbers that can be represented by points on the number line are called *real numbers.*

Real Numbers

$\{x \mid x$ is a number that can be represented by a point on the number line$\}$ is the set of **real numbers.**

Real numbers can be written as decimal numbers. Any rational number can be written as a decimal that will come to an end (terminate), or repeat in a fixed "block" of digits. For example, $\frac{2}{5} = .4$ and $\frac{27}{100} = .27$ are rational numbers with terminating decimals; $\frac{1}{3} = .3333\ldots$ and $\frac{3}{11} = .27272727\ldots$ are repeating decimals. The decimal representation of an irrational number will neither terminate nor repeat. Decimal representations of rational and irrational numbers will be discussed further later in this chapter.

Figure 5 illustrates two ways to represent the relationships among the various sets of real numbers.

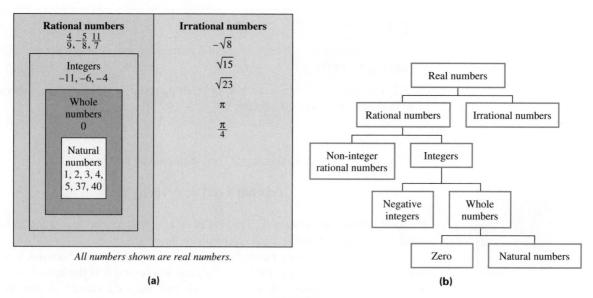

FIGURE 5

EXAMPLE 1   Identifying Elements of a Set of Numbers

List the numbers in the set

$$\left\{-5, -\frac{2}{3}, 0, \sqrt{2}, \frac{13}{4}, 5, 5.8\right\}$$

that belong to each set of numbers.

(a) natural numbers   (b) whole numbers   (c) integers
(d) rational numbers   (e) irrational numbers   (f) real numbers

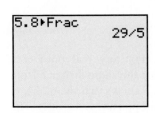

The TI-83/84 Plus calculator will convert a decimal to a fraction. See Example 1(d).

SOLUTION

(a) The only natural number in the set is 5.
(b) The whole numbers consist of the natural numbers and 0. So, the elements of the set that are whole numbers are 0 and 5.
(c) The integers in the set are -5, 0, and 5.
(d) The rational numbers are -5, $-\frac{2}{3}$, 0, $\frac{13}{4}$, 5, and 5.8, because each of these numbers *can* be written as the quotient of two integers. For example, $5.8 = \frac{58}{10} = \frac{29}{5}$.
(e) The only irrational number in the set is $\sqrt{2}$.
(f) All the numbers in the set are real numbers.   ■

Order in the Real Numbers

Two real numbers may be compared, or ordered, using the ideas of equality and inequality. Suppose that a and b represent two real numbers. If their graphs on the number line are the same point, they are **equal.** If the graph of a lies to the left of b, a **is less than** b, and if the graph of a lies to the right of b, a **is greater than** b. The **law of trichotomy** says that for two numbers a and b, one and only one of the following is true:

$$a = b, \quad a < b, \quad \text{or} \quad a > b.$$

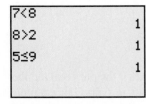

The calculator returns a 1 for these statements of inequality, signifying that each is true.

When read from left to right, the symbol $<$ means "is less than," so

$$7 < 8. \quad \text{7 is less than 8.}$$

The symbol $>$ means "is greater than." For example,

$$8 > 2. \quad \text{8 is greater than 2.}$$

Notice that the symbol always points to the lesser number. For example,

$$\text{Lesser number} \longrightarrow 8 < 15.$$

The symbol $\leq$ means "is less than or equal to," so

$$5 \leq 9. \quad \text{5 is less than or equal to 9.}$$

This statement is true, since $5 < 9$ is true. *If either the $<$ part or the $=$ part is true, then the inequality $\leq$ is true.* Also, $8 \leq 8$ is true since $8 = 8$ is true. But it is not true that $13 \leq 9$ because neither $13 < 9$ nor $13 = 9$ is true.

The symbol $\geq$ means "is greater than or equal to." Again,

$$9 \geq 5 \quad \text{9 is greater than or equal to 5.}$$

is true because $9 > 5$ is true.

The symbol for equality, =, was first introduced by the Englishman Robert Recorde in his 1557 algebra text *The Whetstone of Witte.* He used two parallel line segments, because, he claimed, no two things can be more equal.

The symbols for order relationships, $<$ and $>$, were first used by Thomas Harriot (1560–1621), another Englishman. These symbols were not immediately adopted by other mathematicians.

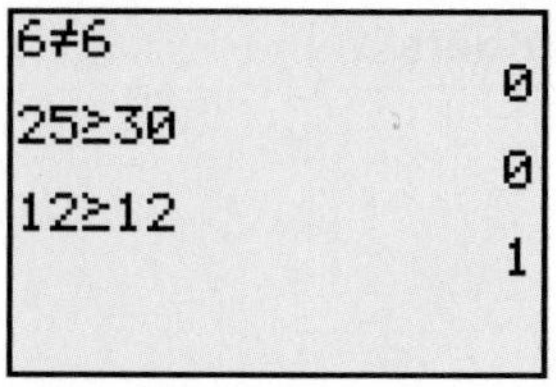

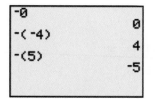

EXAMPLE 2 Comparing Real Numbers

Determine whether each statement is *true* or *false*.

(a) $6 \neq 6$ (b) $5 < 19$ (c) $15 \leq 20$ (d) $25 \geq 30$ (e) $12 \geq 12$

SOLUTION

(a) The statement $6 \neq 6$ is false, because 6 *is equal to* 6.
(b) Since 5 is indeed less than 19, this statement is true.
(c) The statement $15 \leq 20$ is true, since $15 < 20$.
(d) Both $25 > 30$ and $25 = 30$ are false, so $25 \geq 30$ is false.
(e) Since $12 = 12$, the statement $12 \geq 12$ is true.

Additive Inverses and Absolute Value For any real number x (except 0), there is exactly one number on the number line the same distance from 0 as x but on the opposite side of 0. For example, Figure 6 shows that the numbers 3 and -3 are both the same distance from 0 but are on opposite sides of 0. The numbers 3 and -3 are called **additive inverses, negatives,** or **opposites,** of each other.

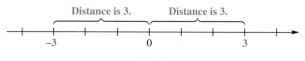

Distance is 3.   Distance is 3.

FIGURE 6

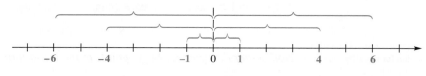

The additive inverse of the number 0 is 0 itself. This makes 0 the only real number that is its own additive inverse. Other additive inverses occur in pairs. For example, 4 and -4, and 5 and -5, are additive inverses of each other. Several pairs of additive inverses are shown in Figure 7.

FIGURE 7

The additive inverse of a number can be indicated by writing the symbol $-$ in front of the number. With this symbol, the additive inverse of 7 is written -7. The additive inverse of -4 is written $-(-4)$, and can also be read "the opposite of -4" or "the negative of -4." Figure 7 suggests that 4 is an additive inverse of -4. Since a number can have only one additive inverse, the symbols 4 and $-(-4)$ must represent the same number, which means that

$$-(-4) = 4.$$

This idea can be generalized as follows.

Double Negative Rule

For any real number x,

$$-(-x) = x.$$

TABLE 1

Number	Additive Inverse
-4	$-(-4)$ or 4
0	0
19	-19
$-\dfrac{2}{3}$	$\dfrac{2}{3}$

Table 1 shows several numbers and their additive inverses. An important property of additive inverses will be studied later in this chapter: $a + (-a) = (-a) + a = 0$ for all real numbers a.

As mentioned above, additive inverses are numbers that are the same distance from 0 on the number line. See Figure 7. This idea can also be expressed by saying that a number and its additive inverse have the same absolute value. The **absolute value** of a real number can be defined as the distance between 0 and the number on the number line. The symbol for the absolute value of the number x is $|x|$, read **"the absolute value of x."** For example, the distance between 2 and 0 on the number line is 2 units, so

$$|2| = 2.$$

Because the distance between -2 and 0 on the number line is also 2 units,

$$|-2| = 2.$$

Since distance is a physical measurement, which is never negative, **the absolute value of a number is never negative.** For example, $|12| = 12$ and $|-12| = 12$, since both 12 and -12 lie at a distance of 12 units from 0 on the number line. Also, since 0 is a distance of 0 units from 0, $|0| = 0$.

In symbols, the absolute value of x is defined as follows.

Formal Definition of Absolute Value

For any real number x,

$$|x| = \begin{cases} x & \text{if } x \geq 0 \\ -x & \text{if } x < 0. \end{cases}$$

By this definition, if x is a positive number or 0, then its absolute value is x itself. For example, since 8 is a positive number, $|8| = 8$. However, if x is a negative number, then its absolute value is the additive inverse of x. This means that if $x = -9$, then $|-9| = -(-9) = 9$, since the additive inverse of -9 is 9.

The formal definition of absolute value can be confusing if it is not read carefully. The "$-x$" in the second part of the definition *does not* represent a negative number. Since x is negative in the second part, $-x$ represents the opposite of a negative number, that is, a positive number.

EXAMPLE 3   Using Absolute Value

Simplify by finding the absolute value.

(a) $|5|$ **(b)** $|-5|$ **(c)** $-|5|$

(d) $-|-14|$ **(e)** $|8 - 2|$ **(f)** $-|8 - 2|$

```
abs(-5)
                 5
-abs(-14)
               -14
-abs(8-2)
                -6
```

This screen supports the results of Example 3(b), (d), and (f).

SOLUTION

(a) $|5| = 5$　　　　　　　　(b) $|-5| = -(-5) = 5$

(c) $-|5| = -(5) = -5$　　　(d) $-|-14| = -(14) = -14$

(e) $|8 - 2| = |6| = 6$　　　(f) $-|8 - 2| = -|6| = -6$ ▪

Part (e) of Example 3 shows that absolute value bars also serve as grouping symbols. You must perform any operations that appear inside absolute value symbols before finding the absolute value.

Applications A table of data provides a concise way of relating information.

EXAMPLE 4 Interpreting Change Using a Table

The projected annual rates of employment change (in percent) in some of the fastest growing and most rapidly declining industries from 1994 through 2005 are shown in Table 2. What industry in the list is expected to see the greatest change? the least change?

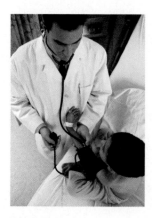

TABLE 2

Industry (1994–2005)	Percent Rate of Change
Health services	5.7
Computer and data processing services	4.9
Child day care services	4.3
Footware, except rubber and plastic	−6.7
Household audio and video equipment	−4.2
Luggage, handbags, and leather products	−3.3

Source: U.S. Bureau of Labor Statistics.

SOLUTION

We want the greatest *change,* without regard to whether the change is an increase or a decrease. Look for the number in the list with the greatest absolute value. That number is found in footware, since $|-6.7| = 6.7$. Similarly, the least change is in the luggage, handbags, and leather products industry: $|-3.3| = 3.3$. ▪

6.1 EXERCISES

In Exercises 1– 6, give a number that satisfies the given condition.

1. An integer between 3.5 and 4.5

2. A rational number between 3.8 and 3.9

3. A whole number that is not positive and is less than 1

4. A whole number greater than 4.5

5. An irrational number that is between $\sqrt{11}$ and $\sqrt{13}$

6. A real number that is neither negative nor positive

In Exercises 7–10, decide whether each statement is true or false.

7. Every natural number is positive.

8. Every whole number is positive.

9. Every integer is a rational number.

10. Every rational number is a real number.

In Exercises 11 and 12, list all numbers from each set that are **(a)** *natural numbers;* **(b)** *whole numbers;* **(c)** *integers;* **(d)** *rational numbers;* **(e)** *irrational numbers;* **(f)** *real numbers.*

11. $\left\{-9, -\sqrt{7}, -1\frac{1}{4}, -\frac{3}{5}, 0, \sqrt{5}, 3, 5.9, 7\right\}$

12. $\left\{-5.3, -5, -\sqrt{3}, -1, -\frac{1}{9}, 0, 1.2, 1.8, 3, \sqrt{11}\right\}$

13. Explain in your own words the different sets of numbers introduced in this section, and give an example of each kind.

14. What two possible situations exist for the decimal representation of a rational number?

Use an integer to express each number representing a change or measurement in the following applications.

15. *Height of the Sears Tower* The Sears Tower in Chicago is 1450 feet high. (*Source:* Council on Tall Buildings and Urban Habitat.)

16. *Population of Laredo* Between 2000 and 2004, the population of Laredo, TX increased by 26,636. (*Source:* Estimate of the U.S. Census Bureau.

17. *Height of Mt. Arenal* The height of Mt. Arenal, an active volcano in Costa Rica, is 5436 feet above sea level. (*Source: The New York Times Almanac 2006.*)

18. *Boiling Point of Chlorine* The boiling point of chlorine is approximately 30° below 0° Fahrenheit.

19. *Melting Point of Fluorine* The melting point of fluorine gas is 220° below 0° Celsius.

20. *Population of Detroit* Between 2000 and 2004, the population of Detroit, MI decreased by 51,072. (*Source:* Estimate of the U.S. Census Bureau.)

21. *Windchill* When the wind speed is 20 miles per hour and the actual temperature is 10° Fahrenheit, the windchill factor is 9° below 0° Fahrenheit. (Give three responses.)

22. *Elevation of New Orleans* The city of New Orleans lies 8 feet below sea level. (*Source:* U.S. Geological Survey, *Elevations and Distances in the United States.*)

23. *Depths and Heights of Seas and Mountains* The chart gives selected depths and heights of bodies of water and mountains.

Bodies of Water	Average Depth in Feet (as a negative number)	Mountains	Altitude in Feet (as a positive number)
Pacific Ocean	−12,925	McKinley	20,320
South China Sea	−4802	Point Success	14,150
Gulf of California	−2375	Matlalcueyetl	14,636
Caribbean Sea	−8448	Ranier	14,410
Indian Ocean	−12,598	Steele	16,644

Source: The World Almanac and Book of Facts.

(a) List the bodies of water in order, starting with the deepest and ending with the shallowest.

(b) List the mountains in order, starting with the lowest and ending with the highest.

(c) *True or false:* The absolute value of the depth of the Pacific Ocean is greater than the absolute value of the depth of the Indian Ocean.

(d) *True or false:* The absolute value of the depth of the Gulf of California is greater than the absolute value of the depth of the Caribbean Sea.

24. *Personal Savings* The bar graph in the figure illustrates the amount of personal savings, in billions of dollars, accumulated during the years 1997 through 2001.

(a) Which year had the greatest amount of savings? Which had the least?

(b) Which years had amounts greater than $200 billion?

(c) Estimate the amounts for 1997 and 1998.

(d) Estimate the difference of the amounts for the years 1997 and 1998.

(e) How did personal savings in 1998 compare to personal savings in 1999?

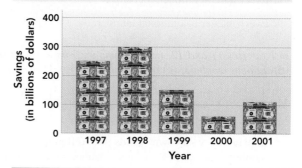

Source: U.S. Bureau of Economic Analysis.

Graph each group of numbers on a number line.

25. $-2, -6, -4, 3, 4$

26. $-5, -3, -2, 0, 4$

27. $\frac{1}{4}, 2\frac{1}{2}, -3\frac{4}{5}, -4, -1\frac{5}{8}$

28. $5\frac{1}{4}, 4\frac{5}{9}, -2\frac{1}{3}, 0, -3\frac{2}{5}$

29. Match each expression in Column I with its value in Column II. Some choices in Column II may not be used.

I	II
(a) $\|-7\|$	**A.** 7
(b) $-(-7)$	**B.** -7
(c) $-\|-7\|$	**C.** neither A nor B
(d) $-\|-(-7)\|$	**D.** both A and B

30. Fill in the blanks with the correct values: The opposite of -2 is _____, while the absolute value of -2 is _____. The additive inverse of -2 is _____, while the additive inverse of the absolute value of -2 is _____.

Find **(a)** *the additive inverse (or opposite) of each number and* **(b)** *the absolute value of each number.*

31. -2

32. -8

33. 6

34. 11

35. $7 - 4$

36. $8 - 3$

37. $7 - 7$

38. $3 - 3$

39. Use the results of Exercises 35 and 36 to complete the following: If $a - b > 0$, then the absolute value of $a - b$ in terms of a and b is _____.

40. Look at Exercises 37 and 38 and use the results to complete the following: If $a - b = 0$, then the absolute value of $a - b$ is _____.

Select the lesser of the two given numbers.

41. $-12, -4$

42. $-9, -14$

43. $-8, -1$

44. $-15, -16$

45. $3, |-4|$

46. $5, |-2|$

47. $|-3|, |-4|$

48. $|-8|, |-9|$

49. $-|-6|, -|-4|$

50. $-|-2|, -|-3|$

51. $|5 - 3|, |6 - 2|$

52. $|7 - 2|, |8 - 1|$

Decide whether each statement is true or false.

53. $6 > -(-2)$

54. $-8 > -(-2)$

55. $-4 \leq -(-5)$

56. $-6 \leq -(-3)$

57. $|-6| < |-9|$

58. $|-12| < |-20|$

59. $-|8| > |-9|$

60. $-|12| > |-15|$

61. $-|-5| \geq -|-9|$

62. $-|-12| \leq -|-15|$

63. $|6 - 5| \geq |6 - 2|$

64. $|13 - 8| \leq |7 - 4|$

Producer Price Index *The table shows the percent change in the Producer Price Index (PPI) for selected industries from 2002 to 2003 and from 2003 to 2004. Use the table to answer Exercises 65–68.*

65. Which industry in which year represents the greatest percentage increase?

66. Which industry in which year represents the greatest percentage decrease?

67. Which industry in which year represents the least change?

68. Which industries represent a decrease for both years?

Industry	Change from 2002 to 2003	Change from 2003 to 2004
Book publishers	3.7	3.8
Telephone apparatus manufacturing	−3.5	−5.1
Construction machinery manufacturing	1.4	3.1
Petroleum refineries	25.9	25.0
Electronic computer manufacturing	−19.6	−12.3

Source: U.S. Bureau of Labor Statistics.

69. ***Comparing Employment Data*** Refer to the table in Example 4. Of the household audio/video equipment industry and computer/data processing services, which shows the greater change (without regard to sign)?

70. Students often say "Absolute value is always positive." Is this true? If not, explain why.

Give three numbers between -6 *and* 6 *that satisfy each given condition.*

71. Positive real numbers but not integers

72. Real numbers but not positive numbers

73. Real numbers but not whole numbers

74. Rational numbers but not integers

75. Real numbers but not rational numbers

76. Rational numbers but not negative numbers

6.2 Operations, Properties, and Applications of Real Numbers

Operations • Order of Operations • Properties of Addition and Multiplication of Real Numbers • Applications of Real Numbers

Operations   The result of adding two numbers is called their **sum.** The numbers being added are called **addends** (or **terms**).

Adding Real Numbers

Like Signs   Add two numbers with the *same* sign by adding their absolute values. The sign of the sum (either $+$ or $-$) is the same as the sign of the two numbers.

Unlike Signs   Add two numbers with *different* signs by subtracting the smaller absolute value from the larger to find the absolute value of the sum. The sum is positive if the positive number has the larger absolute value. The sum is negative if the negative number has the larger absolute value.

Practical Arithmetic From the time of Egyptian and Babylonian merchants, practical aspects of arithmetic complemented mystical (or "Pythagorean") tendencies. This was certainly true in the time of **Adam Riese** (1489–1559), a "reckon master" influential when commerce was growing in Northern Europe. Riese's likeness on the stamp above comes from the title page of one of his popular books on *Rechnung* (or "reckoning"). He championed new methods of reckoning using Hindu-Arabic numerals and quill pens. (The Roman methods then in common use moved counters on a ruled board.) Riese thus fulfilled Fibonacci's efforts 300 years earlier to supplant Roman numerals and methods.

For example, to add -12 and -8, first find their absolute values:

$$|-12| = 12 \quad \text{and} \quad |-8| = 8.$$

Since -12 and -8 have the *same* sign, add their absolute values: $12 + 8 = 20$. Give the sum the sign of the two numbers. Since both numbers are negative, the sum is negative and

$$-12 + (-8) = -20.$$

Find $-17 + 11$ by subtracting the absolute values, because these numbers have different signs.

$$|-17| = 17 \quad \text{and} \quad |11| = 11$$
$$17 - 11 = 6$$

Give the result the sign of the number with the larger absolute value.

$$-17 + 11 = -6$$
↑————Negative since $|-17| > |11|$

EXAMPLE 1 Adding Signed Numbers

Find each sum.

(a) $-6 + (-3)$ **(b)** $-12 + (-4)$ **(c)** $4 + (-1)$
(d) $-9 + 16$ **(e)** $-16 + 12$

SOLUTION

(a) $-6 + (-3) = -(6 + 3) = -9$
(b) $-12 + (-4) = -(12 + 4) = -16$
(c) $4 + (-1) = 3$ **(d)** $-9 + 16 = 7$ **(e)** $-16 + 12 = -4$ ▪

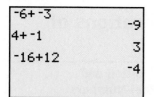

The calculator supports the results of Example 1(a), (c), and (e).

The result of subtracting two numbers is called their **difference.** In $a - b$, a is called the **minuend,** and b is called the **subtrahend.** Compare the two statements below.

$$7 - 5 = 2$$
$$7 + (-5) = 2$$

In a similar way, $9 - 3 = 9 + (-3)$. That is, to subtract 3 from 9, add the additive inverse of 3 to 9.

These examples suggest the following rule for subtraction.

Definition of Subtraction

For all real numbers a and b,

$$a - b = a + (-b).$$

(Change the sign of the subtrahend and add.)

EXAMPLE 2   Subtracting Signed Numbers

Find each difference.

(a) $6 - 8$ **(b)** $-12 - 4$
(c) $-10 - (-7)$ **(d)** $15 - (-3)$

SOLUTION

——— Change to addition.
——— Change sign of the subtrahend.

(a) $6 - 8 = 6 + (-8) = -2$

——— Change to addition.
——— Sign changed.

(b) $-12 - 4 = -12 + (-4) = -16$
(c) $-10 - (-7) = -10 + [-(-7)]$ This step can be omitted.
$\qquad\qquad\qquad = -10 + 7$
$\qquad\qquad\qquad = -3$
(d) $15 - (-3) = 15 + 3 = 18$

The result of multiplying two numbers is called their **product.** The two numbers being multiplied are called **factors.** Any rules for multiplication with negative real numbers should be consistent with the usual rules for multiplication of positive real numbers and zero. To inductively obtain a rule for multiplying a positive real number and a negative real number, observe the pattern of products below.

$$4 \cdot 5 = 20$$
$$4 \cdot 4 = 16$$
$$4 \cdot 3 = 12$$
$$4 \cdot 2 = 8$$
$$4 \cdot 1 = 4$$
$$4 \cdot 0 = 0$$
$$4 \cdot (-1) = ?$$

What number must be assigned as the product $4 \cdot (-1)$ so that the pattern is maintained? The numbers just to the left of the equality signs decrease by 1 each time, and the products to the right decrease by 4 each time. To maintain the pattern, the number to the right in the bottom equation must be 4 less than 0, which is -4, so

$$4 \cdot (-1) = -4.$$

The pattern continues with

$$4 \cdot (-2) = -8$$
$$4 \cdot (-3) = -12$$
$$4 \cdot (-4) = -16,$$

and so on. In the same way,

$$-4 \cdot 2 = -8$$
$$-4 \cdot 3 = -12$$
$$-4 \cdot 4 = -16,$$

Left margin:

```
6-8
            -2
-12-4
            -16
-10-(-7)
            -3
```

The calculator supports the results of Example 2(a), (b), and (c).

Early ways of writing the basic operation symbols were quite different from those used today. The **addition symbol** shown below was derived from the Italian word *piú* (plus) in the sixteenth century. The $+$ sign used today is shorthand for the Latin *et* (and).

The **subtraction symbol** shown below was used by Diophantus in Greece sometime during the second or third century A.D. Our subtraction bar may be derived from a bar used by medieval traders to mark differences in weights of products.

Early ways of writing the multiplication and division symbols were also quite different. In the seventeenth century, Leibniz used the **multiplication symbol** below to avoid ✕ as too similar to the "unknown" *x*. The multiplication symbol ✕ is based on St. Andrew's Cross.

The **division symbol** shown below was used by Gallimard in the eighteenth century. The familiar ÷ symbol may come from the fraction bar, embellished with the dots above and below.

and so on. A similar observation can be made about the product of two negative real numbers. Look at the pattern that follows.

$$-5 \cdot 4 = -20$$
$$-5 \cdot 3 = -15$$
$$-5 \cdot 2 = -10$$
$$-5 \cdot 1 = -5$$
$$-5 \cdot 0 = 0$$
$$-5 \cdot (-1) = \text{?}$$

The numbers just to the left of the equality signs decrease by 1 each time. The products on the right increase by 5 each time. To maintain the pattern, the product $-5 \cdot (-1)$ must be 5 more than 0, so

$$-5 \cdot (-1) = 5.$$

Continuing this pattern gives

$$-5 \cdot (-2) = 10$$
$$-5 \cdot (-3) = 15$$
$$-5 \cdot (-4) = 20,$$

and so on. These observations lead to the following rules for multiplication.

$(+) \cdot (+) = +$
$(-) \cdot (-) = +$
$(+) \cdot (-) = -$
$(-) \cdot (+) = -$

Multiplying Real Numbers

Like Signs Multiply two numbers with the *same* sign by multiplying their absolute values to find the absolute value of the product. The product is positive.

Unlike Signs Multiply two numbers with *different* signs by multiplying their absolute values to find the absolute value of the product. The product is negative.

EXAMPLE 3 Multiplying Signed Numbers

Find each product.

(a) $-9 \cdot 7$ **(b)** $14 \cdot (-5)$ **(c)** $-8 \cdot (-4)$

SOLUTION

(a) $-9 \cdot 7 = -63$ **(b)** $14 \cdot (-5) = -70$ **(c)** $-8 \cdot (-4) = 32$ ▪

The result of dividing two numbers is called their **quotient.** In the quotient $a \div b$ (or $\frac{a}{b}$), where $b \neq 0$, a is called the **dividend** (or numerator), and b is called the **divisor** (or denominator). For real numbers a, b, and c, if

$$\frac{a}{b} = c, \quad \text{then} \quad a = b \cdot c.$$

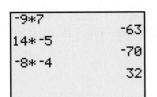

An asterisk (*) represents multiplication on this screen. The display supports the results of Example 3.

To illustrate this, consider the quotient $\frac{10}{-2}$. The value of this quotient is obtained by asking, "What number multiplied by -2 gives 10?" From our discussion of multiplication, the answer to this question must be "-5." Therefore,

$$\frac{10}{-2} = -5,$$

because $-2 \cdot (-5) = 10$. Similar reasoning leads to the following results.

$$\frac{-10}{2} = -5 \quad \text{and} \quad \frac{-10}{-2} = 5$$

These facts, along with the fact that the quotient of two positive numbers is positive, lead to the following rule for division.

$(+)/(+) = +$
$(-)/(-) = +$
$(+)/(-) = -$
$(-)/(+) = -$

Dividing Real Numbers

Like Signs   Divide two numbers with the *same* sign by dividing their absolute values to find the absolute value of the quotient. The quotient is positive.

Unlike Signs   Divide two numbers with *different* signs by dividing their absolute values to find the absolute value of the quotient. The quotient is negative.

EXAMPLE 4   Dividing Signed Numbers

Find each quotient.

(a) $\dfrac{15}{-5}$ **(b)** $\dfrac{-100}{-25}$ **(c)** $\dfrac{-60}{3}$

SOLUTION

(a) $\dfrac{15}{-5} = -3$ This is true because $-5 \cdot (-3) = 15$.

(b) $\dfrac{-100}{-25} = 4$ **(c)** $\dfrac{-60}{3} = -20$ ∎

The division operation is represented by a slash (/). This screen supports the results of Example 4.

If 0 is divided by a nonzero number, the quotient is 0. That is,

$$\frac{0}{a} = 0, \quad \text{for } a \neq 0.$$

This is true because $a \cdot 0 = 0$. However, we cannot divide by 0. There is a good reason for this. Whenever a division is performed, we want to obtain one and only one quotient. Now consider the division problem

$$\frac{7}{0}.$$

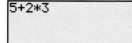

Dividing by zero leads to this message on the TI-83/84 Plus.

We must ask ourselves "What number multiplied by 0 gives 7?" There is no such number, since the product of 0 and any number is zero. On the other hand, if we consider the quotient

$$\frac{0}{0},$$

there are infinitely many answers to the question, "What number multiplied by 0 gives 0?" Since division by 0 does not yield a *unique* quotient, it is not permitted. To summarize these two situations, we make the following statement.

Division by Zero

Division by 0 is undefined.

5+2∗3

What result does the calculator give? The order of operations determines the answer. (See Example 5(a).)

Order of Operations

Given a problem such as $5 + 2 \cdot 3$, should 5 and 2 be added first or should 2 and 3 be multiplied first? When a problem involves more than one operation, we use the following **order of operations.**

Order of Operations

If parentheses or square brackets are present:

Step 1 Work separately above and below any **fraction bar.**

Step 2 Use the rules below within each set of **parentheses or square brackets.** Start with the innermost set and work outward.

If no parentheses or brackets are present:

Step 1 Apply any **exponents.**

Step 2 Do any **multiplications or divisions** in the order in which they occur, working from left to right.

Step 3 Do any **additions or subtractions** in the order in which they occur, working from left to right.

The sentence **"Please excuse my dear Aunt Sally"** is often used to help us remember the rule for order of operations. The letters **P, E, M, D, A, S** are the first letters of the words of the sentence, and they stand for *parentheses, exponents, multiply, divide, add, subtract.* (*Remember also that M and D have equal priority, as do A and S. Operations with equal priority are performed in order from left to right.*)

When evaluating an exponential expression that involves a negative sign, be aware that $(-a)^n$ and $-a^n$ do not necessarily represent the same quantity. For example, if $a = 2$ and $n = 6$,

$$(-2)^6 = (-2)(-2)(-2)(-2)(-2)(-2) = 64 \quad \text{The base is } -2.$$

while

$$-2^6 = -(2 \cdot 2 \cdot 2 \cdot 2 \cdot 2 \cdot 2) = -64. \quad \text{The base is } 2.$$

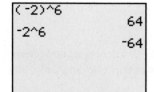

Notice the difference in the two expressions. This supports $(-2)^6 \neq -2^6$.

EXAMPLE 5 Using the Order of Operations

Use the order of operations to simplify each expression.

(a) $5 + 2 \cdot 3$

(b) $4 \cdot 3^2 + 7 - (2 + 8)$

(c) $\dfrac{2(8 - 12) - 11(4)}{5(-2) - 3}$

(d) -4^4

(e) $(-4)^4$

(f) $(-8)(-3) - [4 - (3 - 6)]$

SOLUTION

(a) $5 + 2 \cdot 3 = 5 + 6$ Multiply.

Be careful! $= 11$ Add.

Multiply first.

(b) $4 \cdot 3^2 + 7 - (2 + 8) = 4 \cdot 3^2 + 7 - 10$ Work within parentheses first.

$3^2 = 3 \cdot 3$, not $3 \cdot 2$. $= 4 \cdot 9 + 7 - 10$ Apply the exponent.

$= 36 + 7 - 10$ Multiply.

$= 43 - 10$ Add.

$= 33$ Subtract.

(c) $\dfrac{2(8 - 12) - 11(4)}{5(-2) - 3} = \dfrac{2(-4) - 11(4)}{5(-2) - 3}$ Work separately above and below fraction bar.

$= \dfrac{-8 - 44}{-10 - 3}$ Multiply.

$= \dfrac{-52}{-13}$ Subtract.

$= 4$ Divide.

(d) $-4^4 = -(4 \cdot 4 \cdot 4 \cdot 4) = -256$

The base is 4, not -4.

(e) $(-4)^4 = (-4)(-4)(-4)(-4) = 256$

The base is -4 here.

(f) $-8(-3) - [4 - (3 - 6)] = -8(-3) - [4 - (-3)]$ Work within parentheses.

Start here. $= -8(-3) - [4 + 3]$ Definition of subtraction

$= -8(-3) - 7$ Work within brackets.

$= 24 - 7$ Multiply.

$= 17$ Subtract.   ■

```
5+2*3
             11
-4^4
           -256
-8*-3-(4-(3-6))
             17
```

The calculator supports the results in Example 5(a), (d), and (f).

Properties of Addition and Multiplication of Real Numbers

Properties of Addition and Multiplication

For real numbers a, b, and c, the following properties hold.

Closure Properties $a + b$ and ab are real numbers.

Commutative Properties $a + b = b + a$ $ab = ba$

Associative Properties $(a + b) + c = a + (b + c)$

$(ab)c = a(bc)$

Identity Properties   There is a real number 0 such that

$$a + 0 = a \quad \text{and} \quad 0 + a = a.$$

There is a real number 1 such that

$$a \cdot 1 = a \quad \text{and} \quad 1 \cdot a = a.$$

(continued)

Properties of Addition and Multiplication, Continued	
Inverse Properties	For each real number a, there is a single real number $-a$ such that
	$$a + (-a) = 0 \quad \text{and} \quad (-a) + a = 0.$$
	For each nonzero real number a, there is a single real number $\frac{1}{a}$ such that
	$$a \cdot \frac{1}{a} = 1 \quad \text{and} \quad \frac{1}{a} \cdot a = 1.$$
Distributive Property of Multiplication with Respect to Addition	$$a(b + c) = ab + ac$$ $$(b + c)a = ba + ca$$

The set of real numbers is said to be closed with respect to the operations of addition and multiplication. This means that the sum of two real numbers and the product of two real numbers are themselves real numbers. The commutative properties state that two real numbers may be added or multiplied in either order without affecting the result. The associative properties allow us to group terms or factors in any manner we wish without affecting the result.

The number 0 is called the **identity element for addition,** and it may be added to any real number to obtain that real number as a sum. Similarly, 1 is called the **identity element for multiplication,** and multiplying a real number by 1 will always yield that real number. Each real number a has an **additive inverse,** $-a$, such that the sum of a and its additive inverse is the additive identity element 0. Each nonzero real number a has a **multiplicative inverse,** or **reciprocal,** $\frac{1}{a}$, such that the product of a and its multiplicative inverse is the multiplicative identity element 1. The distributive property allows us to change certain products to sums and certain sums to products.

```
X+Y=Y+X
                    1
X+(Y+Z)=(X+Y)+Z
                    1
5(X+Y)=5X+5Y
                    1
```

No matter what values are stored in X, Y, and Z, the commutative, associative, and distributive properties assure us that these statements are true.

EXAMPLE 6 Identifying Properties of Addition and Multiplication

Identify the property of addition or multiplication illustrated in each statement.

(a) $5 + 7$ is a real number.

(b) $5 + (6 + 8) = (5 + 6) + 8$

(c) $8 + 0 = 8$

(d) $-4\left(-\dfrac{1}{4}\right) = 1$

(e) $4 + (3 + 9) = 4 + (9 + 3)$

(f) $5(x + y) = 5x + 5y$

SOLUTION

(a) The statement that the sum of two real numbers is also a real number is an example of the closure property of addition.

(b) Because the grouping of the terms is different on the two sides of the equation, this illustrates the associative property of addition.

(c) Adding 0 to a number yields the number itself. This is an example of the identity property of addition.

(d) Multiplying a number by its reciprocal yields 1, and this illustrates the inverse property of multiplication.

(e) The order of the addends (terms) 3 and 9 is different, so this is justified by the commutative property of addition.

(f) The factor 5 is distributed to the terms x and y. This is an example of the distributive property of multiplication with respect to addition. ▪

Applications of Real Numbers

The usefulness of negative numbers can be seen by considering situations that arise in everyday life. For example, we need negative numbers to express the temperatures on January days in Anchorage, Alaska, where they often drop below zero. The phrases "in the red" and "in the black" mean losing money and making money, respectively. (These descriptions go back to the days when bookkeepers used red ink to represent losses and black ink to represent gains.)

> **PROBLEM-SOLVING HINT** When problems deal with gains and losses, the gains may be interpreted as positive numbers and the losses as negative numbers. Temperatures below 0° are negative, and those above 0° are positive. Altitudes above sea level are considered positive, and those below sea level are considered negative.

EXAMPLE 7 Analyzing the Producer Price Index

The Producer Price Index is the oldest continuous statistical series published by the Bureau of Labor Statistics. It measures the average changes in prices received by producers of all commodities produced in the United States. The bar graph in Figure 8 gives the Producer Price Index (PPI) for construction materials between 1996 and 2003.

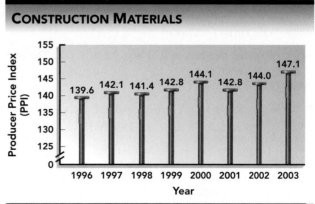

Source: U.S. Bureau of Labor Statistics, Producer Price Indexes, monthly and annual.

FIGURE 8

Use a signed number to represent the change in the PPI from

(a) 1999 to 2000.   **(b)** 2000 to 2001.

SOLUTION

(a) To find this change, we start with the index number from 2000 and subtract from it the index number from 1999.

$$144.1 \quad - \quad 142.8 \quad = \quad 1.3$$

The 2000 index   The 1999 index   A positive number indicates an increase.

(b) Use the same procedure as in part (a).

$$142.8 \quad - \quad 144.1 \quad = 142.8 + (-144.1) = -1.3$$

The 2001 index   The 2000 index   A negative number indicates a decrease. ■

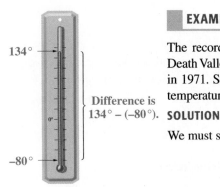

FIGURE 9

134°

Difference is 134° − (−80°).

−80°

EXAMPLE 8 Determining Difference of Temperatures

The record high temperature in the United States was 134° Fahrenheit, recorded at Death Valley, California, in 1913. The record low was −80°F, at Prospect Creek, Alaska, in 1971. See Figure 9. How much greater was the highest temperature than the lowest temperature? (*Source: The World Almanac and Book of Facts 2006.*)

SOLUTION

We must subtract the lower temperature from the higher temperature.

$$134 - (-80) = 134 + 80 \quad \text{Use the definition of subtraction.}$$
$$= 214 \quad \text{Add.}$$

The difference of the two temperatures is 214°F. ■

6.2 EXERCISES

Fill in each blank with the correct response.

1. The sum of two negative numbers will always be a _____ number.
(positive/negative)

2. The sum of a number and its opposite will always be _____.

3. To simplify the expression 8 + [−2 + (−3 + 5)], I should begin by adding _____ and _____, according to the rule for order of operations.

4. If I am adding a positive number and a negative number, and the negative number has the larger absolute value, the sum will be a _____ number.
(positive/negative)

5. Explain in words how to add signed numbers. Consider the various cases and give examples.

6. Explain in words how to multiply signed numbers.

Perform the indicated operations, using the order of operations as necessary.

7. −12 + (−8)

8. −5 + (−2)

9. 12 + (−16)

10. −6 + 17

11. −12 − (−1)

12. −3 − (−8)

13. −5 + 11 + 3

14. −9 + 16 + 5

15. 12 − (−3) − (−5)

16. $15 - (-6) - (-8)$

17. $-9 - (-11) - (4 - 6)$

18. $-4 - (-13) + (-5 + 10)$

19. $(-12)(-2)$

20. $(-3)(-5)$

21. $9(-12)(-4)(-1)3$

22. $-5(-17)(2)(-2)4$

23. $\dfrac{-18}{-3}$

24. $\dfrac{-100}{-50}$

25. $\dfrac{36}{-6}$

26. $\dfrac{52}{-13}$

27. $\dfrac{0}{12}$

28. $\dfrac{0}{-7}$

29. $-6 + [5 - (3 + 2)]$

30. $-8[4 + (7 - 8)]$

31. $-8(-2) - [(4^2) + (7 - 3)]$

32. $-7(-3) - [2^3 - (3 - 4)]$

33. $-4 - 3(-2) + 5^2$

34. $-6 - 5(-8) + 3^2$

35. $(-8 - 5)(-2 - 1)$

36. $\dfrac{(-10 + 4) \cdot (-3)}{-7 - 2}$

37. $\dfrac{(-6 + 3) \cdot (-4)}{-5 - 1}$

38. $\dfrac{2(-5 + 3)}{-2^2} - \dfrac{(-3^2 + 2)3}{3 - (-4)}$

39. $\dfrac{2(-5) + (-3)(-2^2)}{-3^2 + 9}$

40. $\dfrac{3(-4) + (-5)(-2)}{2^3 - 2 + (-6)}$

41. $-\dfrac{1}{4}[3(-5) + 7(-5) + 1(-2)]$

42. $\dfrac{5 - 3\left(\dfrac{-5 - 9}{-7}\right) - 6}{-9 - 11 + 3 \cdot 7}$

43. Which of the following expressions are undefined?

 A. $\dfrac{8}{0}$ **B.** $\dfrac{9}{6 - 6}$ **C.** $\dfrac{4 - 4}{5 - 5}$ **D.** $\dfrac{0}{-1}$

44. If you have no money in your pocket and you divide it equally among your three siblings, how much does each get? Use this situation to explain division of zero by a positive integer.

Identify the property illustrated by each statement.

45. $6 + 9 = 9 + 6$

46. $8 \cdot 4 = 4 \cdot 8$

47. $7 + (2 + 5) = (7 + 2) + 5$

48. $(3 \cdot 5) \cdot 4 = 4 \cdot (3 \cdot 5)$

49. $9 + (-9) = 0$

50. $12 + 0 = 12$

51. $9 \cdot 1 = 9$

52. $\left(\dfrac{1}{-3}\right) \cdot (-3) = 1$

53. $0 + 283 = 283$

54. $6 \cdot (4 \cdot 2) = (6 \cdot 4) \cdot 2$

55. $2 \cdot (4 + 3) = 2 \cdot 4 + 2 \cdot 3$

56. $9 \cdot 6 + 9 \cdot 8 = 9 \cdot (6 + 8)$

57. $0 = -8 + 8$

58. $19 + 12$ is a real number.

59. $19 \cdot 12$ is a real number.

60. Work the following problem in two ways, first using the order of operations, and then using the distributive property: Evaluate $9(11 + 15)$.

Exercises 61– 68 are designed to explore the properties of real numbers in further detail.

61. (a) Evaluate $6 - 8$ and $8 - 6$.
 (b) By the results of part (a), we may conclude that subtraction is not a(n) _____ operation.
 (c) Are there *any* real numbers a and b for which $a - b = b - a$? If so, give an example.

62. (a) Evaluate $4 \div 8$ and $8 \div 4$.
 (b) By the results of part (a), we may conclude that division is not a(n) _____ operation.
 (c) Are there *any* real numbers a and b for which $a \div b = b \div a$? If so, give an example.

63. Many everyday occurrences can be thought of as operations that have opposites or inverses. For example, the inverse operation for "going to sleep" is "waking up." For each of the given activities, specify its inverse activity.
(a) cleaning up your room
(b) earning money
(c) increasing the volume on your MP3 player

64. Many everyday activities are commutative; that is, the order in which they occur does not affect the outcome. For example, "putting on your shirt" and "putting on your pants" are commutative operations. Decide whether the given activities are commutative.
(a) putting on your shoes; putting on your socks
(b) getting dressed; taking a shower
(c) combing your hair; brushing your teeth

65. The following conversation actually took place between one of the authors of this text and his son, Jack, when Jack was four years old.

DADDY: "Jack, what is $3 + 0$?"
JACK: "3"
DADDY: "Jack, what is $4 + 0$?"
JACK: "4...and Daddy, *string* plus zero equals *string!*" What property of addition of real numbers did Jack recognize?

66. The phrase *defective merchandise counter* is an example of a phrase that can have different meanings depending upon how the words are grouped (think of the associative properties). For example, (*defective merchandise*) *counter* is a location at which we would return an item that does not work, while *defective* (*merchandise counter*) is a broken place where items are bought and sold. For each of the following phrases, determine why the associative property does not hold.
(a) difficult test question
(b) woman fearing husband
(c) man biting dog

67. The distributive property holds for multiplication with respect to addition. Does the distributive property hold for addition with respect to multiplication? That is, is $a + (b \cdot c) = (a + b) \cdot (a + c)$ true for all values of *a, b,* and *c?* (*Hint:* Let $a = 2$, $b = 3$, and $c = 4$.)

68. Suppose that a student shows you the following work.

$$-3(4 - 6) = -3(4) - 3(6) = -12 - 18 = -30$$

The student has made a very common error in applying the distributive property. Explain the student's mistake, and work the problem correctly.

Each expression in Exercises 69–76 is equal to either 81 *or* −81. *Decide which of these is the correct value.*

69. -3^4

70. $-(3^4)$

71. $(-3)^4$

72. $-(-3^4)$

73. $-(-3)^4$

74. $[-(-3)]^4$

75. $-[-(-3)]^4$

76. $-[-(-3^4)]$

77. *Federal Budget Outlays* The bar graph shows federal budget outlays for the U.S. Treasury Department for the years 2002 through 2005. Use a signed number to represent the change in outlay for each time period.
(a) 2002 to 2003
(b) 2003 to 2004
(c) 2004 to 2005
(d) 2002 to 2005

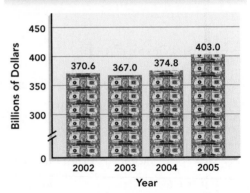

FEDERAL BUDGET OUTLAYS FOR TREASURY DEPARTMENT

Source: U.S. Office of Management and Budget.

78. *Heights of Mountains and Depths of Trenches* The chart shows the heights in feet of some selected mountains and the depths in feet (as negative numbers) of some selected ocean trenches.

Mountain	Height	Trench	Depth
Foraker	17,400	Philippine	−32,995
Wilson	14,246	Cayman	−24,721
Pikes Peak	14,110	Java	−23,376

Source: The World Almanac and Book of Facts 2006.

(a) What is the difference between the height of Mt. Foraker and the depth of the Philippine Trench?

(b) What is the difference between the height of Pikes Peak and the depth of the Java Trench?

(c) How much deeper is the Cayman Trench than the Java Trench?

(d) How much deeper is the Philippine Trench than the Cayman Trench?

79. *Social Security Finances* The table shows Social Security tax revenue and cost of benefits (in billions of dollars).

Year	Tax Revenue	Cost of Benefits
2000	538	409
2010*	916	710
2020*	1479	1405
2030*	2041	2542

*Projected
Source: Social Security Board of Trustees.

(a) Find the difference between Social Security tax revenue and cost of benefits for each year shown in the table.

(b) Interpret your answer for 2030.

80. *House of Representatives* Based on census population projections for 2020, New York will lose 5 seats in the U.S. House of Representatives, Pennsylvania will lose 4 seats, and Ohio will lose 3. Write a signed number that represents the total projected change in the number of seats for these three states. (*Source:* Population Reference Bureau.)

81. *House of Representatives* Michigan is projected to lose 3 seats in the U.S. House of Representatives and Illinois 2 in 2020. The states projected to gain the most seats are California with 9, Texas with 5, Florida with 3, Georgia with 2, and Arizona with 2. Write a signed number that represents the algebraic sum of these changes. (*Source:* Population Reference Bureau.)

82. *Checking Account Balance* Shalita's checking account balance is $54.00. She then takes a gamble by writing a check for $89.00. What is her new balance? (Write the balance as a signed number.)

83. *Checking Account Balance* In August, Marilyn Cazayoux began with a checking account balance of $904.89. Her checks and deposits for August are given below:

Checks	Deposits
$35.84	$85.00
$26.14	$120.76
$3.12	

Assuming no other transactions, what was her account balance at the end of August?

84. *Checking Account Balances* In September, Carter Fenton began with a checking account balance of $904.89. His checks and deposits for September are given below:

Checks	Deposits
$41.29	$80.59
$13.66	$276.13
$84.40	

Assuming no other transactions, what was his account balance at the end of September?

85. *Difference in Elevations* The top of Mt. Whitney, visible from Death Valley, has an altitude of 14,494 feet above sea level. The bottom of Death Valley is 282 feet below sea level. Using 0 as sea level, find the difference of these two elevations. (*Source: World Almanac and Book of Facts 2006.*)

86. *Altitude of Hikers* The surface, or rim, of a canyon is at altitude 0. On a hike down into the canyon, a party of hikers stops for a rest at 130 meters below the surface. They then descend another 54 meters. What is their new altitude? (Write the altitude as a signed number.)

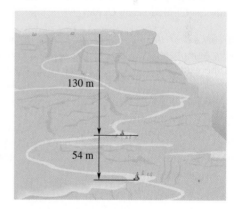

87. *Drastic Temperature Change* On January 23, 1943, the temperature rose 49°F in two minutes in Spearfish, South Dakota. If the starting temperature was −4°F, what was the temperature two minutes later? (*Source: Guinness World Records 2006.*)

88. *Drastic Temperature Change* The largest change in temperature ever recorded within a 24-hour period occurred in Browning, Montana, on January 23–24, 1916. The temperature fell 100°F from a starting temperature of 44°F. What was the low temperature during this period? (*Source: Guinness World Records, 2006.*)

89. ***Extreme Temperatures in Little Rock*** The lowest temperature ever recorded in Little Rock, Arkansas, was −5°F. The highest temperature ever recorded there was 117°F more than the lowest. What was this highest temperature? (*Source: The World Almanac and Book of Facts 2006.*)

90. ***Extreme Temperatures in Tennessee*** The lowest temperature ever recorded in Tennessee was −32°F. The highest temperature ever recorded there was 145°F more than the lowest. What was this highest temperature? (*Source:* National Climatic Data Center.)

91. ***Low Temperatures in Chicago and Huron*** The lowest temperature recorded in Chicago, Illinois, was −27°F in 1985. The record low in Huron, South Dakota, was set in 1994 and was 14°F lower than −27°F. What was the record low in Huron? (*Source: The World Almanac and Book of Facts 2006.*)

92. ***Low Temperatures in Illinois and Utah*** The lowest temperature ever recorded in Illinois was −36°F on January 5, 1999. The lowest temperature ever recorded in Utah was observed on February 1, 1985 and was 33°F lower than Illinois's record low. What is the record low temperature for Utah? (*Source:* National Climatic Data Center.)

93. ***Breaching of Humpback Whales*** No one knows just why humpback whales heave their 45-ton bodies out of the water, but leap they do. (This activity is called *breaching*.) Mark and Debbie, two researchers based on the island of Maui, noticed that one of their favorite whales, "Pineapple," leaped 15 feet above the surface of the ocean while her mate cruised 12 feet below the surface. (See the diagram at the top of the next column.) What is the difference between these two levels?

94. ***Highest Point in Louisiana*** The highest point in Louisiana is Driskill Mountain, at an altitude of 535 feet. The lowest point is at Spanish Fort, 8 feet below sea level. Using zero as sea level, find the difference of these two elevations. (*Source: The World Almanac and Book of Facts 2002.*)

95. ***Birth Date of a Greek Mathematician*** A certain Greek mathematician was born in 426 B.C. Her father was born 43 years earlier. In what year was her father born?

96. ***Federal Budget*** In 2000, the federal budget had a surplus of $236 billion. In 2004, the federal budget had a deficit of $413 billion. Find the difference of these amounts. (*Source:* Treasury Department.)

97. ***Credit Card Balance*** In 1998, undergraduate college students had an average credit card balance of $1879. The average balance increased $869 by 2000 and then dropped $579 by 2004. What was the average credit card balance of undergraduate college students in 2004? (*Source:* Nellie Mae.)

98. ***Airline Ticket Price*** In 1999, companies paid an average of $243 for an airline ticket. This average price had increased $16 by 2001 and then had decreased $40 by 2005. What was the average price companies paid for an airline ticket in 2005? (*Source:* American Express.)

6.3 | Rational Numbers and Decimal Representation

Definition and the Fundamental Property • Operations with Rational Numbers • Density and the Arithmetic Mean • Decimal Form of Rational Numbers

Definition and the Fundamental Property
The set of real numbers is composed of two important mutually exclusive subsets: the rational numbers and the irrational numbers. (Two sets are *mutually exclusive* if they contain no elements in common.)

Benjamin Banneker (1731–1806) spent the first half of his life tending a farm in Maryland. He gained a reputation locally for his mechanical skills and abilities in mathematical problem solving. In 1772 he acquired astronomy books from a neighbor and devoted himself to learning astronomy, observing the skies, and making calculations. In 1789 Banneker joined the team that surveyed what is now the District of Columbia.

Banneker published almanacs yearly from 1792 to 1802. He sent a copy of his first almanac to Thomas Jefferson along with an impassioned letter against slavery. Jefferson subsequently championed the cause of this early African-American mathematician.

Recall from Section 6.1 that quotients of integers are called **rational numbers.** Think of the rational numbers as being made up of all the fractions (quotients of integers with denominator not equal to zero) and all the integers. Any integer can be written as the quotient of two integers. For example, the integer 9 can be written as the quotient $\frac{9}{1}$, or $\frac{18}{2}$, or $\frac{27}{3}$, and so on. Also, -5 can be expressed as a quotient of integers as $\frac{-5}{1}$ or $\frac{-10}{2}$, and so on. (How can the integer 0 be written as a quotient of integers?)

Rational Numbers

Rational numbers $= \{x \mid x$ is a quotient of two integers, with denominator not $0\}$

A rational number is said to be in **lowest terms** if the greatest common factor of the numerator (top number) and the denominator (bottom number) is 1. (The greatest common factor and least common multiple were discussed in Section 5.3.) Rational numbers are written in lowest terms by using the *fundamental property of rational numbers.*

Fundamental Property of Rational Numbers

If a, b, and k are integers with $b \neq 0$ and $k \neq 0$, then

$$\frac{a \cdot k}{b \cdot k} = \frac{a}{b}.$$

EXAMPLE 1   Writing a Fraction in Lowest Terms

Write $\frac{36}{54}$ in lowest terms.

SOLUTION

Since the greatest common factor of 36 and 54 is 18,

$$\frac{36}{54} = \frac{2 \cdot 18}{3 \cdot 18} = \frac{2}{3}.$$

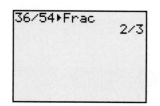

The calculator gives 36/54 in lowest terms, as illustrated in Example 1.

In Example 1, $\frac{36}{54} = \frac{2}{3}$. If we multiply the numerator of the fraction on the left by the denominator of the fraction on the right, we obtain $36 \cdot 3 = 108$. If we multiply the denominator of the fraction on the left by the numerator of the fraction on the right, we obtain $54 \cdot 2 = 108$. The result is the same in both cases.

One way of determining whether two fractions are equal is to perform this test. If the product of the **"extremes"** (36 and 3 in this case) equals the product of the **"means"** (54 and 2), the fractions are equal. This test for equality of rational numbers is called the **cross-product test.**

Cross-Product Test for Equality of Rational Numbers

For rational numbers $\frac{a}{b}$ and $\frac{c}{d}$, $b \neq 0$, $d \neq 0$,

$$\frac{a}{b} = \frac{c}{d} \quad \text{if and only if} \quad a \cdot d = b \cdot c.$$

Operations with Rational Numbers The operation of addition of rational numbers can be illustrated by the sketches in Figure 10. The rectangle at the top left is divided into three equal portions, with one of the portions in color. The rectangle at the top right is divided into five equal parts, with two of them in color.

The total of the areas in color is represented by the sum

$$\frac{1}{3} + \frac{2}{5}.$$

To evaluate this sum, the areas in color must be redrawn in terms of a common unit. Since the least common multiple of 3 and 5 is 15, redraw both rectangles with 15 parts. See Figure 11. In the figure, 11 of the small rectangles are in color, so

$$\frac{1}{3} + \frac{2}{5} = \frac{5}{15} + \frac{6}{15} = \frac{11}{15}.$$

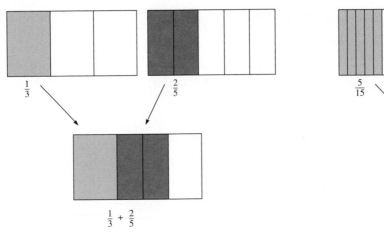

FIGURE 10

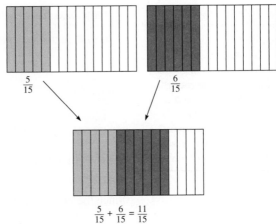

FIGURE 11

A similar example could be given for the difference of rational numbers. A formal definition of addition and subtraction of rational numbers follows.

Adding and Subtracting Rational Numbers

If $\frac{a}{b}$ and $\frac{c}{d}$ are rational numbers, then

$$\frac{a}{b} + \frac{c}{d} = \frac{ad + bc}{bd} \quad \text{and} \quad \frac{a}{b} - \frac{c}{d} = \frac{ad - bc}{bd}.$$

This formal definition is seldom used in practice. In practical problems involving addition and subtraction of rational numbers, we usually rewrite the fractions with the least common multiple of their denominators, called the **least common denominator**.

```
2/15+1/10▶Frac
            7/30
173/180-69/1200▶
Frac
        3253/3600
```

The results of Example 2 are
illustrated in this screen.

EXAMPLE 2 Adding and Subtracting Rational Numbers

Perform each operation.

(a) $\dfrac{2}{15} + \dfrac{1}{10}$ (b) $\dfrac{173}{180} - \dfrac{69}{1200}$

SOLUTION

(a) The least common multiple of 15 and 10 is 30. Now write $\frac{2}{15}$ and $\frac{1}{10}$ with denominators of 30, and then add the numerators. Proceed as follows:

$$\text{Since } 30 \div 15 = 2, \qquad \frac{2}{15} = \frac{2 \cdot 2}{15 \cdot 2} = \frac{4}{30},$$

$$\text{and since } 30 \div 10 = 3, \qquad \frac{1}{10} = \frac{1 \cdot 3}{10 \cdot 3} = \frac{3}{30}.$$

$$\text{Thus,} \qquad \frac{2}{15} + \frac{1}{10} = \frac{4}{30} + \frac{3}{30} = \frac{7}{30}.$$

(b) The least common multiple of 180 and 1200 is 3600.

$$\frac{173}{180} - \frac{69}{1200} = \frac{3460}{3600} - \frac{207}{3600} = \frac{3460 - 207}{3600} = \frac{3253}{3600}$$

The product of two rational numbers is defined as follows.

Multiplying Rational Numbers

If $\frac{a}{b}$ and $\frac{c}{d}$ are rational numbers, then

$$\frac{a}{b} \cdot \frac{c}{d} = \frac{ac}{bd}.$$

```
(3/4)*(7/10)▶Fra
c
          21/40
(5/18)*(3/10)▶Fr
ac
            1/12
```

To illustrate the results of Example
3, we use parentheses around the
fraction factors.

EXAMPLE 3 Multiplying Rational Numbers

Find each product.

(a) $\dfrac{3}{4} \cdot \dfrac{7}{10}$ (b) $\dfrac{5}{18} \cdot \dfrac{3}{10}$

SOLUTION

(a) $\dfrac{3}{4} \cdot \dfrac{7}{10} = \dfrac{3 \cdot 7}{4 \cdot 10} = \dfrac{21}{40}$

(b) $\dfrac{5}{18} \cdot \dfrac{3}{10} = \dfrac{5 \cdot 3}{18 \cdot 10} = \dfrac{15}{180} = \dfrac{1 \cdot 15}{12 \cdot 15} = \dfrac{1}{12}$

In practice, a multiplication problem such as this is often solved by using slash marks to indicate that common factors have been divided out of the numerator and denominator.

$$\frac{\overset{1}{\cancel{5}}}{\underset{6}{\cancel{18}}} \cdot \frac{\overset{1}{\cancel{3}}}{\underset{2}{\cancel{10}}} = \frac{1}{6} \cdot \frac{1}{2}$$

3 is divided out of the terms 3 and 18;
5 is divided out of 5 and 10.

$$= \frac{1}{12}$$

In a fraction, the fraction bar indicates the operation of division. Recall that, in the previous section, we defined the multiplicative inverse, or reciprocal, of the nonzero number b. The multiplicative inverse of b is $\frac{1}{b}$. We can now define division using multiplicative inverses.

For Further Thought

The Influence of Spanish Coinage on Stock Prices

Until August 28, 2000, when decimalization of the U.S. stock market began, market prices were reported with fractions having denominators with powers of 2, such as $17\frac{3}{4}$ and $112\frac{5}{8}$. Did you ever wonder why this was done?

During the early years of the United States, prior to the minting of its own coinage, the Spanish eight-reales coin, also known as the Spanish milled dollar, circulated freely in the states. Its fractional parts, the four reales, two reales, and one real, were known as **pieces of eight,** and were described as such in pirate and treasure lore. When the New York Stock Exchange was founded in 1792, it chose to use the Spanish milled dollar as its price basis, rather than the decimal base as proposed by Thomas Jefferson that same year.

In the September 1997 issue of *COINage*, Tom Delorey's article "The End of 'Pieces of Eight'" gives the following account:

As the Spanish dollar and its fractions continued to be legal tender in America alongside the decimal coins until 1857, there was no urgency to change the system—and by the time the Spanish-American money was

withdrawn in 1857, pricing stocks in eighths of a dollar—and no less—was a tradition carved in stone. Being somewhat a conservative organization, the NYSE saw no need to fix what was not broken.

All prices on the U.S. stock markets are now reported in decimals. (*Source:* "Stock price tables go to decimal listings," *The Times Picayune*, June 27, 2000.)

For Group Discussion or Individual Investigation

Consider this: Have you ever heard this old cheer? "Two bits, four bits, six bits, a dollar. All for the (home team), stand up and holler." The term **two bits** refers to 25 cents. Discuss how this cheer is based on the Spanish eight-reales coin.

Early U.S. cents and **half cents** used fractions to denote their denominations. The half cent used $\frac{1}{200}$ and the cent used $\frac{1}{100}$. (See Exercise 18 for a photo of an interesting error coin.)

The coins shown here were part of the collection of Louis E. Eliasberg, Sr. **Louis Eliasberg** was the only person ever to assemble a complete collection of United States coins. The Eliasberg gold coins were auctioned in 1982, while the copper, nickel, and silver coins were auctioned in two sales in 1996 and 1997. The half cent pictured sold for $506,000 and the cent sold for $27,500. The cent shown in Exercise 18 went for a mere $2970.

Definition of Division

If a and b are real numbers, $b \neq 0$, then

$$\frac{a}{b} = a \cdot \frac{1}{b}.$$

You have probably heard the rule, "To divide fractions, invert the divisor and multiply." But have you ever wondered why this rule works? To illustrate it, suppose that you have $\frac{7}{8}$ of a gallon of milk and you wish to find how many quarts you have. Since a quart is $\frac{1}{4}$ of a gallon, you must ask yourself, "How many $\frac{1}{4}$s are there in $\frac{7}{8}$?" This would be interpreted as

$$\frac{7}{8} \div \frac{1}{4} \quad \text{or} \quad \frac{\frac{7}{8}}{\frac{1}{4}}.$$

The fundamental property of rational numbers discussed earlier can be extended to rational number values of a, b, and k. With $a = \frac{7}{8}$, $b = \frac{1}{4}$, and $k = 4$ (the reciprocal of $b = \frac{1}{4}$),

$$\frac{a}{b} = \frac{a \cdot k}{b \cdot k} = \frac{\frac{7}{8} \cdot 4}{\frac{1}{4} \cdot 4} = \frac{\frac{7}{8} \cdot 4}{1} = \frac{7}{8} \cdot \frac{4}{1}.$$

Now notice that we began with the division problem $\frac{7}{8} \div \frac{1}{4}$ which, through a series of equivalent expressions, led to the multiplication problem $\left(\frac{7}{8} \cdot \frac{4}{1}\right)$. So dividing by $\frac{1}{4}$ is equivalent to multiplying by its reciprocal, $\frac{4}{1}$. By the definition of multiplication of fractions,

$$\frac{7}{8} \cdot \frac{4}{1} = \frac{28}{8} = \frac{7}{2},$$

and thus there are $\frac{7}{2}$ or $3\frac{1}{2}$ quarts in $\frac{7}{8}$ gallon.*

We now state the rule for dividing $\frac{a}{b}$ by $\frac{c}{d}$.

Dividing Rational Numbers

If $\frac{a}{b}$ and $\frac{c}{d}$ are rational numbers, where $\frac{c}{d} \neq 0$, then

$$\frac{a}{b} \div \frac{c}{d} = \frac{a}{b} \cdot \frac{d}{c} = \frac{ad}{bc}.$$

---

*$3\frac{1}{2}$ is a **mixed number.** Mixed numbers are covered in the exercises for this section.

```
(-4/7)/(3/14)▶Fr
ac
                -8/3
(2/9)/4▶Frac
                1/18
```

This screen supports the results in Example 4(b) and (c).

EXAMPLE 4   Dividing Rational Numbers

Find each quotient.

(a) $\dfrac{3}{5} \div \dfrac{7}{15}$ **(b)** $\dfrac{-4}{7} \div \dfrac{3}{14}$ **(c)** $\dfrac{2}{9} \div 4$

SOLUTION

(a) $\dfrac{3}{5} \div \dfrac{7}{15} = \dfrac{3}{5} \cdot \dfrac{15}{7} = \dfrac{45}{35} = \dfrac{9 \cdot 5}{7 \cdot 5} = \dfrac{9}{7}$

(b) $\dfrac{-4}{7} \div \dfrac{3}{14} = \dfrac{-4}{7} \cdot \dfrac{14}{3} = \dfrac{-56}{21} = \dfrac{-8 \cdot 7}{3 \cdot 7} = \dfrac{-8}{3} = -\dfrac{8}{3}$

$\dfrac{-a}{b}, \dfrac{a}{-b},$ and $-\dfrac{a}{b}$ are all equal.

(c) $\dfrac{2}{9} \div 4 = \dfrac{2}{9} \div \dfrac{4}{1} = \dfrac{\overset{1}{2}}{9} \cdot \dfrac{1}{\underset{2}{4}} = \dfrac{1}{9} \cdot \dfrac{1}{4} = \dfrac{1}{18}$

Density and the Arithmetic Mean   There is no integer between two consecutive integers, such as 3 and 4. However, a rational number can always be found between any two distinct rational numbers. For this reason, the set of rational numbers is said to be *dense*.

Density Property of the Rational Numbers

If r and t are distinct rational numbers, with $r < t$, then there exists a rational number s such that

$$r < s < t.$$

Repeated applications of the density property lead to the conclusion that there are *infinitely many* rational numbers between two distinct rational numbers.

To find the **arithmetic mean,** or **average,** of n numbers, we add the numbers and then divide the sum by n. For two numbers, the number that lies halfway between them is their average.

EXAMPLE 5   Finding the Arithmetic Mean (Average)

Find the rational number halfway between $\frac{2}{3}$ and $\frac{5}{6}$ (that is, their arithmetic mean, or average).

SOLUTION

First, find their sum.

$$\frac{2}{3} + \frac{5}{6} = \frac{4}{6} + \frac{5}{6} = \frac{9}{6} = \frac{3}{2} \qquad \text{Find a common denominator.}$$

Now divide by 2.

$$\frac{3}{2} \div 2 = \frac{3}{2} \cdot \frac{1}{2} = \frac{3}{4} \qquad \text{To divide, multiply by the reciprocal.}$$

The number $\frac{3}{4}$ is halfway between $\frac{2}{3}$ and $\frac{5}{6}$.

TABLE 3

Year	Number (in thousands)
1998	16,211
1999	16,477
2000	16,258
2001	16,289
2002	15,979
2003	15,776

Source: U.S. Bureau of Labor Statistics.

```
(16211+16477+162
58+16289+15979+1
5776)/6
           16165
```

The computation in Example 6 is shown here.

```
    .375           .3636...
8)3.000       11)4.00000...
  24             33
  ──             ──
  60             70
  56             66
  ──             ──
  40             40
  40             33
  ──             ──
   0             70
                 66
                 ──
                 40
                  .
                  .
                  .
```

EXAMPLE 6   Finding the Arithmetic Mean (Average)

Table 3 shows the number of labor union or employee association members, in thousands, for the years 1998–2003. What is the average number, in thousands, for this six-year period?

SOLUTION

To find this average, divide the sum by 6.

$$\frac{16,211 + 16,477 + 16,258 + 16,289 + 15,979 + 15,776}{6} = \frac{96,990}{6} = 16,165$$

The average number of workers for the six-year period is 16,165 thousand (or 16,165,000). ∎

It is also true that between any two *real* numbers there is another *real* number. Thus, we say that the set of real numbers is dense.

Decimal Form of Rational Numbers

We have discussed rational numbers in the form of quotients of integers. Rational numbers can also be expressed as decimals. Decimal numerals have place values that are powers of 10. For example, the decimal numeral 483.039475 is read "four hundred eighty-three and thirty-nine thousand, four hundred seventy-five millionths." The place values are as shown here.

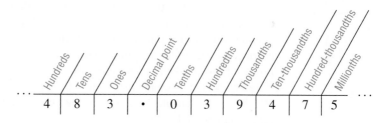

Given a rational number in the form $\frac{a}{b}$, it can be expressed as a decimal most easily by entering it into a calculator. For example, to write $\frac{3}{8}$ as a decimal, enter 3, then enter the operation of division, then enter 8. Press the equals key to find the following equivalence.

$$\frac{3}{8} = .375$$

This same result may be obtained by long division, as shown in the margin. By this result, the rational number $\frac{3}{8}$ is the same as the decimal .375. A decimal such as .375, which stops, is called a **terminating decimal.** Other examples of terminating decimals are

$$\frac{1}{4} = .25, \quad \frac{7}{10} = .7, \quad \text{and} \quad \frac{89}{1000} = .089. \quad \text{Terminating decimals}$$

Not all rational numbers can be represented by terminating decimals. For example, convert $\frac{4}{11}$ into a decimal by dividing 11 into 4 using a calculator. The display shows

.3636363636,   or perhaps   .363636364.

However, we see that the long division process, shown in the margin, indicates that we will actually get .3636 . . . , with the digits 36 repeating over and over indefinitely.

```
2/3
      .6666666667
```

While 2/3 has a repeating decimal representation (2/3 = . $\overline{6}$), the calculator rounds off in the final decimal place displayed.

To indicate this, we write a bar (called a *vinculum*) over the "block" of digits that repeats. Therefore, we can write

$$\frac{4}{11} = .\overline{36}.$$

A decimal such as $.\overline{36}$, which continues indefinitely, is called a **repeating decimal.** Other examples of repeating decimals are

$$\frac{5}{11} = .\overline{45}, \quad \frac{1}{3} = .\overline{3}, \quad \text{and} \quad \frac{5}{6} = .8\overline{3}. \quad \text{Repeating decimals}$$

Because of the limitations of the display of a calculator, and because some rational numbers have repeating decimals, it is important to be able to interpret calculator results accordingly when obtaining repeating decimals.

```
5/11
      .4545454545
1/3
      .3333333333
5/6
      .8333333333
```

Although only ten decimal digits are shown, all three fractions have decimals that repeat endlessly.

While we shall distinguish between *terminating* and *repeating* decimals in this book, some mathematicians prefer to consider all rational numbers as repeating decimals. This can be justified by thinking this way: if the division process leads to a remainder of 0, then zeros repeat without end in the decimal form. For example, we can consider the decimal form of $\frac{3}{4}$ as follows.

$$\frac{3}{4} = .75\overline{0}$$

By considering the possible remainders that may be obtained when converting a quotient of integers to a decimal, we can draw an important conclusion about the decimal form of rational numbers. If the remainder is never zero, the division will produce a repeating decimal. This happens because each step of the division process must produce a remainder that is less than the divisor. Since the number of different possible remainders is less than the divisor, the remainders must eventually begin to repeat. This makes the digits of the quotient repeat, producing a repeating decimal.

Decimal Representation of Rational Numbers

Any rational number can be expressed as either a terminating decimal or a repeating decimal.

To determine whether the decimal form of a quotient of integers will terminate or repeat, we use the following rule.

Simon Stevin (1548–1620) worked as a bookkeeper in Belgium and became an engineer in the Netherlands army. He is usually given credit for the development of **decimals.**

Criteria for Terminating and Repeating Decimals

A rational number $\frac{a}{b}$ in lowest terms results in a **terminating decimal** if the only prime factor of the denominator is 2 or 5 (or both).

A rational number $\frac{a}{b}$ in lowest terms results in a **repeating decimal** if a prime other than 2 or 5 appears in the prime factorization of the denominator.

To find a baseball player's batting average, we divide the number of hits by the number of al-bats. A surprising paradox exists concerning averages; it is possible for Player *A* to have a higher batting average than Player *B* in each of two successive years, yet for the two-year period, Player *B* can have a higher total batting average. Look at the chart.

Year	Player *A*	Player *B*
1998	$\frac{20}{40} = .500$	$\frac{90}{200} = .450$
1999	$\frac{60}{200} = .300$	$\frac{10}{40} = .250$
Two-year total	$\frac{80}{240} = .333$	$\frac{100}{240} = .417$

In both individual years, Player *A* had a higher average, but for the two-year period, Player *B* had the higher average. This is an example of **Simpson's paradox** from statistics.

Justification of this rule is based on the fact that the prime factors of 10 are 2 and 5, and the decimal system uses ten as its base.

EXAMPLE 7　Determining Whether a Decimal Terminates or Repeats

Without actually dividing, determine whether the decimal form of the given rational number terminates or repeats.

(a) $\frac{7}{8}$　**(b)** $\frac{13}{150}$　**(c)** $\frac{6}{75}$

SOLUTION

(a) The rational number $\frac{7}{8}$ is in lowest terms. Its denominator is 8, and since 8 factors as 2^3, the decimal form will terminate. No primes other than 2 or 5 divide the denominator.

(b) The rational number $\frac{13}{150}$ is in lowest terms with denominator $150 = 2 \cdot 3 \cdot 5^2$. Since 3 appears as a prime factor of the denominator, the decimal form will repeat.

(c) First write the rational number $\frac{6}{75}$ in lowest terms.

$$\frac{6}{75} = \frac{2}{25} \qquad \text{Denominator is 25.}$$

Since $25 = 5^2$, the decimal form will terminate. ◼

We have seen that a rational number will be represented by either a terminating or a repeating decimal. Must a terminating decimal or a repeating decimal represent a rational number? The answer is *yes*. For example, the terminating decimal .6 represents a rational number.

$$.6 = \frac{6}{10} = \frac{3}{5}$$

```
.437▶Frac
           437/1000
8.2▶Frac
              41/5
```

The results of Example 8 are supported in this screen.

EXAMPLE 8　Writing Terminating Decimals as Quotients of Integers

Write each terminating decimal as a quotient of integers.

(a) .437　　**(b)** 8.2

SOLUTION

(a) $.437 = \dfrac{437}{1000}$　　Read as "four hundred thirty-seven thousandths" and then write as a fraction.

(b) $8.2 = 8 + \dfrac{2}{10} = \dfrac{82}{10} = \dfrac{41}{5}$　　Read as a decimal, write as a sum, and then add. ◼

Repeating decimals cannot be converted into quotients of integers quite so quickly.

EXAMPLE 9　Writing a Repeating Decimal as a Quotient of Integers

Find a quotient of two integers equal to $.\overline{85}$.

SOLUTION

Step 1　Let $x = .\overline{85}$, so $x = .858585 \ldots$.

$1 = .999999^{99999^{99999^{99}}}$

Terminating or Repeating?
One of the most baffling truths of elementary mathematics is the following:

$$1 = .9999\ldots.$$

Most people believe that $.\overline{9}$ has to be less than 1, but this is not the case. The following argument shows why. Let $x = .9999\ldots$. Then

$$10x = 9.9999\ldots$$
$$\underline{x = .9999\ldots}$$
$$9x = 9 \qquad \text{Subtract.}$$
$$x = 1. \qquad \text{Divide.}$$

Therefore, $1 = .9999\ldots$. Similarly, it can be shown that any terminating decimal can be represented as a repeating decimal with an endless string of 9s. For example, $.5 = .49999\ldots$ and $2.6 = 2.59999\ldots$. This is a way of justifying that any rational number may be represented as a repeating decimal.

Step 2 Multiply both sides of the equation $x = .858585\ldots$ by 100. (Use 100 since there are **two** digits in the part that repeats, and $100 = 10^2$.)

$$x = .858585\ldots$$
$$100x = 100(.858585\ldots)$$
$$100x = 85.858585\ldots$$

Step 3 Subtract the expressions in Step 1 from the final expressions in Step 2.

$$100x = 85.858585\ldots \qquad \text{(Recall that } x = 1x \text{ and}$$
$$\underline{x = .858585\ldots} \qquad 100x - x = 99x.\text{)}$$
$$99x = 85 \qquad \text{Subtract.}$$

Step 4 Solve the equation $99x = 85$ by dividing both sides by 99.

$$99x = 85$$
$$\frac{99x}{99} = \frac{85}{99} \qquad \text{Divide by 99.}$$
$$x = \frac{85}{99} \qquad \frac{99x}{99} = x$$
$$.\overline{85} = \frac{85}{99} \qquad x = .\overline{85}$$

When checking with a calculator, remember that the calculator will only show a finite number of decimal places and may round off in the final decimal place shown. ▪

6.3 EXERCISES

Choose the expression(s) that is (are) equivalent to the given rational number.

1. $\dfrac{4}{8}$

   A. $\dfrac{1}{2}$ **B.** $\dfrac{8}{4}$ **C.** $.5$

   D. $.5\overline{0}$ **E.** $.\overline{55}$

2. $\dfrac{2}{3}$

   A. $.67$ **B.** $.\overline{6}$ **C.** $\dfrac{20}{30}$

   D. $.666\ldots$ **E.** $.6$

3. $\dfrac{5}{9}$

   A. $.56$ **B.** $.55$ **C.** $.\overline{5}$

   D. $\dfrac{9}{5}$ **E.** $1\dfrac{4}{5}$

4. $\dfrac{1}{4}$

   A. $.25$ **B.** $.24\overline{9}$ **C.** $\dfrac{25}{100}$

   D. 4 **E.** $\dfrac{10}{400}$

Use the fundamental property of rational numbers to write each fraction in lowest terms.

5. $\dfrac{16}{48}$ **6.** $\dfrac{21}{28}$

7. $-\dfrac{15}{35}$ **8.** $-\dfrac{8}{48}$

Use the fundamental property to write each fraction in three other ways.

9. $\dfrac{3}{8}$ **10.** $\dfrac{9}{10}$

11. $-\dfrac{5}{7}$

12. $-\dfrac{7}{12}$

13. Write a fraction in lowest terms that represents the portion of each figure that is in color.

(a)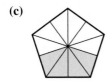

(b)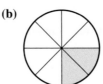

(c)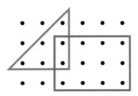

(d)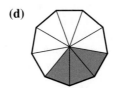

14. Write a fraction in lowest terms that represents the region described.

(a) the dots in the rectangle as a part of the dots in the entire figure

(b) the dots in the triangle as a part of the dots in the entire figure

(c) the dots in the rectangle as a part of the dots in the union of the triangle and the rectangle

(d) the dots in the intersection of the triangle and the rectangle as a part of the dots in the union of the triangle and the rectangle

15. Refer to the figure for Exercise 14 and write a description of the region that is represented by the fraction $\frac{1}{12}$.

16. *Batting Averages* In a softball league, the first six games produced the following results: Greg Tobin got 8 hits in 20 at-bats, and Jason Jordan got 12 hits in 30 at-bats. Which player (if either) had the higher batting average?

17. *Batting Averages* After ten games, the statistics at the top of the next column were obtained.

Player	At-bats	Hits	Home Runs
Anne Kelly	40	9	2
Christine O'Brien	36	12	3
Joanne Ha	11	5	1
Otis Taylor	16	8	0
Carol Britz	20	10	2

Answer each of the following, using estimation skills as necessary.

(a) Which player got a hit in exactly $\frac{1}{3}$ of his or her at-bats?

(b) Which player got a hit in just less than $\frac{1}{2}$ of his or her at-bats?

(c) Which player got a home run in just less than $\frac{1}{10}$ of his or her at-bats?

(d) Which player got a hit in just less than $\frac{1}{4}$ of his or her at-bats?

(e) Which two players got hits in exactly the same fractional parts of their at-bats? What was the fractional part, reduced to lowest terms?

18. Refer to the margin note discussing the use of common fractions on early U.S. copper coinage. The photo here shows an error near the bottom that occurred on an 1802 large cent. Discuss the error and how it represents a mathematical impossibility.

Perform the indicated operations and express answers in lowest terms. Use the order of operations as necessary.

19. $\dfrac{3}{8} + \dfrac{1}{8}$

20. $\dfrac{7}{9} + \dfrac{1}{9}$

21. $\dfrac{5}{16} + \dfrac{7}{12}$

22. $\dfrac{1}{15} + \dfrac{7}{18}$

23. $\dfrac{2}{3} - \dfrac{7}{8}$

24. $\dfrac{13}{20} - \dfrac{5}{12}$

25. $\dfrac{5}{8} - \dfrac{3}{14}$

26. $\dfrac{19}{15} - \dfrac{7}{12}$

27. $\dfrac{3}{4} \cdot \dfrac{9}{5}$

28. $\dfrac{3}{8} \cdot \dfrac{2}{7}$

29. $-\dfrac{2}{3} \cdot -\dfrac{5}{8}$

30. $-\dfrac{2}{4} \cdot \dfrac{3}{9}$

31. $\dfrac{5}{12} \div \dfrac{15}{4}$

32. $\dfrac{15}{16} \div \dfrac{30}{8}$

33. $-\dfrac{9}{16} \div -\dfrac{3}{8}$

34. $-\dfrac{3}{8} \div \dfrac{5}{4}$

35. $\left(\dfrac{1}{3} \div \dfrac{1}{2}\right) + \dfrac{5}{6}$

36. $\dfrac{2}{5} \div \left(-\dfrac{4}{5} \div \dfrac{3}{10}\right)$

37. *Recipe for Grits* The following chart appears on a package of Quaker® Quick Grits.

	Microwave		Stove Top	
Servings	1	1	4	6
Water	$\dfrac{3}{4}$ cup	1 cup	3 cups	4 cups
Grits	3 Tbsp	3 Tbsp	$\dfrac{3}{4}$ cup	1 cup
Salt (optional)	dash	dash	$\dfrac{1}{4}$ tsp	$\dfrac{1}{2}$ tsp

(a) How many cups of water would be needed for 6 microwave servings?

(b) How many cups of grits would be needed for 5 stove-top servings? (*Hint:* 5 is halfway between 4 and 6.)

38. *U.S. Immigrants* More than 8 million immigrants were admitted to the United States during the first eight years of the 1990s. The circle graph gives the fractional number from each region of birth for these immigrants.

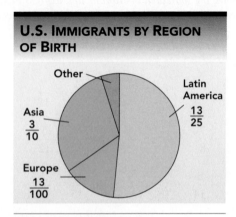

U.S. IMMIGRANTS BY REGION OF BIRTH

Other

Latin America $\dfrac{13}{25}$

Asia $\dfrac{3}{10}$

Europe $\dfrac{13}{100}$

Source: U.S. Census Bureau

(a) What fractional part of the immigrants were from other regions?

(b) What fractional part of the immigrants were from Latin America or Asia?

(c) How many (in millions) were from Europe?

The **mixed number** $2\frac{5}{8}$ *represents the sum* $2 + \frac{5}{8}$. *We can convert* $2\frac{5}{8}$ *to a fraction as follows:*

$$2\frac{5}{8} = 2 + \frac{5}{8} = \frac{2}{1} + \frac{5}{8} = \frac{16}{8} + \frac{5}{8} = \frac{21}{8}.$$

The fraction $\frac{21}{8}$ *can be converted back to a mixed number by dividing 8 into 21. The quotient is 2, the remainder is 5, and the divisor is 8.*

Convert each mixed number to a fraction, and convert each fraction to a mixed number.

39. $4\dfrac{1}{3}$

40. $3\dfrac{7}{8}$

41. $2\dfrac{9}{10}$

42. $\dfrac{18}{5}$

43. $\dfrac{27}{4}$

44. $\dfrac{19}{3}$

It is possible to add mixed numbers by first converting them to fractions, adding, and then converting the sum back to a mixed number. For example,

$$2\frac{1}{3} + 3\frac{1}{2} = \frac{7}{3} + \frac{7}{2} = \frac{14}{6} + \frac{21}{6} = \frac{35}{6} = 5\frac{5}{6}.$$

The other operations with mixed numbers may be performed in a similar manner.

Perform each operation and express your answer as a mixed number.

45. $3\dfrac{1}{4} + 2\dfrac{7}{8}$

46. $6\dfrac{1}{5} - 2\dfrac{7}{15}$

47. $-4\dfrac{7}{8} \cdot 3\dfrac{2}{3}$

48. $-4\dfrac{1}{6} \div 1\dfrac{2}{3}$

Solve each problem.

49. *Socket Wrench Measurements* A hardware store sells a 40-piece socket wrench set. The measure of the largest socket is $\frac{3}{4}$ in., while the measure of the smallest socket is $\frac{3}{16}$ in. What is the difference between these measures?

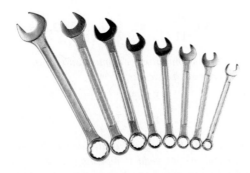

50. **Swiss Cheese Hole Sizes** Under existing standards, most of the holes in Swiss cheese must have diameters between $\frac{11}{16}$ and $\frac{13}{16}$ in. To accommodate new high-speed slicing machines, the USDA wants to reduce the minimum size to $\frac{3}{8}$ in. How much smaller is $\frac{3}{8}$ in. than $\frac{11}{16}$ in.? (*Source:* U.S. Department of Agriculture.)

A quotient of quantities containing fractions (with denominator not zero) is called a **complex fraction.** *There are two methods that are used to simplify a complex fraction.*

Method 1 *Simplify the numerator and denominator separately. Then rewrite as a division problem, and proceed as you would when dividing fractions.*

Method 2 *Multiply both the numerator and denominator by the least common denominator of all the fractions found within the complex fraction. (This is, in effect, multiplying the fraction by 1, which does not change its value.) Apply the distributive property, if necessary, and simplify.*

Use one of the methods above to simplify each complex fraction.

51. $\dfrac{\frac{1}{2}+\frac{1}{4}}{\frac{1}{2}-\frac{1}{4}}$

52. $\dfrac{\frac{2}{3}+\frac{1}{6}}{\frac{2}{3}-\frac{1}{6}}$

53. $\dfrac{\frac{5}{8}-\frac{1}{4}}{\frac{1}{8}+\frac{3}{4}}$

54. $\dfrac{\frac{3}{16}-\frac{1}{2}}{\frac{5}{16}+\frac{1}{8}}$

55. $\dfrac{\frac{7}{11}+\frac{3}{10}}{\frac{1}{11}-\frac{9}{10}}$

56. $\dfrac{\frac{11}{15}+\frac{1}{9}}{\frac{13}{15}-\frac{2}{3}}$

The expressions in Exercises 57 and 58 are called **continued fractions.** *Write each in the form $\frac{p}{q}$ reduced to lowest terms. (Hint: Start at the bottom and work up.)*

57. $2+\dfrac{1}{1+\dfrac{1}{3+\dfrac{1}{2}}}$

58. $4+\dfrac{1}{2+\dfrac{1}{1+\dfrac{1}{3}}}$

Find the rational number halfway between the two given rational numbers.

59. $\dfrac{1}{2},\dfrac{3}{4}$

60. $\dfrac{1}{3},\dfrac{5}{12}$

61. $\dfrac{3}{5},\dfrac{2}{3}$

62. $\dfrac{7}{12},\dfrac{5}{8}$

63. $-\dfrac{2}{3},-\dfrac{5}{6}$

64. $-3,-\dfrac{5}{2}$

Solve each problem.

65. **Average Annual Salary** The table shows the average annual salary in the eight highest-paying metropolitan areas in the United States. Find the average of these amounts to the nearest dollar.

Metropolitan Area	Average Annual Salary
San Jose, CA	$63,056
New York, NY	$57,708
San Francisco, CA	$56,602
New Haven, CT, area	$51,170
Middlesex, NJ, area	$50,457
Jersey City, NJ	$49,562
Newark, NJ	$48,781
Washington, DC, area	$48,430

Source: Bureau of Labor Statistics.

66. **Adoption of Chinese Babies** Since 2000, the country of China has been the most popular foreign country for U.S. adoptions. Find the average annual number of adoptions during the period 2000–2004, based on the figures in the table.

Year	Number of Adoptions
2000	4943
2001	4629
2002	6062
2003	6638
2004	7033

Source: Department of Homeland Security, Office of Immigration Statistics.

In the March 1973 issue of The Mathematics Teacher *there appeared an article by Laurence Sherzer, an eighth-grade mathematics teacher, that immortalized one of his students, Robert McKay. The class was studying the density property and Sherzer was explaining how to find a rational number between two given positive rational numbers by finding the average. McKay pointed out that there was no need to go to all that trouble. To find a number (not necessarily their average) between two positive rational numbers $\frac{a}{b}$ and $\frac{c}{d}$, he claimed, simply add the numerators and add the denominators. Much to Sherzer's surprise, this method really does work.*

For example, to find a rational number between $\frac{1}{3}$ and $\frac{1}{4}$, add $1 + 1 = 2$ to get the numerator and $3 + 4 = 7$ to get the denominator. Therefore, by **McKay's theorem,** $\frac{2}{7}$ *is between $\frac{1}{3}$ and $\frac{1}{4}$. Sherzer provided a proof of this method in the article.*

Use McKay's theorem *to find a rational number between the two given rational numbers.*

67. $\frac{5}{6}$ and $\frac{9}{13}$

68. $\frac{10}{11}$ and $\frac{13}{19}$

69. $\frac{4}{13}$ and $\frac{9}{16}$

70. $\frac{6}{11}$ and $\frac{13}{14}$

71. 2 and 3

72. 3 and 4

73. Apply McKay's theorem to any pair of consecutive integers, and make a conjecture about what always happens in this case.

74. Explain in your own words how to find the rational number that is one-fourth of the way between two different rational numbers.

Convert each rational number into either a repeating or a terminating decimal. Use a calculator if your instructor so allows.

75. $\frac{3}{4}$ **76.** $\frac{7}{8}$ **77.** $\frac{3}{16}$ **78.** $\frac{9}{32}$

79. $\frac{3}{11}$ **80.** $\frac{9}{11}$ **81.** $\frac{2}{7}$ **82.** $\frac{11}{15}$

Convert each terminating decimal into a quotient of integers. Write each in lowest terms.

83. .4   **84.** .9   **85.** .85

86. .105   **87.** .934   **88.** .7984

Use the method of Example 7 to decide whether each rational number would yield a repeating or a terminating decimal. (Hint: Write in lowest terms before trying to decide.)

89. $\frac{8}{15}$ **90.** $\frac{8}{35}$ **91.** $\frac{13}{125}$

92. $\frac{3}{24}$ **93.** $\frac{22}{55}$ **94.** $\frac{24}{75}$

95. Follow through on all parts of this exercise in order.
   (a) Find the decimal for $\frac{1}{3}$.
   (b) Find the decimal for $\frac{2}{3}$.
   (c) By adding the decimal expressions obtained in parts (a) and (b), obtain a decimal expression for $\frac{1}{3} + \frac{2}{3} = \frac{3}{3} = 1$.
   (d) Does your result seem bothersome? Read the margin note on terminating and repeating decimals in this section, which refers to this idea.

96. It is a fact that $\frac{1}{3} = .333\ldots$. Multiply both sides of this equation by 3. Does your answer bother you? See the margin note on terminating and repeating decimals in this section.

Use the method of Example 9 to write each rational number as a quotient of integers in lowest terms.

97. (a) .8   (b) $.7\overline{9}$

98. (a) .75   (b) $.74\overline{9}$

99. (a) .66   (b) $.65\overline{9}$

100. Based on your results in Exercises 97–99, predict the lowest terms form of the rational number $.4\overline{9}$.

6.4   Irrational Numbers and Decimal Representation

Definition and Basic Concepts • Irrationality of $\sqrt{2}$ and Proof by Contradiction • Operations with Square Roots • The Irrational Numbers π, ϕ, and e

Definition and Basic Concepts   In the previous section, we saw that every rational number has a decimal form that terminates or repeats. Also, every repeating or terminating decimal represents a rational number. Some decimals, however, neither repeat nor terminate. For example, the decimal

.102001000200001000002 . . .

does not terminate and does not repeat. (It is true that there is a pattern in this decimal, but no single block of digits repeats indefinitely.)*

Tsu Ch'ung-chih (about 500 A.D.), the Chinese mathematician honored on the above stamp, investigated the digits of π. **Aryabhata,** his Indian contemporary, gave 3.1416 as the value.

Irrational Numbers

Irrational numbers $= \{x \mid x$ is a number represented by a nonrepeating, nonterminating decimal$\}$.

    As the name implies, an irrational number cannot be represented as a quotient of integers.

The decimal number mentioned above is an irrational number. Other irrational numbers include $\sqrt{2}$, $\frac{1+\sqrt{5}}{2}$ (ϕ, from Section 5.5), π (the ratio of the circumference of a circle to its diameter), and e (a constant *approximately equal to* 2.71828). There are infinitely many irrational numbers.

The irrational number $\sqrt{2}$ was discovered by the Pythagoreans in about 500 B.C. This discovery was a great setback to their philosophy that everything is based upon the whole numbers. The Pythagoreans kept their findings secret, and legend has it that members of the group who divulged this discovery were sent out to sea, and, according to Proclus (410–485), "perished in a shipwreck, to a man."

Irrationality of $\sqrt{2}$ and Proof by Contradiction
Figure 12 illustrates how a point with coordinate $\sqrt{2}$ can be located on a number line.

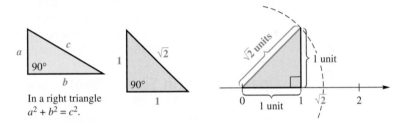

FIGURE 12

    The proof that $\sqrt{2}$ is irrational is a classic example of a **proof by contradiction.** We begin by assuming that $\sqrt{2}$ is rational, which leads to a contradiction, or absurdity. The method is also called **reductio ad absurdum** (Latin for "reduce to the absurd"). In order to understand the proof, we consider three preliminary facts:

1. When a rational number is written in lowest terms, the greatest common factor of the numerator and denominator is 1.

2. If an integer is even, then it has 2 as a factor and may be written in the form $2k$, where k is an integer.

3. If a perfect square is even, then its square root is even.

---

*In this section, we will assume that the digits of a number such as this continue indefinitely in the pattern established. The next few digits would be 000000100000002, and so on.

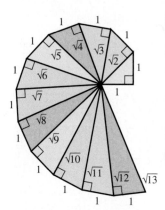

An interesting way to represent the lengths corresponding to $\sqrt{2}$, $\sqrt{3}$, $\sqrt{4}$, $\sqrt{5}$, and so on, is shown in the figure. Use the **Pythagorean theorem** to verify the lengths in the figure.

THEOREM

Statement: $\sqrt{2}$ is an irrational number.

Proof: Assume that $\sqrt{2}$ is a rational number. Then by definition,

$$\sqrt{2} = \frac{p}{q}, \quad \text{for some integers } p \text{ and } q.$$

Furthermore, assume that $\frac{p}{q}$ is the form of $\sqrt{2}$ that is written in lowest terms, so the greatest common factor of p and q is 1.

$$2 = \frac{p^2}{q^2} \qquad \text{Square both sides of the equation.}$$

$$2q^2 = p^2 \qquad \text{Multiply by } q^2.$$

This last equation indicates that 2 is a factor of p^2. So p^2 is even, and thus p is even. Since p is even, it may be written in the form $2k$, where k is an integer.

Now, substitute $2k$ for p in the last equation and simplify:

$$2q^2 = (2k)^2 \qquad \text{Let } p = 2k.$$

$$2q^2 = 4k^2 \qquad (2k)^2 = 2k \cdot 2k = 4k^2$$

$$q^2 = 2k^2. \qquad \text{Divide by 2.}$$

Since 2 is a factor of q^2, q^2 must be even, and thus q must be even. This leads to a contradiction: p and q cannot both be even because they would then have a common factor of 2, although it was assumed that their greatest common factor is 1.

Therefore, since the original assumption that $\sqrt{2}$ is rational has led to a contradiction, it must follow that $\sqrt{2}$ is irrational. ▪

Operations with Square Roots

In everyday mathematical work, nearly all of our calculations deal with rational numbers, usually in decimal form. In our study of mathematics, however, we must sometimes perform operations with irrational numbers, and in many instances, the irrational numbers are square roots. Some examples are

$$\sqrt{2}, \quad \sqrt{3}, \quad \text{and} \quad \sqrt{13}. \qquad \text{Square roots that are irrational.}$$

However, not all square roots are irrational. For example,

$$\sqrt{4} = 2, \quad \sqrt{36} = 6, \quad \text{and} \quad \sqrt{100} = 10 \qquad \text{Square roots that are rational.}$$

are all rational numbers. If n is a positive integer that is not the square of an integer, then $\sqrt{n}$ is an irrational number.

A calculator with a square root key can give approximations of square roots of numbers that are not perfect squares. To show that they are approximations, we use the ≈ symbol to indicate "is approximately equal to." Some such calculator approximations are as follows:

$$\sqrt{2} \approx 1.414213562, \quad \sqrt{6} \approx 2.449489743, \quad \text{and} \quad \sqrt{1949} \approx 44.14748011.$$

Recall that $\sqrt{a}$, for $a \geq 0$, is the nonnegative number whose square is a; that is, $\left(\sqrt{a}\right)^2 = a$. We will now look at some simple operations with square roots.

Notice that

$$\sqrt{4} \cdot \sqrt{9} = 2 \cdot 3 = 6$$

```
√(2)
          1.414213562
√(6)
          2.449489743
√(1949)
          44.14748011
```

These are calculator approximations of irrational numbers.

and
$$\sqrt{4 \cdot 9} = \sqrt{36} = 6.$$
Thus, $\sqrt{4} \cdot \sqrt{9} = \sqrt{4 \cdot 9}$. This is a particular case of the following product rule.

Product Rule for Square Roots

For nonnegative real numbers a and b,
$$\sqrt{a} \cdot \sqrt{b} = \sqrt{a \cdot b}.$$

Just as every rational number $\frac{a}{b}$ can be written in simplest (lowest) terms (by using the fundamental property of rational numbers), every square root radical has a simplified form.

Conditions Necessary for the Simplified Form of a Square Root Radical

A square root radical is in **simplified form** if the following three conditions are met.

1. The number under the radical **(radicand)** has no factor (except 1) that is a perfect square.
2. The radicand has no fractions.
3. No denominator contains a radical.

√(27)=3√(3)
                           1
√(27)
            5.196152423
3√(3)
            5.196152423

The 1 after the first line indicates that the equality is true. The calculator also shows the same approximations for $\sqrt{27}$ and $3\sqrt{3}$ in the second and third answers. (See Example 1.)

EXAMPLE 1   Simplifying a Square Root Radical (Product Rule)

Simplify $\sqrt{27}$.

SOLUTION

Since 9 is a factor of 27 and 9 is a perfect square, $\sqrt{27}$ is not in simplified form. The first condition of simplified form is not met. We simplify as follows.

$$\sqrt{27} = \sqrt{9 \cdot 3}$$
$$= \sqrt{9} \cdot \sqrt{3} \qquad \text{Use the product rule.}$$
$$= 3\sqrt{3} \qquad \sqrt{9} = 3, \text{ since } 3^2 = 9.$$

Expressions such as $\sqrt{27}$ and $3\sqrt{3}$ are *exact values* of the square root of 27. If we use the square root key of a calculator, we find
$$\sqrt{27} \approx 5.196152423.$$

If we find $\sqrt{3}$ and then multiply the result by 3, we get
$$3\sqrt{3} \approx 3(1.732050808) \approx 5.196152423.$$

Notice that these approximations are the same, as we would expect. (Due to various methods of calculating, there may be a discrepancy in the final digit of the calculation.) Understand, however, that the calculator approximations do not actually

The radical symbol above comes from the Latin word for root, *radix*. It was first used by **Leonardo of Pisa** (Fibonacci) in 1220. The sixteenth-century German symbol we use today probably is also derived from the letter r.

prove that the two numbers are equal, but only strongly suggest equality. The work done in Example 1 actually provides the mathematical justification that they are indeed equal.

A rule similar to the product rule exists for quotients.

Quotient Rule for Square Roots

For nonnegative real numbers a and positive real numbers b,

$$\frac{\sqrt{a}}{\sqrt{b}} = \sqrt{\frac{a}{b}}.$$

EXAMPLE 2 Simplifying Square Root Radicals (Quotient Rule)

Simplify each radical.

(a) $\sqrt{\dfrac{25}{9}}$ **(b)** $\sqrt{\dfrac{3}{4}}$ **(c)** $\sqrt{\dfrac{1}{2}}$

SOLUTION

(a) Because the radicand contains a fraction, the radical expression is not simplified. (See condition 2 of simplified form preceding Example 1.) Use the quotient rule as follows.

$$\sqrt{\frac{25}{9}} = \frac{\sqrt{25}}{\sqrt{9}} = \frac{5}{3}$$

(b) $\sqrt{\dfrac{3}{4}} = \dfrac{\sqrt{3}}{\sqrt{4}} = \dfrac{\sqrt{3}}{2}$

(c) $\sqrt{\dfrac{1}{2}} = \dfrac{\sqrt{1}}{\sqrt{2}} = \dfrac{1}{\sqrt{2}}$

This expression is not yet in simplified form, since condition 3 of simplified form is not met. To give an equivalent expression with no radical in the denominator, we use a procedure called **rationalizing the denominator.** Multiply $\frac{1}{\sqrt{2}}$ by $\frac{\sqrt{2}}{\sqrt{2}}$, which is a form of 1, the identity element for multiplication.

$$\frac{1}{\sqrt{2}} = \frac{1}{\sqrt{2}} \cdot \frac{\sqrt{2}}{\sqrt{2}} = \frac{\sqrt{2}}{2} \qquad \sqrt{2} \cdot \sqrt{2} = 2$$

The simplified form of $\sqrt{\frac{1}{2}}$ is $\frac{\sqrt{2}}{2}$.

Is $\sqrt{4} + \sqrt{9} = \sqrt{4 + 9}$ a true statement? Computation shows that the answer is *no*, since $\sqrt{4} + \sqrt{9} = 2 + 3 = 5$, while $\sqrt{4 + 9} = \sqrt{13}$, and $5 \neq \sqrt{13}$. *Square root radicals may be combined, however, if they have the same radicand.* Such radicals are **like radicals.** We add (and subtract) like radicals using the distributive property.

> **EXAMPLE 3** **Adding and Subtracting Square Root Radicals**

Add or subtract as indicated.

(a) $3\sqrt{6} + 4\sqrt{6}$ **(b)** $\sqrt{18} - \sqrt{32}$

SOLUTION

(a) Since both terms contain $\sqrt{6}$, they are like radicals, and may be combined.

$$3\sqrt{6} + 4\sqrt{6} = (3 + 4)\sqrt{6} \qquad \text{Distributive property}$$
$$= 7\sqrt{6} \qquad \text{Add.}$$

(b) If we simplify $\sqrt{18}$ and $\sqrt{32}$, then this operation can be performed.

$$\sqrt{18} - \sqrt{32} = \sqrt{9 \cdot 2} - \sqrt{16 \cdot 2} \qquad \text{Factor so that perfect squares are in the radicands.}$$
$$= \sqrt{9} \cdot \sqrt{2} - \sqrt{16} \cdot \sqrt{2} \qquad \text{Product rule}$$
$$= 3\sqrt{2} - 4\sqrt{2} \qquad \text{Take square roots.}$$
$$= (3 - 4)\sqrt{2} \qquad \text{Distributive property}$$
$$= -1\sqrt{2} \qquad \text{Subtract.}$$
$$= -\sqrt{2} \qquad -1 \cdot a = -a$$

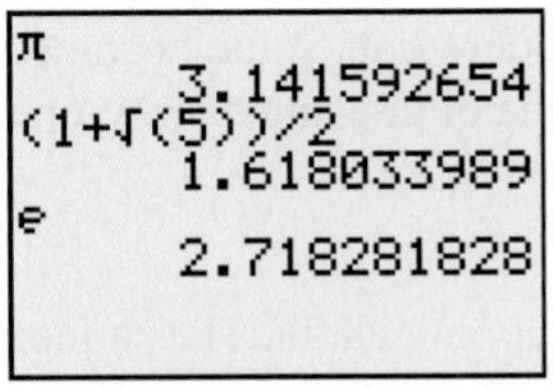

From Example 3, we see that like radicals may be added or subtracted by adding or subtracting their coefficients (the numbers by which they are multiplied) and keeping the same radical. For example,

$$9\sqrt{7} + 8\sqrt{7} = 17\sqrt{7} \quad (\text{since } 9 + 8 = 17)$$
$$4\sqrt{3} - 12\sqrt{3} = -8\sqrt{3}, \quad (\text{since } 4 - 12 = -8)$$

and so on.

In the statements of the product and quotient rules for square roots, the radicands could not be negative. While $-\sqrt{2}$ is a real number, for example, $\sqrt{-2}$ is not: there is no real number whose square is -2. The same may be said for any negative radicand. In order to handle this situation, mathematicians have extended our number system to include *complex numbers*, discussed in the Extension at the end of this chapter.

The Irrational Numbers π, ϕ, and e

Figure 13 shows approximations for three of the most interesting and important irrational numbers in mathematics. The first of these, π, represents the ratio of the circumference of a circle to its diameter. The second, ϕ, is the Golden Ratio, covered in detail in Section 5.5. Its exact value is $\frac{1+\sqrt{5}}{2}$. The third is e, a fundamental number in our universe. It is the base of the *natural exponential* and *natural logarithmic* functions, as seen in Section 8.6. The letter e was chosen to honor Leonhard Euler, who published extensive research on the number in 1746.

Pi (π)
$\pi \approx 3.14159265358979323846264338327

9$ |

The computation of the digits of π has fascinated mathematicians since ancient times. Archimedes was the first to explore it extensively, and mathematicians have

---

π
3.141592654
(1+√(5))/2
1.618033989
e
2.718281828

FIGURE 13

This poem, dedicated to **Archimedes** ("the immortal Syracusan"), allows us to learn the first 31 digits of the decimal representation of π. By replacing each word with the number of letters it contains, with a decimal point following the initial 3, the decimal is found. The poem was written by A. C. Orr, and appeared in the *Literary Digest* in 1906.

Now I, even I, would celebrate
In rhymes unapt, the great
Immortal Syracusan, rivaled
 nevermore,
Who in his wondrous lore
Passed on before,
Left men his guidance
How to circles mensurate.

today computed its value to over 1 trillion digits. Yasumasa Kanada of the University of Tokyo and the brothers Gregory and David Chudnovsky are among the foremost of today's pi researchers. The book *A History of π* by Petr Beckmann is a classic, now in its third edition. Numerous Web sites are devoted to the history and methods of computation of pi. Some of them are as follows:

www.joyofpi.com/

www.math.utah.edu/~alfeld/Archimedes/Archimedes.html

www.super-computing.org/

www.pbs.org/wgbh/nova/sciencenow/3210/04.html

One of the methods of computing pi involves the topic of *infinite series,* as seen in Example 4.

EXAMPLE 4 Computing the Digits of Pi Using an Infinite Series

It is shown in higher mathematics that the *infinite series*

$$1 - \frac{1}{3} + \frac{1}{5} - \frac{1}{7} + \frac{1}{9} + \dots$$

"converges" to $\frac{\pi}{4}$. That is, as more and more terms are considered, its value becomes closer and closer to $\frac{\pi}{4}$. With a calculator, approximate the value of pi using twenty-one terms of this series.

SOLUTION

Figure 14 shows the necessary calculation on the TI-83/84 Plus calculator. The sum of the first twenty-one terms is multiplied by 4, to obtain the approximation

3.189184782.

(While this is only correct to the first decimal place, better approximations are obtained using more terms of the series.)

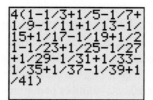

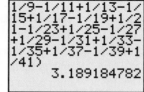

This is a continuation of the previous screen.

FIGURE 14

A rectangle that satisfies the condition that the ratio of its length to its width is equal to the ratio of the sum of its length and width to its length is called a **Golden Rectangle.** This ratio is called the **Golden Ratio.** (See Section 5.5.) The exact value of the Golden Ratio is the irrational number $\frac{1 + \sqrt{5}}{2}$, and it is represented by the Greek letter ϕ (phi).

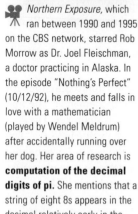

Northern Exposure, which ran between 1990 and 1995 on the CBS network, starred Rob Morrow as Dr. Joel Fleischman, a doctor practicing in Alaska. In the episode "Nothing's Perfect" (10/12/92), he meets and falls in love with a mathematician (played by Wendel Meldrum) after accidentally running over her dog. Her area of research is **computation of the decimal digits of pi.** She mentions that a string of eight 8s appears in the decimal relatively early in the expansion. A search at The Pi Searcher (www.angio.net/pi/bigpi/cgi) confirms that this string starts at position 46,663,520 counting from the first digit after the decimal point.

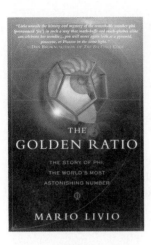

THE GOLDEN RATIO
THE STORY OF PHI,
THE WORLD'S MOST
ASTONISHING NUMBER

MARIO LIVIO

In 1767 **J. H. Lambert** proved that π is irrational (and thus its decimal will never terminate and never repeat). Nevertheless, the 1897 Indiana state legislature considered a bill that would have *legislated* the value of π. In one part of the bill, the value was stated to be 4, and in another part, 3.2. Amazingly, the bill passed the House, but the Senate postponed action on the bill indefinitely.

```
233/144
       1.618055556
377/233
       1.618025751
610/377
       1.618037135
```

FIGURE 15

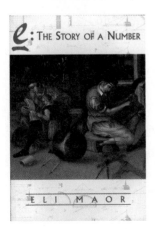

ℓ: THE STORY OF A NUMBER

ELI MAOR

Phi (ϕ)

$$\phi = \frac{1 + \sqrt{5}}{2} \approx 1.6180339887498948482045868343 65$$

Two readily accessible books on phi are *The Divine Proportion, A Study in Mathematical Beauty* by H. E. Huntley, and the more recent *The Golden Ratio* by Mario Livio. Some popular Web sites devoted to this irrational number are as follows:

www.mcs.surrey.ac.uk/Personal/R.Knott/Fibonacci/

www.goldennumber.net/

www.mathforum.org/dr.math/faq/faq.golden.ratio.html

www.geom.uiuc.edu/~demo5337/s97b/art.htm

EXAMPLE 5 **Computing the Digits of Phi Using the Fibonacci Sequence**

The first twelve terms of the Fibonacci sequence are

$$1, 1, 2, 3, 5, 8, 13, 21, 34, 55, 89, 144.$$

Each term after the first two terms is obtained by adding the two previous terms. Thus, the thirteenth term is $89 + 144 = 233$. As one goes farther and farther out in the sequence, the ratio of a term to its predecessor gets closer and closer to ϕ. How far out must one go in order to approximate ϕ so that the first five decimal places agree?

SOLUTION

After 144, the next three Fibonacci numbers are 233, 377, and 610. Figure 15 shows that $\frac{610}{377} \approx 1.618037135$, which agrees with ϕ to the fifth decimal place. ◼

Most applications of the irrational number e are beyond the scope of this text. However, e is a fundamental constant in mathematics, and if there are intelligent beings elsewhere in the universe, they will no doubt know about this number. If you study Section 8.6, you will encounter it as a base of the important exponential and logarithmic functions.

e

$$e \approx 2.7182818284590452353602874713 53$$

The nature of e has made it less understood by the layman than π (or even ϕ, for that matter). The 1994 book *e: The Story of a Number* by Eli Maor has attempted to rectify this situation. These Web sites also give information on e:

www.mathforum.org/dr.math/faq/faq.e.html

www-groups.dcs.st-and.ac.uk/~history/HistTopics/e.html

http://antwrp.gsfc.nasa.gov/htmltest/gifcity/e.1mil

www.math.toronto.edu/mathnet/answers/ereal.html

Example 6 illustrates another infinite series, but this one converges to e.

EXAMPLE 6 Computing the Digits of *e* Using an Infinite Series

The infinite series

$$2 + \frac{1}{1 \cdot 2} + \frac{1}{1 \cdot 2 \cdot 3} + \frac{1}{1 \cdot 2 \cdot 3 \cdot 4} + \cdots$$

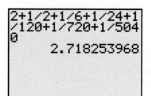

converges to *e*. Use a calculator to approximate *e* using the first seven terms of this series.

SOLUTION

Figure 16 shows the sum of the first seven terms. (The denominators have all been multiplied out.) The sum is 2.718253968, which agrees with *e* to four decimal places. This series converges more rapidly than the one for π in Example 4. ▪

FIGURE 16

6.4 EXERCISES

Identify each number as rational *or* irrational.

1. $\dfrac{4}{9}$

2. $\dfrac{7}{8}$

3. $\sqrt{10}$

4. $\sqrt{14}$

5. 1.618

6. 2.718

7. $.\overline{41}$

8. $.\overline{32}$

9. π

10. $\dfrac{1 + \sqrt{5}}{2}$

11. .878778777877778. . .

12. *e*

13. 3.14159

14. $\dfrac{22}{7}$

15. **(a)** Find the sum.

$$\begin{aligned}
&.272772777277772. . . \\
&+.616116111611116. . .
\end{aligned}$$

(b) Based on the result of part (a), we can conclude that the sum of two _____ numbers may be a(n) _____ number.

16. **(a)** Find the sum.

$$\begin{aligned}
&.010110111011110. . . \\
&+.252552555255552. . .
\end{aligned}$$

(b) Based on the result of part (a), we can conclude that the sum of two _____ numbers may be a(n) _____ number.

Use a calculator to find a rational decimal approximation for each irrational number. Give as many places as your calculator shows.

17. $\sqrt{39}$

18. $\sqrt{44}$

19. $\sqrt{15.1}$

20. $\sqrt{33.6}$

21. $\sqrt{884}$

22. $\sqrt{643}$

23. $\sqrt{\dfrac{9}{8}}$

24. $\sqrt{\dfrac{6}{5}}$

Use the methods of Examples 1 and 2 to simplify each expression. Then, use a calculator to approximate both the given expression and the simplified expression. (Both should be the same.)

25. $\sqrt{50}$

26. $\sqrt{32}$

27. $\sqrt{75}$

28. $\sqrt{150}$

29. $\sqrt{288}$

30. $\sqrt{200}$

31. $\dfrac{5}{\sqrt{6}}$

32. $\dfrac{3}{\sqrt{2}}$

33. $\sqrt{\dfrac{7}{4}}$

34. $\sqrt{\dfrac{8}{9}}$

35. $\sqrt{\dfrac{7}{3}}$

36. $\sqrt{\dfrac{14}{5}}$

Use the method of Example 3 to perform the indicated operations.

37. $\sqrt{17} + 2\sqrt{17}$ **38.** $3\sqrt{19} + \sqrt{19}$ **39.** $5\sqrt{7} - \sqrt{7}$ **40.** $3\sqrt{27} - \sqrt{27}$

41. $3\sqrt{18} + \sqrt{2}$ **42.** $2\sqrt{48} - \sqrt{3}$ **43.** $-\sqrt{12} + \sqrt{75}$ **44.** $2\sqrt{27} - \sqrt{300}$

Exercises 45–58 deal with π, ϕ, or e. Use a calculator or computer as necessary.

45. Move one matchstick to make the equation approximately true. (*Source:* www.joyofpi.com)

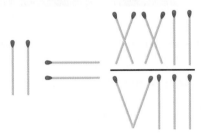

46. Find the square root of $\frac{2143}{22}$ using a calculator. Then find the square root of that result. Compare your result to the decimal given for π in the margin note. What do you notice?

47. Find the first eight digits in the decimal for $\frac{355}{113}$. Compare the result to the decimal for π given in the text. What do you notice?

48. You may have seen the statements "use $\frac{22}{7}$ for π" and "use 3.14 for π." Since $\frac{22}{7}$ is the quotient of two integers, and 3.14 is a terminating decimal, do these statements suggest that π is rational?

49. In the Bible (I Kings 7:23), a verse describes a circular pool at King Solomon's temple, about 1000 B.C. The pool is said to be ten cubits across, "and a line of 30 cubits did compass it round about." What value of π does this imply?

50. The ancient Egyptians used a method for finding the area of a circle that is equivalent to a value of 3.1605 for π. Write this decimal as a mixed number.

51. The computation of π has fascinated mathematicians and laymen for centuries. In the nineteenth century, the British mathematician William Shanks spent many years of his life calculating π to 707 decimal places. It turned out that only the first 527 were correct. Use an Internet search to find the 528th decimal digit of π (following the whole number part 3.).

52. One of the reasons for computing so many digits of π is to determine how often each digit appears and to identify any interesting patterns among the digits. Gregory and David Chudnovsky have spent a great deal of time and effort looking for patterns in the digits. For example, six 9s in a row appear relatively early in the decimal, within the first 800 decimal places. Use an Internet search to find the positions of these six 9s in a row.

53. The expression $\frac{2 \cdot 2 \cdot 4 \cdot 4 \cdot 6 \cdot 6 \cdot 8 \cdots}{1 \cdot 3 \cdot 3 \cdot 5 \cdot 5 \cdot 7 \cdot 7 \cdots}$ converges to $\frac{\pi}{2}$. Use a calculator to evaluate only the digits of the expression as shown here, and then multiply by 2. What value for an approximation for π does this give (to one decimal place)?

54. A *mnemonic device* is a scheme whereby one is able to recall facts by memorizing something completely unrelated to the facts. One way of learning the first few digits of the decimal for π is to memorize a sentence (or several sentences) and count the letters in each word of the sentence. For example, "See, I know a digit," will give the first 5 digits of π: "See" has 3 letters, "I" has 1 letter, "know" has 4 letters, "a" has 1 letter, and "digit" has 5 letters. So the first five digits are 3.1415.

Verify that the following mnemonic devices work.

(a) "May I have a large container of coffee?"

(b) "See, I have a rhyme assisting my feeble brain, its tasks ofttimes resisting."

(c) "How I want a drink, alcoholic of course, after the heavy lectures involving quantum mechanics."

55. Use a calculator to find the decimal approximations for $\phi = \frac{1 + \sqrt{5}}{2}$ and its *conjugate*, $\frac{1 - \sqrt{5}}{2}$. Comment on the similarities and differences in the two decimals.

56. In some literature, the Golden Ratio is defined to be the reciprocal of $\frac{1 + \sqrt{5}}{2}$ — that is, $\frac{2}{1 + \sqrt{5}}$. Use a calculator to find a decimal approximation for $\frac{2}{1 + \sqrt{5}}$ and compare it to ϕ as defined in this text. What do you observe?

57. An approximation for e is 2.718281828. A student noticed that there seems to be a repetition of four digits in this number (1, 8, 2, 8) and concluded that it is rational, because repeating decimals represent rational numbers. Was the student correct? Why or why not?

58. Use a calculator with an exponential key to find values for the following: $(1.1)^{10}$, $(1.01)^{100}$, $(1.001)^{1000}$, $(1.0001)^{10,000}$, and $(1.00001)^{100,000}$. Compare your results to the approximation given for e in this section. What do you find?

Solve each problem. Use a calculator as necessary, and give approximations to the nearest tenth unless specified otherwise.

59. *Period of a Pendulum* The period of a pendulum in seconds depends on its length, *L,* in feet, and is given by the formula

$$P = 2\pi\sqrt{\frac{L}{32}}.$$

If a pendulum is 5.1 feet long, what is its period? Use 3.14 for π.

60. *Radius of an Aluminum Can* The radius of the circular top or bottom of an aluminum can with surface area S and height h is given by

$$r = \frac{-h + \sqrt{h^2 + .64S}}{2}.$$

What radius should be used to make a can with height 12 inches and surface area 400 square inches?

61. *Distance to the Horizon* Jack Adrian, a friend of one of the authors of this text, has a beautiful 14th floor condo, with a stunning view, in downtown Chicago. The floor is 150 feet above the ground. Knowing that this author is a mathematics teacher, Jack emailed the author and told him that he recalled once having studied a formula for calculating the distance to the horizon, but could not remember it. He wanted to know how far he can see from his condo. The author responded:

> *To find the distance to the horizon in miles, take the square root of the height of your view and multiply that result by 1.224. That will give you the number of miles to the horizon.*

Assuming Jack's eyes are 6 feet above his floor, the total height from the ground is $150 + 6 = 156$ feet.

To the nearest tenth of a mile, how far can he see to the horizon?

62. *Electronics Formula* The formula

$$I = \sqrt{\frac{2P}{L}}$$

relates the coefficient of self-induction L (in henrys), the energy P stored in an electronic circuit (in joules), and the current I (in amps). Find I if $P = 120$ joules and $L = 80$ henrys.

63. *Area of the Bermuda Triangle* *Heron's formula* gives a method of finding the area of a triangle if the lengths of its sides are known. Suppose that a, b, and c are the lengths of the sides. Let s denote one-half of the perimeter of the triangle (called the *semiperimeter*); that is,

$$s = \frac{1}{2}(a + b + c).$$

Then the area A of the triangle is given by

$$A = \sqrt{s(s - a)(s - b)(s - c)}.$$

Find the area of the Bermuda Triangle, if the "sides" of this triangle measure approximately 850 miles, 925 miles, and 1300 miles. Give your answer to the nearest thousand square miles.

64. *Area Enclosed by the Vietnam Veterans' Memorial* The Vietnam Veterans' Memorial in Washington, D.C., is in the shape of an unenclosed isosceles triangle with equal sides of length 246.75 feet. If the triangle were enclosed, the third side would have length 438.14 feet. Use Heron's formula from the previous exercise to find the area of this enclosure to the nearest hundred square feet. (*Source:* Information pamphlet obtained at the Vietnam Veterans' Memorial.)

65. Perfect Triangles A *perfect triangle* is a triangle whose sides have whole number lengths and whose area is numerically equal to its perimeter. Use Heron's formula to show that the triangle with sides of length 9, 10, and 17 is perfect.

66. Heron Triangles A *Heron triangle* is a triangle having integer sides and area. Use Heron's formula to show that each of the following is a Heron triangle.
(a) $a = 11, b = 13, c = 20$
(b) $a = 13, b = 14, c = 15$
(c) $a = 7, b = 15, c = 20$

67. Diagonal of a Box The length of the diagonal of a box is given by

$$D = \sqrt{L^2 + W^2 + H^2},$$

where L, W, and H are the length, the width, and the height of the box. Find the length of the diagonal, D, of a box that is 4 feet long, 3 feet wide, and 2 feet high.

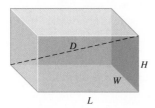

68. Rate of Return of an Investment If an investment of P dollars grows to A dollars in two years, the annual rate of return on the investment is given by

$$r = \frac{\sqrt{A} - \sqrt{P}}{\sqrt{P}}.$$

First rationalize the denominator and then find the annual rate of return (as a decimal) if $50,000 increases to $58,320.

69. Accident Reconstruction Police sometimes use the following procedure to estimate the speed at which a car was traveling at the time of an accident. A police officer drives the car involved in the accident under conditions similar to those during which the accident took place and then skids to a stop. If the car is driven at 30 miles per hour, then the speed at the time of the accident is given by

$$s = 30\sqrt{\frac{a}{p}},$$

where a is the length of the skid marks left at the time of the accident and p is the length of the skid marks in the police test. Find s for the following values of a and p.
(a) $a = 862$ feet; $p = 156$ feet
(b) $a = 382$ feet; $p = 96$ feet
(c) $a = 84$ feet; $p = 26$ feet

70. Law of Tensions In the study of sound, one version of the law of tensions is

$$f_1 = f_2\sqrt{\frac{F_1}{F_2}}.$$

Find f_1 to the nearest unit if $F_1 = 300$, $F_2 = 60$, and $f_2 = 260$.

The concept of square (second) root can be extended to **cube (third) root, fourth root,** *and so on. If $n \geq 2$ and a is a nonnegative number, $\sqrt[n]{a}$ represents the nonnegative number whose nth power is a. For example,*

$$\sqrt[3]{8} = 2 \text{ because } 2^3 = 8,$$
$$\sqrt[3]{1000} = 10 \text{ because } 10^3 = 1000,$$
$$\sqrt[4]{81} = 3 \text{ because } 3^4 = 81,$$

and so on. Find each root.

71. $\sqrt[3]{64}$ **72.** $\sqrt[3]{125}$

73. $\sqrt[3]{343}$ **74.** $\sqrt[3]{729}$

75. $\sqrt[3]{216}$ **76.** $\sqrt[3]{512}$

77. $\sqrt[4]{1}$ **78.** $\sqrt[4]{16}$

79. $\sqrt[4]{256}$ **80.** $\sqrt[4]{625}$

81. $\sqrt[4]{4096}$ **82.** $\sqrt[4]{2401}$

Use a calculator to approximate each root. Give as many places as your calculator shows. (Hint: To find the fourth root, find the square root of the square root.)

83. $\sqrt[3]{43}$ **84.** $\sqrt[3]{87}$

85. $\sqrt[3]{198}$ **86.** $\sqrt[4]{2107}$

87. $\sqrt[4]{10,265.2}$ **88.** $\sqrt[4]{863.5}$

6.5 Applications of Decimals and Percents

Operations with Decimals • Rounding Decimals • Percent • Applications

Operations with Decimals Because calculators have, for the most part, replaced paper-and-pencil methods for operations with decimals and percent, we will only briefly mention these latter methods. *We strongly suggest that the work in this section be done with a calculator at hand.*

```
.46+3.9+12.58
            16.94
12.1-8.723
             3.377
```

This screen supports the results in Example 1.

Addition and Subtraction of Decimals

To add or subtract decimal numbers, line up the decimal points in a column and perform the operation.

EXAMPLE 1 Adding and Subtracting Decimal Numbers

Find each of the following.

(a) .46 + 3.9 + 12.58 **(b)** 12.1 − 8.723

SOLUTION

(a) To compute the sum .46 + 3.9 + 12.58, use the following method.

$$
\begin{array}{rl}
.46 & \text{Line up decimal points.}\\
3.9\mathbf{0} & \text{Attach a zero as a placeholder.}\\
+12.58 &\\
\hline
16.94 & \leftarrow\text{Sum}
\end{array}
$$

(b) To compute the difference 12.1 − 8.723, use this method.

$$
\begin{array}{rl}
12.1\mathbf{00} & \text{Attach zeros.}\\
-\ 8.723 &\\
\hline
3.377 & \leftarrow\text{Difference}
\end{array}
$$

Recall that when two numbers are multiplied, the numbers are called *factors* and the answer is called the *product.* When two numbers are divided, the number being divided is called the *dividend,* the number doing the dividing is called the *divisor,* and the answer is called the *quotient.*

Technology pervades the world outside school. There is no question that students will be expected to use calculators in other settings; this technology is now part of our culture. . . students no longer have the same need to perform these (paper-and-pencil) procedures with large numbers of lengthy expressions that they might have had in the past without ready access to technology.

From Computation, Calculators, and Common Sense (A Position of the National Council of Teachers of Mathematics).

Multiplication and Division of Decimals

Multiplication To multiply decimals, multiply in the same manner as integers are multiplied. The number of decimal places to the right of the decimal point in the product is the *sum* of the numbers of places to the right of the decimal points in the factors.

Division To divide decimals, move the decimal point to the right the same number of places in the divisor and the dividend so as to obtain a whole number in the divisor. Divide in the same manner as integers are divided. The number of decimal places to the right of the decimal point in the quotient is the same as the number of places to the right in the dividend.

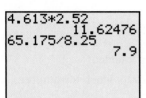

This screen supports the results in Example 2.

EXAMPLE 2 **Multiplying and Dividing Decimal Numbers**

Find each of the following.

(a) 4.613×2.52 **(b)** $65.175 \div 8.25$

SOLUTION

(a) To find the product 4.613×2.52, use the following method.

$$
\begin{array}{r}
4.613 \quad \leftarrow 3 \text{ decimal places} \\
\times \quad 2.52 \quad \leftarrow 2 \text{ decimal places} \\
\hline
9226 \\
23065 \\
9226 \\
\hline
11.62476 \quad \leftarrow 3 + 2 = 5 \text{ decimal places}
\end{array}
$$

(b) To find the quotient $65.175 \div 8.25$, follow these steps.

$$
\longrightarrow 825\overline{)6517.5} \quad
\begin{array}{l}
7.9
\end{array}
$$

Bring the decimal point straight up in the answer.

$$
\begin{array}{r}
5775 \\
\hline
7425 \\
7425 \\
\hline
0
\end{array}
$$

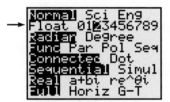

TI-83 Plus

TI-84 Plus

Here the TI-83/84 Plus is set to round the answer to two decimal places.

Rounding Decimals Operations with decimals often result in long strings of digits in the decimal places. Since all these digits may not be needed in a practical problem, it is common to *round* a decimal to the necessary number of decimal places. For example, in preparing federal income tax, money amounts are rounded to the nearest dollar. Round as shown in the next example.

EXAMPLE 3 **Rounding a Decimal Number**

Round 3.917 to the nearest hundredth.

SOLUTION

The hundredths place in 3.917 contains the digit 1.

$$3.917$$

↑ Hundredths place

To round this decimal, locate 3.91 and 3.92 on a number line as in Figure 17.

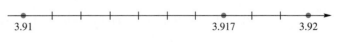

FIGURE 17

The distance from 3.91 to 3.92 is divided into ten equal parts. The seventh of these ten parts locates the number 3.917. As the number line shows, 3.917 is closer to 3.92 than it is to 3.91, so 3.917 rounded to the nearest hundredth is 3.92.

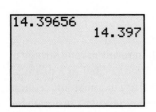

The calculator rounds 3.917 to the nearest hundredth.

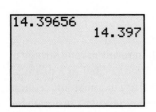

The calculator rounds 3.915 *up* to 3.92.

If the number line method of Example 3 were used to round 3.915 to the nearest hundredth, a problem would develop—the number 3.915 is exactly halfway between 3.91 and 3.92. An arbitrary decision is then made to round *up:* 3.915 rounded to the nearest hundredth is 3.92.

Rules for Rounding Decimals

Step 1   Locate the **place** to which the number is being rounded.

Step 2   Look at the next **digit to the right** of the place to which the number is being rounded.

Step 3A   If this digit is **less than 5,** drop all digits to the right of the place to which the number is being rounded. Do *not change* the digit in the place to which the number is being rounded.

Step 3B   If this digit is **5 or greater,** drop all digits to the right of the place to which the number is being rounded. *Add one* to the digit in the place to which the number is being rounded.

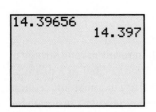

With the calculator set to round to three decimal places, the result of Example 4 is supported.

EXAMPLE 4   Rounding a Decimal Number

Round 14.39656 to the nearest thousandth.

SOLUTION

Step 1   Use an arrow to locate the place to which the number is being rounded.

$$14.39656$$

Thousandths place

Step 2   Check to see if the first digit to the right of the arrow is 5 or greater.

14.396   5   6   Digit to the right of the arrow is 5.

Step 3   Since the digit to the right of the arrow is 5 or greater, increase by 1 the digit to which the arrow is pointing. Drop all digits to the right of the arrow.

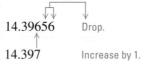

14.39656   Drop.

14.397   Increase by 1.

Finally, 14.39656 rounded to the nearest thousandth is 14.397.   ■

The percent sign, %, probably evolved from a symbol introduced in an Italian manuscript of 1425. Instead of "per 100," "P 100," or "P cento," which were common at that time, the author used "Pȓ." By about 1650 the ȓ had become $\frac{0}{0}$, so "per $\frac{0}{0}$," was often used. Finally the "per" was dropped, leaving $\frac{0}{0}$ or %.

From *Historical Topics for the Mathematics Classroom,* the Thirty-first Yearbook of the National Council of Teachers of Mathematics, 1969.

Percent
One of the main applications of decimals comes from problems involving **percents.** In consumer mathematics, interest rates and discounts are often given as percents. The word *percent* means "per hundred." The symbol % represents "percent."

🎥 Gene Wilder has appeared in nearly 40 movies in his career. Among his most notable characters are accountant Leo Bloom in the 1969 version of *The Producers* and Willy Wonka in *Willy Wonka and the Chocolate Factory,* both of whom deliver interesting lines involving **percent.**

In *The Producers,* he and Max Bialystock (Zero Mostel) scheme to make a fortune by overfinancing what they think will be a Broadway flop. After enumerating the percent of profits all of Max's little old ladies have been offered in the production, reality sets in.

MAX: Leo, how much percentage of a play can there be altogether?
LEO: Max, you can only sell 100% of anything.
MAX: And how much for *Springtime for Hitler* have we sold?
LEO: 25,000%
MAX (reaching for Leo's blue security blanket): 25,000%. . . Give me that blue thing.

As Willy Wonka, upon preparing a mixture in his laboratory, Wilder delivers the following as he drinks his latest concoction.

WILLY WONKA: Invention, my dear friends, is 93% perspiration, 6% electricity, 4% evaporation, and 2% butterscotch ripple.
FEMALE VOICE: That's 105%.
MALE VOICE: Any good?
WILLY WONKA: Yes!

Percent

$$1\% = \frac{1}{100} = .01$$

EXAMPLE 5   Converting Percents to Decimals

Convert each percent to a decimal.

(a) 98%   **(b)** 3.4%   **(c)** .2%

SOLUTION

(a) $98\% = 98(1\%) = 98(.01) = .98$
(b) $3.4\% = 3.4(1\%) = 3.4(.01) = .034$
(c) $.2\% = .2(1\%) = .2(.01) = .002$

EXAMPLE 6   Converting Decimals to Percents

Convert each decimal to a percent.

(a) .13   **(b)** .532   **(c)** 2.3

SOLUTION

(a) $.13 = 13(.01) = 13(1\%) = 13\%$
(b) $.532 = 53.2(.01) = 53.2(1\%) = 53.2\%$
(c) $2.3 = 230(.01) = 230(1\%) = 230\%$

From Examples 5 and 6, we see that the following procedures can be used when converting between percents and decimals.

Converting Between Decimals and Percents

To convert a percent to a decimal, drop the % sign and move the decimal point two places to the left, inserting zeros as placeholders if necessary.

To convert a decimal to a percent, move the decimal point two places to the right, inserting zeros as placeholders if necessary, and attach a % sign.

EXAMPLE 7   Converting Fractions to Percents

Convert each fraction to a percent.

(a) $\frac{3}{5}$ **(b)** $\frac{14}{25}$

SOLUTION

(a) First write $\frac{3}{5}$ as a decimal. Dividing 5 into 3 gives $\frac{3}{5} = .6 = 60\%$.

The 2004 movie *Mean Girls* stars Lindsay Lohan as Cady Heron, who has been home-schooled until her senior year in high school. A scene in the school cafeteria features her sitting with The Plastics (the "mean girls" of the title). Regina George, played by Rachel McAdams, is reading a candy bar wrapper.

REGINA: 120 calories and 48 calories from fat. What **percent** is that? I'm only eating food with less than 30% calories from fat.
CADY: It's 40%. (Responding to a quizzical look from Regina.) Well, 48 over 120 equals *x* over 100, and then you cross-multiply and get the value of *x*.
REGINA: Whatever. I'm getting cheese fries.

(b) $\dfrac{14}{25} = .56 = 56\%$

The procedure of Example 7 is summarized as follows.

Converting a Fraction to a Percent

To convert a fraction to a percent, convert the fraction to a decimal, and then convert the decimal to a percent.

In the following examples involving percents, three methods are shown. The second method in each case involves using cross-products. The third method involves the percent key of a basic calculator.

EXAMPLE 8 Finding a Percent of a Number

Find 18% of 250.

SOLUTION

Method 1   The key word here is "of." The word "of" translates as "times," with 18% of 250 given by

$$(18\%)\,(250) = (.18)\,(250) = 45.$$

Method 2   Think "18 is to 100 as what (*x*) is to 250?" This translates into the equation

$$\frac{18}{100} = \frac{x}{250}$$

$$100x = 18 \cdot 250 \qquad \tfrac{a}{b} = \tfrac{c}{d} \text{ if and only if } ad = bc$$

$$x = \frac{18 \cdot 250}{100} \qquad \text{Divide by 100.}$$

$$x = 45. \qquad\qquad \text{Simplify.}$$

Method 3   Use the percent key on a calculator with the following keystrokes:

With any of these methods, we find that 18% of 250 is 45.

EXAMPLE 9 Finding What Percent One Number Is of Another

What percent of 500 is 75?

SOLUTION

Method 1   Let the phrase "what percent" be represented by $x \cdot 1\%$ or $.01x$. Again the word "of" translates as "times," while "is" translates as "equals." Thus,

$$.01x \cdot 500 = 75$$
$$5x = 75 \quad \text{Multiply on the left side.}$$
$$x = 15. \quad \text{Divide by 5.}$$

Method 2   Think "What (x) is to 100 as 75 is to 500?" This translates as

$$\frac{x}{100} = \frac{75}{500}$$
$$500x = 7500 \quad \text{Cross-products}$$
$$x = 15. \quad \text{Divide by 500.}$$

Method 3 | 7 | 5 | ÷ | 5 | 0 | 0 | % | **15**

In each case, 15 is the percent, so we conclude that 75 is 15% of 500.   ▪

▪ **EXAMPLE 10   Finding a Number of Which a Given Number Is a Given Percent**

---

38 is 5% of what number?

SOLUTION

Method 1 $$38 = .05x$$
$$x = \frac{38}{.05} \quad \text{Divide by .05.}$$
$$x = 760 \quad \text{Simplify.}$$

Method 2   Think "38 is to what number (x) as 5 is to 100?"

$$\frac{38}{x} = \frac{5}{100}$$
$$5x = 3800 \quad \text{Cross-products}$$
$$x = 760 \quad \text{Divide by 5.}$$

Method 3 | 3 | 8 | ÷ | 5 | % | **760**

Each method shows us that 38 is 5% of 760.   ▪

There are various shortcuts that can be used to work with percents. Suppose that you need to compute 20% of 50. Here are two such shortcuts.

1. You think "20% means $\frac{1}{5}$, and to find $\frac{1}{5}$ of something I divide by 5, so 50 divided by 5 is 10. The answer is 10."

2. You think "20% is twice 10%, and to find 10% of something I move the decimal point one place to the left. So, 10% of 50 is 5, and 20% is twice 5, or 10. The answer is 10."

Applications

> **PROBLEM-SOLVING HINT** When applying percent it is often a good idea to restate the problem as a question similar to those found in Examples 8–10, and then answer that question. One strategy of problem solving deals with solving a simpler, similar problem.

EXAMPLE 11 Interpreting Percents from a Graph

In 2003, people in the United States spent an estimated $29.7 billion on their pets. Use the graph in Figure 18 to determine how much of this amount was spent on pet food.

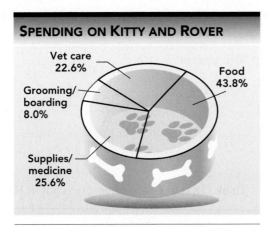

SPENDING ON KITTY AND ROVER

Vet care 22.6%
Grooming/boarding 8.0%
Supplies/medicine 25.6%
Food 43.8%

Dotty

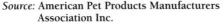

Source: American Pet Products Manufacturers Association Inc.

FIGURE 18

SOLUTION

According to the graph, 43.8% was spent on food. We use Method 1 of Example 8 to find 43.8% of $29.7 billion.

$$.438 \quad \times \quad \$29.7 \text{ billion} \quad = \quad \$13.0 \text{ billion}$$

43.8% of Total amount Amount spent on pet food

In many applications we are asked to find the percent increase or percent decrease from one quantity to another. The following guidelines summarize how to do this.

Finding Percent Increase or Decrease

1. To find the **percent increase from *a* to *b*,** where $b > a$, subtract a from b, and divide this result by a. Convert to a percent.

Example: The percent increase from 4 to 7 is $\frac{7-4}{4} = \frac{3}{4} = 75\%$.

2. To find the **percent decrease from *a* to *b*,** where $b < a$, subtract b from a, and divide this result by a. Convert to a percent.

Example: The percent decrease from 8 to 6 is $\frac{8-6}{8} = \frac{2}{8} = \frac{1}{4} = 25\%$.

EXAMPLE 12 Finding Percent Increase of Las Vegas Population

Las Vegas, Nevada, is the fastest-growing city in the United States. In 1990, the population of Las Vegas was 258,295. By 2000, it had grown to 478,434. (*Source:* U.S. Census Bureau.)

(a) Estimate the percent increase over this period.
(b) Find the actual percent increase, to the nearest tenth of a percent, over this period.

SOLUTION

(a) For easy computation, think of the 2000 population as 470,000 and the 1990 population as 270,000. The difference is

$$470{,}000 - 270{,}000 = 200{,}000.$$

Now, think of the 1990 population as 250,000 and answer the question "What percent of 250,000 (the *original* population) is 200,000?" The fraction $\frac{200{,}000}{250{,}000}$ simplifies to $\frac{20}{25} = \frac{4}{5}$, which is 80%. Therefore, the population increased by about 80% over the ten-year period.

(b) We must find the difference between the two populations, and then determine what percent of 258,295 this difference comprises.

$$\underbrace{478{,}434}_{\substack{\text{Population}\\\text{in 2000}}} - \underbrace{258{,}295}_{\substack{\text{Population}\\\text{in 1990}}} = \underbrace{220{,}139}_{\substack{\text{Increase in}\\\text{population}}}$$

Now solve the problem "What percent of 258,295 is 220,139?" This is similar to the problem in Example 9. Any of the methods explained there will indicate that the answer is approximately 85.2%.

For Further Thought

It's Time to End Decimal Point Abuse

Using a decimal point erroneously with a ¢ symbol is seen almost on a daily basis. Think about it. . . $.99 represents $\frac{99}{100}$ of a dollar, or 99 cents, while 99¢ also represents 99 cents (since ¢ is the symbol for *cent*). So what does .99¢ represent? That's right, $\frac{99}{100}$ of one cent!

Look at the photos provided by one of the authors. A 20-oz single of FlavorSplash is advertised for .99¢. What do you think would happen if you gave the clerk a dime and asked for ten bottles and change? You would most likely get a dumbfounded look. A similar response would probably be forthcoming if you asked for Sierra Mist, which costs even less: .79¢. To vacuum your car, it costs .50¢, a mere half cent. At The Floor Place, fabulous floors really do cost less. . . a lot less: less than half a cent per square foot for Berber flooring. Now here's a deal: a 2 liter bottle of Coca Cola for .09¢! (No doubt, the 1 preceding the decimal point fell off. Even then, one such bottle would cost only a tiny bit more than one penny.) On the Cherokee Turnpike, you are expected to provide exact change of .25¢. Could you possibly do it?

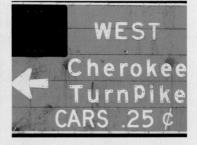

For Group Discussion or Individual Investigation

Assume that the products shown in the photos are actually being sold for the indicated prices. Answer each of the following.

1. How many 20-oz singles of FlavorSplash should you get for $1.00? How much change would the store owe you?
2. How much does one ounce of Sierra Mist cost?
3. If you deposit two quarters to have your car vacuumed, how many times should you be able to vacuum?
4. You want to cover your room area with 400 square feet of Berber flooring. How much will this cost?
5. How many 2 liter bottles of Coca Cola would nine cents get you?
6. How many trips on the Cherokee Turnpike should you get for a quarter?

6.5 EXERCISES

Decide whether each statement is true or false.

1. 300% of 12 is 36.

2. 25% of a quantity is the same as $\frac{1}{4}$ of that quantity.

3. When 759.367 is rounded to the nearest hundredth, the result is 759.40.

4. When 759.367 is rounded to the nearest hundred, the result is 759.37.

5. To find 50% of a quantity, we may simply divide the quantity by 2.

6. A soccer team that has won 12 games and lost 8 games has a winning percentage of 60%.

7. If 70% is the lowest passing grade on a quiz that has 50 items of equal value, then answering at least 35 items correctly will assure you of a passing grade.

8. 30 is more than 40% of 120.

9. .99¢ = 99 cents

10. If an item usually costs $70.00 and it is discounted 10%, then the discount price is $7.00.

Calculate each of the following using either a calculator or paper-and-pencil methods, as directed by your instructor.

11. 8.53 + 2.785

12. 9.358 + 7.2137

13. 8.74 − 12.955

14. 2.41 − 3.997

15. 25.7 × .032

16. 45.1 × 8.344

17. 1019.825 ÷ 21.47

18. −262.563 ÷ 125.03

19. $\dfrac{118.5}{1.45 + 2.3}$

20. 2.45(1.2 + 3.4 − 5.6)

Change in Population The table shows the percent change in population from 1990 through 2000 for some large cities in the United States.

City	Percent Change
New York	8.8
Los Angeles	9.7
Cleveland	2.2
Pittsburgh	−1.5
Baltimore	7.2
Buffalo	−1.6

Source: U.S. Census Bureau.

21. Which city had the greatest percent change? What was this change? Was it an increase or a decrease?

22. Which city had the least percent change? What was this change? Was it an increase or a decrease?

Postage Stamp Pricing *Refer to* For Further Thought *on decimal point abuse. At one time, the United States Postal Service sold rolls of 33-cent stamps that featured fruit berries. One such stamp is shown on the left. On the right is a photo of the pricing information found on the cellophane wrapper of such a roll.*

100 STAMPS PSA
.33¢ ea. TOTAL $33.00
FRUIT BERRIES
ITEM 7757
BCA

23. Look at the second line of the pricing information. According to the price listed *per stamp,* how many stamps should you be able to purchase for one cent?

24. The total price listed is the amount the Postal Service actually charges. If you were to multiply the listed price *per stamp* by the number of stamps, what should the total price be?

Pricing of Pie and Coffee *The photos here were taken at a flea market near Natchez, MS. The handwritten signs indicate that a piece of pie costs .10¢ and a cup of coffee ("ffee") costs .5¢. Assuming these are the actual prices, answer the questions in Exercises 25–28.*

25. How much will 10 pieces of pie and 10 cups of coffee cost?

26. How much will 20 pieces of pie and 10 cups of coffee cost?

27. How many pieces of pie can you get for $1.00?

28. How many cups of coffee can you get for $1.00?

Exercises 29–32 are based on formulas found in Auto Math Handbook: Mathematical Calculations, Theory, and Formulas for Automotive Enthusiasts, *by John Lawlor (1991, HP Books).*

29. *Blood Alcohol Concentration* The Blood Alcohol Concentration (BAC) of a person who has been drinking is given by the formula

$$\text{BAC} = \frac{(\text{ounces} \times \text{percent alcohol} \times .075)}{\text{body weight in lb}}$$

$$- (\text{hours of drinking} \times .015).$$

Suppose a policeman stops a 190-pound man who, in two hours, has ingested four 12-ounce beers, each having a 3.2 percent alcohol content. The formula would then read

$$\text{BAC} = \frac{[(4 \times 12) \times 3.2 \times .075]}{190} - (2 \times .015).$$

(a) Find this BAC.
(b) Find the BAC for a 135-pound woman who, in three hours, has drunk three 12-ounce beers, each having a 4.0 percent alcohol content.

30. *Approximate Automobile Speed* The approximate speed of an automobile in miles per hour (MPH) can be found in terms of the engine's revolutions per minute (rpm), the tire diameter in inches, and the overall gear ratio by the formula

$$\text{MPH} = \frac{\text{rpm} \times \text{tire diameter}}{\text{gear ratio} \times 336}.$$

If a certain automobile has an rpm of 5600, a tire diameter of 26 inches, and a gear ratio of 3.12, what is its approximate speed (MPH)?

31. *Engine Horsepower* Horsepower can be found from indicated mean effective pressure (mep) in pounds per square inch, engine displacement in cubic inches, and revolutions per minute (rpm) using the formula

$$\text{Horsepower} = \frac{\text{mep} \times \text{displacement} \times \text{rpm}}{792,000}.$$

Suppose that an engine has displacement of 302 cubic inches, and indicated mep of 195 pounds per square inch at 4000 rpm. What is its approximate horsepower?

32. *Torque Approximation* To determine the torque at a given value of rpm, the formula below applies:

$$\text{Torque} = \frac{5252 \times \text{horsepower}}{\text{rpm}}.$$

If the horsepower of a certain vehicle is 400 at 4500 rpm, what is the approximate torque?

Round each number to the nearest **(a)** *tenth;* **(b)** *hundredth. Always round from the original number.*

33. 78.414

34. 3689.537

35. .0837

36. .0658

37. 12.68925

38. 43.99613

Convert each decimal to a percent.

39. .42	**40.** .87
41. .365	**42.** .792
43. .008	**44.** .0093
45. 2.1	**46.** 8.9

Convert each fraction to a percent.

47. $\dfrac{1}{5}$	**48.** $\dfrac{2}{5}$
49. $\dfrac{1}{100}$	**50.** $\dfrac{1}{50}$
51. $\dfrac{3}{8}$	**52.** $\dfrac{5}{6}$
53. $\dfrac{3}{2}$	**54.** $\dfrac{7}{4}$

55. Explain the difference between $\frac{1}{2}$ of a quantity and $\frac{1}{2}\%$ of the quantity.

56. On the next page Group I shows some common percents, found in many everyday situations. In Group II are fractional equivalents of these percents. Match the fractions in Group II with their equivalent percents in Group I.

I		II	
(a) 25%	**(b)** 10%	**A.** $\dfrac{1}{3}$	**B.** $\dfrac{1}{50}$
(c) 2%	**(d)** 20%	**C.** $\dfrac{3}{4}$	**D.** $\dfrac{1}{10}$
(e) 75%	**(f)** $33\dfrac{1}{3}\%$	**E.** $\dfrac{1}{4}$	**F.** $\dfrac{1}{5}$

57. Fill in each blank with the appropriate numerical response.
(a) 5% means _____ in every 100.
(b) 25% means 6 in every _____ .
(c) 200% means _____ for every 4.
(d) .5% means _____ in every 100.
(e) _____ % means 12 for every 2.

58. The Venn diagram shows the number of elements in the four regions formed.

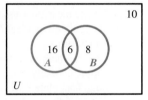

(a) What percent of the elements in the universe are in $A \cap B$?
(b) What percent of the elements in the universe are in A but not in B?
(c) What percent of the elements in $A \cup B$ are in $A \cap B$?
(d) What percent of the elements in the universe are in neither A nor B?

59. *Discount and Markup* Suppose that an item regularly costs $60.00 and it is discounted 20%. If it is then marked up 20%, is the resulting price $60.00? If not, what is it?

60. The figures in Exercise 13 of Section 6.3 are reproduced here. Express the fractional parts represented by the shaded areas as percents.

(a)
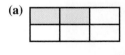

(b)

(c)
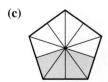

(d)

Win-Loss Record Exercises 61 and 62 deal with winning percentage in the standings of sports teams.

61. At the end of the regular 2005 Major League Baseball season, the standings of the Central Division of the American League were as shown. Winning percentage is commonly expressed as a decimal rounded to the nearest thousandth. To find the winning percentage of a team, divide the number of wins (W) by the total number of games played (W + L). Find the winning percentage of each team.
(a) Chicago   (b) Cleveland   (c) Detroit

Team	W	L
Chicago	99	63
Cleveland	93	69
Minnesota	83	79
Detroit	71	91
Kansas City	56	106

62. Repeat Exercise 61 for the following standings for the East Division of the National League.
(a) Atlanta   (b) Philadelphia
(c) Florida and New York

Team	W	L
Atlanta	90	72
Philadelphia	88	74
Florida	83	79
New York	83	79
Washington	81	81

Work each problem involving percent.

63. What is 26% of 480?

64. Find 38% of 12.

65. Find 10.5% of 28.

66. What is 48.6% of 19?

67. What percent of 30 is 45?

68. What percent of 48 is 20?

69. 25% of what number is 150?

70. 12% of what number is 3600?

71. .392 is what percent of 28?

72. 78.84 is what percent of 292?

Use mental techniques to answer the questions in Exercises 73–76. Try to avoid using paper and pencil or a calculator.

73. Allowance Increase Dierdre Lynch's allowance was raised from $4.00 per week to $5.00 per week. What was the percent of the increase?
A. 25%   **B.** 20%   **C.** 50%   **D.** 30%

74. Boat Purchase and Sale Jane Gunton bought a boat five years ago for $5000 and sold it this year for $2000. What percent of her original purchase did she lose on the sale?
A. 40%   **B.** 50%   **C.** 20%   **D.** 60%

75. Population of Alabama The 2000 U.S. census showed that the population of Alabama was 4,447,000, with 26.0% represented by African Americans. What is the best estimate of the African American population in Alabama? (*Source:* U.S. Census Bureau.)
A. 500,000   **B.** 1,500,000
C. 1,100,000   **D.** 750,000

76. Population of Hawaii The 2000 U.S. census showed that the population of Hawaii was 1,212,000, with 21.4% of the population being of two or more races. What is the best estimate of this population of Hawaii? (*Source:* U.S. Census Bureau.)
A. 240,000   **B.** 300,000
C. 21,400   **D.** 24,000

Gasoline Prices *The line graph shows the average price, adjusted for inflation, that Americans have paid for a gallon of gasoline for selected years between 1970 and 2000. Use this information in Exercises 77 and 78.*

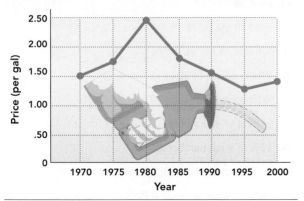

AVERAGE GASOLINE PRICES

Source: American Petroleum Institute; AP research.

77. By what percent did prices increase from 1970 to 1980?

78. By what percent did prices decrease from 1980 to 1990?

Metabolic Units *One way to measure a person's cardio fitness is to calculate how many METs, or metabolic units, he or she can reach at peak exertion. One MET is the amount of energy used when sitting quietly. To calculate ideal METs, we can use one of the following expressions.*

$$14.7 - \text{age} \cdot .13 \quad \text{For women}$$
$$14.7 - \text{age} \cdot .11 \quad \text{For men}$$

(*Source: New England Journal of Medicine*, August, 2005.)

79. A 40-year-old woman wishes to calculate her ideal MET.
   (a) Write the expression using her age.
   (b) Calculate her ideal MET. (*Hint:* Use the order of operations.)
   (c) Researchers recommend that a person reach approximately 85% of their MET when exercising. Calculate 85% of the ideal MET from part (b). Then refer to the following table. What activity can the woman do that is approximately this value?

Activity	METs	Activity	METs
Golf (with cart)	2.5	Skiing (water or downhill)	6.8
Walking (3 mph)	3.3	Swimming	7.0
Mowing lawn (power mower)	4.5	Walking (5 mph)	8.0
Ballroom or square dancing	5.5	Jogging	10.2
Cycling	5.7	Rope skipping	12.0

Source: Harvard School of Public Health.

80. Repeat parts **(a)**–**(c)** of Exercise 79 for a 55-year-old man.

81. *Value of 1916-D Mercury Dime* The 1916 Mercury dime minted in Denver is quite rare. In 1979 its value in Extremely Fine condition was $625. The 2005 value had increased to $6000. What was the percent increase in the value of this coin from 1979 to 2005? (*Sources: A Guide Book of United States Coins; Coin World Coin Values.*)

82. *Value of 1903-O Morgan Dollar* In 1963, the value of a 1903 Morgan dollar minted in New Orleans in typical Uncirculated condition was $1500. Due to a discovery of a large hoard of these dollars late that year, the value plummeted. Its value in 2005 was $550. What was the percent decrease in its value from 1963 to 2005? (*Sources: A Guide Book of United States Coins; Coin World Coin Values.*)

Tipping Procedure *It is customary in our society to "tip" waiters and waitresses when dining in restaurants. One common rate for tipping is 15%. A quick way of figuring a tip that will give a close approximation of 15% is as follows:*

1 *Round off the bill to the nearest dollar.*

2 *Find 10% of this amount by moving the decimal point one place to the left.*

3 *Take half of the amount obtained in Step 2 and add it to the result of Step 2.*

This will give you approximately 15% of the bill. The amount obtained in Step 3 is 5%, and

$$10\% + 5\% = 15\%.$$

Use the method above to find an approximation of 15% for each restaurant bill.

83. $29.57   **84.** $38.32

85. $5.15   **86.** $7.89

Suppose that you get extremely good service and decide to tip 20%. You can use the first two steps listed, and then in Step 3, double the amount you obtained in Step 2. Use this method to find an approximation of 20% for each restaurant bill.

87. $59.96   **88.** $40.24

89. $180.43   **90.** $199.86

91. A television reporter once asked a professional wrist-wrestler what percent of his sport was physical and what percent was mental. The athlete responded "I would say it's 50% physical and 90% mental." Comment on this response.

92. According to *The Yogi Book,* consisting of quotes by baseball Hall-of-Famer Yogi Berra, he claims that "90% of the game is half mental." Comment on this statement.

EXTENSION
Complex Numbers

Numbers such as $\sqrt{-5}$ and $\sqrt{-16}$ were called *imaginary* by the early mathematicians who would not permit these numbers to be used as solutions to problems. Gradually, however, applications were found that required the use of these numbers, making it necessary to expand the set of real numbers to form the set of **complex numbers.**

Consider the equation $x^2 + 1 = 0$. It has no real number solution, since any solution must be a number whose square is -1. In the set of real numbers all squares are nonnegative numbers, because the product of either two positive numbers or two negative numbers is positive. To provide a solution for the equation $x^2 + 1 = 0$, a new number i is defined so that

$$i^2 = -1.$$

(continued)

That is, i is a number whose square is -1. This definition of i makes it possible to define the square root of any negative number as follows.

$\sqrt{-b}$

For any positive real number b, $\quad \sqrt{-b} = i\sqrt{b}.$

■ EXAMPLE 1 Writing Square Roots Using i

Write each number as a product of a real number and i.

(a) $\sqrt{-100}$ **(b)** $\sqrt{-2}$

SOLUTION

(a) $\sqrt{-100} = i\sqrt{100} = 10i$

(b) $\sqrt{-2} = \sqrt{2}i = i\sqrt{2}$

It is easy to mistake $\sqrt{2}i$ for $\sqrt{2i}$, with the i under the radical. For this reason, it is common to write $\sqrt{2}i$ as $i\sqrt{2}$.

When finding a product such as $\sqrt{-4} \cdot \sqrt{-9}$, the product rule for radicals cannot be used, since that rule applies only when both radicals represent real numbers. For this reason, always change $\sqrt{-b}$ ($b > 0$) to the form $i\sqrt{b}$ before performing any multiplications or divisions. For example,

$$\sqrt{-4} \cdot \sqrt{-9} = i\sqrt{4} \cdot i\sqrt{9} = i \cdot 2 \cdot i \cdot 3 = 6i^2.$$

Since $i^2 = -1$,

$$6i^2 = 6(-1) = -6.$$

An *incorrect* use of the product rule for radicals would give a wrong answer.

$$\sqrt{-4} \cdot \sqrt{-9} = \sqrt{(-4)(-9)} = \sqrt{36} = 6 \quad \text{Incorrect}$$

■ EXAMPLE 2 Multiplying Expressions Involving i

Multiply.

(a) $\sqrt{-3} \cdot \sqrt{-7}$ **(b)** $\sqrt{-2} \cdot \sqrt{-8}$ **(c)** $\sqrt{-5} \cdot \sqrt{6}$

SOLUTION

(a) $\sqrt{-3} \cdot \sqrt{-7} = i\sqrt{3} \cdot i\sqrt{7} = i^2\sqrt{3 \cdot 7} = (-1)\sqrt{21} = -\sqrt{21}$

(b) $\sqrt{-2} \cdot \sqrt{-8} = i\sqrt{2} \cdot i\sqrt{8} = i^2\sqrt{2 \cdot 8} = (-1)\sqrt{16} = (-1)4 = -4$

(c) $\sqrt{-5} \cdot \sqrt{6} = i\sqrt{5} \cdot \sqrt{6} = i\sqrt{30}$

■ EXAMPLE 3 Dividing Expressions Involving i

Divide.

(a) $\dfrac{\sqrt{-75}}{\sqrt{-3}}$ **(b)** $\dfrac{\sqrt{-32}}{\sqrt{8}}$

Gauss and the Complex Numbers The stamp shown above honors the many contributions made by Gauss to our understanding of complex numbers. In about 1831 he was able to show that numbers of the form $a + bi$ can be represented as points on the plane (as the stamp shows) just as real numbers are. He shared this contribution with **Robert Argand,** a bookkeeper in Paris, who wrote an essay on the geometry of the complex numbers in 1806. This went unnoticed at the time.

When the TI-83/84 Plus calculator is in complex mode, denoted by $a + bi$, it will perform complex number arithmetic.

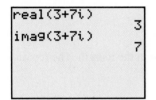

This screen supports the results of Examples 2(b), 3(a), and 3(b).

SOLUTION

(a) $\dfrac{\sqrt{-75}}{\sqrt{-3}} = \dfrac{i\sqrt{75}}{i\sqrt{3}} = \sqrt{\dfrac{75}{3}} = \sqrt{25} = 5$

(b) $\dfrac{\sqrt{-32}}{\sqrt{8}} = \dfrac{i\sqrt{32}}{\sqrt{8}} = i\sqrt{\dfrac{32}{8}} = i\sqrt{4} = 2i$ ∎

Complex numbers are defined as follows.

Complex Numbers

If a and b are real numbers, then any number of the form $a + bi$ is called a **complex number.**

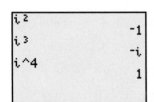

The TI-83/84 Plus calculator identifies the real and imaginary parts of $3 + 7i$.

In the complex number $a + bi$, the number a is called the **real part** and b is called the **imaginary part.*** When $b = 0$, $a + bi$ is a real number, so the real numbers are a subset of the complex numbers. Complex numbers of the form bi, where $b \neq 0$, are called **pure imaginary numbers.** In spite of their name, such numbers are very useful in applications, particularly in work with electricity.

An interesting pattern emerges when we consider various powers of i. By definition, $i^0 = 1$, and $i^1 = i$. We have seen that $i^2 = -1$, and greater powers of i can be found as shown in the following list.

$$i^3 = i \cdot i^2 = i(-1) = -i \qquad\qquad i^6 = i^2 \cdot i^4 = (-1) \cdot 1 = -1$$
$$i^4 = i^2 \cdot i^2 = (-1)(-1) = 1 \qquad i^7 = i^3 \cdot i^4 = (-i) \cdot 1 = -i$$
$$i^5 = i \cdot i^4 = i \cdot 1 = i \qquad\qquad i^8 = i^4 \cdot i^4 = 1 \cdot 1 = 1$$

A few powers of i are listed here.

The calculator computes powers of i. Compare to the powers in the chart.

Powers of i

$i^1 = i$	$i^5 = i$	$i^9 = i$	$i^{13} = i$
$i^2 = -1$	$i^6 = -1$	$i^{10} = -1$	$i^{14} = -1$
$i^3 = -i$	$i^7 = -i$	$i^{11} = -i$	$i^{15} = -i$
$i^4 = 1$	$i^8 = 1$	$i^{12} = 1$	$i^{16} = 1$

As these examples suggest, the powers of i rotate through the four numbers i, -1, $-i$, and 1. Larger powers of i can be simplified by using the fact that $i^4 = 1$. For example,

$$i^{75} = (i^4)^{18} \cdot i^3 = 1^{18} \cdot i^3 = 1 \cdot i^3 = -i.$$

---

*In some texts, bi is called the imaginary part.

(continued)

> **Simplifying Large Powers of *i***
>
> **Step 1** Divide the exponent by 4.
>
> **Step 2** Observe the remainder obtained in Step 1. The large power of *i* is the same as *i* raised to the power determined by this remainder. Refer to the previous chart to complete the simplification. (If the remainder is 0, the power simplifies to $i^0 = 1$.)

EXAMPLE 4   Simplifying Powers of *i*

Simplify each power of *i*.

(a) i^{12} **(b)** i^{39}

SOLUTION

(a) $i^{12} = (i^4)^3 = 1^3 = 1$

(b) To find i^{39}, start by dividing 39 by 4 (Step 1), as shown in the margin. The remainder is 3. So $i^{39} = i^3 = -i$ (Step 2).

Another way to simplify i^{39} is as follows.

$$i^{39} = i^{36} \cdot i^3 = (i^4)^9 \cdot i^3 = 1^9 \cdot (-i) = -i$$

$$\begin{array}{r} 9 \\ 4\overline{)39} \\ 36 \\ \hline 3 \end{array} \leftarrow \text{Remainder}$$

EXTENSION EXERCISES

Use the method of Examples 1–3 to write each expression as a real number or a product of a real number and i.

1. $\sqrt{-144}$ **2.** $\sqrt{-196}$ **3.** $-\sqrt{-225}$ **4.** $-\sqrt{-400}$

5. $\sqrt{-3}$ **6.** $\sqrt{-19}$ **7.** $\sqrt{-75}$ **8.** $\sqrt{-125}$

9. $\sqrt{-5} \cdot \sqrt{-5}$ **10.** $\sqrt{-3} \cdot \sqrt{-3}$ **11.** $\sqrt{-9} \cdot \sqrt{-36}$

12. $\sqrt{-4} \cdot \sqrt{-81}$ **13.** $\sqrt{-16} \cdot \sqrt{-100}$ **14.** $\sqrt{-81} \cdot \sqrt{-121}$

15. $\dfrac{\sqrt{-200}}{\sqrt{-100}}$ **16.** $\dfrac{\sqrt{-50}}{\sqrt{-2}}$ **17.** $\dfrac{\sqrt{-54}}{\sqrt{6}}$

18. $\dfrac{\sqrt{-90}}{\sqrt{10}}$ **19.** $\dfrac{\sqrt{-288}}{\sqrt{-8}}$ **20.** $\dfrac{\sqrt{-48} \cdot \sqrt{-3}}{\sqrt{-2}}$

21. Why is it incorrect to use the product rule for radicals to multiply $\sqrt{-3} \cdot \sqrt{-12}$?

22. In your own words describe the relationship between complex numbers and real numbers.

Use the method of Example 4 to simplify each power of i.

23. i^8 **24.** i^{16} **25.** i^{42} **26.** i^{86}

27. i^{47} **28.** i^{63} **29.** i^{101} **30.** i^{141}

COLLABORATIVE INVESTIGATION
Budgeting to Buy a Car

You are shopping for a sports car and have put aside a certain amount of money each month for a car payment. Your instructor will assign this amount to you. After looking through a variety of resources, you have narrowed your choices to the cars listed in the table.

Year/Make/Model	Retail Price	Fuel Tank Size (in gallons)	Miles per Gallon (city)	Miles per Gallon (highway)
2006 Ford Mustang	$26,320	16.0	18	23
2006 Ford Five Hundred	$22,230	20.0	20	27
2006 Toyota Camry	$25,805	18.5	20	28
2006 Mazda MX-5 Miata	$26,700	12.7	23	30
2006 Honda CR-V XLE	$25,450	15.3	22	27
2006 Chevrolet Tracker	$23,900	17.0	19	25

Source: www.edmunds.com

As a group, work through the following steps to determine which car you can afford to buy.

A. Decide which cars you think are within your budget.

B. Select one of the cars you identified in part A. Have each member of the group calculate the monthly payment for this car using a different financing option. Use the formula given below, where *P* is principal, *r* is interest rate, and *m* is the number of monthly payments, along with the financing options table.

Financing Options

Time (in years)	Interest Rate
4	7.0%
5	8.5%
6	10.0%

$$\text{Monthly Payment} = \frac{\dfrac{Pr}{12}}{1 - \left(\dfrac{12}{12 + r}\right)^m}$$

C. Have each group member determine the amount of money paid in interest over the duration of the loan for his or her financing option.

D. Consider fuel expenses.
   1. Assume you will travel an average of 75 miles in the city and 400 miles on the highway each week. How many gallons of gas will you need to buy each month?
   2. Using typical prices for gas in your area at this time, how much money will you need to have available for buying gas?

E. Repeat parts B–D as necessary until your group can reach a consensus on the car you will buy and the financing option you will use. Write a paragraph to explain your choices.

CHAPTER 6 TEST

1. Consider $\{-4, -\sqrt{5}, -\frac{3}{2}, -.5, 0, \sqrt{3}, 4.1, 12\}$. List the elements of the set that belong to each of the following.
   (a) natural numbers
   (b) whole numbers
   (c) integers
   (d) rational numbers
   (e) irrational numbers
   (f) real numbers

2. Match each set in (a)–(d) with the correct set-builder notation description in A–D.
   (a) $\{\ldots, -4, -3, -2, -1\}$
   (b) $\{3, 4, 5, 6, \ldots\}$
   (c) $\{1, 2, 3, 4, \ldots\}$
   (d) $\{-12, \ldots, -2, -1, 0, 1, 2, \ldots, 12\}$

   A. $\{x \mid x$ is an integer with absolute value less than or equal to 12$\}$
   B. $\{x \mid x$ is an integer greater than 2.5$\}$
   C. $\{x \mid x$ is a negative integer$\}$
   D. $\{x \mid x$ is a positive integer$\}$

3. Decide whether each statement is true or false.
   (a) The absolute value of a number is always positive.
   (b) $|-7| = -(-7)$
   (c) $\frac{2}{5}$ is an example of a real number that is not an integer.
   (d) Every real number is either positive or negative.

Perform the indicated operations. Use the order of operations as necessary.

4. $6^2 - 4(9 - 1)$

5. $(-3)(-2) - [5 + (8 - 10)]$

6. $\dfrac{(-8 + 3) - (5 + 10)}{7 - 9}$

7. **Changes in Car Sales** The graph shows the percent change in car sales from January 2000 to January 2001 for various automakers. Use this graph to answer the following. (Consider absolute value.)
   (a) Which automaker had the greatest change in sales? What was that change?
   (b) Which automaker had the least change in sales? What was that change?

CAR SALES

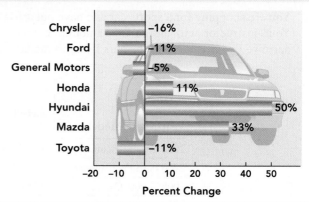

Source: Automakers.

   (c) *True* or *false:* The absolute value of the percent change for Honda was greater than the absolute value of the percent change for Toyota.
   (d) *True* or *false:* The percent change for Hyundai was more than four times greater than the percent change for Honda.

8. **Altitude of a Plane** The surface of the Dead Sea has altitude 1299 ft below sea level. Vangie is flying 80 ft above that surface. How much altitude must she gain to clear a 3852 ft pass by 225 ft? (*Source: The World Almanac and Book of Facts.*)

9. **Median Home Prices** Median pricings for existing homes in the United States for the years 1997 through 2002 are shown in the table. Complete the table, determining the change from one year to the next by subtraction.

	Year	Median-Priced Existing Homes	Change from Previous Year
	1997	$121,800	
	1998	$128,400	$6600
(a)	1999	$133,300	
(b)	2000	$139,000	
(c)	2001	$147,800	
(d)	2002	$158,100	

Source: National Association of Realtors.

10. Match each statement in (a)–(f) with the property that justifies it in A–F.

(a) $7 \cdot (8 \cdot 5) = (7 \cdot 8) \cdot 5$
(b) $3x + 3y = 3(x + y)$
(c) $8 \cdot 1 = 1 \cdot 8 = 8$
(d) $7 + (6 + 9) = (6 + 9) + 7$
(e) $9 + (-9) = -9 + 9 = 0$
(f) $5 \cdot 8$ is a real number.

A. Distributive property
B. Identity property
C. Closure property
D. Commutative property
E. Associative property
F. Inverse property

11. *Basketball Shot Statistics* Six players on the local high school basketball team had the following shooting statistics.

Player	Field Goal Attempts	Field Goals Made
Ed Moura	40	13
Jack Pritchard	10	4
Chuck Miller	20	8
Ben Whitney	6	4
Charlie Dawkins	7	2
Jason McElwain ("J-Mac")	7	6

Answer each question, using estimation skills as necessary.

(a) Which player made more than half of his attempts?
(b) Which players made just less than $\frac{1}{3}$ of the attempts?
(c) Which player made exactly $\frac{2}{3}$ of his attempts?
(d) Which two players made the same fractional parts of their attempts? What was the fractional part, reduced to lowest terms?
(e) Which player had the greatest fractional part of shots made?

Perform each operation. Write your answer in lowest terms.

12. $\dfrac{3}{16} + \dfrac{1}{2}$

13. $\dfrac{9}{20} - \dfrac{3}{32}$

14. $\dfrac{3}{8} \cdot \left(-\dfrac{16}{15}\right)$

15. $\dfrac{7}{9} \div \dfrac{14}{27}$

16. Convert each rational number into a repeating or terminating decimal. Use a calculator if your instructor so allows.

(a) $\dfrac{9}{20}$

(b) $\dfrac{5}{12}$

17. Convert each decimal into a quotient of integers, reduced to lowest terms.

(a) $.72$

(b) $.\overline{58}$

18. Identify each number as rational or irrational.

(a) $\sqrt{10}$
(b) $\sqrt{16}$
(c) $.01$
(d) $.\overline{01}$
(e) $.0101101110\ldots$
(f) π

For each of the following, (a) use a calculator to find a decimal approximation and (b) simplify the radical according to the guidelines in this chapter.

19. $\sqrt{150}$

20. $\dfrac{13}{\sqrt{7}}$

21. $2\sqrt{32} - 5\sqrt{128}$

22. A student using her powerful new calculator states that the *exact* value of $\sqrt{65}$ is 8.062257748. Is she correct? If not, explain.

23. Work each of the following using either a calculator or paper-and-pencil methods, as directed by your instructor.

(a) $4.6 + 9.21$
(b) $12 - 3.725 - 8.59$
(c) $86(.45)$
(d) $236.439 \div (-9.73)$

24. Round 9.0449 to the following place values:
(a) hundredths
(b) thousandths.

25. (a) Find 18.5% of 90.
(b) What number is 145% of 70?

26. Consider the figure.
(a) What percent of the total number of shapes are circles?
(b) What percent of the total number of shapes are not stars?

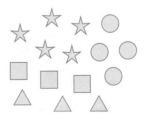

27. **Sales of Books** Use estimation techniques to answer the following: In 2005, Bill Schoof sold $300,000 worth of books. In 2006, he sold $900,000. His 2006 sales were _____ of his 2005 sales.

A. 30%   **B.** $33\frac{1}{3}$%

C. 200%   **D.** 300%

28. **Creature Comforts** From a list of "everyday items" often taken for granted, adults were recently surveyed as to those items they wouldn't want to live without. Complete the results shown in the table if 1200 adults were surveyed.

Item	Percent That Wouldn't Want to Live Without	Number That Wouldn't Want to Live Without
Toilet paper	69%	
Zipper	42%	
Frozen Food		190
Self-stick note pads		75

(Other items included tape, hairspray, pantyhose, paper clips, and Velcro.)
Source: Market Facts for Kleenex Cottonelle.

29. **Composition of U.S. Workforce** The U.S. Bureau of Labor Statistics projected the composition of the U.S. workforce for the year 2006. The projected total number of people in the workforce for that year is 148,847,000. To the nearest thousand, how many of these will be in the Hispanic category?

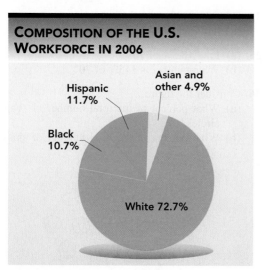

Source: U.S. Bureau of Labor Statistics.

30. **Medicare Funding** Current projections indicate that funding for Medicare will not cover its costs unless the program changes. The line graph shows projections for the years 2004 through 2013. What signed number represents how much the funding will have changed from 2004 to 2013?

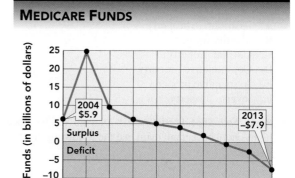

Source: Centers for Medicare and Medicaid Services.

THE METRIC SYSTEM

Joseph Louis Lagrange
(1736–1813) was born in Turin, Italy, and became a professor at age 19. In 1776 he came to Berlin at the request of Frederick the Great to take the position Euler left. A decade later Lagrange settled permanently in Paris. Napoleon was among many who admired and honored him.

Lagrange's greatest work was in the theory and application of **calculus.** He carried forward Euler's work of putting calculus on firm algebraic ground in his theory of functions. His *Analytic Mechanics* (1788) applied calculus to the motion of objects. Lagrange's contributions to algebra had great influence on Galois and hence the theory of groups. He also wrote on number theory; he proved, for example, that every integer is the sum of at most four squares. His study of the moon led to methods for finding longitude.

The metric system was developed by a committee of the French Academy just after the French Revolution of 1789. The president of the committee was the mathematician Joseph Louis Lagrange.

The advantages of the metric system can be seen when compared to our English system. In the English system, one inch is one-twelfth of a foot, while one foot is one-third of a yard. One mile is equivalent to 5280 feet, or 1760 yards. Obviously, there is no consistency in subdivisions. In the metric system, prefixes are used to indicate multiplications or divisions by powers of ten. For example, the basic unit of length in the metric system is the *meter* (which is a little longer than one yard). To indicate one thousand meters, attach the prefix **"kilo-"** to get **kilo**meter. To indicate one one-hundredth of a meter, use the prefix **"centi-"** to obtain **centi**meter. A complete list of the prefixes of the metric system is shown in Table 1 below, with the most commonly used prefixes appearing in heavy type.

TABLE 1   Metric Prefixes

Prefix	Multiple	Prefix	Multiple
exa	1,000,000,000,000,000,000	deci	.1
peta	1,000,000,000,000,000	**centi**	.01
tera	1,000,000,000,000	**milli**	.001
giga	1,000,000,000	micro	.000001
mega	1,000,000	nano	.000000001
kilo	1000	pico	.000000000001
hecto	100	femto	.000000000000001
deka	10	atto	.000000000000000001

Length and Area

Lagrange urged the committee devising the metric system to find some natural measure for length from which weight and volume measures could be derived. It was decided that one **meter (m)** would be the basic unit of length, with a meter being defined as one ten-millionth of the distance from the equator to the North Pole.

To obtain measures longer than one meter, Greek prefixes were added. For measures smaller than a meter, Latin prefixes were used. A meter is a little longer than a yard (about 39.37 inches). A **centimeter (cm)** is one one-hundredth of a meter and is about $\frac{2}{5}$ of an inch. See Figure 1.

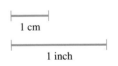

1 cm

1 inch

FIGURE 1

A Comparison of Distances

Length in Meters	Approximate Related Distances
10^{19}	Distance to the North Star
10^{12}	Distance of Saturn from the sun
10^{11}	Distance of Venus from the sun
10^{9}	Diameter of the sun
10^{8}	Diameter of Jupiter
10^{7}	Diameter of Earth; distance from Washington, D.C. to Tokyo
10^{6}	Distance from Chicago to Wichita, Kansas
10^{5}	Average distance across Lake Michigan
10^{4}	Average width of the Grand Canyon
10^{3}	Length of the Golden Gate Bridge
10^{2}	Length of a football field
10^{1}	Average height of a two-story house
10^{0}	Width of a door
10^{-1}	Width of your hand
10^{-2}	Diameter of a piece of chalk
10^{-3}	Thickness of a dime
10^{-4}	Thickness of a piece of paper
10^{-5}	Diameter of a red blood cell
10^{-7}	Thickness of a soap bubble
10^{-8}	Average distance between molecules of air in a room
10^{-9}	Diameter of a molecule of oil
10^{-14}	Diameter of an atomic nucleus
10^{-15}	Diameter of a proton

According to Paul G. Hewitt, in *Conceptual Physics,* 7th edition (HarperCollins, 1993):

The distance from the equator to the North Pole was thought at the time to be close to 10,000 kilometers. One ten-millionth of this, the meter, was carefully determined and marked off by means of scratches on a bar of platinum-iridium alloy. This bar is kept at the International Bureau of Weights and Measures in France. The standard meter in France has since been calibrated in terms of the wavelength of light—it is 1,650,763.73 times the wavelength of orange light emitted by the atoms of the gas krypton-86. The meter is now defined as being the length of the path traveled by light in a vacuum during a time interval of 1/299,792,458 of a second.

Because the metric system is based on decimals and powers of ten, conversions within the system involve multiplying and dividing by powers of ten. For example, to convert 2.5 m to centimeters, multiply 2.5 by 100 (since 100 cm = 1 m) to obtain 250 cm. On the other hand, to convert 18.6 cm to meters, divide by 100 to obtain .186 m. Other conversions are made in the same manner, using the meanings of the prefixes. Why is 42 m equal to 42,000 millimeters (mm)?

Long distances usually are measured in kilometers. A **kilometer (km)** is 1000 meters. (According to a popular dictionary, the word *kilometer* may be pronounced with the accent on either the first or the second syllable. Scientists usually stress the second syllable.) A kilometer is equal to about .6 mile. Figure 2 shows the ratio of 1 kilometer to 1 mile.

Conversions from meters to kilometers, and vice versa, are made by multiplying or dividing by 1000 as necessary. For example, 37 kilometers equals 37,000 meters, while 583 meters equals .583 km.

The area of a figure can be measured in square metric units. Figure 3 shows a square that is 1 cm on each side; thus, it is a **square centimeter (cm^2).** One square meter (m^2) is the area of a square with sides one meter long. How many cm^2 are in one m^2?

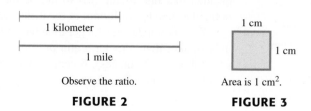

| 1 kilometer |
| 1 mile |

Observe the ratio.

FIGURE 2

1 cm

1 cm

Area is 1 cm^2.

FIGURE 3

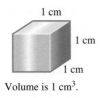

Volume is 1 cm³.

FIGURE 4

In September 1999, the **Mars Climate Orbiter** was lost due to "a failure to use metric units in the coding of a ground software file…." According to Edward Weiler, associate administrator for NASA's Office of Space Science, the metric conversion error that led to the loss "should have been caught five ways to Sunday," but it wasn't. (*Source:* "NASA's Mars Losses Spark Anger and Opportunity" by Leonard David, Washington Contributing Editor to www.space.com.)

Volume, Mass, and Weight

The volume of a three-dimensional figure is measured in cubic units. If, for example, the dimensions are given in centimeters, the volume may be determined by the appropriate formula from geometry, and it will be in **cubic centimeters (cm³).** See Figure 4 for a sketch of a box whose volume is one cm³.

In the metric system, one **liter (l)** is the quantity assigned to the volume of a box that is 10 cm on a side. (See Figure 5.) A liter is a little more than a quart. (See Figure 6.) Notice the advantage of this definition over the equivalent one in the English system—using a ruler marked in centimeters, a volume of 1 liter (symbolized 1 L) can be constructed. On the other hand, given a ruler marked in inches, it would be difficult to construct a volume of 1 quart.

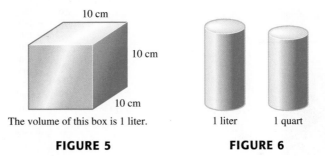

The volume of this box is 1 liter.   1 liter   1 quart

FIGURE 5   **FIGURE 6**

The prefixes mentioned earlier are used throughout the metric system, so one **milliliter (ml)** is one one-thousandth of a liter, one **centiliter (cl)** is one one-hundredth of a liter, one **kiloliter (kl)** is 1000 liters, and so on. Milliliters are used extensively in science and medicine. Many beverages now are sold by milliliters and by liters. For example, 750 ml is a common size for wine bottles, and many soft drinks now are sold in 1- and 2-liter bottles.

Because of the way a liter is defined as the volume of a box 10 cm on a side,

$$1 \text{ L} = 10 \text{ cm} \times 10 \text{ cm} \times 10 \text{ cm} = 1000 \text{ cm}^3 \quad \text{or} \quad \frac{1}{1000} \text{L} = 1 \text{ cm}^3.$$

Since $\frac{1}{1000}$ L = 1 ml, we have the following relationship:

$$\textbf{1 ml} = \textbf{1 cm}^3.$$

For example, the volume of a box which is 8 cm by 6 cm by 5 cm may be given as 240 cm³ or as 240 ml.

The box in Figure 4 is 1 cm by 1 cm by 1 cm. The volume of this box is 1 cm³, or 1 ml. By definition, the mass of the water that fills such a box is **1 gram (g).** A nickel five-cent piece has a mass close to 5 grams, or 5 g. The volume of water used to define a gram is very small, so a gram is a very small mass. For everyday use, a **kilogram (kg),** or one thousand grams, is more practical. A kilogram weighs about 2.2 pounds. A common abbreviation for kilogram is the word **kilo.**

Extremely small masses can be measured with **milligrams (mg)** and **centigrams (cg).** These measures are so small that they, like centiliters and milliliters, are used mainly in science and medicine.

Temperature

In the metric system temperature is measured in **degrees Celsius.** On the Celsius temperature scale, water freezes at 0° and boils at 100°. These two numbers are easier to remember than the corresponding numbers on the Fahrenheit scale, 32° and 212°. The thermometer in Figure 7 shows some typical temperatures in both Fahrenheit and Celsius.

Anders Celsius and his scale for measuring temperature are honored on this Swedish stamp. The original scale had the freezing point of water at 100° and the boiling point at 0°, but biologist Carl von Linne inverted the scale, giving us the familiar Celsius scale of today.

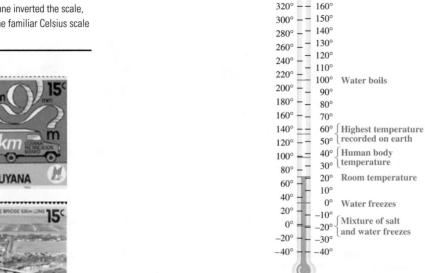

FIGURE 7

The formulas given below can be used to convert between Celsius and Fahrenheit temperatures.

Celsius-Fahrenheit Conversion Formulas
To convert a reading from Fahrenheit to Celsius, use $C = \frac{5}{9}(F - 32)$.
To convert from Celsius to Fahrenheit, use $F = \frac{9}{5}C + 32$.

Metric Conversions

Switching a country to the metric system requires a tremendous educational campaign. The stamps shown here were issued as part of one such campaign. They show the various metric units and items measured in those units.

Due to legislation enacted by Congress, the metric system is used in the United States, and an ultimate goal is for the two systems to be in use, side-by-side, with public acceptance of both systems. Many industries now use the metric system. In particular,

Further information on the **metric system** can be obtained from the U.S. Metric Association, 10245 Andasol Avenue, Northridge, CA 91325-1504.

industries that export a great many goods are using the metric system, since this is compatible with most of the countries with which they trade.

Some scientific calculators are programmed to do conversions between the English and metric systems. Approximate conversions can be made with the aid of Tables 2 and 3 below.

TABLE 2	Metric to English	
To Convert from	**To**	**Multiply by**
meters	yards	1.0936
meters	feet	3.2808
meters	inches	39.37
kilometers	miles	.6214
grams	pounds	.0022
kilograms	pounds	2.20
liters	quarts	1.0567
liters	gallons	.2642

TABLE 3	English to Metric	
To Convert from	**To**	**Multiply by**
yards	meters	.9144
feet	meters	.3048
inches	meters	.0254
miles	kilometers	1.609
pounds	grams	454
pounds	kilograms	.454
quarts	liters	.9464
gallons	liters	3.785

APPENDIX EXERCISES

Perform each conversion by multiplying or dividing by the appropriate powers of 10.

1. 8 m to millimeters

2. 14.76 m to centimeters

3. 8500 cm to meters

4. 250 mm to meters

5. 68.9 cm to millimeters

6. 3.25 cm to millimeters

7. 59.8 mm to centimeters

8. 3.542 mm to centimeters

9. 5.3 km to meters

10. 9.24 km to meters

11. 27,500 m to kilometers

12. 14,592 m to kilometers

Use a metric ruler to perform each measurement, first in centimeters, then in millimeters.

13. ├─────────────┤

14. ├──────────────────────┤

15. ├────────────────────────────────┤

16. Based on your measurement of the line segment in Exercise 13, one inch is about how many centimeters? how many millimeters?

Perform each conversion by multiplying or dividing by the appropriate powers of 10.

17. 6 L to centiliters

18. 4.1 L to milliliters

19. 8.7 L to milliliters

20. 12.5 L to centiliters

21. 925 cl to liters

22. 412 ml to liters

23. 8974 ml to liters

24. 5639 cl to liters

25. 8000 g to kilograms

26. 25,000 g to kilograms

27. 5.2 kg to grams

28. 12.42 kg to grams

29. 4.2 g to milligrams

30. 3.89 g to centigrams

31. 598 mg to grams

32. 7634 cg to grams

Use the formulas given in the text to perform each conversion. If necessary, round to the nearest degree.

33. 86°F to Celsius

34. 536°F to Celsius

35. −114°F to Celsius

36. −40°F to Celsius

37. 10°C to Fahrenheit

38. 25°C to Fahrenheit

39. −40°C to Fahrenheit

40. −15°C to Fahrenheit

Solve each problem. Refer to geometry formulas as necessary.

41. One nickel weighs 5 g. How many nickels are in 1 kg of nickels?

42. Sea water contains about 3.5 g salt per 1000 ml of water. How many grams of salt would be in one liter of sea water?

43. Helium weighs about .0002 g per milliliter. How much would one liter of helium weigh?

44. About 1500 g sugar can be dissolved in a liter of warm water. How much sugar could be dissolved in one milliliter of warm water?

45. Northside Foundry needed seven metal strips, each 67 cm long. Find the total cost of the strips, if they sell for $8.74 per meter.

46. Uptown Dressmakers bought fifteen pieces of lace, each 384 mm long. The lace sold for $54.20 per meter. Find the cost of the fifteen pieces.

47. Imported marble for desktops costs $174.20 per square meter. Find the cost of a piece of marble 128 cm by 174 cm.

48. A special photographic paper sells for $63.79 per square meter. Find the cost to buy 80 pieces of the paper, each 9 cm by 14 cm.

49. An importer received some special coffee beans in a box measuring 82 cm by 1.1 m by 1.2 m. Give the volume of the box, both in cubic centimeters and cubic meters.

50. A fabric center receives bolts of woolen cloth in crates measuring 1.5 m by 74 cm by 97 cm. Find the volume of a crate, both in cubic centimeters and cubic meters.

51. A medicine is sold in small bottles holding 800 ml each. How many of these bottles can be filled from a vat holding 160 L of the medicine?

52. How many 2-liter bottles of soda pop would be needed for a wedding reception if 80 people are expected, and each drinks 400 ml of soda?

Perform each conversion. Use a calculator and/or the table in the text as necessary.

53. 982 yd to meters

54. 12.2 km to miles

55. 125 mi to kilometers

56. 1000 mi to kilometers

57. 1816 g to pounds

58. 1.42 lb to grams

59. 47.2 lb to grams

60. 7.68 kg to pounds

61. 28.6 L to quarts

62. 59.4 L to quarts

63. 28.2 gal to liters

64. 16 qt to liters

Metric measures are very common in medicine. Since we convert among metric measures by moving the decimal point, errors in locating the decimal point in medical doses are not unknown. Decide whether each dose of medicine seems reasonable *or* unreasonable.

65. Take 2 kg of aspirin three times a day.

66. Take 4 L of liquid Mylanta every evening just before bedtime.

67. Take 25 ml of cough syrup daily.

68. Soak your feet in 6 L of hot water.

69. Inject $\frac{1}{2}$ L of insulin every morning.

70. Apply 40 g of salve to a cut on your finger.

Select the most reasonable choice for each of the following.

71. length of an adult cow
   A. 1 m   **B.** 3 m   **C.** 5 m

72. length of a Cadillac
   A. 1 m   **B.** 3 m   **C.** 5 m

73. distance from Seattle to Miami
   A. 500 km   **B.** 5000 km   **C.** 50,000 km

74. length across an average nose
   A. 3 cm   **B.** 30 cm   **C.** 300 cm

75. distance across a page of a book
   A. 1.93 mm   **B.** 19.3 mm   **C.** 193 mm

76. weight of a book
   A. 1 kg   **B.** 10 kg   **C.** 1000 kg

77. weight of a large automobile
   A. 1300 kg   **B.** 130 kg   **C.** 13 kg

78. volume of a 12-ounce bottle of beverage
   A. 35 ml   **B.** 355 ml   **C.** 3550 ml

79. height of a person
   A. 180 cm   **B.** 1800 cm   **C.** 18 cm

80. diameter of the earth
   A. 130 km   **B.** 1300 km   **C.** 13,000 km

81. length of a long freight train
   A. 8 m   **B.** 80 m   **C.** 800 m

82. volume of a grapefruit
   A. 1 L   **B.** 4 L   **C.** 8 L

83. the length of a pair of Levis
   A. 70 cm   **B.** 700 cm   **C.** 7 cm

84. a person's weight
   A. 700 kg   **B.** 7 kg   **C.** 70 kg

85. diagonal measure of the picture tube of a table model TV set
   A. 5 cm   **B.** 50 cm   **C.** 500 cm

86. width of a standard bedroom door
   A. 1 m   **B.** 3 m   **C.** 5 m

87. thickness of a marking pen
   A. .9 mm   **B.** 9 mm   **C.** 90 mm

88. length around the rim of a coffee mug
   A. 300 mm   **B.** 30 mm   **C.** 3000 mm

89. the temperature at the surface of a frozen lake
   A. 0°C   **B.** 10°C   **C.** 32°C

90. the temperature in the middle of Death Valley on a July afternoon
   A. 25°C   **B.** 40°C   **C.** 65°C

91. surface temperature of desert sand on a hot summer day
   A. 30°C   **B.** 60°C   **C.** 90°C

92. temperature of boiling water
   A. 100°C   **B.** 120°C   **C.** 150°C

93. air temperature on a day when you need a sweater
   A. 30°C   **B.** 20°C   **C.** 10°C

94. air temperature when you go swimming
   A. 30°C   **B.** 15°C   **C.** 10°C

95. temperature when baking a cake
   A. 120°C   **B.** 170°C   **C.** 300°C

96. temperature of bath water
   A. 35°C   **B.** 50°C   **C.** 65°C

ANSWERS TO SELECTED EXERCISES

CHAPTER 1   **The Art of Problem Solving**

1.1 Exercises   (Pages 7–10)

1. deductive   **3.** inductive   **5.** deductive   **7.** deductive   **9.** inductive   **11.** inductive
13. Answers will vary.   **15.** 21   **17.** 3072   **19.** 63   **21.** $\frac{11}{12}$ **23.** 216
25. 52   **27.** 5   **29.** One such list is 10, 20, 30, 40, 50, ...   **31.** $(98{,}765 \times 9) + 3 = 888{,}888$
33. $3367 \times 15 = 50{,}505$ **35.** $33{,}334 \times 33{,}334 = 1{,}111{,}155{,}556$ **37.** $3 + 6 + 9 + 12 + 15 = \frac{15(6)}{2}$
39. $5(6) + 5(36) + 5(216) + 5(1296) + 5(7776) = 6(7776 - 1)$ **41.** $\frac{1}{2} + \frac{1}{4} + \frac{1}{8} + \frac{1}{16} + \frac{1}{32} = 1 - \frac{1}{32}$
43. 20,100   **45.** 320,400   **47.** 15,400   **49.** 2550   **51.**

53. 1 (These are the numbers of chimes a clock rings, starting with 12 o'clock, if it rings the number of hours on the hour, and 1 chime on the half-hour.)   **55. (a)** The middle digit is always 9, and the sum of the first and third digits is always 9 (considering 0 as the first digit if the difference has only two digits).   **(b)** Answers will vary.   **57.** 142,857; 285,714; 428,571; 571,428; 714,285; 857,142. Each result consists of the same six digits, but in a different order. $142{,}857 \times 7 = 999{,}999$ **59.** 21   **61.** Answers will vary.

1.2 Exercises   (Pages 17–19)

1. 79   **3.** 450   **5.** 4032   **7.** 32,758   **9.** 57; 99   **11.** $(4321 \times 9) - 1 = 38{,}888$ **13.** $999{,}999 \times 4 = 3{,}999{,}996$ **15.** $21^2 - 15^2 = 6^3$ **17.** $5^2 - 4^2 = 5 + 4$ **19.** $1 + 5 + 9 + 13 = 4 \times 7$ **21.** 45,150
23. 228,150   **25.** 2601   **27.** 250,000   **29.** $S = n(n + 1)$ **31.** Answers will vary.   **33.** row 1: 28, 36; row 2: 36, 49, 64;   row 3: 35, 51, 70, 92;   row 4: 28, 45, 66, 91, 120;   row 5: 18, 34, 55, 81, 112, 148;   row 6: 8, 21, 40, 65, 96, 133, 176   **35.** $8(1) + 1 = 9 = 3^2$; $8(3) + 1 = 25 = 5^2$; $8(6) + 1 = 49 = 7^2$; $8(10) + 1 = 81 = 9^2$
37. The pattern is 1, 0, 1, 0, 1, 0, ...   **39.**

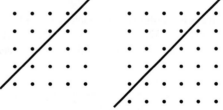

41. (a) a triangular number   **(b)** a triangular number   **43.** 256   **45.** 117   **47.** 235   **49.** $N_n = \frac{n(7n - 5)}{2}$
51. a square number   **53.** a perfect cube

1.3 Exercises   (Pages 27–33)

1. 42   **3.** 6   **5.** If you multiply the two digits in the numbers in the first row, you will get the second row of numbers. The second row of numbers is a pattern of two numbers (8 and 24) repeating.   **7.** I put the ring in the box and put my lock on the box. I send you the box. You put your lock on, as well, and send it back to me. I then remove my lock with my key and send the box (with your lock still on) back to you, so you can remove your lock with your key and get the ring.   **9.** 59   **11.** You should choose a sock from the box labeled *red and green socks*. Because it is mislabeled, it contains only red socks or only green socks, determined by the

sock you choose. If the sock is green, relabel this box *green socks*. Since the other two boxes were mislabeled, switch the remaining label to the other box and place the label that says *red and green socks* on the unlabeled box. No other choice guarantees a correct relabeling because you can remove only one sock.
13. D   **15.** A

17. One example of a solution follows:

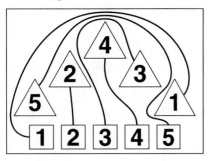

19. | 9 | 7 | 2 | 14 | 11 | 5 | 4 | 12 | 13 | 3 | 6 | 10 | 15 | 1 | 8 |

(or the same arrangement reading right to left)

21. Here is one solution.

23. D   **25.** $\frac{1}{3}$

27. One possible sequence is shown here. The numbers represent the number of gallons in each bucket in each successive step.

Big	7	4	4	1	1	0	7	5	5
Small	0	3	0	3	0	1	1	3	0

29. 90   **31.** 55 miles per hour   **33.** 07

35. A kilogram of $10 gold pieces is worth twice as much as half a kilogram of $20 gold pieces. (The denomination has nothing to do with the answer!)   **37.** 3   **39.** 5   **41.** 3 socks   **43.** 35   **45.** 6
47. the nineteenth day   **49.** 1967   **51.** Eve has $5, and Adam has $7.

53.
$$\begin{array}{r} 4\ \ 0\ \ 2 \\ \times \quad\ \ 3\ \ 9 \\ \hline 1\ \ 5,\ 6\ \ 7\ \ 8 \end{array}$$

55.

6	12	7	9
1	15	4	14
11	5	10	8
16	2	13	3

57. 25 pitches (The visiting team's pitcher retires 24 consecutive batters through the first eight innings, using only one pitch per batter. His team does not score either. Going into the bottom of the ninth tied 0–0, the first batter for the home team hits his first pitch for a home run. The pitcher threw 25 pitches and loses the game by a score of 1–0.)

59. Q   **61.** Here is one solution.   **63.** 8   **65.** The CEO is a woman.

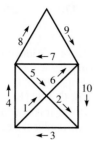

67. Dan (36) is married to Jessica (29); James (30) is married to Cathy (31).   **69.** 12; All months have 28 days.
71. The products always differ by 1.   **73.** 6

One of several
possibilities

1.4 Exercises   (Pages 38–41)

1. 43.8   **3.** 2.3589   **5.** 7.48   **7.** 7.1289   **9.** 6340.338097   **11.** 1   **13.** 1.061858759
15. 2.221441469   **17.** 3.141592653   **19.** .7782717162   **21.** yes   **23.** positive   **25.** 1   **27.** the same as
29. 0   **31.** positive   **33.** Answers will vary.   **35.** Answers will vary.   **37.** ShELLOIL   **39.** BOSE
41. Answers will vary.   **43.** 63   **45.** 14   **47.** B   **49.** A   **51.** D   **53.** 5%   **55.** 260,000
57. 1998; 2000   **59.** $250 billion; $300 billion   **61.** from 2004 to 2005   **63.** They are approximately the same.

Chapter 1 Test   (Pages 48–49)

1. inductive   **2.** deductive   **3.** 256, 3125   (The nth term in the sequence is n^n.)   **4.** 65,359,477,124,183 × 68 =
4,444,444,444,444,444   **5.** 351   **6.** 31,375   **7.** 65; 65 = 1 + 7 + 13 + 19 + 25   **8.** 1, 8, 21, 40, 65, 96,
133, 176; The pattern is 1, 0, 1, 0, 1, 0, 1, 0, ...   **9.** The first two terms are both 1. Each term after the second is found
by adding the two previous terms.   **10.** $\frac{1}{4}$ **11.** 9   **12.** 35   **13.** 629 + 154 = 783 is one of several solutions.
14. 8, 53, and 54   **15.** 3   **16.** The sum of the digits is always 9.   **17.** 9.907572861 (Answers may vary due to
the model of calculator used.)   **18.** 34.328125   **19.** B   **20. (a)** 1990–2000   **(b)** 1990   **(c)** 1980

CHAPTER 2   The Basic Concepts of Set Theory
2.1 Exercises   (Pages 56–58)

1. C   **3.** E   **5.** B   **7.** H   **9.** {1, 2, 3, 4, 5, 6}   **11.** {0, 1, 2, 3, 4}   **13.** {6, 7, 8, 9, 10, 11, 12, 13, 14}
15. {−15, −13, −11, −9, −7, −5, −3, −1}   **17.** {2, 4, 8, 16, 32, 64, 128, 256}   **19.** {0, 2, 4, 6, 8, 10}
21. {21, 22, 23, . . .}   **23.** {Lake Erie, Lake Huron, Lake Michigan, Lake Ontario, Lake Superior}   **25.** {5, 10,
15, 20, 25, . . .}   **27.** $\left\{1, \frac{1}{2}, \frac{1}{3}, \frac{1}{4}, \frac{1}{5}, \dots\right\}$ **In Exercises 29 and 31, there are other ways to describe the sets.**
29. $\{x \mid x \text{ is a rational number}\}$ **31.** $\{x \mid x \text{ is an odd natural number less than 76}\}$ **33.** finite   **35.** infinite
37. infinite   **39.** infinite   **41.** 8   **43.** 500   **45.** 26   **47.** 39   **49.** 28   **51.** Answers will vary.
53. well defined   **55.** not well defined   **57.** not well defined   **59.** ∈   **61.** ∉   **63.** ∈   **65.** ∉
67. ∈   **69.** false   **71.** true   **73.** true   **75.** true   **77.** false   **79.** true   **81.** true   **83.** true
85. false   **87.** true   **89.** Answers will vary.   **91.** {2} and {3, 4} (Other examples are possible.)   **93.** {a, b}
and {a, c} (Other examples are possible.)   **95. (a)** {LU, NT, PFE, GE}   **(b)** {GE, MOT, TWX, C, TXN, EMC, AWE}

2.2 Exercises (Pages 63–65)

1. F **3.** C **5.** A **7.** ⊄ **9.** ⊆ **11.** ⊆ **13.** ⊄ **15.** both **17.** ⊆ **19.** both
21. neither **23.** true **25.** false **27.** true **29.** true **31.** true **33.** true **35.** false **37.** false
39. true **41.** false **43. (a)** 8 **(b)** 7 **45. (a)** 64 **(b)** 63 **47. (a)** 32 **(b)** 31 **49.** {2, 3, 5, 7, 9, 10}
51. {2} **53.** {1, 2, 3, 4, 5, 6, 7, 8, 9, 10} or U **55.** {Higher cost, Lower cost, Educational, More time to see the sights, Less time to see the sights, Cannot visit relatives along the way, Can visit relatives along the way} **57.** {Higher cost, More time to see the sights, Cannot visit relatives along the way} **59.** ∅ **61.** {A, B, C, D, E} (All are present.) **63.** {A, B, C}, {A, B, D}, {A, B, E}, {A, C, D}, {A, C, E}, {A, D, E}, {B, C, D}, {B, C, E}, {B, D, E}, {C, D, E} **65.** {A}, {B}, {C}, {D}, {E} **67.** 32 **69. (a)** 15 **(b)** 16; It is now possible to select *no* bills. **71. (a)** s **(b)** s **(c)** $2s$ **(d)** Adding one more element will always double the number of subsets, so the expression 2^n is true in general.

2.3 Exercises (Pages 75–79)

1. B **3.** A **5.** E **7.** {a, c} **9.** {a, b, c, d, e, f} **11.** {a, b, c, d, e, f, g} **13.** {b, d, f} **15.** {d, f}
17. {a, b, c, e, g} **19.** {a, c, e, g} **21.** {a} **23.** {e, g} **25.** {e, g} **27.** {d, f} **29.** {e, b, g}
In Exercises 31–35, there may be other acceptable descriptions. **31.** the set of all elements that either are in A, or are not in B and not in C **33.** the set of all elements that are in C but not in B, or are in A **35.** the set of all elements that are in A but not in C, or in B but not in C **37.** {e, h, c, l, b} **39.** {l, b} **41.** {e, h, c, l, b} **43.** the set of all tax returns showing business income or filed in 2005 **45.** the set of all tax returns filed in 2005 without itemized deductions **47.** the set of all tax returns with itemized deductions or showing business income, but not selected for audit **49.** always true **51.** always true **53.** not always true **55. (a)** {1, 3, 5, 2} **(b)** {1, 2, 3, 5} **(c)** For any sets X and Y, $X \cup Y = Y \cup X$. **57. (a)** {1, 3, 5, 2, 4} **(b)** {1, 3, 5, 2, 4} **(c)** For any sets X, Y, and Z, $X \cup (Y \cup Z) = (X \cup Y) \cup Z$. **59. (a)** {4} **(b)** {4} **(c)** For any sets X and Y, $(X \cup Y)' = X' \cap Y'$. **61.** $X \cup \emptyset = X$; For any set X, $X \cup \emptyset = X$. **63.** true **65.** false **67.** true **69.** true **71.** $A \times B = \{(2, 4), (2, 9), (8, 4), (8, 9), (12, 4), (12, 9)\}$; $B \times A = \{(4, 2), (4, 8), (4, 12), (9, 2), (9, 8), (9, 12)\}$ **73.** $A \times B = \{(d, p), (d, i), (d, g), (o, p), (o, i), (o, g), (g, p), (g, i), (g, g)\}$; $B \times A = \{(p, d), (p, o), (p, g), (i, d), (i, o), (i, g), (g, d), (g, o), (g, g)\}$ **75.** $n(A \times B) = 6$; $n(B \times A) = 6$ **77.** $n(A \times B) = 210$; $n(B \times A) = 210$ **79.** 6

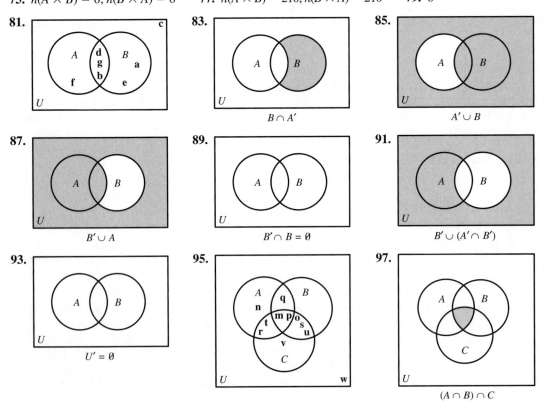

99.

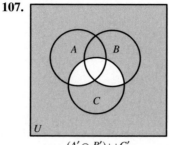

$(A \cap B) \cup C'$

101.

$(A' \cap B') \cap C$

103.

$(A \cap B') \cup C$

105.

$(A \cap B') \cap C'$

107.

$(A' \cap B') \cup C'$

109. $A' \cap B'$ or $(A \cup B)'$ **111.** $(A \cup B) \cap (A \cap B)'$ or $(A \cup B) - (A \cap B)$ **113.** $(A \cap B) \cup (A \cap C)$ or $A \cap (B \cup C)$ **115.** $(A \cap B) \cap C'$ or $(A \cap B) - C$ **117.** $A \cap B = \emptyset$ **119.** This statement is true for any set A. **121.** $A = \emptyset$ **123.** $A = \emptyset$ **125.** $A = \emptyset$ **127.** $B \subseteq A$ **129.** always true **131.** always true **133.** not always true **135.** always true **137.** no

2.4 Exercises (Pages 82–86)

1. (a) 6 **(b)** 8 **(c)** 0 **(d)** 2 **(e)** 9 **3. (a)** 1 **(b)** 3 **(c)** 4 **(d)** 0 **(e)** 2 **(f)** 10 **(g)** 2 **(h)** 5 **5.** 17 **7.** 2 **9.** 35

11.

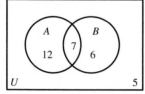

13.

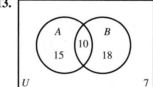

15.

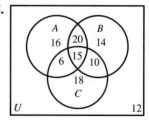

17.

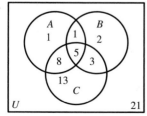

19. (a) 3 **(b)** 5 **21. (a)** 18 **(b)** 15 **(c)** 20 **(d)** 5 **23.** Yes, he should be reassigned to the job in Siberia. His figures add up to 142 people.

25. (a) 37 **(b)** 22 **(c)** 50 **(d)** 11 **(e)** 25 **(f)** 11 **27. (a)** 31 **(b)** 24 **(c)** 11 **(d)** 45 **29. (a)** 1 **(b)** 1, 2, 3, 4, 5, 6, 7, 8, 9, 10, 11, 12, 13, 14, 15 **(c)** 1, 2, 3, 4, 5, 9, 11 **(d)** 5, 8, 13 **31. (a)** 9 **(b)** 9 **(c)** 20 **(d)** 20 **(e)** 27 **(f)** 15 **33.** Answers will vary.

2.5 Exercises   (Pages 92–94)

1. B; 1   **3.** A; $\aleph_0$ **5.** F; 0
7. (Other correspondences are possible.)   **9.** (Other correspondences are possible.)

$$\{I, \quad II, \quad III\}$$
$$\updownarrow \quad \updownarrow \quad \updownarrow$$
$$\{x, \quad y, \quad z\}$$

$$\{a, \quad d, \quad i, \quad t, \quad o, \quad n\}$$
$$\updownarrow \quad \updownarrow \quad \updownarrow \quad \updownarrow \quad \updownarrow \quad \updownarrow$$
$$\{a, \quad n, \quad s, \quad w, \quad e, \quad r\}$$

11. 11   **13.** 0   **15.** $\aleph_0$ **17.** $\aleph_0$ **19.** $\aleph_0$ **21.** 12   **23.** $\aleph_0$ **25.** both   **27.** equivalent   **29.** equivalent

31. $\{2, \quad 4, \quad 6, \quad 8, \quad \ldots, \quad 2n, \quad \ldots\}$
$\quad\;\; \updownarrow \quad \updownarrow \quad \updownarrow \quad \updownarrow \qquad\;\;\; \updownarrow$
$\quad\;\; \{1, \quad 2, \quad 3, \quad 4, \quad \ldots, \quad n, \quad \ldots\}$

33. $\{1{,}000{,}000, \quad 2{,}000{,}000, \quad 3{,}000{,}000, \quad \ldots, \quad 1{,}000{,}000n, \quad \ldots\}$
$\qquad\quad \updownarrow \qquad\qquad\;\; \updownarrow \qquad\qquad\;\; \updownarrow \qquad\qquad\qquad \updownarrow$
$\quad\;\; \{ \quad 1, \qquad\qquad 2, \qquad\qquad 3, \qquad \ldots, \qquad n, \qquad \ldots\}$

35. $\{2, \quad 4, \quad 8, \quad 16, \quad 32, \quad \ldots, \quad 2^n, \quad \ldots\}$
$\quad\;\; \updownarrow \quad \updownarrow \quad \updownarrow \quad \updownarrow \quad \updownarrow \qquad\;\; \updownarrow$
$\quad\;\; \{1, \quad 2, \quad 3, \quad 4, \quad 5, \quad \ldots, \quad n, \quad \ldots\}$

37. This statement is not always true. For example, let A = the set of counting numbers, B = the set of real numbers.
39. This statement is not always true. For example, A could be the set of all subsets of the set of reals. Then $n(A)$ would be an infinite number *greater* than c.   **41. (a)** Rays emanating from point P will establish a geometric pairing of the points on the semicircle with the points on the line.

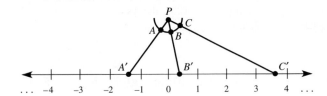

(b) The set of real numbers is infinite, having been placed in a one-to-one correspondence with a proper subset of itself.

43. $\{3, \quad 6, \quad 9, \quad 12, \quad \ldots, \quad 3n, \quad \ldots\}$
$\quad\;\; \updownarrow \quad \updownarrow \quad \updownarrow \quad \updownarrow \qquad\quad \updownarrow$
$\quad\;\; \{6, \quad 9, \quad 12, \quad 15, \quad \ldots, \quad 3n + 3, \quad \ldots\}$

45. $\left\{\dfrac{3}{4}, \quad \dfrac{3}{8}, \quad \dfrac{3}{12}, \quad \dfrac{3}{16}, \quad \ldots, \quad \dfrac{3}{4n}, \quad \ldots\right\}$
$\qquad\; \updownarrow \quad\; \updownarrow \quad\;\; \updownarrow \quad\;\; \updownarrow \qquad\qquad \updownarrow$
$\left\{\dfrac{3}{8}, \quad \dfrac{3}{12}, \quad \dfrac{3}{16}, \quad \dfrac{3}{20}, \quad \ldots, \quad \dfrac{3}{4n + 4}, \quad \ldots\right\}$

47. $\left\{\dfrac{1}{9}, \quad \dfrac{1}{18}, \quad \dfrac{1}{27}, \quad \ldots, \quad \dfrac{1}{9n}, \quad \ldots\right\}$
$\qquad \updownarrow \quad\;\; \updownarrow \quad\;\; \updownarrow \qquad\qquad \updownarrow$
$\left\{\dfrac{1}{18}, \quad \dfrac{1}{27}, \quad \dfrac{1}{36}, \quad \ldots, \quad \dfrac{1}{9n + 9}, \quad \ldots\right\}$

49. Answers will vary.   **51.** Answers will vary.

Chapter 2 Test   (Pages 95–96)

1. $\{a, b, c, d, e\}$ **2.** $\{a, b, d\}$ **3.** $\{c, f, g, h\}$ **4.** $\{a, c\}$ **5.** true   **6.** false   **7.** true   **8.** true
9. false   **10.** true   **11.** true   **12.** true   **13.** 8   **14.** 15   **Answers may vary for Exercises 15–18.**
15. the set of odd integers between -4 and 10   **16.** the set of months of the year   **17.** $\{x \mid x \text{ is a negative integer}\}$
18. $\{x \mid x \text{ is a multiple of 8 between 20 and 90}\}$ **19.** $\subseteq$ **20.** neither

21.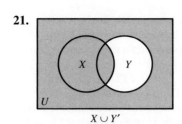
$X \cup Y'$

22.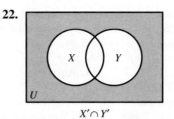
$X' \cap Y'$

23.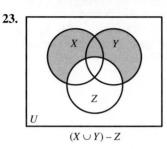
$(X \cup Y) - Z$

24.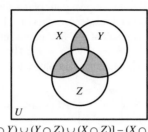
$[(X \cap Y) \cup (Y \cap Z) \cup (X \cap Z)] - (X \cap Y \cap Z)$

25. {Electric razor}   **26.** {Adding machine, Barometer, Pendulum clock, Thermometer}   **27.** {Electric razor}
28. Answers will vary.   **29. (a)** 22   **(b)** 12   **(c)** 28   **30. (a)** 16   **(b)** 32   **(c)** 33   **(d)** 45   **(e)** 14   **(f)** 26

CHAPTER 3   Introduction to Logic

3.1 Exercises   (Pages 103–104)

1. statement   **3.** not a statement   **5.** statement   **7.** statement   **9.** statement   **11.** not a statement
13. statement   **15.** compound   **17.** not compound   **19.** not compound   **21.** compound   **23.** Her
aunt's name is not Hildegard.   **25.** At least one dog does not have its day.   **27.** No book is longer than this
book.   **29.** At least one computer repairman can play poker.   **31.** Someone does not love somebody sometime.
33. $x \le 12$ **35.** $x < 5$ **37.** Answers will vary.   **39.** She does not have green eyes.   **41.** She has green
eyes and he is 56 years old.   **43.** She does not have green eyes or he is 56 years old.   **45.** She does not have
green eyes or he is not 56 years old.   **47.** It is not the case that she does not have green eyes and he is 56 years
old.   **49.** $p \wedge \sim q$ **51.** $\sim p \vee q$ **53.** $\sim (p \vee q)$ or, equivalently, $\sim p \wedge \sim q$ **55.** Answers will vary.
57. C   **59.** A, B   **61.** A, C   **63.** B   **65.** true   **67.** true   **69.** true   **71.** true   **73.** false
75. Answers will vary.   **77.** Everyone here has done that at one time or another.

3.2 Exercises   (Pages 115–117)

1. false   **3.** true   **5.** They must both be false.   **7.** T   **9.** T   **11.** F   **13.** T   **15.** T   **17.** T
19. It is a disjunction, because it means "5 > 2 or 5 = 2."   **21.** T   **23.** F   **25.** T   **27.** T   **29.** F
31. F   **33.** T   **35.** T   **37.** T   **39.** 4   **41.** 16   **43.** 128   **45.** seven   **47.** FFTF   **49.** FTTT
51. TTTT   **53.** FFFT   **55.** TFFF   **57.** FFFFTFFF   **59.** FTFTTTTT   **61.** TTTTTTTTTTTTFTTT
63. You can't pay me now and you can't pay me later.   **65.** It is not summer or there is snow.   **67.** I did not say
yes or she did not say no.   **69.** $5 - 1 \ne 4$ or $9 + 12 = 7$ **71.** Neither Dasher nor Blitzen will lead Santa's sleigh
next Christmas.   **73.** T   **75.** T   **77.**

p	q	$p \vee q$
T	T	F
T	F	T
F	T	T
F	F	F

79. F   **81.** T

3.3 Exercises   (Pages 124–127)

1. If you see it on the Internet, then you can believe it.   **3.** If the person is Garrett Olinde, then his area code is 225.
5. If the soldier is a marine, then the soldier loves boot camp.   **7.** If it is a koala, then it does not live in Iowa.

9. If it is an opium-eater, then it has no self-command. **11.** true **13.** true **15.** true **17.** false
19. Answers will vary. **21.** F **23.** T **25.** T **27.** If they do not raise alpacas, then he trains dogs.
29. If she has a ferret for a pet, then they raise alpacas and he trains dogs. **31.** If he does not train dogs, then they do not raise alpacas or she has a ferret for a pet. **33.** $b \rightarrow p$ **35.** $p \rightarrow {\sim}r$ **37.** $p \wedge (r \rightarrow {\sim}b)$ **39.** $p \rightarrow r$
41. T **43.** F **45.** T **47.** F **49.** T **51.** T **53.** Answers will vary. **55.** TTTF **57.** TTFT
59. TTTT; tautology **61.** TFTF **63.** TTTTTTFT **65.** TTTFTTTTTTTTTTTT **67.** one
69. That is an authentic Persian rug and I am not surprised. **71.** The English measures are not converted to metric measures and the spacecraft does not crash on the surface of Saturn. **73.** You want to be happy for the rest of your life and you make a pretty woman your wife. **75.** You do not give your plants tender, loving care or they flourish.
77. She does or he will. **79.** The person is not a resident of Oregon City or is a resident of Oregon. **81.** equivalent
83. equivalent **85.** equivalent **87.** not equivalent **89.** equivalent **91.** $(p \wedge q) \vee (p \wedge {\sim}q)$; The statement simplifies to p. **93.** $p \vee ({\sim}q \wedge r)$ **95.** ${\sim}p \vee (p \vee q)$; The statement simplifies to T.
97. The statement simplifies to $p \wedge q$. **99.** The statement simplifies to F.

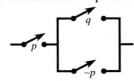

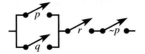

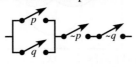

101. The statement simplifies to $(r \wedge {\sim}p) \wedge q$. **103.** The statement simplifies to $p \vee q$.

3.4 Exercises (Pages 132–134)

1. (a) If you were an hour, then beauty would be a minute. **(b)** If beauty were not a minute, then you would not be an hour. **(c)** If you were not an hour, then beauty would not be a minute. **3. (a)** If you don't fix it, then it ain't broke. **(b)** If it's broke, then fix it. **(c)** If you fix it, then it's broke. **5. (a)** If it is dangerous to your health, then you walk in front of a moving car. **(b)** If you do not walk in front of a moving car, then it is not dangerous to your health. **(c)** If it is not dangerous to your health, then you do not walk in front of a moving car. **7. (a)** If they flock together, then they are birds of a feather. **(b)** If they are not birds of a feather, then they do not flock together. **(c)** If they do not flock together, then they are not birds of a feather. **9. (a)** If he comes, then you built it. **(b)** If you don't build it, then he won't come. **(c)** If he doesn't come, then you didn't build it. **11. (a)** ${\sim}q \rightarrow p$ **(b)** ${\sim}p \rightarrow q$ **(c)** $q \rightarrow {\sim}p$
13. (a) ${\sim}q \rightarrow {\sim}p$ **(b)** $p \rightarrow q$ **(c)** $q \rightarrow p$ **15. (a)** $(q \vee r) \rightarrow p$ **(b)** ${\sim}p \rightarrow ({\sim}q \wedge {\sim}r)$ **(c)** $({\sim}q \wedge {\sim}r) \rightarrow {\sim}p$
17. Answers will vary. **19.** If it is muddy, then I'll wear my galoshes. **21.** If 18 is positive, then $18 + 1$ is positive. **23.** If a number is an integer, then it is a rational number. **25.** If I do crossword puzzles, then I am driven crazy. **27.** If Gerald Guidroz is to shave, then he must have a day's growth of beard. **29.** If I go from Park Place to Baltic Avenue, then I pass GO. **31.** If a number is a whole number, then it is an integer. **33.** If their pitching improves, then the Orioles will win the pennant. **35.** If the figure is a rectangle, then it is a parallelogram with a right angle. **37.** If a triangle has two sides of the same length, then it is isosceles. **39.** If a two-digit number whose units digit is 5 is squared, then it will end in 25. **41.** D **43.** Answers will vary. **45.** true **47.** false
49. false **51.** contrary **53.** consistent **55.** contrary **57.** Answers will vary. One example is: That man is Carter Fenton. That man sells books.

3.5 Exercises (Pages 137–138)

1. valid **3.** invalid **5.** valid **7.** invalid **9.** invalid **11.** invalid **13.** yes
15. All people with blue eyes have blond hair. **17.** invalid **19.** valid **21.** invalid **23.** valid **25.** invalid
Dinya Norris does not have blond hair.
_____
Dinya Norris does not have blue eyes.
27. invalid **29.** valid **31.** Answers will vary.

Extension Exercises (Pages 141–144)

1. First, Piotr Knightovich, Yorki; Second, Ivan Rookov, Porki; Third, Boris Bishopnik, Gorki; Fourth, Yuri Pawnchev, Corki. **3.** Ben Ashby, Jane Kenny, Dirk and Daisy, American; Hans Gruber, Sue Rogers, Merlyns, English; Peter Owen, Carol Dodds, Starr Twins, own composition; Steven Thorp, Nancy O'Hara, Rose and Thorn, Irish.

5.
7	2	6	4	9	1	5	3	8
9	4	5	8	6	3	2	1	7
8	1	3	7	5	2	4	9	6
6	8	1	3	2	4	7	5	9
2	9	7	6	1	5	3	8	4
3	5	4	9	8	7	1	6	2
4	7	9	1	3	8	6	2	5
5	3	8	2	4	6	9	7	1
1	6	2	5	7	9	8	4	3

7.
2	7	5	3	8	4	6	1	9
8	3	6	5	9	1	4	2	7
4	1	9	7	6	2	8	3	5
3	4	7	2	5	8	1	9	6
6	2	8	1	4	9	7	5	3
5	9	1	6	7	3	2	4	8
9	5	4	8	1	6	3	7	2
7	8	2	4	3	5	9	6	1
1	6	3	9	2	7	5	8	4

9.
1	8	2	5	7	9	3	4	6
5	3	4	8	1	6	2	9	7
7	6	9	2	3	4	8	1	5
4	1	8	7	9	2	6	5	3
3	7	6	1	8	5	4	2	9
2	9	5	4	6	3	7	8	1
9	2	1	3	4	7	5	6	8
8	5	7	6	2	1	9	3	4
6	4	3	9	5	8	1	7	2

11.
9	8	3	2	4	5	7	1	6
2	6	1	3	9	7	8	4	5
7	5	4	8	6	1	9	3	2
1	7	6	4	5	3	2	9	8
4	9	5	7	2	8	3	6	1
3	2	8	6	1	9	4	5	7
5	4	7	9	8	6	1	2	3
8	1	2	5	3	4	6	7	9
6	3	9	1	7	2	5	8	4

3.6 Exercises (Pages 151–154)

1. valid by reasoning by transitivity **3.** valid by modus ponens **5.** fallacy by fallacy of the converse **7.** valid by modus tollens **9.** fallacy by fallacy of the inverse **11.** valid by disjunctive syllogism **13.** invalid **15.** valid **17.** invalid **19.** valid **21.** invalid **23.** invalid **25.** Every time something squeaks, I use WD-40.

Every time I use WD-40, I go to the hardware store.
_____

Every time something squeaks, I go to the hardware store. **27.** valid

29. invalid **31.** invalid **33.** valid **35.** valid **37.** If tell you the time, then my life will be miserable. **39.** If it is my poultry, then it is a duck. **41.** If it is a guinea pig, then it is hopelessly ignorant of music. **43.** If it is a teachable kitten, then it does not have green eyes. **45.** If I can read it, then I have not filed it. **47. (a)** $p \rightarrow \sim s$ **(b)** $r \rightarrow s$ **(c)** $q \rightarrow p$ **(d)** None of my poultry are officers. **49. (a)** $r \rightarrow \sim s$ **(b)** $u \rightarrow t$ **(c)** $\sim r \rightarrow p$ **(d)** $\sim u \rightarrow \sim q$ **(e)** $t \rightarrow s$ **(f)** All pawnbrokers are honest. **51. (a)** $r \rightarrow w$ **(b)** $\sim u \rightarrow \sim t$ **(c)** $v \rightarrow \sim s$ **(d)** $x \rightarrow r$ **(e)** $\sim q \rightarrow t$ **(f)** $y \rightarrow p$ **(g)** $w \rightarrow s$ **(h)** $\sim x \rightarrow \sim q$ **(i)** $p \rightarrow \sim u$ **(j)** I can't read any of Brown's letters.

Collaborative Investigation (Page 155)

1. 1, *Death in Beijing*, John Gunn, red; 2, *A Killer Abroad*, Mary Hemlock, brown; 3, *Murder in the Sun*, Geoffrey Stringer, green; 4, *The Final Case*, Sandra Bludgeon, blue; 5, *Mayhem in Madagascar*, Dahlia Dagger, yellow; 6, *Lurking in the Shadows*, Philip G Rott, black.

Chapter 3 Test (Pages 156–157)

1. $6 - 3 \neq 3$ **2.** Some men are not created equal. **3.** No members of the class went on the field trip. **4.** That's the way you feel and I won't accept it. **5.** She did not apply or did not get a FEMA trailer. **6.** $\sim p \rightarrow q$ **7.** $p \rightarrow q$ **8.** $\sim q \leftrightarrow \sim p$ **9.** You won't love me and I will love you. **10.** It is not the case that you will love me or I will not love you. (Equivalently: You won't love me and I will love you.) **11.** T **12.** T **13.** T **14.** F **15.** Answers will vary. **16. (a)** The antecedent must be true and the consequent must be false. **(b)** Both component statements must be true. **(c)** Both component statements must be false. **17.** TFFF **18.** TTTT (tautology) **19.** false **20.** true

Wording may vary in the answers for Exercises 21–25. **21.** If the number is an integer, then it is a rational number.
22. If a polygon is a rhombus, then it is a quadrilateral. **23.** If a number is divisible by 9, then it is divisible by 3.
24. If she digs dinosaur bones, then she is a paleontologist. **25. (a)** If the graph helps me understand it, then a picture
paints a thousand words. **(b)** If a picture doesn't paint a thousand words, then the graph won't help me understand it.
(c) If the graph doesn't help me understand it, then a picture doesn't paint a thousand words. **26. (a)** $(q \wedge r) \to \sim p$
(b) $p \to (\sim q \vee \sim r)$ **(c)** $(\sim q \vee \sim r) \to p$ **27.** valid **28. (a)** A **(b)** F **(c)** C **(d)** D **29.** valid
30. invalid

CHAPTER 4 Numeration and Mathematical Systems

4.1 Exercises (Pages 166–168)

1. 13,036 **3.** 7,630,729 **5.** **7.**

9. **11.** **13.** **15.** 935

17. 3007 **19.** **21.** **23.** to **25.** to **27.** 216 **29.** 53,601 **31.** 113

33. 7598 **35.** 1378 **37.** 5974 **39.** 622,500 shekels **41.** Answers will vary. **43.** Answers will vary.
45. 99,999 **47.** 3124 **49.** $10^d - 1$ **51.** $7^d - 1$ **53.** Answers will vary.

4.2 Exercises (Pages 177–178)

1. $(7 \cdot 10^1) + (3 \cdot 10^0)$ **3.** $(3 \cdot 10^3) + (7 \cdot 10^2) + (7 \cdot 10^1) + (4 \cdot 10^0)$ **5.** $(4 \cdot 10^3) + (9 \cdot 10^2) + (2 \cdot 10^1)$
$+ (4 \cdot 10^0)$ **7.** $(1 \cdot 10^7) + (4 \cdot 10^6) + (2 \cdot 10^5) + (0 \cdot 10^4) + (6 \cdot 10^3) + (0 \cdot 10^2) + (4 \cdot 10^1) + (0 \cdot 10^0)$
9. 42 **11.** 6209 **13.** 70,401,009 **15.** 89 **17.** 32 **19.** 109 **21.** 733 **23.** 6 **25.** 206
27. 256 **29.** 63,259 **31.** **33.** **35.** 1885 **37.** 38,325

39. 3,035,154 **41.** 496 **43.** 217,204 **45.** 242 **47.** 49,801 **49.** 460 **51.** 32,798

4.3 Exercises (Pages 187–189)

1. 1, 2, 3, 4, 5, 6, 10, 11, 12, 13, 14, 15, 16, 20, 21, 22, 23, 24, 25, 26 **3.** 1, 2, 3, 4, 5, 6, 7, 8, 10, 11, 12, 13, 14, 15, 16,
17, 18, 20, 21, 22 **5.** 13_{five}; 20_{five} **7.** $\text{B6E}_{\text{sixteen}}$; $\text{B70}_{\text{sixteen}}$ **9.** 3 **11.** 11 **13.** least: $1000_{\text{three}} = 27$;
greatest: $2222_{\text{three}} = 80$ **15.** 14 **17.** 11 **19.** 956 **21.** 881 **23.** 28,854 **25.** 139 **27.** 5601
29. 321_{five} **31.** 10011_{two} **33.** 93_{sixteen} **35.** 2131101_{five} **37.** 1001001010_{two} **39.** 102112101_{three}
41. 111134_{six} **43.** 32_{seven} **45.** 1031321_{four} **47.** 11110111_{two} **49.** 467_{eight} **51.** 11011100_{two}
53. $2D_{\text{sixteen}}$ **55.** 37_{eight} **57.** 1427 **59.** 1000011_{two} **61.** 1101011_{two} **63.** HELP
65. $100111011001011110111_{\text{two}}$ **67.** Answers will vary. **69. (a)** The binary ones digit is 1. **(b)** The binary
twos digit is 1. **(c)** The binary fours digit is 1. **(d)** The binary eights digit is 1. **(e)** The binary sixteens digit is 1.
71. 6 **73.** yes **75.** yes **77.** yes **79.** yes **81.** Answers will vary. **83.** no **85.** yes
87. Answers will vary. **89.** 20120011_{three} **91.** 25657_{nine}

4.4 Exercises (Pages 199–203)

1. 5 **3.** 6 **5.** row 2: 0, 6, 10; row 3: 9, 0, 9; row 4: 0, 4, 0, 8, 0; row 5: 1, 9, 2, 7; row 6: 6, 0, 0; row 7: 4, 11, 6, 8, 3, 5; row 8: 8, 4, 0, 0; row 9: 6, 3, 9, 3, 9, 6, 3; row 10: 6, 4, 0, 10, 8, 6, 4; row 11: 10, 9, 8, 7, 6, 5, 4, 3, 2
7. yes **9.** row 1: 0; row 2: 0; row 3: 0, 1, 2 row 4: 0, 1, 2 **11.** yes **13.** yes (0 is its own inverse, 1 and 4 are inverses of each other, and 2 and 3 are inverses of each other.) **15.** yes **17.** yes (1 is the identity element.)
19. 3 **21.** 4 **23.** Answers will vary. **25.** 0700 **27.** 0000 **29.** false **31.** true **33.** 3 **35.** 3
37. 1 **39.** 10 **41.** Answers will vary. **43.** 5 **45.** 4 **47.** row 1: 0; row 2: 2, 3, 4, 5, 6, 0, 1; row 3: 3, 4, 5, 6, 0, 1, 2; row 4: 4, 5, 6, 0, 1, 2, 3; row 5: 5, 6, 0, 1, 2, 3, 4; row 6: 6, 0, 1, 2, 3, 4, 5 **49.** row 2: 1
51. row 2: 1, 3, 7; row 3: 3, 0; row 4: 3, 2, 1; row 5: 6, 7, 4; row 7: 3, 1, 6, 4; row 8: 6, 5, 2 **53.** {3, 10, 17, 24, 31, 38, . . . } **55.** {1, 2, 3, 4, 5, 6, . . . } **57.** 100,000 **59. (a)** 365 **(b)** Friday **61.** 62 **63.** Chicago: July 23 and 29; New Orleans: July 5 and August 16; San Francisco: August 9 **65.** Sunday **67.** Wednesday
69. June **71.** June **73.** yes **75.** 6 **77.** 2

4.5 Exercises (Pages 208–210)

1. all properties; 1 is the identity element; 1 is its own inverse, as is 2. **3.** closure, commutative, associative, and identity properties; 1 is the identity element; 2, 4, and 6 have no inverses. **5.** all properties except the inverse; 1 is the identity element; 5 has no inverse. **7.** all properties; F is the identity element; A and B are inverses; F is its own inverse.
9. all properties; t is the identity element; s and r are inverses; t and u are their own inverses. **11.** a **13.** a
15. row b: d; row c: d, b; row d: b, c **17.** associative, commutative, identity (U), closure **19.** Answers may vary. One possibility is shown.

	a	b	c	d
a	a	b	c	d
b	b	a	d	c
c	c	d	a	b
d	d	c	b	a

21. no **23. (a)** true **(b)** true **(c)** true **(d)** true

25. $a + b + c = 1$ or $a = 0$ **27. (a)** $a = 0$ **(b)** $a = 0$ **29.** Each side simplifies to e. **31.** Each side simplifies to d. **33.**

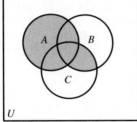

$A \cup (B \cap C) = (A \cup B) \cap (A \cup C)$

35. Both final columns read TTTTTFFF, when set up in the manner described in Chapter 3.

4.6 Exercises (Pages 216–218)

1. No operation is specified. **3.** yes **5.** no; closure, inverse **7.** yes **9.** no; inverse **11.** no; associative, identity, inverse **13.** no; inverse **15.** yes **17.** no; closure, identity, inverse **19.** Answers will vary.
21. S **23.** N **25.** Each side is equal to M. **27.** Each side is equal to Q. **29.** N **31.** R **33.** T
35. no **37.** yes **39.** Answers will vary. **41.** Answers will vary. **43.** row B: D; row C: D, B; row D: C, B
45. (a) yes **(b)** Answers will vary. **47. (a)** no **(b)** Answers will vary.

Chapter 4 Test (Pages 219–220)

1. ancient Egyptian; 2426 **2.** 7561 **3.** $(6 \cdot 10^4) + (0 \cdot 10^3) + (9 \cdot 10^2) + (2 \cdot 10^1) + (3 \cdot 10^0)$ **4.** 1998
5. 22,184 **6.** 12,827 **7.** 89 **8.** 50 **9.** 57,007 **10.** 110001_{two} **11.** 43210_{five} **12.** 256_{eight}
13. {2, 7, 12, 17, 22, 27, . . . } **14. (a)** 5 **(b)** 4 **(c)** 9 **(d)** 8 **15. (a)** 3 **(b)** 1 **16.** 48 **17.** There is less repetition of symbols. **18.** There are fewer symbols to learn. **19.** There are fewer digits in the numerals.
20. 0 **21.** $\frac{1}{3}$ **22.** commutative **23.** row 3: 1, 7; row 5: 7, 3; row 7: 5, 1 **24. (a)** yes **(b)** 1
25. (a) yes **(b)** Answers will vary. **26. (a)** yes **(b)** Answers will vary. **27. (a)** no **(b)** Answers will vary.
28. (a) yes **(b)** Answers will vary.

CHAPTER 5 Number Theory

5.1 Exercises (Pages 230–233)

1. true **3.** false **5.** false **7.** true **9.** false **11.** false **13.** 1, 2, 3, 4, 6, 12 **15.** 1, 2, 4, 5, 10, 20
17. 1, 2, 3, 4, 5, 6, 8, 10, 12, 15, 20, 24, 30, 40, 60, 120 **19. (a)** no **(b)** yes **(c)** no **(d)** yes **(e)** no **(f)** no
(g) yes **(h)** no **(i)** no **21. (a)** no **(b)** no **(c)** no **(d)** yes **(e)** no **(f)** no **(g)** no **(h)** no **(i)** no
23. (a) no **(b)** yes **(c)** no **(d)** no **(e)** no **(f)** no **(g)** yes **(h)** no **(i)** no **25. (a)** Answers will vary.
(b) 13 **(c)** square root; square root; square root **(d)** prime **27.** 2, 3; no **29.** It must be 0.
31.

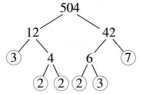

$504 = 3 \cdot 2^3 \cdot 3 \cdot 7$
$= 2^3 \cdot 3^2 \cdot 7$

33. $2^4 \cdot 3 \cdot 5$ **35.** $2^3 \cdot 3^2 \cdot 5$ **37.** $3 \cdot 13 \cdot 17$

39. yes **41.** no **43.** yes **45.** no **47.** The number must be divisible by both 3 and 5. That is, the sum of the
digits must be divisible by 3, and the last digit must be 5 or 0. **49.** $75 = 3 \cdot 25$, $75 = 5 \cdot 15$ **51.** 0, 2, 4, 6, 8
53. 0, 4, 8 **55.** 0, 6 **57.** 6 **59.** 10 **61.** 27 **63.** leap year **65.** leap year **67.** Answers will vary.
69. Answers will vary. **71.** $41^2 - 41 + 41 = 41^2$, and 41^2 is not a prime. **72. (a)** 1763 **(b)** 1847 **73.** B
75. (a) 65,537 **(b)** 251 **77.** Answers will vary. **79.** Answers will vary. **81.** composite: $30{,}031 = 59 \cdot 509$
83. 63 **85.** $2^p - 1$ **87.** 3 and 31

5.2 Exercises (Pages 238–240)

1. true **3.** true **5.** true **7.** false **9.** true **11.** The sum of the proper divisors is 496: $1 + 2 + 4 + 8 +$
$16 + 31 + 62 + 124 + 248 = 496$. **13.** 8191 is prime; 33,550,336 **15.** $1 + \frac{1}{2} + \frac{1}{3} + \frac{1}{6} = 2$ **17.** abundant
19. deficient **21.** 12, 18, 20, 24 **23.** $1 + 3 + 5 + 7 + 9 + 15 + 21 + 27 + 35 + 45 + 63 + 105 + 135 +$
$189 + 315 = 975$, and $975 > 945$, so 945 is abundant. **25.** $1 + 2 + 4 + 8 + 16 + 32 + 37 + 74 + 148 + 296 +$
$592 = 1210$ and $1 + 2 + 5 + 10 + 11 + 22 + 55 + 110 + 121 + 242 + 605 = 1184$ **27.** $3 + 11$ **29.** $3 + 23$
31. Let $a = 5$ and $b = 3$; $11 = 5 + 2 \cdot 3$ **33.** 71 and 73 **35.** 137 and 139 **37. (a)** $5 = 9 - 4 = 3^2 - 2^2$
(b) $11 = 36 - 25 = 6^2 - 5^2$ **39.** $5^2 + 2 = 27 = 3^3$ **41.** Answers will vary. **43.** No; for the first six,
the sequence is 6, 8, 6, 8, 6, 6. **45.** one; not happy **47.** both; happy **49.** Answers will vary. **51.** B
53. 7; yes **55.** 15; no **57.** 27; no **59.** 24; 23; 25; yes; no **61.** Answers will vary. **63.** B

5.3 Exercises (Pages 247–249)

1. true **3.** true **5.** false **7.** true **9.** true **11.** 10 **13.** 120 **15.** 7 **17.** 12 **19.** 10
21. 6 **23.** 12 **25.** 12 **27.** 70 **29.** Answers will vary. **31.** 120 **33.** 672 **35.** 840 **37.** 96
39. 225 **41.** 2160 **43.** 180 **45.** 1260 **47.** 1680 **49. (a)** $p^b q^c r^c$ **(b)** $p^a q^a r^b$ **51.** 30 **53.** 15
55. 12 **57. (a)** 6 **(b)** 36 **59. (a)** 18 **(b)** 216 **61.** p and q are relatively prime. **63.** Answers will vary.
65. 144th **67.** 48 **69.** $600; 25 books

Extension Exercises (Pages 256–257)

1. 3 **3.** 4 **5.** 5 **7.** 2 **9.** 2 **11.** 13 **13.** 12 **15.** 3 **17.** 55; 40 **19.** 65; 48 **21.** 5
23. 61 **25. (a)** 27 **(b)** 35 **27. (a)** 11 **(b)** 23 **29.** Answers will vary.

5.4 Exercises (Pages 262–265)

1. 2584 **3.** 46,368 **5.** $\frac{1 + \sqrt{5}}{2}$ **7.** $1 + 1 + 2 + 3 + 5 + 8 = 21 - 1$; Each expression is equal to 20.
9. $1 + 2 + 5 + 13 + 34 + 89 = 144$; Each expression is equal to 144. **11.** $13^2 - 5^2 = 144$; Each expression is equal
to 144. **13.** $1 - 2 + 5 - 13 + 34 - 89 = -8^2$; Each expression is equal to -64. **15.** (There are other ways to do
this.) **(a)** $37 = 34 + 3$ **(b)** $40 = 34 + 5 + 1$ **(c)** $52 = 34 + 13 + 5$ **17. (a)** The greatest common factor of 10
and 4 is 2, and the greatest common factor of $F_{10} = 55$ and $F_4 = 3$ is $F_2 = 1$. **(b)** The greatest common factor of 12 and 6
is 6, and the greatest common factor of $F_{12} = 144$ and $F_6 = 8$ is $F_6 = 8$. **(c)** The greatest common factor of 14 and 6 is 2,
and the greatest common factor of $F_{14} = 377$ and $F_6 = 8$ is $F_2 = 1$. **19. (a)** $5 \cdot 34 - 13^2 = 1$ **(b)** $13^2 - 3 \cdot 55 = 4$
(c) $2 \cdot 89 - 13^2 = 9$ **(d)** The difference will be 25, because we are obtaining the squares of the terms of the
Fibonacci sequence. $13^2 - 1 \cdot 144 = 25 = 5^2$. **21.** 199 **23.** Each sum is 2 less than a Lucas number.
25. (a) $8 \cdot 18 = 144$; Each expression is equal to 144. **(b)** $8 + 21 = 29$; Each expression is equal to 29.

(c) $8 + 18 = 2 \cdot 13$; Each expression is equal to 26. **27.** 3, 4, 5 **29.** 16, 30, 34 **31.** The sums are 1, 1, 2, 3, 5, 8, 13. They are terms of the Fibonacci sequence. **33.** $\dfrac{1 + \sqrt{5}}{2} \approx 1.618033989$ and $\dfrac{1 - \sqrt{5}}{2} \approx -.618033989$. After the decimal point, the digits are the same. **35.** 377 **37.** 17,711

Extension Exercises (Pages 267–269)

1.

2	7	6
9	5	1
4	3	8

3.

11	10	4	23	17
18	12	6	5	24
25	19	13	7	1
2	21	20	14	8
9	3	22	16	15

5.

15	16	22	3	9
8	14	20	21	2
1	7	13	19	25
24	5	6	12	18
17	23	4	10	11

7.

24	9	12
3	15	27
18	21	6

Magic sum is 45.

9.

$\frac{17}{2}$	12	$\frac{1}{2}$	4	$\frac{15}{2}$
$\frac{23}{2}$	$\frac{5}{2}$	$\frac{7}{2}$	7	8
2	3	$\frac{13}{2}$	10	11
5	6	$\frac{19}{2}$	$\frac{21}{2}$	$\frac{3}{2}$
$\frac{11}{2}$	9	$\frac{25}{2}$	1	$\frac{9}{2}$

Magic sum is $32\frac{1}{2}$.

11. 479 **13.** 467 **15.** 269 **17.** (a) 73 (b) 70 (c) 74 (d) 69
19. (a) 7 (b) 22 (c) 5 (d) 4 (e) 15 (f) 19 (g) 6 (h) 23

21.

30	39	48	1	10	19	28
38	47	7	9	18	27	29
46	6	8	17	26	35	37
5	14	16	25	34	36	45
13	15	24	33	42	44	4
21	23	32	41	43	3	12
22	31	40	49	2	11	20

23. Each sum is equal to 34. **25.** Each sum is equal to 68. **27.** Each sum is equal to 9248. **29.** Each sum is equal to 748. **31.**

16	2	3	13
5	11	10	8
9	7	6	12
4	14	15	1

The second and third columns are interchanged.

33.

18	20	10
8	16	24
22	12	14

35.

39	48	57	10	19	28	37
47	56	16	18	27	36	38
55	15	17	26	35	44	46
14	23	25	34	43	45	54
22	24	33	42	51	53	13
30	32	41	50	52	12	21
31	40	49	58	11	20	29

Magic sum is 238.

37. 260 **39.** $52 + 45 + 16 + 17 + 54 + 43 + 10 + 23 = 260$

41.

5	13	21	9	17
6	19	2	15	23
12	25	8	16	4
18	1	14	22	10
24	7	20	3	11

Chapter 5 Test (Pages 270–271)

1. false **2.** true **3.** true **4.** true **5.** true **6.** (a) yes (b) yes (c) no (d) yes (e) yes (f) no
(g) yes (h) yes (i) no **7.** (a) composite (b) neither (c) prime **8.** $2^5 \cdot 3^2 \cdot 5$ **9.** Answers will vary.
10. (a) deficient (b) perfect (c) abundant **11.** C **12.** 41 and 43 **13.** 90 **14.** 360

15. Monday **16.** 46,368 **17.** $89 - (8 + 13 + 21 + 34) = 13$; Each expression is equal to 13. **18.** B **19. (a)** 1, 5, 6, 11, 17, 28, 45, 73 **(b)** The process will yield 19 for any term chosen. **20.** A **21.** Answers will vary. **22.** Answers will vary.

CHAPTER 6 The Real Numbers and Their Representations

6.1 Exercises (Pages 280–283)

1. 4 **3.** 0 **5.** $\sqrt{12}$ (There are others.) **7.** true **9.** true **11. (a)** 3, 7 **(b)** 0, 3, 7 **(c)** $-9, 0, 3, 7$ **(d)** $-9, -1\frac{1}{4}, -\frac{3}{5}, 0, 3, 5.9, 7$ **(e)** $-\sqrt{7}, \sqrt{5}$ **(f)** All are real numbers. **13.** Answers will vary. **15.** 1450 **17.** 5436 **19.** $-220°$ **21.** 20; 10°; $-9°$ **23. (a)** Pacific Ocean, Indian Ocean, Caribbean Sea, South China Sea, Gulf of California **(b)** Point Success, Ranier, Matlalcueyetl, Steele, McKinley **(c)** true **(d)** false

25. [number line: $-6\ -4\ -2\ 0\ 2\ 4$] **27.** [number line: $-3\frac{4}{5}\ -1\frac{5}{8}\ \frac{1}{4}\ 2\frac{1}{2}$; $-4\ -2\ 0\ 2\ 4$] **29. (a)** A **(b)** A **(c)** B **(d)** B **31. (a)** 2 **(b)** 2

33. (a) -6 **(b)** 6 **35. (a)** -3 **(b)** 3 **37. (a)** 0 **(b)** 0 **39.** $a - b$ **41.** -12 **43.** -8 **45.** 3 **47.** $|-3|$ or 3 **49.** $-|-6|$ or -6 **51.** $|5 - 3|$ or 2 **53.** true **55.** true **57.** true **59.** false **61.** true **63.** false **65.** petroleum refineries, 2002 to 2003 **67.** construction machinery manufacturing, 2002 to 2003 **69.** computer/data processing services **Answers will vary in Exercises 71–75.** **71.** $\frac{1}{2}, \frac{5}{8}, 1\frac{3}{4}$ **73.** $-3\frac{1}{2}, -\frac{2}{3}, \frac{3}{7}$ **75.** $\sqrt{5}, \pi, -\sqrt{3}$

6.2 Exercises (Pages 292–296)

1. negative **3.** $-3; 5$ **5.** Answers will vary. **7.** -20 **9.** -4 **11.** -11 **13.** 9 **15.** 20 **17.** 4 **19.** 24 **21.** -1296 **23.** 6 **25.** -6 **27.** 0 **29.** -6 **31.** -4 **33.** 27 **35.** 39 **37.** -2 **39.** not a real number **41.** 13 **43.** A, B, C **45.** commutative property of addition **47.** associative property of addition **49.** inverse property of addition **51.** identity property of multiplication **53.** identity property of addition **55.** distributive property **57.** inverse property of addition **59.** closure property of multiplication **61. (c)** Yes; choose $a = b$. For example, $a = b = 2 : 2 - 2 = 2 - 2$. **63. (a)** messing up your room **(b)** spending money **(c)** decreasing the volume on your MP3 player **65.** identity **67.** No, it does not hold true. **69.** -81 **71.** 81 **73.** -81 **75.** -81 **77. (a)** -3.6 (billion dollars) **(b)** 7.8 (billion dollars) **(c)** 28.2 (billion dollars) **(d)** 32.4 (billion dollars) **79. (a)** 2000: $129 billion; 2010: $206 billion; 2020: $74 billion; 2030: $-$501 billion **(b)** The cost of Social Security will exceed revenue in 2030 by $501 billion. **81.** 16 **83.** $1045.55 **85.** 14,776 feet **87.** 45°F **89.** 112°F **91.** $-41°$F **93.** 27 feet **95.** 469 B.C. **97.** $2169

6.3 Exercises (Pages 306–310)

1. A, C, D **3.** C **5.** $\frac{1}{3}$ **7.** $-\frac{3}{7}$ **Answers will vary in Exercises 9 and 11.** **9.** $\frac{6}{16}, \frac{9}{24}, \frac{12}{32}$ **11.** $-\frac{10}{14}, -\frac{15}{21}, -\frac{20}{28}$ **13. (a)** $\frac{1}{3}$ **(b)** $\frac{1}{4}$ **(c)** $\frac{2}{5}$ **(d)** $\frac{1}{3}$ **15.** the dots in the intersection of the triangle and the rectangle as a part of the dots in the entire figure **17. (a)** O'Brien **(b)** Ha **(c)** Ha **(d)** Kelly **(e)** Taylor and Britz; $\frac{1}{2}$ **19.** $\frac{1}{2}$ **21.** $\frac{43}{48}$ **23.** $-\frac{5}{24}$ **25.** $\frac{23}{56}$ **27.** $\frac{27}{20}$ **29.** $\frac{5}{12}$ **31.** $\frac{1}{9}$ **33.** $\frac{3}{2}$ **35.** $\frac{3}{2}$ **37. (a)** $4\frac{1}{2}$ cups **(b)** $\frac{7}{8}$ cup **39.** $\frac{13}{3}$ **41.** $\frac{29}{10}$ **43.** $6\frac{3}{4}$ **45.** $6\frac{1}{8}$ **47.** $-17\frac{7}{8}$ **49.** $\frac{9}{16}$ inch **51.** 3 **53.** $\frac{3}{7}$ **55.** $-\frac{103}{89}$ **57.** $\frac{25}{9}$ **59.** $\frac{5}{8}$ **61.** $\frac{19}{30}$ **63.** $-\frac{3}{4}$ **65.** $53,221 **67.** $\frac{14}{19}$ **69.** $\frac{13}{29}$ **71.** $\frac{5}{2}$ **73.** It gives the rational number halfway between the two integers (their average). **75.** .75 **77.** .1875 **79.** $.\overline{27}$ **81.** $.2\overline{85714}$ **83.** $\frac{2}{5}$ **85.** $\frac{17}{20}$ **87.** $\frac{467}{500}$ **89.** repeating **91.** terminating **93.** terminating **95. (a)** $.\overline{3}$ or .333 ... **(b)** $.\overline{6}$ or .666... **(c)** $.\overline{9}$ or .999... **(d)** $1 = .\overline{9}$ **97. (a)** $\frac{4}{5}$ **(b)** $\frac{4}{5}$ **99. (a)** $\frac{33}{50}$ **(b)** $\frac{33}{50}$

6.4 Exercises (Pages 318–321)

1. rational **3.** irrational **5.** rational **7.** rational **9.** irrational **11.** irrational **13.** rational **15. (a)** $.\overline{8}$ **(b)** irrational; rational **17.** 6.244997998 **19.** 3.885871846 **21.** 29.73213749 **23.** 1.060660172 **25.** $5\sqrt{2}$; 7.071067812 **27.** $5\sqrt{3}$; 8.660254038 **29.** $12\sqrt{2}$; 16.97056275 **31.** $\frac{5\sqrt{6}}{6}$; 2.041241452 **33.** $\frac{\sqrt{7}}{2}$; 1.322875656 **35.** $\frac{\sqrt{21}}{3}$; 1.527525232 **37.** $3\sqrt{17}$ **39.** $4\sqrt{7}$ **41.** $10\sqrt{2}$

43. $3\sqrt{3}$ **45.**

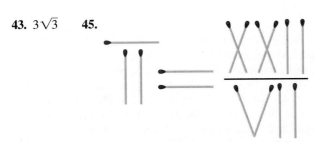

47. The result is 3.1415929, which agrees with the first seven digits in the decimal for π.
49. 3   **51.** 4   **53.** 3.3   **55.** ϕ is positive, while its conjugate is negative. The units digit of ϕ is 1, and the units digit of its conjugate is 0. The decimal digits agree.   **57.** It is just a coincidence that 1828 appears back-to-back early in the decimal. There is no repetition indefinitely, which would be indicative of a rational number.   **59.** 2.5 seconds

61. 15.3 miles   **63.** 392,000 square miles   **65.** The area and the perimeter are both numerically equal to 36.
67. 5.4 feet   **69.** (a) 70.5 mph   (b) 59.8 mph   (c) 53.9 mph   **71.** 4   **73.** 7   **75.** 6   **77.** 1
79. 4   **81.** 8   **The number of decimal digits shown will vary among caculator models in Exercises 83–87.**
83. 3.50339806   **85.** 5.828476683   **87.** 10.06565066

6.5 Exercises   (Pages 331–335)

1. true   **3.** false   **5.** true   **7.** true   **9.** false   **11.** 11.315   **13.** −4.215   **15.** .8224   **17.** 47.5
19. 31.6   **21.** Los Angeles; The population increased, as represented by 9.7%.   **23.** three (and you would have .01¢ left over)   **25.** $.06 or 6¢   **27.** 1000   **29.** (a) .031   (b) .035   **31.** 297   **33.** (a) 78.4   (b) 78.41
35. (a) .1   (b) .08   **37.** (a) 12.7   (b) 12.69   **39.** 42%   **41.** 36.5%   **43.** .8%   **45.** 210%   **47.** 20%
49. 1%   **51.** $37\frac{1}{2}$%   **53.** 150%   **55.** Answers will vary.   **57.** (a) 5   (b) 24   (c) 8   (d) .5 or $\frac{1}{2}$
(e) 600   **59.** No, the price is $57.60.   **61.** (a) .611   (b) .574   (c) .438   **63.** 124.8   **65.** 2.94
67. 150%   **69.** 600   **71.** 1.4%   **73.** A   **75.** C   **77.** about 67%   **79.** (a) $14.7 - 40 \cdot .13$ (b) 9.5
(c) 8.075; walking (5 mph)   **81.** 860%   **83.** $4.50   **85.** $.75   **87.** $12.00   **89.** $36.00
91. Answers will vary.

Extension Exercises   (Page 338)

1. $12i$ **3.** $-15i$ **5.** $i\sqrt{3}$ **7.** $5i\sqrt{3}$ **9.** −5   **11.** −18   **13.** −40   **15.** $\sqrt{2}$ **17.** $3i$
19. 6   **21.** The product rule requires that a and b be nonnegative.   **23.** 1   **25.** −1   **27.** −i **29.** i

Chapter 6 Test   (Pages 340–342)

1. (a) 12   (b) 0, 12   (c) −4, 0, 12   (d) $-4, -\frac{3}{2}, -.5, 0, 4.1, 12$ (e) $-\sqrt{5}, \sqrt{3}$ (f) $-4, -\sqrt{5}, -\frac{3}{2}, -.5, 0, \sqrt{3},$
4.1, 12   **2.** (a) C   (b) B   (c) D   (d) A   **3.** (a) false   (b) true   (c) true   (d) false   **4.** 4   **5.** 3
6. 10   **7.** (a) Hyundai; 50%   (b) General Motors; −5%   (c) false   (d) true   **8.** 5296 ft   **9.** (a) $4900
(b) $5700   (c) $8800   (d) $10,300   **10.** (a) E   (b) A   (c) B   (d) D   (e) F   (f) C   **11.** (a) Whitney
(b) Moura and Dawkins   (c) Whitney   (d) Pritchard and Miller; $\frac{2}{5}$ (e) McElwain ("J-Mac")   **12.** $\frac{11}{16}$ **13.** $\frac{57}{160}$
14. $-\frac{2}{5}$ **15.** $\frac{3}{2}$ **16.** (a) .45   (b) .41$\overline{6}$ **17.** (a) $\frac{18}{25}$ (b) $\frac{58}{99}$ **18.** (a) irrational   (b) rational   (c) rational
(d) rational   (e) irrational   (f) irrational   **19.** (a) 12.247448714   (b) $5\sqrt{6}$ **20.** (a) 4.913538149   (b) $\frac{13\sqrt{7}}{7}$
21. (a) −45.254834   (b) $-32\sqrt{2}$ **22.** Answers will vary.   **23.** (a) 13.81   (b) −.315   (c) 38.7   (d) −24.3
24. (a) 9.04   (b) 9.045   **25.** (a) 16.65   (b) 101.5   **26.** (a) $26\frac{2}{3}$%   (b) $66\frac{2}{3}$%   **27.** D   **28.** 828; 504;
16%; 6%   **29.** 17,415,000   **30.** − 13.8 (billion dollars)

CHAPTER 7   The Basic Concepts of Algebra

7.1 Exercises   (Pages 351–354)

1. A and C   **3.** Both sides are evaluated as 30, so 6 is a solution.   **5.** solution set   **7.** B   **9.** {−1}
11. {3}   **13.** {−7}   **15.** {0}   **17.** $\{-\frac{5}{3}\}$ **19.** $\{-\frac{1}{2}\}$ **21.** {2}   **23.** {−2}   **25.** {7}   **27.** {2}
29. $\{\frac{3}{2}\}$ **31.** {−5}   **33.** {3}   **35.** 2 (that is, 10^2, or 100)   **37.** {4}   **39.** {0}   **41.** {0}   **43.** {2000}
45. {25}   **47.** {40}   **49.** identity, contradiction   **51.** contradiction; $\emptyset$ **53.** conditional; {−8}
55. conditional; {0}   **57.** identity; {all real numbers}   **59.** D   **61.** $t = \frac{d}{r}$ **63.** $b = \frac{A}{h}$ **65.** $a = P - b - c$
67. $b = \frac{2A}{h}$ **69.** $h = \frac{S - 2\pi r^2}{2\pi r}$ or $h = \frac{S}{2\pi r} - r$ **71.** $F = \frac{9}{5}C + 32$ **73.** $H = \frac{A - 2LW}{2W + 2L}$ **75.** (a) 16.8 million
(b) 2009   **77.** (a) .0352   (b) approximately .015 or 1.5%   (c) approximately 1 case   **79.** (a) 800 cubic feet
(b) 107,680 μg (c) $F = 107,680x$ (d) approximately .25 day, or 6 hr

7.2 Exercises   (Pages 364–369)

1. expression   **3.** equation   **5.** expression   **7.** yes   **9.** $x - 14$ **11.** $(x - 7)(x + 5)$ **13.** $\frac{15}{x}$ $(x \neq 0)$
15. Answers will vary.   **17.** 3   **19.** 6   **21.** -3 **23.** Springsteen: \$115.9 million; Dion:
\$80.5 million   **25.** wins: 62; losses: 20   **27.** Democrats: 44; Republicans: 55   **29.** shortest piece: 15 inches;
middle piece: 20 inches; longest piece: 24 inches   **31.** gold: 35; silver: 39; bronze: 29   **33.** 35 milliliters   **35.** \$350
37. \$14.15   **39.** 4 liters   **41.** $18\frac{2}{11}$ liters   **43.** 5 liters   **45.** \$4000 at 3%; \$8000 at 4%   **47.** \$10,000 at
4.5%; \$19,000 at 3%   **49.** \$58,000   **51.** 17 pennies, 17 dimes, 10 quarters   **53.** 305 students, 105 nonstudents
55. 54 seats on Row 1; 51 seats on Row 2   **57.** 39-cent stamps: 28; 24-cent stamps: 17   **59.** 3.173 hours
61. 1.715 hours   **63.** 8.08 meters per second   **65.** 8.40 meters per second   **67.** 530 miles   **69.** No, it is not
correct. The distance is $45\left(\frac{1}{2}\right) = 22.5$ miles.   **71.** $1\frac{3}{4}$ hours   **73.** 10:00 A.M.   **75.** 18 miles   **77.** 8 hours

7.3 Exercises   (Pages 378–383)

1. $\frac{5}{8}$ **3.** $\frac{1}{4}$ **5.** $\frac{2}{1}$ **7.** $\frac{3}{1}$ **9.** D   **11.** Answers will vary.   **13.** true   **15.** false   **17.** true
19. $\{35\}$ **21.** $\{-1\}$ **23.** $\left\{-\frac{27}{4}\right\}$ **25.** \$30.00   **27.** \$8.75   **29.** \$67.50   **31.** \$38.85   **33.** 4 feet
35. 2.7 inches   **37.** 2.0 inches   **39.** $2\frac{5}{8}$ cups   **41.** \$363.84   **43.** 12,500 fish   **45.** 10-lb size; \$.439
47. 32-oz size; \$.093   **49.** 128-oz size; \$.044   **51.** 36-oz size; \$.049   **53.** $x = 4$ **55.** $x = 1; y = 4$
57. (a)   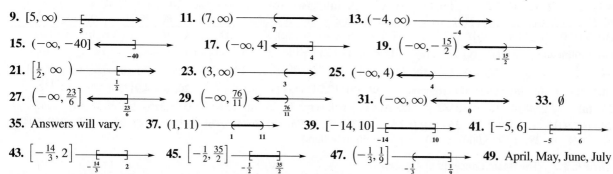   (b) 54 feet   **59.** \$144   **61.** \$165   **63.** 9   **65.** 125   **67.** $\frac{4}{9}$
69. \$40.32   **71.** 20 miles per hour   **73.** about 302 pounds
75. 100 pounds per square inch   **77.** 20 pounds per square foot
79. 144 feet   **81.** 1.105 liters   **83.** $\frac{8}{9}$ metric ton
85. 6.2 pounds

7.4 Exercises   (Pages 391–394)

1. D   **3.** B   **5.** F   **7.** Use parentheses when the symbol is $<$ or $>$. Use brackets when the symbol is $\leq$ or $\geq$.

9. $[5, \infty)$ **11.** $(7, \infty)$ **13.** $(-4, \infty)$

15. $(-\infty, -40]$ **17.** $(-\infty, 4]$ **19.** $\left(-\infty, -\frac{15}{2}\right)$

21. $\left[\frac{1}{2}, \infty\right)$ **23.** $(3, \infty)$ **25.** $(-\infty, 4)$

27. $\left(-\infty, \frac{23}{6}\right]$ **29.** $\left(-\infty, \frac{76}{11}\right)$ **31.** $(-\infty, \infty)$ **33.** $\emptyset$

35. Answers will vary.   **37.** $(1, 11)$ **39.** $[-14, 10]$ **41.** $[-5, 6]$

43. $\left[-\frac{14}{3}, 2\right]$ **45.** $\left[-\frac{1}{2}, \frac{35}{2}\right]$ **47.** $\left(-\frac{1}{3}, \frac{1}{9}\right]$ **49.** April, May, June, July

51. January, February, March, August, September, October, November, December   **53.** from about 2:30 P.M. to 6:00 P.M.
55. about 84°F–91°F   **57.** 2 miles   **59.** at least 80   **61.** 50 miles   **63.** (a) 140 to 184 pounds   (b) Answers
will vary.   **65.** 26 DVDs

7.5 Exercises   (Pages 404–407)

1. A   **3.** A   **5.** D   **7.** 625   **9.** -32 **11.** -8 **13.** -81 **15.** $\frac{1}{49}$ **17.** $-\frac{1}{49}$ **19.** -128
21. $\frac{16}{5}$ **23.** 125   **25.** $\frac{25}{16}$ **27.** $\frac{9}{20}$ **29.** 1   **31.** 1   **33.** 0   **35.** reciprocal, additive inverse
37. D   **39.** x^{16} **41.** 5   **43.** $\frac{1}{27}$ **45.** $\frac{1}{81}$ **47.** $\frac{1}{t^7}$ **49.** $9x^2$ **51.** $\frac{1}{a^5}$ **53.** x^{11} **55.** r^6
57. $-\frac{56}{k^2}$ **59.** $\frac{1}{z^4}$ **61.** $-\frac{3}{r^7}$ **63.** $\frac{27}{a^{18}}$ **65.** $\frac{x^5}{y^2}$ **67.** D   **69.** 2.3×10^2 **71.** 2×10^{-2} **73.** 6500

75. .0152 **77.** 6×10^5 **79.** 2×10^5 **81.** 2×10^5 **83.** 1×10^9; 1×10^{12}; 2.128×10^{12}; 1.44419×10^5
85. $\$1.61964 \times 10^{10}$ **87.** 1×10^{10} **89.** 2,000,000,000 **91.** $1392 **93.** approximately 9.474×10^{-7} parsec **95.** 300 seconds **97.** approximately 5.87×10^{12} miles **99.** 20,000 hours

7.6 Exercises (Pages 415–417)

1. $x^2 - x + 3$ **3.** $9y^2 - 4y + 4$ **5.** $6m^4 - 2m^3 - 7m^2 - 4m$ **7.** $-2x^2 - 13x + 11$ **9.** $x^2 - 5x - 24$
11. $28r^2 + r - 2$ **13.** $12x^5 + 8x^4 - 20x^3 + 4x^2$ **15.** $4m^2 - 9$ **17.** $16m^2 + 16mn + 4n^2$
19. $25r^2 + 30rt^2 + 9t^4$ **21.** $-2z^3 + 7z^2 - 11z + 4$ **23.** $m^2 + mn - 2n^2 - 2km + 5kn - 3k^2$
25. $a^2 - 2ab + b^2 + 4ac - 4bc + 4c^2$ **27.** A **29.** Answers will vary. **31.** $2m^2(4m^2 + 3m - 6)$
33. $4k^2m^3(1 + 2k^2 - 3m)$ **35.** $2(a + b)(1 + 2m)$ **37.** $(m - 1)(2m^2 - 7m + 7)$ **39.** $(2s + 3)(3t - 5)$
41. $(t^3 + s^2)(r - p)$ **43.** $(8a + 5b)(2a - 3b)$ **45.** $(5z - 2x)(4z - 9x)$ **47.** $(1 - a)(1 - b)$
49. $(x - 5)(x + 3)$ **51.** $(y + 7)(y - 5)$ **53.** $6(a - 10)(a + 2)$ **55.** $3m(m + 1)(m + 3)$
57. $(3k - 2p)(2k + 3p)$ **59.** $(5a + 3b)(a - 2b)$ **61.** $(7x + 2y)(3x - y)$ **63.** $2a^2(4a - b)(3a + 2b)$
65. Answers will vary. **67.** $(3m - 2)^2$ **69.** $2(4a - 3b)^2$ **71.** $(2xy + 7)^2$ **73.** $(x + 6)(x - 6)$
75. $(y + w)(y - w)$ **77.** $(3a + 4)(3a - 4)$ **79.** $(5s^2 + 3t)(5s^2 - 3t)$ **81.** $(p^2 + 25)(p + 5)(p - 5)$
83. $(2 - a)(4 + 2a + a^2)$ **85.** $(5x - 3)(25x^2 + 15x + 9)$ **87.** $(3y^3 + 5z^2)(9y^6 - 15y^3z^2 + 25z^4)$
89. $(x + y)(x - 5)$ **91.** $(m - 2n)(p^4 + q)$ **93.** $(2z + 7)^2$ **95.** $(10x + 7y)(100x^2 - 70xy + 49y^2)$
97. $(5m^2 - 6)(25m^4 + 30m^2 + 36)$ **99.** $(6m - 7n)(2m + 5n)$

7.7 Exercises (Pages 422–426)

1. $4, 5, -9$ **3.** two **5.** $\{-3, 9\}$ **7.** $\left\{\frac{7}{2}, -\frac{1}{5}\right\}$ **9.** $\{-3, 4\}$ **11.** $\{-7, -2\}$ **13.** $\left\{-\frac{1}{2}, \frac{1}{6}\right\}$

15. $\{-2, 4\}$ **17.** $\{\pm 8\}$ **19.** $\left\{\pm 2\sqrt{6}\right\}$ **21.** $\emptyset$ **23.** $\{1, 7\}$ **25.** $\left\{4 \pm \sqrt{3}\right\}$ **27.** $\left\{\frac{5 \pm \sqrt{13}}{2}\right\}$

29. $\left\{\frac{2 \pm \sqrt{3}}{2}\right\}$ **31.** $\left\{\frac{1 \pm \sqrt{3}}{2}\right\}$ **33.** $\left\{\frac{1 \pm \sqrt{5}}{2}\right\}$ **35.** $\left\{\frac{-1 \pm \sqrt{2}}{2}\right\}$ **37.** $\left\{\frac{1 \pm \sqrt{29}}{2}\right\}$

39. $\emptyset$ **41.** Answers will vary. $\left\{\pm \frac{\sqrt{10}}{2}\right\}$ **43.** The presence of $2x^3$ makes it a *cubic* equation (degree 3).
45. 0; (c) **47.** 121; (a) **49.** 360; (b) **51.** 5.2 seconds **53.** Find s when $t = 0$. **55.** (a) 1 second and
8 seconds (b) 9 seconds after it is projected **57.** 2.3, 5.3, 5.8 **59.** 412.3 feet **61.** eastbound ship: 80 miles;
southbound ship: 150 miles **63.** 5 centimeters, 12 centimeters, 13 centimeters **65.** length: 2 centimeters; width:
1.5 centimeters **67.** 1 foot **69.** length: 26 meters; width: 16 meters **71.** length: 20 inches; width: 12 inches
73. $.80 **75.** 5.5 meters per second **77.** 5 or 14 **79.** $\{2\}$

Chapter 7 Test (Pages 428–429)

1. $\{2\}$ **2.** $\{4\}$ **3.** identity; {all real numbers} **4.** $v = \frac{S + 16t^2}{t}$ **5.** Hawaii: 4021 square miles; Maui:
728 square miles; Kauai: 551 square miles **6.** 5 liters **7.** 2.2 hours **8.** 8 slices for $2.19 **9.** 2300 miles
10. 200 amps **11.** $(-\infty, 4]$ ←———→ **12.** $(-2, 6]$ ←——→ **13.** C **14.** at least 82
15. $\frac{16}{9}$ **16.** -64 **17.** $\frac{64}{27}$ **18.** 0 **19.** $\frac{216}{p^4}$ **20.** $\frac{1}{m^{14}}$ **21.** (a) 693,000,000 (b) .000000125
22. 3×10^{-4} **23.** about 15,300 seconds **24.** $4k^2 + 6k + 10$ **25.** $15x^2 - 14x - 8$ **26.** $16x^4 - 9$
27. $3x^3 + 20x^2 + 23x - 36$ **28.** One example is $t^5 + 2t^4 + 3t^3 - 4t^2 + 5t + 6$. **29.** $(2p - 3q)(p - q)$
30. $(10x + 7y)(10x - 7y)$ **31.** $(3y - 5x)(9y^2 + 15yx + 25x^2)$ **32.** $(4 - m)(x + y)$ **33.** $\left\{-\frac{3}{2}, \frac{1}{3}\right\}$
34. $\{\pm \sqrt{13}\}$ **35.** $\left\{\frac{1 \pm \sqrt{29}}{2}\right\}$ **36.** .87 second

CHAPTER 8 Graphs, Functions, and Systems of Equations and Inequalities

8.1 Exercises (Pages 438–441)

1. (a) x represents the year; y represents the percent of women in mathematics or computer science professions.
(b) 1990–2000 (c) 1990 (d) 1980 **3.** x **5.** $(0, 0)$ **7.** (a) I (b) III (c) II (d) IV (e) none

9. (a) I or III **(b)** II or IV **(c)** II or IV **(d)** I or III **11.–20.**

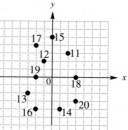

21. (a) $\sqrt{34}$ **(b)** $\left(\frac{1}{2}, \frac{5}{2}\right)$ **23. (a)** $\sqrt{61}$ **(b)** $\left(\frac{1}{2}, 1\right)$ **25. (a)** $\sqrt{146}$ **(b)** $\left(-\frac{1}{2}, \frac{3}{2}\right)$ **27.** B **29.** D
31. $x^2 + y^2 = 36$ **33.** $(x + 1)^2 + (y - 3)^2 = 16$ **35.** $x^2 + (y - 4)^2 = 3$ **37.** center: $(0, 0)$; radius: r
39. $(-2, -3); 2$ **41.** $(-5, 7); 9$ **43.** $(2, 4); 4$ **45.**

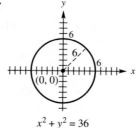

47.

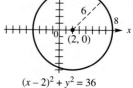

$x^2 + y^2 = 36$ \qquad $(x - 2)^2 + y^2 = 36$

49.

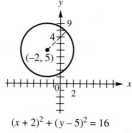

$(x + 2)^2 + (y - 5)^2 = 16$

51.

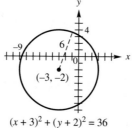

$(x + 3)^2 + (y + 2)^2 = 36$

53. (a) $\sqrt{40} = 2\sqrt{10}$ **(b)** $(-1, 4)$

55. \$17,396 **57.** 1988: \$12,471; 1998: \$16,787 **59.** Answers will vary. **61.** Answers will vary.
63. The epicenter is $(-2, -2)$. **65.** Answers will vary. **67.** $(9, 18)$
69. Answers will vary.

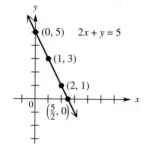

8.2 Exercises (Pages 447–451)

1. $(0, 5)$, $\left(\frac{5}{2}, 0\right)$, $(1, 3)$, $(2, 1)$ **3.** $(0, -4)$, $(4, 0)$, $(2, -2)$, $(3, -1)$ **5.** $(0, 4)$, $(5, 0)$, $\left(3, \frac{8}{5}\right)$, $\left(\frac{5}{2}, 2\right)$

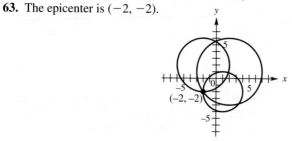

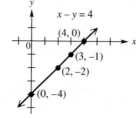

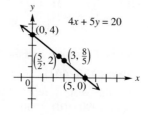

7. $(0, 4)$, $\left(\dfrac{8}{3}, 0\right)$, $(2, 1)$, $(4, -2)$ **9.** Answers will vary.   **11.** A   **13.** $(4, 0)$; $(0, 6)$

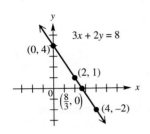

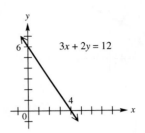

15. $(2, 0)$; $\left(0, \dfrac{5}{3}\right)$ **17.** $\left(\dfrac{5}{2}, 0\right)$; $(0, -5)$ **19.** $(2, 0)$; $\left(0, -\dfrac{2}{3}\right)$

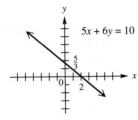

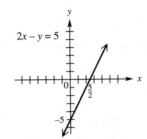

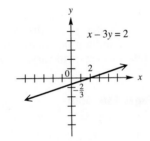

21. $(0, 0)$; $(0, 0)$ **23.** $(0, 0)$; $(0, 0)$ **25.** $(2, 0)$;   none

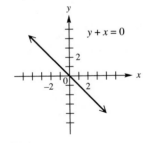

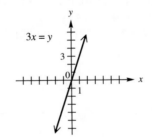

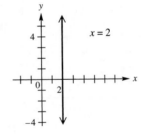

27. none; $(0, 4)$ **29.** C   **31.** A   **33.** D   **35.** B   **37.** $\dfrac{3}{10}$

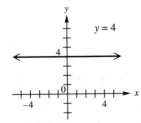

39. (a) $\dfrac{3}{2}$ **(b)** $-\dfrac{7}{4}$ **41.** 8   **43.** $-\dfrac{5}{6}$ **45.** 0   **47. (a)** slope $= 232$ (This represents enrollment in thousands.)
(b) positive; increased   **(c)** 232,000 students   **(d)** -1.66 **(e)** negative; decreased   **(f)** 1.66 students per computer

49.

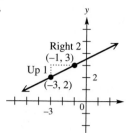

51.

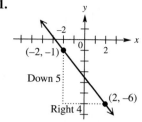

53.

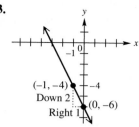

55.

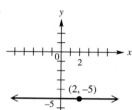

57. parallel   **59.** perpendicular   **61.** neither parallel nor perpendicular

63. $\frac{7}{10}$ **65. (a)** 3.8% per year   **(b)** As the years increase, the number of electronic filings also increases. **67.** In each case, 1000 million per year; The average rate of change is the same. The data points lie on the same straight line.   **69.** Answers will vary.

8.3 Exercises (Pages 456–460)

1. D   **3.** B   **5.** $y = 3x - 3$ **7.** $y = -x + 3$ **9.** A   **11.** C   **13.** H   **15.** B   **17.** $y = -\frac{3}{4}x + \frac{5}{2}$
19. $y = -2x + 18$ **21.** $y = \frac{1}{2}x + \frac{13}{2}$ **23.** $y = 4x - 12$ **25.** $y = 5$ **27.** $x = 9$ **29.** $x = .5$
31. $y = 8$ **33.** $y = 2x - 2$ **35.** $y = -\frac{1}{2}x + 4$ **37.** $y = \frac{2}{13}x + \frac{6}{13}$ **39.** $y = 5$ **41.** $x = 7$ **43.** $y = -3$
45. $y = 5x + 15$ **47.** $y = -\frac{2}{3}x + \frac{4}{5}$ **49.** $y = \frac{2}{5}x + 5$ **51.** Answers will vary.   **53. (a)** $y = -x + 12$
(b) -1 **(c)** $(0, 12)$ **55. (a)** $y = -\frac{5}{2}x + 10$ **(b)** $-\frac{5}{2}$ **(c)** $(0, 10)$ **57. (a)** $y = \frac{2}{3}x - \frac{10}{3}$ **(b)** $\frac{2}{3}$ **(c)** $\left(0, -\frac{10}{3}\right)$
59. $y = 3x - 19$ **61.** $y = \frac{1}{2}x - 1$ **63.** $y = -\frac{1}{2}x + 9$ **65.** $y = 7$
67. (a) yes   **(b)** $y = 763.6x + 9391$ **(c)** \$23,136

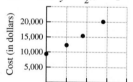

69. (a) $y = -108.3x + 28,959$ **(b)** 27,335   **71. (a)** $y = 14.55x + 262.42$ **(b)** 2525 light-years
73. (a) 32°; 212°   **(b)** $(0, 32)$; $(100, 212)$ **(c)** $\frac{9}{5}$ **(d)** $F = \frac{9}{5}C + 32$ **(e)** $C = \frac{5}{9}(F - 32)$
(f) When Celsius temperature is 50°, Fahrenheit temperature is 122°.

8.4 Exercises (Pages 470–473)

1. Answers will vary.   **3.** It is the independent variable.   **5.** function; domain: $\{2, 3, 4, 5\}$; range: $\{5, 7, 9, 11\}$
7. not a function; domain: $(0, \infty)$; range: $(-\infty, 0) \cup (0, \infty)$ **9.** function; domain: {Hispanic, Native American, Asian American, African American, White}; range in millions: $\{21.3, 1.6, 8.2, 24.6, 152.0\}$ **11.** function; domain: $(-\infty, \infty)$; range: $(-\infty, 4]$ **13.** not a function; domain: $[-4, 4]$; range: $[-3, 3]$ **15.** function; domain: $(-\infty, \infty)$ **17.** not a function; domain: $[0, \infty)$ **19.** not a function; domain: $(-\infty, \infty)$ **21.** function; domain: $[0, \infty)$ **23.** function; domain: $(-\infty, 0) \cup (0, \infty)$ **25.** function; domain: $\left[-\frac{1}{2}, \infty\right)$ **27.** function; domain: $(-\infty, 9) \cup (9, \infty)$
29. (a) $[0, 3000]$ **(b)** 25 hours; 25 hours   **(c)** 2000 gallons   **(d)** $g(0) = 0$; The pool is empty at time zero.

31. Here is one example: The cost of gasoline; number of gallons purchased; cost; number of gallons   **33.** 5   **35.** 2
37. -1 **39.** -13

41.

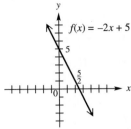

domain and range: $(-\infty, \infty)$

43.

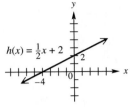

domain and range: $(-\infty, \infty)$

45.

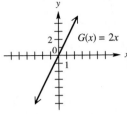

domain and range: $(-\infty, \infty)$

47.

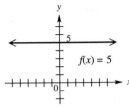

domain: $(-\infty, \infty)$; range: $\{5\}$

49. (a) $f(x) = 3 - 2x^2$ (b) -15 **51.** (a) $f(x) = \dfrac{8 - 4x}{-3}$ (b) $\dfrac{4}{3}$

53. line; -2; $-2x + 4$; -2; $3, -2$ **55.** (a) \$0; \$1.50; \$3.00; \$4.50   (b) $1.50x$ (c)

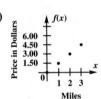

57. (a) 194.53 centimeters   (b) 177.29 centimeters   (c) 177.41 centimeters   (d) 163.65 centimeters   **59.** (a) \$160
(b) 70 mph   (c) 66 mph   (d) for speeds more than 80 mph

61. (a) $C(x) = .02x + 200$
(b) $R(x) = .04x$
(c) 10,000
(d)

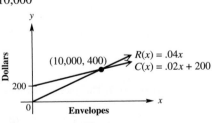

For $x < 10,000$, a loss
For $x > 10,000$, a profit

63. (a) $C(x) = 3.00x + 2300$
(b) $R(x) = 5.50x$
(c) 920
(d)

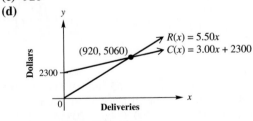

For $x < 920$, a loss
For $x > 920$, a profit

8.5 Exercises   **(Pages 481–484)**

1. F   **3.** C   **5.** E   **7.** Answers will vary   **9.** $(0, 0)$ **11.** $(0, 4)$ **13.** $(1, 0)$ **15.** $(-3, -4)$
17. Answers will vary   **19.** downward; narrower   **21.** upward; wider   **23.** (a) I   (b) IV   (c) II   (d) III

25.

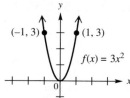

$(-1, 3)$ $(1, 3)$

$f(x) = 3x^2$

27.

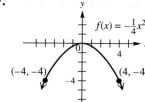

$f(x) = -\frac{1}{4}x^2$

$(-4, -4)$ $(4, -4)$

29.

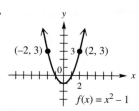

$(-2, 3)$ 3 $(2, 3)$

$f(x) = x^2 - 1$

31.

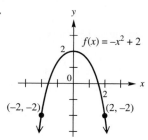

$f(x) = -x^2 + 2$

$(-2, -2)$ $(2, -2)$

33.

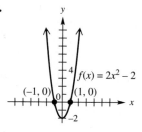

$f(x) = 2x^2 - 2$

$(-1, 0)$ $(1, 0)$

35.

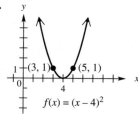

$(3, 1)$ $(5, 1)$

$f(x) = (x - 4)^2$

37.

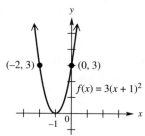

$(-2, 3)$ $(0, 3)$

$f(x) = 3(x + 1)^2$

39.

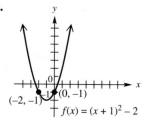

$(-2, -1)$ $(0, -1)$

$f(x) = (x + 1)^2 - 2$

41.

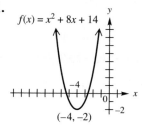

$f(x) = x^2 + 8x + 14$

$(-4, -2)$

43.

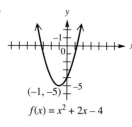

$(-1, -5)$

$f(x) = x^2 + 2x - 4$

45.

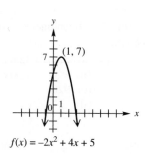

$(1, 7)$

$f(x) = -2x^2 + 4x + 5$

47. 25 meters   **49.** 16 feet; 2 seconds

51. 4.1 seconds; 81.6 meters   **53. (a)** 19.2 hours   **(b)** 84.3 ppm   **55.** $f(45) = 161.5$; This means that when the speed is 45 mph, the stopping distance is 161.5 feet.
57. (a) $R(x) = (100 - x)(200 + 4x) = 20,000 + 200x - 4x^2$ **(b)**   **(c)** 25   **(d)** $22,500

(25, 22,500)

$R(x) = (100 - x)(200 + 4x)$

8.6 Exercises   (Pages 492–494)

1. rises; falls   **3.** does not   **5.** rises; falls   **7.** does not   **9.** 2.56425419972   **11.** 1.25056505582
13. 7.41309466897   **15.** .0000210965628481

17.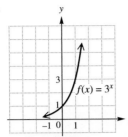

19.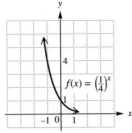

21. 20.0855369232 **23.** .018315638889 **25.** $2 = \log_4 16$ **27.** $-3 = \log_{2/3}\left(\frac{27}{8}\right)$ **29.** $2^5 = 32$
31. $3^1 = 3$ **33.** 1.38629436112 **35.** -1.0498221245 **37.** (a) .5°C (b) .35°C **39.** (a) 1.6°C (b) .5°C
41.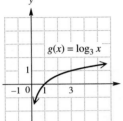
43.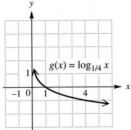
45. (a) $22,510.18 (b) $22,529.85

47. (a) $33,504.35 (b) $33,504.71 **49.** Plan A is better by $102.65 **51.** (a) 828 millibars (b) 232 millibars
53. (a) 146,250 (b) 198,403 (c) It will have increased by almost 36%. **55.** (a) 440 grams (b) 387 grams
(c) 264 grams (d) 21.66 years **57.** 1611.97 years **59.** about 9000 years **61.** about 13,000 years
63. almost 4 times as powerful

8.7 Exercises (Pages 508–514)

1. (a) 1991; about 350 million (b) (1987, 100 million) (c) 1988–1990 (d) CD production generally increased during
these years; positive (e) The slope would be negative, because the line falls from left to right. **3.** yes **5.** no
7. $\{(2, 2)\}$ **9.** $\{(3, -1)\}$ **11.** $\{(2, -3)\}$ **13.** $\left\{\left(\frac{3}{2}, -\frac{3}{2}\right)\right\}$ **15.** $\left\{\left(\frac{6-2y}{7}, y\right)\right\}$

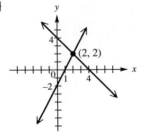

17. $\{(2, -4)\}$ **19.** $\emptyset$ **21.** $\{(1, 2)\}$ **23.** $\left\{\left(\frac{22}{9}, \frac{22}{3}\right)\right\}$ **25.** $\{(2, 3)\}$ **27.** $\{(5, 4)\}$ **29.** $\left\{\left(-5, -\frac{10}{3}\right)\right\}$
31. $\{(2, 6)\}$ **33.** Answers will vary. **35.** $\{(1, 4, -3)\}$ **37.** $\{(0, 2, -5)\}$ **39.** $\left\{\left(-\frac{7}{3}, \frac{22}{3}, 7\right)\right\}$
41. $\{(4, 5, 3)\}$ **43.** $\{(2, 2, 2)\}$ **45.** $\left\{\left(\frac{8}{3}, \frac{2}{3}, 3\right)\right\}$ **47.** wins: 100; losses: 62 **49.** length: 94 feet; width: 50 feet
51. weekend days: 3; weekdays: 3 **53.** square: 12 centimeters; triangle: 8 centimeters **55.** cappuccino: $1.95;
house latte: $2.35 **57.** NHL: $247.32; NBA: $267.37 **59.** Tokyo: $430; New York: $385 **61.** dark clay:
$5 per kilogram; light clay: $4 per kilogram **63.** (a) 12 ounces (b) 30 ounces (c) 48 ounces (d) 60 ounces
65. $1.29x **67.** 15% solution: $26\frac{2}{3}$ liters; 33% solution: $13\frac{1}{3}$ liters **69.** 3 liters **71.** 50% juice: 150 liters;
30% juice: 50 liters **73.** $1.20 candy: 100 pounds; $2.40 candy: 60 pounds **75.** at 4%: $10,000; at 3%: $5000
77. train: 60 kilometers per hour; plane: 160 kilometers per hour **79.** boat: 21 mph; current: 3 mph **81.** gold:
35; silver: 39; bronze: 29 **83.** shortest: 10 inches; middle: 20 inches; longest: 26 inches **85.** type A: 80;
type B: 160; type C: 250 **87.** $10 tickets: 350; $18 tickets: 250; $30 tickets: 50

Extension Exercises **(Page 518)**

1. $\{(2, 3)\}$ **3.** $\{(-3, 0)\}$ **5.** $\left\{\left(-\frac{7}{2}, -1\right)\right\}$ **7.** $\{(1, -4)\}$ **9.** $\{(-1, 23, 16)\}$ **11.** $\{(2, 1, -1)\}$
13. $\{(3, 2, -4)\}$ **15.** $\{(0, 1, 0)\}$ **17.** $\{(-1, 2, 0)\}$

8.8 Exercises **(Pages 524–526)**

1. C **3.** B **5.** 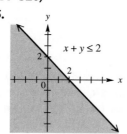 **7.** 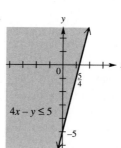 **9.**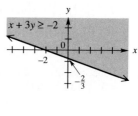

11. 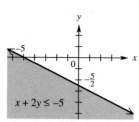 **13.** 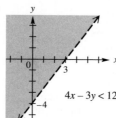 **15.**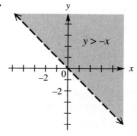

17. 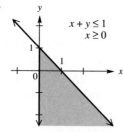 **19.** 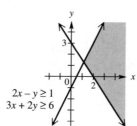 **21.**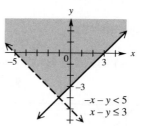

23. maximum of 65 at (5, 10); minimum of 8 at (1, 1) **25.** $\left(\frac{6}{5}, \frac{6}{5}\right)$; $\frac{42}{5}$ **27.** $\left(\frac{17}{3}, 5\right)$; $\frac{49}{3}$ **29.** Ship 20 to A and 80 to B, for a minimum cost of $1040. **31.** Take 3 red pills and 2 blue pills, for a minimum cost of 70¢ per day. **33.** Produce 6.4 million gallons of gasoline and 3.2 million gallons of fuel oil, for a maximum revenue of $16,960,000. **35.** Ship 4000 medical kits and 2000 containers of water.

Chapter 8 Test **(Pages 527–528)**

1. $\sqrt{41}$ **2.** $(x + 1)^2 + (y - 2)^2 = 9$ **3.** x-intercept: $\left(\frac{8}{3}, 0\right)$; y-intercept: $(0, -4)$

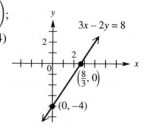

4. $\frac{2}{7}$ **5. (a)** $y = -\frac{2}{5}x + \frac{13}{5}$ **(b)** $y = -\frac{1}{2}x - \frac{3}{2}$ **(c)** $y = -\frac{1}{2}x + 2$ **6.** B **7. (a)** $y = 881x + 38,885$
(b) $41,528; The model value is less than the actual income. **8.** $y = .05x + .50$; (1, .55), (5, .75), (10, 1.00)
9. $y = \frac{2}{3}x + 1$ **10. (a)** $(-\infty, \infty)$ **(b)** 22 **11.** $(-\infty, 3) \cup (3, \infty)$ **12.** 500 calculators; $30,000

13. axis: $x = -3$; vertex: $(-3, 4)$; domain: $(-\infty, \infty)$; range: $(-\infty, 4]$ **14.** 80 feet by 160 feet

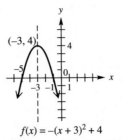

$$f(x) = -(x + 3)^2 + 4$$

15. (a) 2116.31264888   **(b)** .157237166314   **(c)** 3.15955035878   **16.** A   **17. (a)** \$13,521.90   **(b)** \$13,529.96
18. (a) 1.62 grams   **(b)** 1.18 grams   **(c)** .69 gram   **(d)** 2.00 grams   **19.** $\{(4, -2)\}$ **20.** $\{(2, 0, -1)\}$
21. $\{(1, 2z + 3, z)\}$ **22.** *Pretty Woman*: \$463.4 million; *Ocean's Eleven*: \$450.7 million   **23.** \$40,000 at 10%;
\$100,000 at 6%; \$140,000 at 5%   **24.**   **25.** Manufacture 0 VIP rings and 24 SST rings, for a maximum profit of \$960.

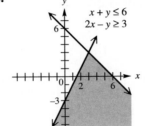

$x + y \leq 6$
$2x - y \geq 3$

CHAPTER 9   GEOMETRY

9.1 Exercises   (Pages 537–540)

1. 90   **3.** equal   **5.** true   **7.** false   **9.** true   **11.** true   **13.** false
15. (a) $\overleftrightarrow{AB}$ **(b)**   **17. (a)** $\overrightarrow{CB}$ **(b)**
19. (a) $\overrightarrow{BC}$ **(b)**   **21. (a)** $\overrightarrow{BA}$ **(b)**
23. (a) $\overleftrightarrow{CA}$ **(b)**   **25.** F   **27.** D   **29.** B   **31.** E   **There may be other correct
forms of the answers in Exercises 33–39.**   **33.** $\overrightarrow{MO}$ **35.** $\overleftrightarrow{MO}$ **37.** $\emptyset$ **39.** $\overleftrightarrow{OP}$ **41.** 62°   **43.** 1°
45. $(90 - x)°$ **47.** 48°   **49.** 154°   **51.** $(180 - y)°$ **53.** $\angle CBD$ and $\angle ABE$; $\angle CBE$ and $\angle DBA$
55. (a) 52°   **(b)** 128°   **57.** 107° and 73°   **59.** 75° and 75°   **61.** 139° and 139°   **63.** 65° and 115°
65. 35° and 55°   **67.** 117° and 117°   **69.** 141° and 141°   **71.** 80°   **73.** 52°   **75.** Measures are given in
numerical order, starting with angle 1: 55°, 65°, 60°, 65°, 60°, 120°, 60°, 60°, 55°, 55°.   **77.** Answers will vary.

9.2 Exercises   (Pages 545–548)

1. chord   **3.** equilateral (or equiangular)   **5.** false   **7.** false   **9.** true   **11.** Answers will vary.
13. both   **15.** closed   **17.** closed   **19.** neither   **21.** convex   **23.** convex   **25.** not convex
27. right, scalene   **29.** acute, equilateral   **31.** right, scalene   **33.** right, isosceles   **35.** obtuse, scalene
37. acute, isosceles   **39.** Answers will vary.   **41.** Answers will vary.   **43.** $A = 50°$; $B = 70°$; $C = 60°$;
45. $A = B = C = 60°$ **47.** $A = B = 52°$; $C = 76°$ **49.** 165°   **51.** 170°   **53. (a)** O **(b)** $\overrightarrow{OA}, \overrightarrow{OC}, \overrightarrow{OB}$,
$\overrightarrow{OD}$ **(c)** $\overleftrightarrow{AC}, \overleftrightarrow{BD}$ **(d)** $\overleftrightarrow{AC}, \overleftrightarrow{BD}, \overleftrightarrow{BC}, \overleftrightarrow{AB}$ **(e)** $\overleftrightarrow{BC}, \overleftrightarrow{AB}$ **(f)** $\overleftrightarrow{AE}$ **55. (e)** The sum of the measures of the angles
of a triangle is 180° (because the pencil has gone through one-half of a complete rotation).

Extension Exercises   (Page 551)

1. With radius of the compasses greater than one-half the length PQ, place the point of the compasses at P and swing
arcs above and below line r. Then with the same radius and the point of the compasses at Q, swing two more arcs
above and below line r. Locate the two points of intersections of the arcs above and below, and call them A and B.
With a straightedge, join A and B. AB is the perpendicular bisector of PQ.   **3.** With the radius of the compasses

greater than the distance from P to r, place the point of the compasses at P and swing an arc intersecting line r in two points. Call these points A and B. Swing arcs of equal radius to the left of line r, with the point of the compasses at A and at B, intersecting at points Q. With a straightedge, join P and Q. PQ is the perpendicular from P to line r.
5. With any radius, place the point of the compasses at P and swing arcs to the left and right, intersecting line r in two points. Call these points A and B. With an arc of sufficient length, place the point of the compasses first at A and then at B, and swing arcs either both above or both below line r, intersecting at point Q. With a straightedge, join P and Q. PQ is perpendicular to line r at P.   **7.** With any radius, place the point of the compasses at A and swing an arc intersecting the sides of angle A at two points. Call the point of intersection on the horizontal side B and call the other point of intersection C. Draw a horizontal working line, and locate any point A' on this line. With the same radius used earlier, place the point of the compasses at A' and swing an arc intersecting the working line at B'. Return to angle A, and set the radius of the compasses equal to BC. On the working line, place the point of the compasses at B' and swing an arc intersecting the first arc at C'. Now draw line $A'C'$. Angle A' is equal to angle A.   **9.** Use Construction 3 to construct a perpendicular to a line at a point. Then use Construction 4 to bisect one of the right angles formed. This yields a 45° angle.   **11.** Answers will vary.

9.3 Exercises   (Pages 559–565)

1. 12   **3.** 6   **5.** circumference   **7.** 12 cm^2 **9.** 5 cm^2 **11.** 8 in.^{2} **13.** 4.5 cm^2 **15.** 418 mm^2
17. 8 cm^2 **19.** 3.14 cm^2 **21.** 1017.36 m^2 **23.** 4 m   **25.** 300 ft, 400 ft, 500 ft   **27.** 46 ft
29. 23,800.10 ft^2 **31.** perimeter   **33.** 12 in., 12π in., 36π in.^{2} **35.** 5 ft, 10π ft, 25π ft^2 **37.** 6 cm,
12 cm, 36π cm^2 **39.** 10 in., 20 in., 20π in.   **41.** 14.5   **43.** 7   **45.** 5.1   **47.** 5   **49.** 5   **51.** 1.5
53. **(a)** 20 cm^2 **(b)** 80 cm^2 **(c)** 180 cm^2 **(d)** 320 cm^2 **(e)** 4 **(f)** 3; 9 **(g)** 4; 16 **(h)** n^2 **55.** $800
57. n^2 **59.** 80   **61.** 76.26   **63.** 132 ft^2 **65.** 5376 cm^2 **67.** 145.34 m^2 **69.** 14-in. pizza
71. 14-in. pizza   **73.** 26 in.   **75.** 625 ft^2 **77.** 648 in.^{2} **79.** $\frac{(4-\pi)r^2}{4}$

9.4 Exercises   (Pages 572–578)

1.

STATEMENTS	REASONS
1. $AC = BD$	**1.** Given
2. $AD = BC$	**2.** Given
3. $AB = AB$	**3.** Reflexive property
4. $\triangle ABD \cong \triangle BAC$	**4.** SSS congruence property

3.

STATEMENTS	REASONS
1. $\overleftrightarrow{DB}$ is perpendicular to $\overleftrightarrow{AC}$.	**1.** Given
2. $AB = BC$	**2.** Given
3. $\angle ABD = \angle CBD$	**3.** Both are right angles by definition of perpendicularity.
4. $DB = DB$	**4.** Reflexive property
5. $\triangle ABD \cong \triangle CBD$	**5.** SAS congruence property

5.

STATEMENTS	REASONS
1. $\angle BAC = \angle DAC$	**1.** Given
2. $\angle BCA = \angle DCA$	**2.** Given
3. $AC = AC$	**3.** Reflexive property
4. $\triangle ABD \cong \triangle ADC$	**4.** ASA congruence property

7. 67°, 67°   **9.** 6 in.   **11.** Answers will vary.   **13.** $\angle A$ and $\angle P$; $\angle C$ and $\angle R$; $\angle B$ and $\angle Q$; $\overline{AC}$ and $\overline{PR}$; $\overline{CB}$ and $\overline{RQ}$; $\overline{AB}$ and $\overline{PQ}$;   **15.** $\angle H$ and $\angle F$; $\angle K$ and $\angle E$; $\angle HGK$ and $\angle FGE$; $\overline{HK}$ and $\overline{FE}$; $\overline{GK}$ and $\overline{GE}$; $\overline{HG}$ and $\overline{FG}$;   **17.** $\angle P = 78°$; $\angle M = 46°$; $\angle A = \angle N = 56°$ **19.** $\angle T = 74°$; $\angle Y = 28°$; $\angle Z = \angle W = 78°$
21. $\angle T = 20°$; $\angle V = 64°$; $\angle R = \angle U = 96°$ **23.** $a = 20$; $b = 15$ **25.** $a = 6$; $b = \frac{15}{2}$ **27.** $x = 6$

29. $x = 110$ **31.** $c = 111\frac{1}{9}$ **33.** 30 m **35.** 500 m, 700 m **37.** 112.5 ft **39.** 8 ft, 11 in.
41. $c = 17$ **43.** $a = 13$ **45.** $c = 50$ m **47.** $a = 20$ in. **49.** The sum of the squares of the two shorter sides of a right triangle is equal to the square of the longest side. **51.** $(3, 4, 5)$ **53.** $(7, 24, 25)$ **55.** $(12, 16, 20)$
57. Answers will vary. **59.** $(3, 4, 5)$ **61.** $(7, 24, 25)$ **63.** Answers will vary. **65.** $(4, 3, 5)$
67. $(8, 15, 17)$ **69.** Answers will vary. **71.** 24 m **73.** 16 ft **75.** 4.55 ft **77.** 19 ft, 3 in.
79. 28 ft, 10 in. **81.** (a) $\frac{1}{2}(a + b)(a + b)$ (b) PWX: $\frac{1}{2}ab$; PZY: $\frac{1}{2}ab$; PXY: $\frac{1}{2}c^2$

(c) $\frac{1}{2}(a + b)(a + b) = \frac{1}{2}ab + \frac{1}{2}ab + \frac{1}{2}c^2$. When simplified, this gives $a^2 + b^2 = c^2$.

83. $24 + 4\sqrt{6}$ **85.** 10 **87.** $256 + 64\sqrt{3}$ **89.** 5 in. **91.** Answers will vary. **93.** Answers will vary.

9.5 Exercises (Pages 584–587)

1. true **3.** true **5.** false **7.** (a) $3\frac{3}{4}$ m³ (b) $14\frac{3}{4}$ m² **9.** (a) 96 in.³ (b) 130.4 in.²
11. (a) 267,946.67 ft³ (b) 20,096 ft² **13.** (a) 549.5 cm³ (b) 376.8 cm² **15.** (a) 65.94 m³ (b) 100.00 m²
17. 168 in.³ **19.** 1969.10 cm³ **21.** 427.29 cm³ **23.** 508.68 cm³ **25.** 2,415,766.67 m³ **27.** .52 m³
29. 12 in., 288 π in.³, 144 π in.² **31.** 5 ft, $\frac{500}{3}\pi$ ft³, 100 π ft² **33.** 2 cm, 4 cm, 16 π cm²
35. 1 m, 2 m, $\frac{4}{3}\pi$ m³ **37.** volume **39.** $\sqrt[3]{2}\,x$ **41.** \$8100 **43.** \$37,500 **45.** 2.5 **47.** 6
49. 210 in.³ **51.** $\frac{62,500}{3}\pi$ in.³ **53.** 2 to 1 **55.** 288 **57.** 4, 4, 6, 2 **59.** 8, 6, 12, 2 **61.** 20, 12, 30, 2

9.6 Exercises (Pages 596–598)

The answers are given in blue for this section.

1.
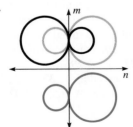

3.

5.

7. The figure is its own reflection image.

9.
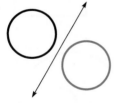

11.

13.
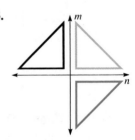

15.
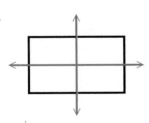

17.
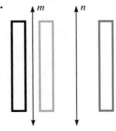

19.
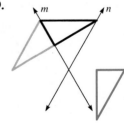

21.

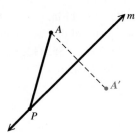

23.

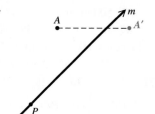

25.

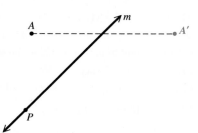

27.

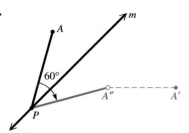

29.

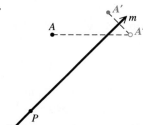

31.

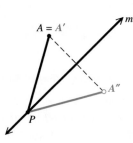

33. no   **35.**

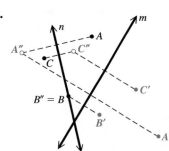

37.

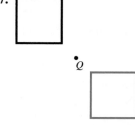

39.

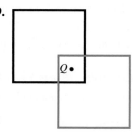

41.

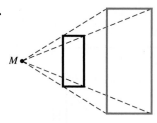

43.

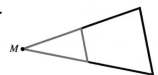

45.

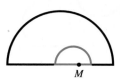

9.7 Exercises   (Pages 606–609)

1. Euclidean   **3.** Lobachevskian   **5.** greater than   **7.** Riemannian   **9.** Euclidean

11. (a)–(g)

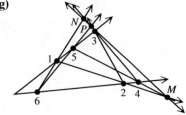

(h) Suppose that a hexagon is inscribed in an angle. Let each pair of opposite sides be extended so as to intersect. Then the three points of intersection thus obtained will lie in a straight line.
13. C   **15.** A, E   **17.** A, E   **19.** none of them
21. no   **23.** yes   **25.** 1   **27.** 3   **29.** 1
31. A, C, D, and F are even; B and E are odd.   **33.** A, B, C, and F are odd; D, E, and G are even.   **35.** A, B, C, and D are odd; E is even

37. traversable

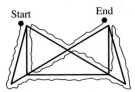

39. not traversable   **41.** traversable

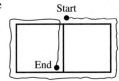

43. yes   **45.** no

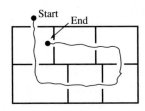

9.8 Exercises (Pages 613–615)

1. 4   **2.** 4   **3.** 2   **4.** $\dfrac{2}{1} = 2$ **5.** $\dfrac{4}{1} = 4$ **6.** $\dfrac{3}{1} = 3;\dfrac{9}{1} = 9$ **7.** $\dfrac{4}{1} = 4;\dfrac{16}{1} = 16$ **8.** 4, 9, 16,

25, 36, 100   **9.** Each ratio in the bottom row is the square of the scale factor in the top row.   **10.** 4
11. 4, 9, 16, 25, 36, 100   **12.** Each ratio in the bottom row is again the square of the scale factor in the top row.
13. Answers will vary. Some examples are: $3^d = 9$, thus $d = 2$; $5^d = 25$, thus $d = 2$; $4^d = 16$, thus $d = 2$.   **14.** 8
15. $\dfrac{2}{1} = 2;\dfrac{8}{1} = 8$ **16.** 8, 27, 64, 125, 216, 1000   **17.** Each ratio in the bottom row is the cube of the scale

factor in the top row.   **18.** Since $2^3 = 8$, the value of d in $2^d = 8$ must be 3.   **19.** $\dfrac{3}{1} = 3$.   **20.** 4

21. 1.262 or $\dfrac{\ln 4}{\ln 3}$ **22.** $\dfrac{2}{1} = 2$ **23.** 3   **24.** It is between 1 and 2.   **25.** 1.585 or $\dfrac{\ln 3}{\ln 2}$ **27.** .842, .452,
.842, .452, ... The two attractors are .842 and .452.

Chapter 9 Test (Pages 617–619)

1. (a) 52° (b) 142° (c) acute   **2.** 40°, 140°   **3.** 45°, 45°   **4.** 30°, 60°   **5.** 130°, 50°   **6.** 117°, 117°
7. Answers will vary.   **8.** C   **9.** both   **10.** neither   **11.** 30°, 45°, 105°   **12.** 72 cm²   **13.** 60 in.²
14. 68 m²   **15.** 180 m²   **16.** 24 π in.   **17.** 1978 ft   **18.** 57 cm²

19.

STATEMENTS	REASONS
1. $\angle CAB = \angle DBA$	**1.** Given
2. $DB = CA$	**2.** Given
3. $AB = AB$	**3.** Reflexive property
4. $\triangle ABD \cong \triangle BAC$	**4.** SAS congruence property

20. 20 ft   **21.** 29 m   **22.**

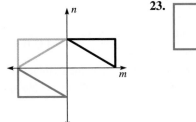

23.

24. (a) 904.32 in.³   (b) 452.16 in.²   **25.** (a) 864 ft² (b) 552 ft²   **26.** (a) 1582.56 m³ (b) 753.60 m²
27. Answers will vary.   **28.** (a) yes   (b) no

29. (a) yes 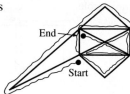 **(b)** no **30.** The only attractor is .5238095238.

CHAPTER 10 Trigonometry

10.1 Exercises (Pages 626–627)

1. (a) 60° **(b)** 150° **3. (a)** 45° **(b)** 135° **5. (a)** 1° **(b)** 91° **7.** $(90 - x)$ degrees **9.** 83°59′
11. 119°27′ **13.** 38°32′ **15.** 17°1′49″ **17.** 20.900° **19.** 91.598° **21.** 274.316° **23.** 31°25′47″
25. 89°54′1″ **27.** 178°35′58″ **29.** 320° **31.** 235° **33.** 179° **35.** 130° **37.** $30° + n \cdot 360°$
39. $60° + n \cdot 360°$

Angles other than those given are possible in Exercises 41–47.

41.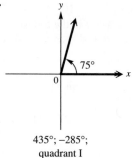

435°; −285°;
quadrant I

43.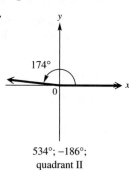

534°; −186°;
quadrant II

45.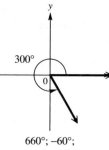

660°; −60°;
quadrant IV

47.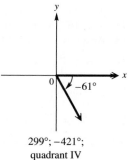

299°; −421°;
quadrant IV

10.2 Exercises (Pages 630–631)

1.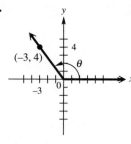

3.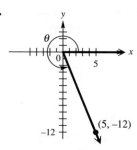

5. $\dfrac{4}{5}; -\dfrac{3}{5}; \dfrac{4}{3}; -\dfrac{3}{4}; -\dfrac{5}{3}; \dfrac{5}{4}$

7. $1; 0;$ undefined; $0;$ undefined; 1

9. $\dfrac{\sqrt{3}}{2}; \dfrac{1}{2}; \sqrt{3}; \dfrac{\sqrt{3}}{3}; 2; \dfrac{2\sqrt{3}}{3}$ **11.** $\dfrac{5\sqrt{34}}{34}; \dfrac{3\sqrt{34}}{34}; \dfrac{5}{3}; \dfrac{3}{5}; \dfrac{\sqrt{34}}{3}; \dfrac{\sqrt{34}}{5}$ **13.** $0; -1; 0;$ undefined; $-1;$ undefined

15. Answers will vary. **17.** It is the distance from a point (x, y) on the terminal side of the angle to the origin.
19. positive **21.** negative **23.** positive **25.** negative **27.** 0 **29.** undefined **31.** undefined
33. 0 **35.** 0 **37.** 1 **39.** 0

10.3 Exercises (Pages 635–636)

1. $-\dfrac{1}{3}$ **3.** $\dfrac{1}{3}$ **5.** -5 **7.** $2\sqrt{2}$ **9.** $-\dfrac{3\sqrt{5}}{5}$ **11.** $\dfrac{2}{3}$ **13.** II **15.** I **17.** II **19.** II or III

21. +; +; + **23.** −; −; + **25.** −; +; − **27.** +; +; + **29.** −; +; − **31.** $-2\sqrt{2}$ **33.** $\dfrac{\sqrt{15}}{4}$

35. $-2\sqrt{2}$ **37.** $-\dfrac{\sqrt{15}}{4}$

In Exercises 39–46, we give, in order, sine, cosine, tangent, cotangent, secant, and cosecant.

39. $\dfrac{15}{17}; -\dfrac{8}{17}; -\dfrac{15}{8}; -\dfrac{8}{15}; -\dfrac{17}{8}; \dfrac{17}{15}$ **41.** $-\dfrac{4}{5}; -\dfrac{3}{5}; \dfrac{4}{3}; \dfrac{3}{4}; -\dfrac{5}{3}; -\dfrac{5}{4}$

43. $-\dfrac{\sqrt{3}}{2}; -\dfrac{1}{2}; \sqrt{3}; \dfrac{\sqrt{3}}{3}; -2; \dfrac{2\sqrt{3}}{3}$ **45.** $\dfrac{\sqrt{5}}{7}; \dfrac{2\sqrt{11}}{7}; \dfrac{\sqrt{55}}{22}; \dfrac{2\sqrt{55}}{5}; \dfrac{7\sqrt{11}}{22}; \dfrac{7\sqrt{5}}{5}$ **47.** Answers will vary.

10.4 Exercises (Pages 644–645)

1. $\dfrac{3}{5}; \dfrac{4}{5}; \dfrac{3}{4}; \dfrac{4}{3}; \dfrac{5}{4}; \dfrac{5}{3}$ **3.** $\dfrac{21}{29}; \dfrac{20}{29}; \dfrac{21}{20}; \dfrac{20}{21}; \dfrac{29}{20}; \dfrac{29}{21}$ **5.** $\dfrac{n}{p}; \dfrac{m}{p}; \dfrac{n}{m}; \dfrac{m}{n}; \dfrac{p}{m}; \dfrac{p}{n}$

In Exercises 7 and 9, we give, in order, the unknown side, sine, cosine, tangent, cotangent, secant, and cosecant.

7. $c = 13; \dfrac{12}{13}; \dfrac{5}{13}; \dfrac{12}{5}; \dfrac{5}{12}; \dfrac{13}{5}; \dfrac{13}{12}$ **9.** $b = \sqrt{13}; \dfrac{\sqrt{13}}{7}; \dfrac{6}{7}; \dfrac{\sqrt{13}}{6}; \dfrac{6\sqrt{13}}{13}; \dfrac{7}{6}; \dfrac{7\sqrt{13}}{13}$ **11.** $\cot 40°$

13. $\sec 43°$ **15.** $\cot 64.6°$ **17.** $\sin 76°30'$ **19.** $\dfrac{\sqrt{3}}{3}$ **21.** $\dfrac{1}{2}$ **23.** $\sqrt{2}$ **25.** $\dfrac{\sqrt{2}}{2}$ **27.** $\dfrac{\sqrt{3}}{2}$

29. $\sqrt{3}$ **31.** $82°$ **33.** $45°$ **35.** $30°$

In Exercises 37–55, we give, in order, sine, cosine, tangent, cotangent, secant, and cosecant.

37. $\dfrac{\sqrt{3}}{2}; -\dfrac{1}{2}; -\sqrt{3}; -\dfrac{\sqrt{3}}{3}; -2; \dfrac{2\sqrt{3}}{3}$ **39.** $\dfrac{1}{2}; -\dfrac{\sqrt{3}}{2}; -\dfrac{\sqrt{3}}{3}; -\sqrt{3}; -\dfrac{2\sqrt{3}}{3}; 2$

41. $-\dfrac{\sqrt{3}}{2}; -\dfrac{1}{2}; \sqrt{3}; \dfrac{\sqrt{3}}{3}; -2; -\dfrac{2\sqrt{3}}{3}$ **43.** $-\dfrac{\sqrt{2}}{2}; \dfrac{\sqrt{2}}{2}; -1; -1; \sqrt{2}; -\sqrt{2}$ **45.** $\dfrac{\sqrt{3}}{2}; \dfrac{1}{2}; \sqrt{3}; \dfrac{\sqrt{3}}{3}; 2; \dfrac{2\sqrt{3}}{3}$

47. $\dfrac{\sqrt{2}}{2}; -\dfrac{\sqrt{2}}{2}; -1; -1; -\sqrt{2}; \sqrt{2}$ **49.** $\dfrac{1}{2}; \dfrac{\sqrt{3}}{2}; \dfrac{\sqrt{3}}{3}; \sqrt{3}; \dfrac{2\sqrt{3}}{3}; 2$ **51.** $\dfrac{\sqrt{3}}{2}; \dfrac{1}{2}; \sqrt{3}; \dfrac{\sqrt{3}}{3}; 2; \dfrac{2\sqrt{3}}{3}$

53. $-\dfrac{1}{2}; \dfrac{\sqrt{3}}{2}; -\dfrac{\sqrt{3}}{3}; -\sqrt{3}; \dfrac{2\sqrt{3}}{3}; -2$ **55.** $\dfrac{\sqrt{3}}{2}; \dfrac{1}{2}; \sqrt{3}; \dfrac{\sqrt{3}}{3}; 2; \dfrac{2\sqrt{3}}{3}$ **57.** $\dfrac{\sqrt{3}}{3}, \sqrt{3}$

59. $\dfrac{\sqrt{3}}{2}, \dfrac{\sqrt{3}}{3}, \dfrac{2\sqrt{3}}{3}$ **61.** $-1, -1$ **63.** $-\dfrac{\sqrt{3}}{2}, -\dfrac{2\sqrt{3}}{3}$ **65.** $210°, 330°$ **67.** $45°, 225°$ **69.** $60°, 120°$

71. $120°, 240°$ **73.** $225°, 315°$ **75.** $120°, 300°$

10.5 Exercises (Pages 651–654)

1. .5657728 **3.** 1.1342773 **5.** 1.0273488 **7.** .6383201 **9.** 1.7768146 **11.** .4771588

13. −5.7297416 **15.** 1.9074147 **17.** 57.997172° **19.** 30.502748° **21.** 46.173581°

23. 81.168073° **25.** $B = 53°40'; a = 571$ m; $b = 777$ m **27.** $M = 38.8°; n = 154$ m; $p = 198$ m

29. $A = 47.9108°; c = 84.816$ cm; $a = 62.942$ cm **31.** $B = 62.00°; a = 8.17$ ft; $b = 15.4$ ft

33. $A = 17.00°; a = 39.1$ in.; $c = 134$ in. **35.** $c = 85.9$ yd; $A = 62°50'; B = 27°10'$ **37.** $b = 42.3$ cm;

$A = 24°10'; B = 65°50'$ **39.** $B = 36°36'; a = 310.8$ ft; $b = 230.8$ ft **41.** $A = 50°51'; a = .4832$ m;

$b = .3934$ m **43.** 9.35 meters **45.** 88.3 meters **47.** 26.92 inches **49.** 583 feet **51.** 28.0 meters

53. 469 meters **55.** 146 meters **57.** 34.0 miles **59.** $a = 12, b = 12\sqrt{3}, d = 12\sqrt{3}, c = 12\sqrt{6}$

10.6 Exercises (Pages 663–668)

1. $C = 95°, b = 13$ m, $a = 11$ m **3.** $B = 37.3°, a = 38.5$ ft, $b = 51.0$ ft **5.** $C = 57.36°, b = 11.13$ ft,

$c = 11.55$ ft **7.** $B = 18.5°, a = 239$ yd, $c = 230$ yd **9.** $A = 56°00', AB = 361$ ft, $BC = 308$ ft

11. $B = 110.0°, a = 27.01$ m, $c = 21.36$ m **13.** $A = 34.72°, a = 3326$ ft, $c = 5704$ ft

15. $C = 97°34', b = 283.2$ m, $c = 415.2$ m **17.** 118 meters **19.** 10.4 inches **21.** 12 **23.** 7 **25.** $30°$

27. $c = 2.83$ in., $A = 44.9°$, $B = 106.8°$ **29.** $c = 6.46$ m, $A = 53.1°$, $B = 81.3°$
31. $a = 156$ cm, $B = 64°50'$, $C = 34°30'$ **33.** $b = 9.529$ in., $A = 64.59°$, $C = 40.61°$
35. $a = 15.7$ m, $B = 21.6°$, $C = 45.6°$ **37.** $A = 30°$, $B = 56°$, $C = 94°$
39. $A = 82°$, $B = 37°$, $C = 61°$ **41.** $A = 42.0°$, $B = 35.9°$, $C = 102.1°$ **43.** 257 meters   **45.** 22 feet

47. 36° with the 45-foot cable, 26° with the 60-foot cable   **49.** $\dfrac{\sqrt{3}}{2}$ **51.** $\dfrac{\sqrt{2}}{2}$ **53.** 46.4 m²   **55.** 356 cm²

57. 722.9 in.²   **59.** $24\sqrt{3}$ **61.** 78 m²   **63.** 12,600 cm²   **65.** 3650 ft²   **67.** 100 m²   **69.** 33 cans

Chapter 10 Test   **(Pages 668–669)**

1. 74.2983°   **2.** 203°   **3.** $\sin \theta = -\dfrac{5\sqrt{29}}{29}$; $\cos \theta = \dfrac{2\sqrt{29}}{29}$; $\tan \theta = -\dfrac{5}{2}$ **4.** III   **5.** $\sin \theta = -\dfrac{3}{5}$;

$\tan \theta = -\dfrac{3}{4}$; $\cot \theta = -\dfrac{4}{3}$; $\sec \theta = \dfrac{5}{4}$; $\csc \theta = -\dfrac{5}{3}$ **6.** $\sin A = \dfrac{12}{13}$; $\cos A = \dfrac{5}{13}$; $\tan A = \dfrac{12}{5}$;

$\cot A = \dfrac{5}{12}$; $\sec A = \dfrac{13}{5}$; $\csc A = \dfrac{13}{12}$ **7. (a)** $\dfrac{1}{2}$ **(b)** 1   **(c)** undefined   **(d)** $-\dfrac{2\sqrt{3}}{3}$ **(e)** undefined
(f) $-\sqrt{2}$

8. (a) .97939940   **(b)** .20834446   **(c)** 1.9362132   **(d)** 4.16529977   **9.** 16.16664145°   **10.** 135°, 225°
11. $B = 31°30'$, $a = 638$, $b = 391$ **12.** 15.5 ft   **13.** 137.5°   **14.** 180 km   **15.** 49.0°   **16.** 4300 km²
17. 264 square units   **18.** 2.7 miles   **19.** 5500 meters   **20.** distance to both first and third bases: 63.7 feet;
distance to second base: 66.8 feet

CHAPTER 11   Counting Methods

11.1 Exercises   **(Pages 678–681)**

1. *AB, AC, AD, AE, BA, BC, BD, BE, CA, CB,*
CD, CE, DA, DB, DC, DE, EA, EB, EC, ED;
20 ways   **3.** *AC, AE, BC, BE, CA, CB, CD,*
DC, DE, EA, EB, ED; 12 ways   **5.** *ACE,*
AEC, BCE, BEC, DCE, DEC; 6 ways
7. *ABC, ABD, ABE, ACD, ACE, ADE, BCD,*
BCE, BDE, CDE; 10 ways   **9.** 1   **11.** 3
13. 5   **15.** 5   **17.** 3   **19.** 1
21. 18   **23.** 15

25.

	1	2	3	4	5	6
1	11	12	13	14	15	16
2	21	22	23	24	25	26
3	31	32	33	34	35	36
4	41	42	43	44	45	46
5	51	52	53	54	55	56
6	61	62	63	64	65	66

27. 11, 22, 33, 44, 55, 66   **29.** 11, 13, 23,
31, 41, 43, 53, 61   **31.** 16, 25, 36, 64
33. 16, 32, 64

35. (a) tttt   **(b)** hhhh,
hhht, hhth, hhtt, hthh, htht,
htth, thhh, thht, thth, tthh
(c) httt, thtt, ttht, ttth, tttt
(d) hhhh, hhht, hhth, hhtt,
hthh, htht, htth, httt, thhh,
thht, thth, thtt, tthh, ttht, ttth

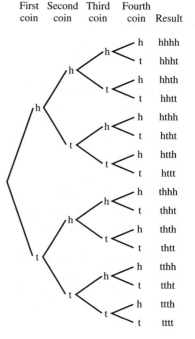

First coin	Second coin	Third coin	Fourth coin	Result
			h	hhhh
		h	t	hhht
	h	t	h	hhth
			t	hhtt
h			h	hthh
	t	h	t	htht
		t	h	htth
			t	httt
			h	thhh
		h	t	thht
	h	t	h	thth
t			t	thtt
			h	tthh
	t	h	t	ttht
		t	h	ttth
			t	tttt

37. 16   **39.** 36   **41.** 17   **43.** 72   **45.** 12   **47.** 10   **49.** 6   **51.** 3   **53.** 54   **55.** 18
57. 138   **59.** 16   **61.** 13   **63.** 4   **65.** 883   **67.** 3   **69.** (a) Determine the number of ordered pairs of digits that can be selected from the set $\{1, 2, 3, 4, 5, 6\}$ if repetition of digits is allowed.   (b) Determine the number of ordered pairs of digits that can be selected from the set $\{1, 2, 3, 4, 5, 6\}$ if the selection is done with replacement.
71. (a) Find the number of ways to select three letters from the set $\{A, B, C, D, E\}$ if repetition of letters is not allowed.   (b) Find the number of ways to select three letters from the set $\{A, B, C, D, E\}$ if the selection is done without replacement.

11.2 Exercises   (Pages 689–692)

1. Answers will vary.   **3.** (a) no   (b) Answers will vary.   **5.** (a) no   (b) Answers will vary.   **7.** 24
9. 336   **11.** 20   **13.** 84   **15.** 840   **17.** 39,916,800   **19.** 95,040   **21.** 1716   **23.** 184,756
25. $4.151586701 \times 10^{12}$ **27.** 362,880   **29.** 1680   **31.** $2^3 = 8$ **33.** Answers will vary.
35. $6^3 = 216$ **37.** $5! = 120$ **39.** $3 \cdot 2 = 6$ **41.** $3 \cdot 3 = 9$ **43.** $3 \cdot 2 \cdot 1 = 6$ **45.** $4 \cdot 2 \cdot 3 = 24$
47. $2^6 = 64$ **49.** $3 \cdot 3 \cdot 4 \cdot 5 = 180$ **51.** $3 \cdot 3 \cdot 4 \cdot 3 = 108$ **53.** $3 \cdot 3 \cdot 1 \cdot 3 = 27$
55. $2 \cdot 5 \cdot 6 = 60$ **57.** $5! = 120$ **59.** (a) 6   (b) 5   (c) 4   (d) 3   (e) 2   (f) 1; 720   **61.** (a) 3
(b) 3   (c) 2   (d) 2   (e) 1   (f) 1; 36   **63.** Answers will vary.   **65.** 450; no

11.3 Exercises   (Pages 702–705)

1. 840   **3.** 495   **5.** 1,028,160   **7.** 70   **9.** $1.805037696 \times 10^{11}$ **11.** Answers will vary.
13. Answers will vary.   **15.** (a) permutation   (b) permutation   (c) combination   (d) combination
(e) permutation   (f) combination   (g) permutation   **17.** $_8P_5 = 6720$ **19.** $_{12}P_2 = 132$
21. $_{25}P_5 = 6,375,600$ **23.** (a) $_4P_4 = 24$ (b) $_4P_4 = 24$ **25.** $_{18}C_5 = 8568$ **27.** (a) $_{13}C_5 = 1287$
(b) $_{26}C_5 = 65,780$ (c) 0 (impossible)   **29.** (a) $_6C_3 = 20$ (b) $_6C_2 = 15$ **31.** $_{10}C_3 = 120$ **33.** (a) 5
(b) 9   **35.** $_{26}P_3 \cdot {}_{10}P_3 \cdot {}_{26}P_3 = 175,219,200,000$ **37.** $2 \cdot {}_{25}P_3 = 27,600$ **39.** $7 \cdot {}_{12}P_8 = 139,708,800$
41. (a) $7^7 = 823,543$ (b) $7! = 5040$ **43.** $_{25}C_3 \cdot {}_{22}C_4 \cdot {}_{18}C_5 \cdot {}_{13}C_6 \approx 2.473653743 \times 10^{14}$
45. $_{20}C_3 = 1140$ **47.** (a) $_7P_2 = 42$ (b) $3 \cdot 6 = 18$ (c) $_7P_2 \cdot 5 = 210$ **49.** $_8P_3 = 336$
51. (a) $_6C_2 \cdot {}_6C_3 \cdot {}_6C_4 = 4500$ (b) $3! \cdot {}_6C_2 \cdot {}_6C_3 \cdot {}_6C_4 = 27,000$ **53.** (a) $8! = 40,320$ (b) $2 \cdot 6! = 1440$
(c) $6! = 720$ **55.** (a) $2 \cdot 4! = 48$ (b) $3 \cdot 4! = 72$ **57.** Each equals 220.   **59.** (a) 1   (b) Answers
will vary.

11.4 Exercises   (Pages 710–712)

1. 6   **3.** 20   **5.** 56   **7.** 36   **9.** $_7C_1 \cdot {}_3C_3 = 7$ **11.** $_7C_3 \cdot {}_3C_1 = 105$ **13.** $_8C_3 = 56$
15. $_8C_5 = 56$ **17.** $_9C_4 = 126$ **19.** $1 \cdot {}_8C_3 = 56$ **21.** 1   **23.** 10   **25.** 5   **27.** 32   **29.** (a) All are multiples of the row number.   (b) The same pattern holds.   (c) The same pattern holds.   **31.** $\ldots 8, 13, 21, 34, \ldots$; A number in this sequence is the sum of the two preceding terms. This is the Fibonacci sequence.   **33.** row 8
35. The sum of the squares of the entries across the top row equals the entry at the bottom vertex.
37. Answers will vary.   **Wording may vary for Exercises 39 and 41.**   **39.** sum = N; Any entry in the array equals the sum of the two entries immediately above it and immediately to its left.   **41.** sum = N; Any entry in the array equals the sum of the row of entries from the cell immediately above it to the left boundary of the array.

11.5 Exercises   (Pages 717–719)

1. $2^4 - 1 = 15$ **3.** $2^7 - 1 = 127$ **5.** 120   **7.** $36 - 6 = 30$ **9.** $6 + 6 - 1 = 11$ **11.** 51
13. $90 - 9 = 81$ **15.** (a) $_8C_3 = 56$ (b) $_7C_3 = 35$ (c) $56 - 35 = 21$ **17.** $_7C_3 - {}_5C_3 = 25$
19. $_8P_3 - {}_6P_3 = 216$ **21.** $_{10}P_3 - {}_7P_3 = 510$ **23.** $_{25}C_4 - {}_{23}C_4 = 3795$ **25.** $13 + 4 - 1 = 16$
27. $30 + 15 - 10 = 35$ **29.** $2,598,960 - {}_{13}C_5 = 2,597,673$ **31.** $2,598,960 - {}_{40}C_5 = 1,940,952$
33. $_{12}C_0 + {}_{12}C_1 + {}_{12}C_2 = 79$ **35.** $2^{12} - 79 = 4017$ **37.** $26^3 \cdot 10^3 - {}_{26}P_3 \cdot {}_{10}P_3 = 6,344,000$
39. Answers will vary.   **41.** $_4C_3 + {}_3C_3 + {}_5C_3 = 15$ **43.** $_{12}C_3 - 4 \cdot 3 \cdot 5 = 160$ **45.** Answers will vary.
47. Answers will vary.   **49.** Answers will vary.

Chapter 11 Test **(Pages 720–721)**

1. $6 \cdot 7 \cdot 7 = 294$ **2.** $6 \cdot 7 \cdot 4 = 168$ **3.** $6 \cdot 6 \cdot 5 = 180$ **4.** $6 \cdot 5 \cdot 1 = 30$ end in 0; $5 \cdot 5 \cdot 1 = 25$ end in 5; $30 + 25 = 55$ **5.** 13

6.

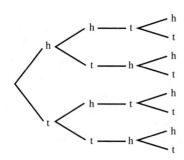

First toss Second toss Third toss Fourth toss

7. $4! = 24$ **8.** 12 **9.** 120 **10.** 336 **11.** 11,880 **12.** 35 **13.** $_{26}P_5 = 7,893,600$
14. $32^5 = 33.554,432$ **15.** $_7P_4 = 840$ **16.** $3! = 6$ **17.** 120 **18.** 30,240 **19.** $_{12}C_4 = 495$
20. $_{12}C_2 \cdot {}_{10}C_2 = 2970$ **21.** $_{12}C_5 \cdot {}_7C_5 = 16,632$ **22.** $2^{12} - [{}_{12}C_0 + {}_{12}C_1 + {}_{12}C_2] = 4017$ **23.** $2^4 = 16$
24. $2^2 = 4$ **25.** $2 \cdot 2^2 = 8$ **26.** 8 **27.** 2 **28.** $16 - (1 + 4) = 11$ **29.** $_6C_3 = 20$
30. $_5C_2 = 10$ **31.** $2 \cdot {}_5C_3 = 20$ **32.** $_5C_2 = 10$ **33.** $_5C_4 + {}_2C_1 \cdot {}_5C_3 = 25$ **34.** Answers will vary.
35. $495 + 220 = 715$ **36.** the counting numbers **37.** Answers will vary.

CHAPTER 12 Probability

12.1 Exercises **(Pages 731–735)**

1. (a) $\dfrac{1}{3}$ (b) $\dfrac{1}{3}$ (c) $\dfrac{1}{3}$ **3.** (a) $\dfrac{1}{2}$ (b) $\dfrac{1}{3}$ (c) $\dfrac{1}{6}$ **5.** (a) $\{1, 2, 3\}$ (b) 2 (c) 1 (d) 3 (e) $\dfrac{2}{3}$ (f) 2 to 1

7. (a) $\{11, 12, 13, 21, 22, 23, 31, 32, 33\}$ (b) $\dfrac{2}{3}$ (c) $\dfrac{1}{3}$ (d) $\dfrac{1}{3}$ (e) $\dfrac{4}{9}$ **9.** (a) 4 to 7 (b) 5 to 6 (c) 2 to 9

11. (a) $\dfrac{1}{50}$ (b) $\dfrac{2}{50} = \dfrac{1}{25}$ (c) $\dfrac{3}{50}$ (d) $\dfrac{4}{50} = \dfrac{2}{25}$ (e) $\dfrac{5}{50} = \dfrac{1}{10}$ **13.** (a) $\dfrac{1}{36}$ (b) $\dfrac{2}{36} = \dfrac{1}{18}$ (c) $\dfrac{3}{36} = \dfrac{1}{12}$
(d) $\dfrac{4}{36} = \dfrac{1}{9}$ (e) $\dfrac{5}{36}$ (f) $\dfrac{6}{36} = \dfrac{1}{6}$ (g) $\dfrac{5}{36}$ (h) $\dfrac{4}{36} = \dfrac{1}{9}$ (i) $\dfrac{3}{36} = \dfrac{1}{12}$ (j) $\dfrac{2}{36} = \dfrac{1}{18}$ (k) $\dfrac{1}{36}$
15. (a) $\dfrac{34,244,000}{288,280,000} \approx .119$ (b) $\dfrac{288,280,000 - 34,244,000}{288,280,000} = \dfrac{254,036,000}{288,280,000} \approx .881$ **17.** Answers will vary.
19. $\dfrac{1}{4}$ **21.** $\dfrac{1}{4}$ **23.** (a) $\dfrac{3}{4}$ (b) $\dfrac{1}{4}$ **25.** $\dfrac{1}{250,000} = .000004$ **27.** $\dfrac{1}{4}$ **29.** $\dfrac{1}{4}$ **31.** $\dfrac{2}{4} = \dfrac{1}{2}$
33. $\dfrac{1}{500} = .002$ **35.** about 160 **37.** $\dfrac{2}{4} = \dfrac{1}{2}$ **39.** (a) 0 (b) no (c) yes **41.** Answers will vary.
43. $\dfrac{12}{31}$ **45.** $\dfrac{36}{2,598,960} \approx .00001385$ **47.** $\dfrac{624}{2,598,960} \approx .00024010$ **49.** $\dfrac{1}{4} \cdot \dfrac{5108}{2,598,960} \approx .00049135$
51. (a) $\dfrac{5}{9}$ (b) $\dfrac{49}{144}$ (c) $\dfrac{5}{48}$ **53.** $3 \cdot 1 \cdot 2 \cdot 1 \cdot 1 \cdot 1 = 6;$ $\dfrac{6}{720} = \dfrac{1}{120} \approx .0083$ **55.** $4 \cdot 3! \cdot 3! = 144;$
$\dfrac{144}{720} = \dfrac{1}{5} = .2$ **57.** $\dfrac{2}{{}_7C_2} = \dfrac{2}{21} \approx .095$ **59.** $\dfrac{{}_5C_3}{{}_{12}C_3} = \dfrac{1}{22} \approx .045$ **61.** $\dfrac{1}{{}_{36}P_3} \approx .000023$ **63.** $\dfrac{3}{28} \approx .107$
65. (a) $\dfrac{8}{9^2} = \dfrac{8}{81} \approx .099$ (b) $\dfrac{4}{{}_9C_2} = \dfrac{1}{9} \approx .111$ **67.** $\dfrac{9 \cdot 10}{9 \cdot 10^2} = \dfrac{1}{10}$

12.2 Exercises (Pages 742–743)

1. yes **3.** Answers will vary. **5.** $\dfrac{1}{2}$ **7.** $\dfrac{5}{6}$ **9.** $\dfrac{2}{3}$ **11. (a)** $\dfrac{2}{13}$ **(b)** 2 to 11 **13. (a)** $\dfrac{11}{26}$ **(b)** 11 to 15

15. (a) $\dfrac{9}{13}$ **(b)** 9 to 4 **17.** $\dfrac{2}{3}$ **19.** $\dfrac{7}{36}$ **21.** $P(A) + P(B) + P(C) + P(D) = 1$ **23.** .005365

25. .971285 **27.** .76 **29.** .92 **31.** 6 to 19

33.

x	$P(x)$
3	.1
4	.1
5	.2
6	.2
7	.2
8	.1
9	.1

35. $n(A') = s - a$ **37.** $P(A) + P(A') = 1$ **39.** 180 **41.** $\dfrac{2}{3}$ **43.** 1

12.3 Exercises (Pages 752–755)

1. independent **3.** not independent **5.** independent **7.** $\dfrac{42}{100} = \dfrac{21}{50}$ **9.** $\dfrac{68}{100} = \dfrac{17}{25}$ **11.** $\dfrac{19}{34}$

13. $\dfrac{4}{7} \cdot \dfrac{4}{7} = \dfrac{16}{49}$ **15.** $\dfrac{2}{7} \cdot \dfrac{1}{7} = \dfrac{2}{49}$ **17.** $\dfrac{4}{7} \cdot \dfrac{3}{6} = \dfrac{2}{7}$ **19.** $\dfrac{1}{6}$ **21.** 0 **23.** $\dfrac{12}{51} = \dfrac{4}{17}$ **25.** $\dfrac{12}{52} \cdot \dfrac{11}{51} = \dfrac{11}{221}$

27. $\dfrac{4}{52} \cdot \dfrac{11}{51} = \dfrac{11}{663}$ **29.** $\dfrac{1}{3}$ **31.** 1 **33.** $\dfrac{3}{10}$ (the same) **35.** $\dfrac{1}{2} \cdot \dfrac{1}{2} \cdot \dfrac{1}{2} = \dfrac{1}{8}$ **37.** .640 **39.** .008

41. .95 **43.** .23 **45.** $\dfrac{1}{35}$ **47.** $\dfrac{3}{7}$ **49.** $\dfrac{3}{7}$ **51. (a)** $\dfrac{3}{4}$ **(b)** $\dfrac{1}{2}$ **(c)** $\dfrac{5}{16}$ **53.** .2704 **55.** .2496

57. Answers will vary. **59.** $\dfrac{1}{64} \approx .0156$ **61.** 10 **63.** .400 **65.** .080 **67.** $(.90)^4 = .6561$

69. $_4C_2 \cdot (.10) \cdot (.20) \cdot (.70)^2 = .0588$ **71.** .30 **73.** .49 **75.** Answers will vary.

12.4 Exercises (Pages 760–762)

1. $\dfrac{1}{8}$ **3.** $\dfrac{3}{8}$ **5.** $\dfrac{3}{4}$ **7.** $\dfrac{1}{2}$ **9.** $\dfrac{3}{8}$ **11.** x; n; n **13.** $\dfrac{7}{128}$ **15.** $\dfrac{35}{128}$ **17.** $\dfrac{21}{128}$ **19.** $\dfrac{1}{128}$

21. $\dfrac{25}{72}$ **23.** $\dfrac{1}{216}$ **25.** .041 **27.** .268 **29.** Answers will vary. **31.** Answers will vary. **33.** .016

35. .020 **37.** .198 **39.** .448 **41.** .656 **43.** .002 **45.** .883 **47.** $\dfrac{1}{1024} \approx .001$ **49.** $\dfrac{45}{1024} \approx .044$

51. $\dfrac{210}{1024} = \dfrac{105}{512} \approx .205$ **53.** $\dfrac{772}{1024} \approx .754$

12.5 Exercises (Pages 770–773)

1. Answers will vary. **3.** $\dfrac{5}{2}$ **5.** $1 **7.** 50¢ **9.** no (expected net winnings: $-\dfrac{3}{4}$¢) **11.** 1.72

13. (a) $-60 **(b)** $36,000 **(c)** $72,000 **15.** 50¢ **17.** $2500 **19.** 2.7 **21.** an increase of 250
23. Answers will vary. **25.** Project C **27.** $2200 **29.** $83,400 **31.** Purchase the insurance (because
$83,400 > $80,400). **33.** 25,000; 60,000; 16,000 **35.** C; C; C; B; C; A; B **37.** about -15¢

Extension Exercises (Pages 777–778)

1. Answers will vary. **3.** no **5.** $\dfrac{18}{50} = .36$ (This is quite close to .375, the theoretical value.) **7.** $\dfrac{11}{50} = .22$

9. Answers will vary. **11.** Answers will vary.

Chapter 12 Test (Pages 779–780)

1. Answers will vary. **2.** Answers will vary. **3.** 3 to 1 **4.** 25 to 1 **5.** 11 to 2 **6.** row 1: CC; row 2: cC, cc

7. $\dfrac{1}{2}$ **8.** 1 to 3 **9.** $\dfrac{7}{7} \cdot \dfrac{6}{7} \cdot \dfrac{5}{7} = \dfrac{30}{49}$ **10.** $\dfrac{7}{19}$ **11.** $1 - \left(\dfrac{30}{49} + \dfrac{1}{49}\right) = \dfrac{18}{49}$ **12.** $\dfrac{_2C_2}{_5C_2} = \dfrac{1}{10}$

13. $\dfrac{_3C_2}{_5C_2} = \dfrac{3}{10}$ **14.** $\dfrac{6}{10} = \dfrac{3}{5}$ **15.** $\dfrac{3}{10}$ **16.** $\dfrac{3}{10}; \dfrac{6}{10}; \dfrac{1}{10},$ **17.** $\dfrac{9}{10}$ **18.** $\dfrac{18}{10} = \dfrac{9}{5}$ **19.** $\dfrac{6}{36} = \dfrac{1}{6}$ **20.** 35 to 1

21. 7 to 2 **22.** $\dfrac{4}{36} = \dfrac{1}{9}$ **23.** $(.78)^3 \approx .475$ **24.** $_3C_2 (.78)^2(.22) \approx .402$ **25.** $1 - (.22)^3 \approx .989$

26. $(.78)(.22)(.78) \approx .134$ **27.** $\dfrac{25}{102}$ **28.** $\dfrac{25}{51}$ **29.** $\dfrac{4}{51}$ **30.** $\dfrac{3}{26}$

CHAPTER 13 Statistics

13.1 Exercises (Pages 788–793)

1. (a)

x	f	f/n
0	10	$\frac{10}{30} \approx 33\%$
1	7	$\frac{7}{30} \approx 23\%$
2	6	$\frac{6}{30} = 20\%$
3	4	$\frac{4}{30} \approx 13\%$
4	2	$\frac{2}{30} \approx 7\%$
5	1	$\frac{1}{30} \approx 3\%$

(b)

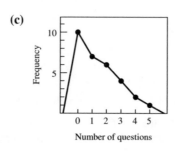

(c)

3. (a)

Class Limits	Tally	Frequency f	Relative Frequency f/n
45–49	|||	3	$\frac{3}{54} \approx 5.6\%$
50–54	卌 卌 ||||	14	$\frac{14}{54} \approx 25.9\%$
55–59	卌 卌 卌		16	$\frac{16}{54} \approx 29.6\%$
60–64	卌 卌 卌 ||	17	$\frac{17}{54} \approx 31.5\%$
65–69	||||	4	$\frac{4}{54} \approx 7.4\%$

Total: $n = 54$

(b)

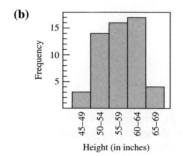

Height (in inches)

(c)

5. (a)

Class Limits	Tally	Frequency f	Relative Frequency f/n
70–74	‖	2	$\frac{2}{30} \approx 6.7\%$
75–79	│	1	$\frac{1}{30} \approx 3.3\%$
80–84	‖‖	3	$\frac{3}{30} = 10.0\%$
85–89	‖	2	$\frac{2}{30} \approx 6.7\%$
90–94	‖‖‖	5	$\frac{5}{30} \approx 16.7\%$
95–99	‖‖‖	5	$\frac{5}{30} \approx 16.7\%$
100–104	‖‖‖ │	6	$\frac{6}{30} = 20.0\%$
105–109	‖‖‖	4	$\frac{4}{30} \approx 13.3\%$
110–114	‖	2	$\frac{2}{30} \approx 6.7\%$

Total: $n = 30$

(b)

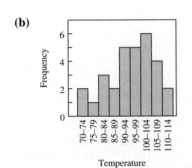

(c)

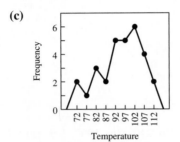

7.

0	7	9	8									
1	1	1	2	8	9	4	3	1	0	5	0	5	5
2	0	9	6	6	2	5	2	3	4	4
3	1

9.

0	8	5	4	9	6	9	4	8				
1	2	0	1	8	8	2	4	0	8	8	6	3
2	6	6	2	5	1	3
3	0	4	6
4	4

11. about 31%　　**13.** CBS; about 4%　　**15.** about .4%; 1998　　**17.** 3.5% in 2005　　**19.** Answers will vary.
21. 184°

23.

25. about 79 years　　**27. (a)** about 6 years　**(b)** Answers will vary.　　**29.** Answers will vary.　　**31.** Answers will vary.　　**33.** Answers will vary.

35. (a)

Letter	Probability
A	.208
E	.338
I	.169
O	.208
U	.078

(b)

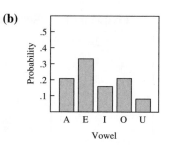

37. Answers will vary.   **39. (a)** .225 **(b)** .275 **(c)** .425 **(d)** .175

41. (a)

Sport	Probability
Sailing	.225
Hang gliding	.125
Bungee jumping	.175
Sky diving	.075
Canoeing	.300
Rafting	.100

(b) empirical   **(c)** Answers will vary.

13.2 Exercises **(Pages 803–807)**

1. (a) 14 **(b)** 10 **(c)** none   **3. (a)** 201.2 **(b)** 210 **(c)** 196   **5. (a)** 5.2 **(b)** 5.35 **(c)** 4.5 and 6.2
7. (a) .8 **(b)** .795 **(c)** none   **9. (a)** 129 **(b)** 128 **(c)** 125 and 128   **11. (a)** 2,154,000 **(b)** 1,320,000
13. (a) 1,292,000 **(b)** 573,000   **15.** 406,000   **17.** 4000 square miles   **19.** 5.27 seconds
21. 2.42 seconds   **23.** the mean   **25.** mean = 77; median = 80; mode = 79   **27.** 92   **29. (a)** 597.42
(b) 598 **(c)** 603   **31.** 2.41   **33.** 711,400 square miles   **35.** 23,303,000   **37.** 716,489
39. $-162,314$ **41.** $946,533.33   **43.** 4   **45. (a)** 17.4 **(b)** 14   **(c)** none   **47. (a)** 74.8 **(b)** 77.5
(c) 78   **49.** Answers will vary.   **51. (a)** mean = 13.7; median = 16; mode = 18   **(b)** median **(c)** Answers
will vary.   **53. (a)** 4 **(b)** 4.25   **55. (a)** 6 **(b)** 9.33   **57.** 80   **59.** no   **61.** Answers will vary.

13.3 Exercises **(Pages 814–817)**

1. the sample standard deviation   **3. (a)** 17 **(b)** 5.53   **5. (a)** 19 **(b)** 6.27   **7. (a)** 23 **(b)** 7.75
9. (a) 1.14 **(b)** .37   **11. (a)** 8 **(b)** 2.41   **13.** $\frac{3}{4}$ **15.** $\frac{45}{49}$ **17.** 88.9%   **19.** 64%   **21.** $\frac{3}{4}$ **23.** $\frac{15}{16}$
25. $\frac{1}{4}$ **27.** $\frac{4}{49}$ **29.** $202.50   **31.** six   **33.** There are at least nine.   **35. (a)** $s_A = 2.35; s_B = 2.58$
(b) $V_A = 46.9; V_B = 36.9$ **(c)** sample B   **(d)** sample A   **37. (a)** $\bar{x}_A = 69.0; \bar{x}_B = 66.6$
(b) $s_A = 4.53; s_B = 5.27$ **(c)** brand A, since $\bar{x}_A > \bar{x}_B$ **(d)** brand A, since $s_A < s_B$ **39.** Brand A
$(s_B = 2235 > 2116)$ **41.** 18.29; 4.35   **43.** 8.29; 4.35   **45.** 54.86; 13.04   **47.** Answers will vary.   **49.** no
51. Answers will vary.   **53. (a)** least **(b)** greatest **(c)** Answers will vary.

13.4 Exercises **(Pages 821–824)**

1. Lynn (since $z = .48 > .19$)   **3.** Arvind (since $z = -1.44 > -1.78$)   **5.** 58   **7.** 62   **9.** 1.3   **11.** 2.4
13. Kuwait   **15.** United Arab Emirates   **17.** Turkey in imports (Turkey's imports z-score was 2.4, Saudi
Arabia's exports z-score was 2.2, and 2.4 > 2.2.)   **19. (a)** The median is $30.5 billion.   **(b)** The range is

$113 - 10 = 103.$ **(c)** The middle half of the items extend from \$13 billion to \$69 billion. **21.** Answers will vary.
23. Answers will vary. **25.** Answers will vary. **27.** the overall distribution **29. (a)** no **(b)** Answers will vary. **31.** Answers will vary. **33.** Answers will vary. **35.** $Q_1 = 61.1, Q_2 = 77.2, Q_3 = 90.9$
37. $P_{65} = 89.7$ **39.** 76.0

41.

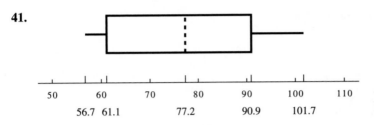

43. 107.5 **45.** high percentage of touchdown passes (about 13.9%)

13.5 Exercises **(Pages 832–834)**

1. discrete **3.** continuous **5.** discrete **7.** 50 **9.** 68 **11.** 50% **13.** 95% **15.** 43.3%
17. 36.0% **19.** 4.5% **21.** 97.9% **23.** 1.28 **25.** −1.34 **27.** 5000 **29.** 640 **31.** 9970
33. 84.1% **35.** 37.8% **37.** 15.9% **39.** 4.7% **41.** .994 or 99.4% **43.** 189 units **45.** .888
47. about 2 eggs **49.** 24.2% **51.** Answers will vary. **53.** 79 **55.** 68 **57.** 90.4 **59.** 40.3
61. Answers will vary.

Extension Exercises **(Pages 841–842)**

1. We have no way of telling. **3.** We can tell only that it rises and then falls **5.** 28% **7.** How long have Toyotas been sold in the United States? How do other makes compare? **9.** The dentists preferred Trident Sugarless Gum to what? Which and how many dentists were surveyed? What percentage responded? **11.** Just how quiet *is* a glider, really? **13.** The maps convey their impressions in terms of *area* distribution, whereas personal income distribution may be quite different. The top map probably implies too high a level of government spending, while the bottom map implies too low a level. **15.** By the time the figures were used, circumstances may have changed greatly. (The Navy was much larger.) Also, New York City was most likely not typical of the nation as a whole.
17. B **19.** C **21. (a)** $m = 1, a = 6, c = 3$ **(b)** There should be 1.4 managers, 5 agents, and 3.6 clerical employees.

13.6 Exercises **(Pages 848–849)**

1. $y' = .3x + 1.5$ **3.** 2.4 decimeters **5.** 48.9° **7.** $y' = 3.35x - 78.4$ **9.** 156 lb

11. **13.** 79 **15.** $r = .996$ **17.**

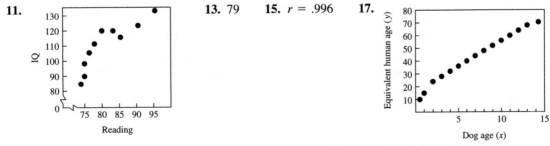

19. Answers will vary. **21.** $y' = 1.44x - .39$ **23.** The linear correlation is strong.
25. $y' = .00197x + 105.7$ **27.** The linear correlation is moderate.

Chapter 13 Test   (Pages 850–852)

1. about 1890   **2.** No. The *percentage* was 4 times as great, not the number of workers   **3.** about 3 million
4. The amount of land farmed in 1940 was about 20% to 28% greater than the amount farmed in 2000   **5. (a)** 8
(b) 7   **(c)** 6 and 7   **6. (a)** 6   **(b)** 2.24

7.

Class Limits	Frequency f	Relative Frequency f/n
6–10	3	$\frac{3}{22} \approx .14$
11–15	6	$\frac{6}{22} \approx .27$
16–20	7	$\frac{7}{22} \approx .32$
21–25	4	$\frac{4}{22} \approx .18$
26–30	2	$\frac{2}{22} \approx .09$

8. (a)

(b)

9. 8   **10.** 12.4   **11.** 12   **12.** 12   **13.** 10

14.

3	3 8
4	3 5 8 9
5	0 2 5
6	1 1 4 5 6 7 7 8
7	0 1 2 3 7 7 8 9 9
8	0 4 4
9	1

15. 35   **16.** 33   **17.** 37   **18.** 31   **19.** 49

20.

21. about 95%   **22.** about .3%   **23.** about 16%

24. about 13.5%   **25.** .684   **26.** .340   **27.** East   **28.** Central   **29.** 78.1   **30.** Phillies ($.79 > .73$)

31.

32. $y' = -.98x + 10.64$ **33.** 7.70   **34.** $-.72$
35. Answers will vary.   **36.** Answers will vary.

CHAPTER 14 Personal Financial Management

14.1 Exercises (Pages 864–867)

1. $112   **3.** $29.25   **5.** $548.38   **7. (a)** $826 **(b)** $835.84   **9. (a)** $2650 **(b)** $2653.02
11. $200   **13.** $15,910   **15.** $168.26   **17.** $817.17   **19.** $17,724.34; $10,224.34
21. (a) $1331 **(b)** $1340.10 **(c)** $1344.89   **23. (a)** $17,631.94 **(b)** $17,762.93 **(c)** $17,831.37
25. (a) $361.56 **(b)** $365.47 **(c)** $368.13 **(d)** $369.44 **(e)** $369.48   **27.** Answers will vary.
29. $1461.04   **31.** $747.26   **33.** $4499.98   **35.** $46,446.11   **37.** $45,370.91   **39.** 4.000%
41. 4.060%   **43.** 4.081%   **45.** 4.081%   **47.** $30,606   **49.** 11 years, 233 days
51. $r = m[(Y + 1)^{1/m} - 1]$ **53. (a)** 3.818% **(b)** Bank A; $6.52 **(c)** no difference; $232.38   **55.** 35 years
57. 8 years   **59.** 10.0%   **61.** 3.2%   **63.** Answers will vary.   **65.** $7.05; $8.61; $14.50; $39.40
67. $22,100; $27,100; $45,500; $124,000   **69.** $198   **71.** $1368   **73.** $81,102,828.75
75. Answers will vary.

Extension Exercises (Pages 873–874)

1. (a) $14,835.10 **(b)** $10,000 **(c)** $4835.10   **3. (a)** $3488.50 **(b)** $3000 **(c)** $488.50
5. (a) $3374.70 **(b)** $3120 **(c)** $254.70   **7.** Answers will vary.   **9.** $3555.94   **11.** $3398.08
13. (a) $1263.86 **(b)** $3791.58 **(c)** $208.42   **15. (a)** $1.80 **(b)** $468.00 **(c)** $32.00
17. (a) $180,000.00 **(b)** $322,257.52   **19.** Answers will vary.

14.2 Exercises (Pages 878–882)

1. $1650   **3.** $2046   **5.** $2546   **7.** $3645   **9.** $476.25   **11.** $1215; $158.75   **13.** $83.25; $46.29
15. $79.18; $38.39   **17.** $229.17   **19.** $330.75   **21.** $10,850   **23.** 6 years   **25.** $3.26   **27.** $2.72
29. $3.51, $358.75; $358.75, $3.95, $396.78; $396.78, $4.36, $368.88; $368.88, $4.06, $361.14   **31.** $7.53,
$708.60; $708.60, $7.79, $850.14; $850.14, $9.35, $825.79; $825.79, $9.08, $791.30   **33.** $2.50   **35.** $12.08
37. (a) $607.33 **(b)** $7.29 **(c)** $646.26   **39. (a)** $473.96 **(b)** $5.69 **(c)** $505.07   **41. (a)** $7.20
(b) $6.62   **43. (a)** $38.18 **(b)** $38.69 **(c)** $39.20   **45.** 16.0%   **47.** $32   **49.** Answers will vary.
51. Answers will vary.   **53.** Answers will vary.   **55. (a)** $127.44 **(b)** $139.08

14.3 Exercises (Pages 887–889)

1. 13.5%   **3.** 8.5%   **5.** $114.58   **7.** $92.71   **9.** 11.0%   **11.** 9.5%   **13. (a)** $8.93 **(b)** $511.60
(c) $6075.70   **15. (a)** $2.79 **(b)** $97.03 **(c)** $4073.57   **17. (a)** $206 **(b)** 9.5%   **19. (a)** $180
(b) 11.0%   **21. (a)** $41.29 **(b)** $39.70   **23. (a)** $420.68 **(b)** $368.47   **25. (a)** $1.80 **(b)** $14.99
(c) $1045.01   **27.** finance company APR: 12.0%; credit union APR: 11.5%; choose credit union   **29.** $32.27
31. Answers will vary.   **33.** Answers will vary.   **35.** 12   **37.** Answers will vary.   **39.** Answers will vary.
41. Answers will vary.   **43.** $\dfrac{5}{39}$

14.4 Exercises (Pages 899–902)

1. $675.52   **3.** $469.14   **5.** $2483.28   **7.** $1034.56   **9. (a)** $513.38 **(b)** $487.50 **(c)** $25.88
(d) $58,474.12   **11. (a)** $1247.43 **(b)** $775.67 **(c)** $471.76 **(d)** $142,728.24 **(e)** $1247.43 **(f)** $773.11
(g) $474.32 **(h)** $142,253.92   **13. (a)** $1390.93 **(b)** $776.61 **(c)** $614.32 **(d)** $113,035.68 **(e)** $1390.93
(f) $772.41 **(g)** $618.52 **(h)** $112,417.16   **15.** $552.18   **17.** $1127.27   **19.** $1168.44   **21.** 360
23. $247,532.80   **25. (a)** $304.01 **(b)** $734.73   **27. (a)** $59,032.06 **(b)** $59,875.11
29. (a) payment 176 **(b)** payment 304   **31.** $25,465.20   **33.** $91,030.80   **35. (a)** $674.79 **(b)** $746.36
(c) an increase of $71.57   **37. (a)** $395.83 **(b)** $466.07   **39.** $65.02   **41.** $140,000   **43.** $4275
45. $240   **47. (a)** $1634 **(b)** $1754 **(c)** $917 **(d)** $997 **(e)** $1555   **49. (a)** $2271 **(b)** $2407
(c) $1083 **(d)** $1174 **(e)** $2055   **51.** Answers will vary.   **53.** Answers will vary.
55. Answers will vary.   **57.** Answers will vary.   **59.** Answers will vary.

14.5 Exercises (Pages 917–921)

1. $29.75 **3.** 7¢ per share lower **5.** $47.48 **7.** $1.72 per share **9.** 7600 shares **11.** 10.6% higher **13.** 35 **15.** $5140.00 **17.** $1161.00 **19.** $2273.82 **21.** $17,822.55 **23.** $24,804.23 **25.** $55,800.00 **27.** $12,424.96 **29.** $5709.88 **31.** $17,441.47 **33.** $56,021.45 **35.** $30.56 net paid out **37.** (a) $800 (b) $80 (c) $960 (d) $1040 (e) 130% **39.** (a) $1250 (b) $108 (c) −$235 (d) −$127 (e) −10.16% **41.** $275 **43.** $177.75 **45.** (a) $10.49 (b) 334 **47.** (a) $8.27 (b) 3080 **49.** (a) $8.39 (b) $100.68 (c) 15.6% **51.** (a) $57.45 (b) $689.40 (c) 27.6% **53.** (a) $1203.75 (b) $18.06 (c) 19.56% **55.** (a) $4179 (b) $76.48 (c) 24.31% **57.** $10.00, $35.17, $29.95 **59.** $400.00, $41.80, $29.95 **61.** $4000.00, $91.40, $120.00 **63.** large; low **65.** $129,258 **67.** $993,383 **69.** (a) $56,473.02 (b) $49,712.70 **71.** (a) $12,851.28 (b) $11,651.81 **73.** (a) $r = m[(\frac{A}{P})^{1/n} - 1]$ (b) 5.4%

	Aggressive Growth	Growth	Growth & Income	Income	Cash
75.	$1400	$ 8600	$ 6200	$ 2800	$ 1000
77.	$8000	$112,000	$144,000	$116,000	$20,000

79. 3.75% **81.** 5.2% **83.** 5.3% **85.** The annual report was available free to *Wall Street Journal* readers. **87.** Answers will vary. **89.** Answers will vary. **91.** Answers will vary. **93.** Answers will vary. **95.** Answers will vary.

Chapter 14 Test (Pages 922–923)

1. $130 **2.** $58.58 **3.** 3.04% **4.** 14 years **5.** $67,297.13 **6.** $10.88 **7.** $450 **8.** $143.75 **9.** 14.0% **10.** $34.13 **11.** 11.5% **12.** Answers will vary. **13.** $1162.95 **14.** $1528.48 **15.** $3488 **16.** Answers will vary. **17.** 12.1% **18.** 112,300 shares **19.** $10 **20.** .078%; No; the given return was not for a 1-year period. **21.** $106,728.55 **22.** Answers will vary.

Chapter 15 Graph Theory

15.1 Exercises (Pages 938–944)

1. 7 vertices, 7 edges **3.** 10 vertices, 9 edges **5.** 6 vertices, 9 edges **7.** Two have degree 3. Three have degree 2. Two have degree 1. Sum of degrees is 14. This is twice the number of edges. **9.** Six have degree 1. Four have degree 3. Sum of degrees is 18. This is twice the number of edges. **11.** not isomorphic **13.** Yes. Corresponding edges should be the same color. AB should match AB, etc.

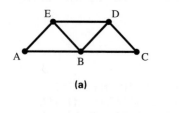

(a)

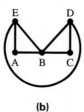

(b)

15. not isomorphic **17.** connected, 1 component **19.** disconnected, 3 components **21.** disconnected, 2 components **23.** 10 **25.** 4 **27.** (a) yes (b) No, because there is no edge A to D. (c) No, because there is no edge A to E. (d) yes (e) yes (f) yes **29.** (a) No, because it does not return to starting vertex. (b) yes (c) No, because there is no edge C to F. (d) No, because it does not return to starting vertex. (e) No, because edge F to D is used more than once. **31.** (a) No, because there is no edge B to C. (b) No, because edge I to G is used more than once. (c) No, because there is no edge E to I. (d) yes (e) yes (f) No, because edge A to D is used more than once. **33.** It is a walk and a path, not a circuit. **35.** It is a walk, not a path, not a circuit.

37. It is a walk and a path, not a circuit.   **39.** No, because there is no edge A to C, for example.

41. No, because there is no edge A to F, for example.   **43.** yes

45.   7 games   **47.** 36 handshakes   **49.** 10 telephone conversations

51. A → B → D → A corresponds to tracing around the edges of a single face. (The circuit is a triangle.)

59. 2   **61.** 3   **63.** 2

65. (a) 2   **(b)** 3   **(c)** 2   **(d)** 3

(e) A cycle with an odd number of vertices has chromatic number 3. A cycle with an even number of vertices has chromatic number 2.

67. 3   **69.** 3   **71.**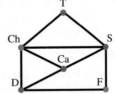

Three times: Choir and Forensics, Service Club and Dance Club, and Theater and Caribbean Club. (There are other possible groupings.)

73.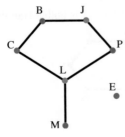

Three gatherings: Brad and Phil and Mary, Joe and Lindsay, and Caitlin and Eva. (There are other possible groupings.)

75. 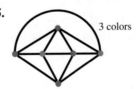 3 colors

77.

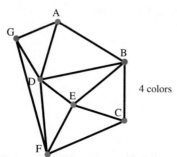

4 colors

79.

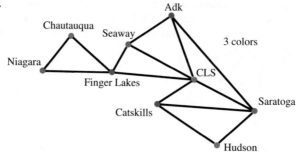

3 colors

In Exercises 81 and 82, there are many different ways to draw the map.
81.

83. By the four-color theorem, this is not possible.

15.2 Exercises **(Pages 954–959)**

1. (a) No, it is not a path. **(b)** yes **(c)** No, it is not a walk. **(d)** No, it is not a circuit. **3. (a)** No, some edges are not used (e.g., B → F). **(b)** yes **(c)** No, it is not a path. **(d)** yes **5.** Yes, all vertices have even degree.
7. No, some vertices have odd degree (e.g., G). **9.** yes **11.** It has an Euler circuit; all vertices have even degree. No circuit visits each vertex exactly once. **13.** It has an Euler circuit; all vertices have even degree.
A → B → H → C → G → D → F → E → A visits each vertex exactly once. **15.** It has no Euler circuit; some vertices have odd degree (e.g., B). It has no circuit that visits each vertex exactly once. **17.** No, some vertices have odd degree. **19.** Yes, all vertices have even degree. **21.** none **23.** B → E or B → D **25.** B → C or B → H **27.** A → C → B → F → E → D → C → F → D → A **29.** Graph has an Euler circuit.
A → G → H → J → I → L → J → K → I → H → F → G → E → F → D → E → C → D → B → C → A → E → B → A **31.** Graph does not have an Euler circuit; some vertices have odd degree (e.g., C). **33.** There is such a route: A → D → B → C → A → H → D → E → B → H → G → E → F → H → J → L → C → M → A → K → M → L → K → J → A **35.** It is not possible; some vertices have odd degree (e.g., room at upper left).
37. no; There are more than two vertices with odd degree. **39.** yes; B and G **41.** possible; Exactly two of the rooms have an odd number of doors. **43.** not possible; All rooms have an even number of doors.
There are other correct answers in Exercises 45–47.
45. A → B → D → C → A; There are 4 edges in any such circuit. **47.** A → B → C → D → E → F → G → H → C → A → H → I → A; There are 12 edges in any such circuit. **49.** A complete graph has an Euler circuit if the number of vertices is an odd number greater than or equal to 3; In a complete graph with n vertices, the degree of each vertex is $n - 1$. "$n - 1$ is even" is equivalent to "n is odd." **51.** Answers will vary.

15.3 Exercises **(Pages 968–972)**

1. (a) No, because it visits vertex E twice. **(b)** yes **(c)** No, because it does not visit C. **(d)** No, because it does not visit A.
3. (a) None, because there is no edge B to C. **(b)** all three **(c)** none; Edge AD is used twice.
5. A → B → D → E → F → C → A **7.** G → H → J → I → G **9.** X → T → U → W → V → X

11. Hamilton circuit: A → B → C → D → A. The graph has no Euler circuit, because at least one of the vertices has odd degree. (In fact, all have odd degree.)

13. A → B → C → D → E → F → A is both a Hamilton and an Euler circuit.

15. Hamilton circuit   **17.** Euler circuit   **19.** Hamilton circuit   **21.** 24   **23.** 362,880   **25.** 9!

27. 17!   **29.** P→Q→R→S→P   P→Q→S→R→P   P→R→Q→S→P   P→R→S→Q→P

P→S→Q→R→P   P→S→R→Q→P

31. E→H→I→F→G→E   E→H→I→G→F→E

33. E→F→G→H→I→E   E→F→G→I→H→E   E→F→H→G→I→E

E→F→H→I→G→E   E→F→I→G→H→E   E→F→I→H→G→E

35. E→G→F→H→I→E   E→G→F→I→H→E   E→G→H→F→I→E

E→G→H→I→F→E   E→G→I→F→H→E   E→G→I→H→F→E

37. A→B→C→D→E→A   A→C→B→D→E→A   A→B→C→E→D→A

A→C→B→E→D→A   A→B→D→C→E→A   A→C→D→B→E→A

A→B→D→E→C→A   A→C→D→E→B→A   A→B→E→C→D→A

A→C→E→B→D→A   A→B→E→D→C→A   A→C→E→D→B→A

A→D→B→C→E→A   A→E→B→C→D→A   A→D→B→E→C→A

A→E→B→D→C→A   A→D→C→B→E→A   A→E→C→B→D→A

A→D→C→E→B→A   A→E→C→D→B→A   A→D→E→B→C→A

A→E→D→B→C→A   A→D→E→C→B→A   A→E→D→C→B→A

39. Minimum Hamilton circuit is P→Q→R→S→P; Weight is 2200.   **41.** Minimum Hamilton circuit is

C→D→E→F→G→C; Weight is 64.   **43. (a)** A→C→E→D→B→A; Total weight is 20.

(b) C→A→B→D→E→C; Total weight is 20.   **(c)** D→C→A→B→E→D; Total weight is 23.

(d) E→C→A→B→D→E; Total weight is 20.   **45. (a)** A→C→D→E→B→A; Total weight is 87.

B→C→A→E→D→B; Total weight is 95. C→A→E→D→B→C; Total weight is 95.

D→C→A→E→B→D; Total weight is 131. E→C→A→D→B→E; Total weight is 137.

(b) A→C→D→E→B→A with total weight 87 **(c)** For example, A→B→C→D→E→A has total weight 52.

47. A→B→C→D→E→F→A   A→B→C→F→E→D→A   A→B→E→D→C→F→A

A→B→E→F→C→D→A   A→D→E→F→C→B→A   A→D→E→B→C→F→A

A→D→C→B→E→F→A   A→D→C→F→E→B→A   A→F→E→B→C→D→A

A→F→E→D→C→B→A   A→F→C→D→E→B→A   A→F→C→B→E→D→A

49. A→B→C→D→E→F→A   A→B→C→E→D→F→A   A→B→C→E→F→D→A

A→B→C→F→E→D→A   A→D→E→F→C→B→A   A→D→F→E→C→B→A

A→F→D→E→C→B→A   A→F→E→D→C→B→A

51. (a) graphs (2) and (4)   **(b)** graphs (2) and (4)   **(c)** No. Graph (1) provides a counterexample.   **(d)** No; if $n < 3$
the graph will have no circuits at all.   **(e)** Degree of each vertex in a complete graph with n vertices is $(n - 1)$. If
$n \geq 3$, then $(n - 1) > n/2$. So we can conclude from Dirac's theorem that the graph has a Hamilton circuit.

53. A→F→G→R→S→T→U→Q→P→N→M→L→K→J→I→H→B→C→D→E→A

55. Answers will vary.   **57.** Answers will vary.

15.4 Exercises   (Pages 981–985)

1. tree   **3.** No, because it is not connected.   **5.** tree   **7.** No, because it has a circuit.

9. It is not possible, since the graph has a circuit.   **11.** tree   **13.** not necessarily a tree   **15.** true

17. false

19.

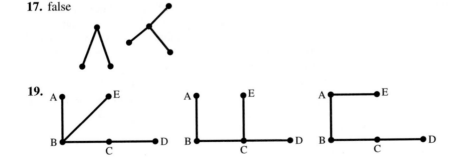

21.

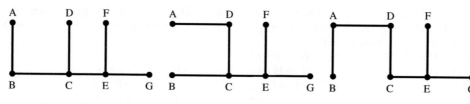

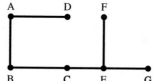

23.

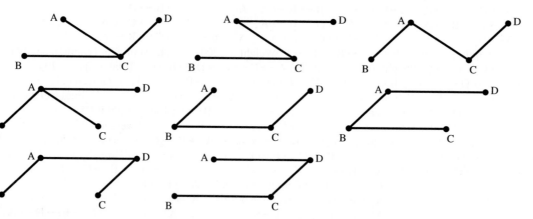

25. 20   **27.** If a connected graph has circuits, none of which have common edges, then the number of spanning trees for the graph is the product of the numbers of edges in all the circuits.

29. Total weight is 51.

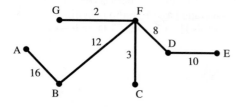

31. Total weight is 66.

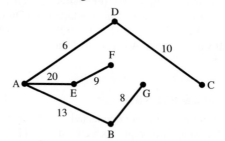

33. Total length to be covered is 140 ft.

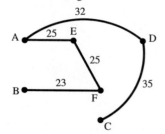

35. 33   **37.** 62   **39.** Different spanning trees must have the same number of edges, because the number of vertices in the tree is the number of vertices in the original graph, and the number of edges has to be one less than this.
41. (a) 9 **(b)** 18 **(c)** 0 **(d)** 2

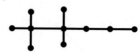

43. 22 cables   **45.** This is possible. Graph must be a tree because it has one fewer edge than vertices.   **47.** This
is possible. Graph cannot be a tree, because it would have at least as many edges as vertices.
49. 3:

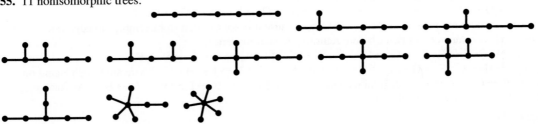

51. 125
53. 3 nonisomorphic trees:

55. 11 nonisomorphic trees:

57. Answers will vary.

Chapter 15 Test   **(Pages 987–989)**

1. 7   **2.** 20   **3.** 10   **4. (a)** No, because edge AB is used twice.   **(b)** yes   **(c)** No, because there is no edge C
to D.   **5. (a)** yes   **(b)** No, because for example, there is no edge B to C.   **(c)** yes
6. For example: **7.** 13 edges

8. The graphs are isomorphic. Corresponding edges should be the same color. AB should match AB, etc.

(a)

(b)

9.

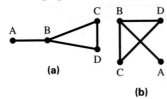

The graph is connected. Tina knows the greatest number of other guests.

10. 28 games   **11.** Yes, because there is an edge from each vertex to each of the remaining 6 vertices.

12. (a)

Chromatic number: 3

(b)

Chromatic number: 5

13.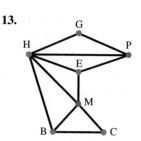

The Chromatic number is 3, so three separate exam times are needed. Exams could be at the same times as follows: Geography, Biology, and English; History and Chemistry; Mathematics and Psychology.

14. (a) No, because it does not use all the edges.   **(b)** No, because it is not a circuit (for example, no edge B to C).
(c) yes   **15.** No, because some vertices have odd degree.   **16.** Yes, because all vertices have even degree.
17. No, because two of the rooms have an odd number of doors.
18. $F \to B \to E \to D \to B \to C \to D \to K \to B \to A \to H \to G \to F \to A \to G \to J \to F$
19. (a) No, because it does not visit all vertices.   **(b)** No, because it is not a circuit (for example, no edge B to C).
(c) No, because it visits some vertices twice before returning to starting vertex.
20. $F \to G \to H \to I \to E \to F$ $F \to G \to H \to E \to I \to F$ $F \to G \to I \to H \to E \to F$
$F \to G \to I \to E \to H \to F$ $F \to G \to E \to H \to I \to F$ $F \to G \to E \to I \to H \to F$. There are 6 such Hamilton
circuits.   **21.** $P \to Q \to S \to R \to P$; Total weight is 27.   **22.** $A \to E \to D \to C \to F \to B \to A$; Total weight is
11.85.   **23.** 24!   **24.** Hamilton circuit
25. Any three of these:

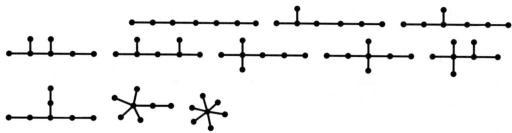

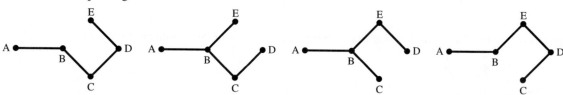

26. false   **27.** true   **28.** true
29. There are 4 spanning trees.

30. Weight is 24.   **31.** 49

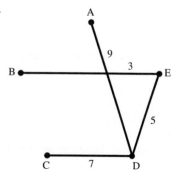

CHAPTER 16   Voting and Apportionment

16.1 Exercises   (Pages 1004–1007)

1. (a) $4! = 24$

(b)

Number of Voters	Ranking
3	$b > c > a > d$
2	$a > d > c > b$
1	$c > d > b > a$
1	$d > c > b > a$
1	$d > a > b > c$
2	$c > a > d > b$
1	$a > c > d > b$
2	$a > b > c > d$

(c) Australian shepherd

3. $5! = 120$; $7! = 5040$ **5.** For any value of $n \geq 5$ there are at least 120 possible rankings of the candidates. This means a voter must select one ranking from a huge number of possibilities. It also means the mechanics of any election method, except the plurality method, are difficult to manage.   **7.** $_6C_2 = 15$; $_8C_2 = 28$ **9.** With 40,320 possible rankings to be examined, finding the outcomes of 28 different pairwise comparisons seems a nearly impossible task.
11. (a) b, with 6 first-place votes   **(b)** c, with 2 (pairwise) points   **(c)** b, with 16 (Borda) points   **(d)** c   **13.** Logo a is selected by all the methods.   **15. (a)** e, with 8 first-place votes   **(b)** j, with 3 (pairwise) points   **(c)** j, with 40 (Borda) points   **(d)** h   **17. (a)** a, with 3 (pairwise) points   **(b)** b, with 24 (Borda) points   **(c)** a, Australian shepherd has 7 of 13 first-place votes—a majority—at the first round of voting.   **19. (a)** t, with 18 first-place votes
(b) h, with 4 (pairwise) points   **(c)** b, with 136 (Borda) points   **(d)** k   **21.** h beats e.   **23.** c beats t.
25. In a runoff between k and c, activity k is selected. Activity k faces activity t, and k is selected.   **27.** Logo a
29. (a) 2   **(b)** c, with 7 pairwise points   **31. (a)** 7   **(b)** e, with 7 pairwise points   **33. (a)** 16   **(b)** c
35. (a) 55   **(b)** c   **37.** j   **39.** Answers will vary.   **41.** Answers will vary.   **43.** Answers will vary.
45. Answers will vary; one possible arrangement of the voters is 2, 4, 5, 7, 3.

16.2 Exercises   (Pages 1017–1022)

1. (a) Alternative a (6 of 11 first-place votes)   **(b)** b   **(c)** yes   **3. (a)** Alternative a (20 of 36 first-place votes)
(b) b   **(c)** yes   **5. (a)** Alternative a (16 of 30 first-place votes)   **(b)** b   **(c)** yes   **7. (a)** a   **(b)** b   **(c)** b   **(d)** a
(e) plurality and Borda methods   **9. (a)** e   **(b)** j   **(c)** e   **(d)** h   **(e)** plurality and Hare methods   **11. (a)** h   **(b)** t
(c) k   **(d)** b   **(e)** all three methods   **13. (a)** m has 2 pairwise points, b and s have $1\frac{1}{2}$ pairwise points each, and c has
1 pairwise point.   **(b)** b has $2\frac{1}{2}$ pairwise points, m has 2 pairwise points, s has 1 pairwise point, c has $\frac{1}{2}$ pairwise point, so b is selected.   **(c)** Yes, the rearranging voters moved m, the winner of the nonbinding election, to the top of their ranking, but b wins the official selection process.   **15. (a)** d drops out after one round of votes; b drops out after Round two; in the third vote a is preferred to c by a margin of 11 to 6.   **(b)** d drops out after one round of votes; c drops out after Round two; in the third vote b is preferred to a by a margin of 9 to 8.   **(c)** Yes, the rearranging voters moved a, the winner of the nonbinding election, to the top of their ranking, but b wins the official selection process.
17. (a) Candidate a has 75 first-place votes.   **(b)** Candidate c has 80 first-place votes.   **(c)** yes   **19.** No; however, the second pairwise comparison results in a tie.   **21. (a)** Round one eliminates b; a is preferred to c in Round two, by a margin of 22 to 12.   **(b)** b   **(c)** yes   **23.** Answers will vary.
25. Answers will vary. One possible voter profile is given.

Number of Voters	Ranking
10	$a > b > c > d > e > f$
9	$b > f > e > c > d > a$

Candidate a is a majority candidate and wins all of its pairwise comparisons by a margin of 10 to 9, earning 5 pairwise points. Candidate b wins all of its comparisons, except the one with a, earning 4 pairwise points.

27. Answers will vary. One possible profile is the voter profile for the animal shelter poster dog contest in Exercises 2 and 17 of Section 16.1.   **29. (a)** a has 2 pair-wise points.   **(b)** Answers will vary. The 3 voters in the bottom row all switch to the ranking a > z > x > y.   **31.** Answers will vary. Delete Candidate c.   **33.** Answers will vary. One possible profile is given.

Number of voters	Ranking
21	g > j > e
12	j > e > g
8	j > g > e

35. Answers will vary.

16.3 Exercises   (Pages 1035–1038)

1.   (a) 29,493; 123.40

(b)

State park	a	b	c	d	e
Number of trees	11	70	62	54	42

(c) $md = 122$

State park	a	b	c	d	e
Number of trees	11	70	62	54	42

(d) The traditionally rounded values of Q sum to 240, which is greater than the number of trees to be apportioned.

State park	a	b	c	d	e
Traditionally rounded Q	12	70	62	54	42

(e) The value of md for the Webster apportionment should be greater than $d = 123.40$, because greater divisors make lesser modified quotas with a lesser total sum.

(f) $md = 124$

State park	a	b	c	d	e
Number of trees	12	70	61	54	42

(g) The Hamilton and Jefferson apportionments are the same. The Webster apportionment is different from the other two apportionments.

3.   (a) 269; 24.45

(b)

Course	Fiction	Poetry	Short Story	Multicultural
Number of sections	2	2	3	4

(c) $md = 20$

Course	Fiction	Poetry	Short Story	Multicultural
Number of sections	2	1	3	5

(d) The traditionally rounded values of Q sum to 10, which is less than the number of sections to be apportioned.

Course	Fiction	Poetry	Short Story	Multicultural
Traditionally rounded Q	2	1	3	4

(e) The value of md for the Webster apportionment should be less than $d = 24.45$ because lesser divisors make greater modified quotas with a greater total sum.

(f) $md = 23$

Course	Fiction	Poetry	Short Story	Multicultural
Number of sections	2	2	3	4

(g) The Hamilton and Webster apportionments are the same. The Jefferson apportionment is different from the other two apportionments.   **(h)** The Hamilton and Webster methods both apportion two sections of poetry; the Jefferson method apportions only one. If there are two sections of poetry, then the 35 enrolled students can be divided into two small sections with 17 and 18 students each instead of all 35 students being forced into one large section.   **(i)** The Jefferson method apportions 5 sections of multicultural literature instead of 4. This means that the average class size will be 20 students, rather than 25 students.

5. (a)

State	Abo	Boa	Cio	Dao	Effo	Foti
Number of seats	15	22	6	19	14	55

(b) $md = 356$

State	Abo	Boa	Cio	Dao	Effo	Foti
Number of seats	15	22	6	19	13	56

(c) The Hamilton, Jefferson, and Webster apportionments all are different.

7.

State	Abo	Boa	Cio	Dao	Effo	Foti	**Total**
Number of seats	15	22	7	18	14	54	130

9. (a) 1721; 43.025

(b)

Hospital	A	B	C	D	E
Number of nurses	3	5	8	11	13

(c) $md = 40$

Hospital	A	B	C	D	E
Number of nurses	3	5	8	11	13

(d) The traditionally rounded values of Q sum to 41, which is greater than the number of nurses to be apportioned.

Hospital	A	B	C	D	E
Traditionally rounded Q	3	6	8	11	13

(e) The value of md for the Webster apportionment should be greater than $d = 43.025$, because greater divisors make lesser modified quotas with a lesser total sum.

(f) $md = 43.1$

Hospital	A	B	C	D	E
Number of nurses	3	5	8	11	13

(g) All three apportionments are the same.

11. Answers will vary. One possible population profile is given.

State	a	b	c	d	e	Total
Population	50	230	280	320	120	1000

13. Answers will vary. One possible ridership profile is given.

Bus route	a	b	c	d	e	Total
Number of riders	131	140	303	178	197	949

15. (a) $md = 29$

Course	Fiction	Poetry	Short Story	Multicultural
Number of sections	2	2	3	4

(b) The Adams apportionment is the same as the Hamilton and Webster apportionments. It is different from the Jefferson apportionment

17. (a) $md = 377.3$

State	Abo	Boa	Cio	Dao	Effo	Foti
Number of seats	16	22	7	18	14	54

(b) All four methods produce different apportionments of the 131 seats in Timmu's legislature.

19. $\sqrt{56 \cdot 57} = 56.498$ **21.** $\sqrt{32 \cdot 33} = 32.496$ **23.** If the sum is greater, then md is found by slowly increasing the value of d, because a greater divisor produces lesser modified quotas with a lesser sum.

25. (a) $md = 24$

Course	Fiction	Poetry	Short Story	Multicultural
Number of sections	2	2	3	4

(b) The Hill-Huntington apportionment is the same as the Hamilton, Webster, and Adams apportionments. It is different from the Jefferson apportionment.

27. (a) $md = 367$

State	Abo	Boa	Cio	Dao	Effo	Foti
Number of seats	15	22	7	19	14	54

(b) The Hill-Huntington apportionment is the same as the Webster apportionment. The other three apportionments differ.
29. Answers will vary.

16.4 Exercises (Pages 1048–1049)

1. $md = 595$

State	a	b	c	d
Q **rounded down/up**	28/29	12/13	**81/82**	9/10
Number of seats	28	12	**83**	9

3. $md = 48.4$

State	a	b	c	d	e
Q **rounded down/up**	52/53	30/31	**164/165**	19/20	22/23
Number of seats	53	30	**166**	19	22

5.

State	a	b	c	d
Number of seats if $n = 204$	**35**	74	42	53
Number of seats if $n = 205$	**34**	75	43	53

7.

State	a	b	c	d	e
Number of seats if $n = 126$	**10**	29	34	28	25
Number of seats if $n = 127$	**9**	30	34	29	25

9.

State	a	b	c
Initial number of seats	1	4	6
Percent growth	10.91%	18.40%	13.16%
Revised number of seats	2	4	5

11.

State	a	b	c
Initial number of seats	6	5	2
Percent growth	4.84%	1.63%	1.45%
Revised number of seats	6	4	3

13. Two additional seats are added for the second apportionment.

State	Original State a	Original State b	New State c
Initial number of seats	20	55	*****
Revised number of seats	21	54	2

15. Seven additional seats are added for the second apportionment.

State	Original State a	Original State b	New State c
Initial number of seats	36	47	*****
Revised number of seats	37	46	7

17. The new states paradox does not occur if the new population is 531, but it does occur if the new population is 532.
19. $md = 208$

State	a	b	c	d	e
Q rounded down	8	16	33	**118**	42
Number of seats	9	17	34	**117**	43

21. Answers will vary.   **23.** Answers will vary.   **25.** Answers will vary.

Chapter 16 Test   (Pages 1051–1053)

1. Cancún   **2.** Aruba   **3.** the Bahamas   **4.** Aruba and Cancún each have two pairwise points and the Bahamas and Dominican Republic each have one pairwise point, so the pairwise comparison method vote results in a tie.
5. $7! = 5040$ **6.** $_{10}C_2 = 45$ **7.** Answers will vary.   **8.** Answers will vary.   **9.** Answers will vary.
10. Answers will vary.   **11.** Alternative a has a majority of the first-place votes, 16 of 31. The Borda method selects alternative b.   **12.** c   **13.** Alternative c is the Condorcet candidate. Plurality and Borda violate the Condorcet criterion and select b. Hare does not violate the criterion because it selects c.   **14.** Alternative c is selected before the five voters rearrange their ranking. Alternative s is selected after they rearrange their ranking. The rearranging voters moved alternative c, the previous pairwise selection, to the top of their ranking, but c is not selected a second time. This shows that the pairwise comparison method can violate the monotonicity criterion.   **15.** Alternative a is selected before the five voters rearrange their ranking. Alternative b is selected after they rearrange their ranking. The rearranging voters moved alternative a, the previous Hare selection, to the top of their ranking, but a is not selected a second time. This shows that the Hare method can violate the monotonicity criterion.   **16.** Alternative a is selected before losing alternative c is dropped. Alternative b is selected after c is dropped. The two outcomes show that the plurality method can violate the irrelevant alternatives criterion. A losing alternative was dropped from the selection process, but the original preferred alternative is not selected a second time.   **17.** Alternative b is selected before losing alternative d is dropped. Alternative a is selected after d is dropped. The two outcomes show that the Borda method can violate the irrelevant alternatives criterion. A losing alternative was dropped from the selection process, but the original preferred alternative is not selected a second time.   **18.** Alternative a is selected before losing alternative b is dropped. Alternative c is selected after b is dropped. The two outcomes show that the Hare method can violate the irrelevant alternatives criterion. A losing alternative was dropped from the selection process, but the original preferred alternative is not selected a second time.   **19.** Answers will vary.
20. standard divisor $d = 133.3692$ (That is, each seat represents 13,337 Smithapolis citizens.)

Ward	1st	2nd	3rd	4th	5th
Number of seats	11	65	57	50	12

21. $md = 131$

Ward	1st	2nd	3rd	4th	5th
Number of seats	10	65	58	50	12

22. $md = 133.7$

Ward	1st	2nd	3rd	4th	5th
Number of seats	11	65	57	50	12

23. Answers will vary.   **24.** Answers will vary.   **25.** Answers will vary.   **26.** Answers will vary.

27. $md = 347$

State	a	b	c	d
Q rounded down	6	12	15	**64**
Number of seats	6	12	16	**66**

28.

State	a	b	c	d	e
Number of seats if $n = 126$	**10**	29	34	28	25
Number of seats if $n = 127$	**9**	30	34	29	25

29.

State	a	b	c
Initial number of seats	**1**	4	**6**
Percent growth	**14.55%**	20.00%	**15.79%**
Revised number of seats	**2**	4	**5**

30. Fifteen additional seats are added for the second apportionment.

State	Original State a	Original State b	New State c
Initial number of seats	23	77	*****
Revised number of seats	24	76	15

31. Answers will vary.

Appendix Exercises   (Pages A-5–A-7)

1. 8000 mm   **3.** 85 m   **5.** 689 mm   **7.** 5.98 cm   **9.** 5300 m   **11.** 27.5 km   **13.** 2.54 cm; 25.4 mm
15. 5 cm; 50 mm   **17.** 600 cl   **19.** 8700 ml   **21.** 9.25 L   **23.** 8.974 L   **25.** 8 kg   **27.** 5200 g
29. 4200 mg   **31.** .598 g   **33.** 30°C   **35.** −81°C   **37.** 50°F   **39.** −40°F   **41.** 200 nickels
43. .2 g   **45.** $40.99   **47.** $387.98   **49.** 1,082,400 cm^3; 1.0824 m^3 **51.** 200 bottles   **53.** 897.9 m
55. 201.1 km   **57.** 3.995 lb   **59.** 21,428.8 g   **61.** 30.22 qt   **63.** 106.7 L   **65.** unreasonable
67. reasonable   **69.** unreasonable   **71.** B   **73.** B   **75.** C   **77.** A   **79.** A   **81.** C   **83.** A
85. B   **87.** B   **89.** A   **91.** B   **93.** C   **95.** B

CREDITS

INDEX OF APPLICATIONS

INDEX

Modern Period (Early) 1450 A.D. to 1800 A.D.
Logarithms; modern number theory; analytic geometry; calculus; the exploitation of the calculus

1700 A.D. to 1750 A.D.

Leonhard Euler pioneers work in topology, organizing calculus and using it to describe motion of objects and forces acting on them.

– – –

Age of French Enlightenment is ushered in by thinkers such as Diderot, Montesquieu, Rousseau, and Voltaire.

First suspension bridge is completed.

James Watt creates steam engine.

1750 A.D. to 1800 A.D.

Benjamin Banneker, a self-taught mathematician and astronomer, compiles a yearly almanac.

Joseph Lagrange develops theory of functions; studies of moon lead to methods for finding longitude.

– – –

Celsius thermometer is invented.

Benjamin Franklin does kite experiment.

American Revolution and French Revolution take place.

1800 A.D. to 1850 A.D.

Carl Gauss publishes masterpiece on theory of numbers (important to development of statistics and geometry).

Non-Euclidean geometry is developed.

Pierre Simon de Laplace works out mathematical formulas describing interacting gravitation forces in the solar system.

Augustin Louis Cauchy does important work in complex analysis.

Evariste Galois develops theory of groups.

Georg Riemann founds second non-Euclidean system.

Arthur Cayley and James Sylvester develop matrix theory.

Joseph Antoine Ferdinand Plateau, a Belgian scientist, develops the phenakistoscope–the first apparatus that allowed "moving pictures".

Napoleon Bonaparte attempts domination of Europe.

Georg Ohm describes principles of electric resistance.

Joseph Jacquard improves mechanical loom, allowing mass production of fabric.

Michael Faraday discovers electromagnetic induction.

Charles Babbage develops analytic engine (forerunner of computers).

Ada Augusta, Lady Lovelace, devises the concept of computer programming.

First telegraph is used.

Mathematical Events

Cultural Events